D1590812

BIOSENSORS
Fundamentals and Applications

EDITED BY

ANTHONY P. F. TURNER
Cranfield Institute of Technology

ISAO KARUBE
Tokyo Institute of Technology

and

GEORGE S. WILSON
University of Arizona

OXFORD NEW YORK TOKYO
OXFORD UNIVERSITY PRESS
1987

Oxford University Press, Walton Street, Oxford OX2 6DP

Oxford New York Toronto
Delhi Bombay Calcutta Madras Karachi
Petaling Jaya Singapore Hong Kong Tokyo
Nairobi Dar es Salaam Cape Town
Melbourne Auckland

and associated companies in
Beirut Berlin Ibadan Nicosia

Oxford is a trade mark of Oxford University Press

Published in the United States
by Oxford University Press, New York

British Library Cataloguing in Publication Data
Biosensors: fundamentals and applications.
1. Biosensors
I. Turner, Anthony P.F.   II. Karube, Isao
III. Wilson, George S.
547   R857.B54
ISBN 0-19-854724-2

Library of Congress Cataloging in Publication Data
Biosensors: fundamentals and applications.
Includes index.
1. Biosensors.   I. Turner, Anthony P.F.
II. Karube, Isao, 1942–   .   III. Wilson, George S.
R857.B54B56   1986   681'.761   86-21811
ISBN 0-19-854724-2

Set by Colset Private Limited, Singapore
Printed in Great Britain by
St Edmundsbury Press, Bury St Edmunds, Suffolk

Preface

A biosensor is a device incorporating a biological sensing element either intimately connected to or integrated within a transducer. The usual aim is to produce a digital electronic signal which is proportional to the concentration of a specific chemical or set of chemicals. The apparently alien marriage of two contrasting disciplines combines the specificity and sensitivity of biological systems with the computing power of the microprocessor. This emerging technology crosses many traditional academic delineations and offers a powerful new tool which threatens to radically alter our attitude to analytical science.

The modern concept of a biosensor owes much to the ideas of Leland C. Clark Jr. and co-workers, 1962 *et seq.* (see Chapter 1). They proposed that enzymes could be immobilized at electrochemical detectors to form 'enzyme electrodes' which would expand the analyte range of the base sensor. A wealth of work ensued, elucidating a myriad of permutations on this theme until slowly the horizons were expanded. The present picture is summarized in Table 1.

All the possible combinations of sensing element and transducer (Table 1) have not yet been explored in true biosensor configurations. This, together with the breadth of multidisciplinary knowledge required to grasp essential concepts, has led the editors to include a few chapters in this monograph falling outside the strict definition given above. In particular, some techniques capable of closely monitoring biological systems have been

Table 1 Components that may be used to construct a biosensor

Biological elements	Transducers
Organisms	Potentiometric
Tissues	Amperometric
Cells	Conductimetric
Organelles	Impedimetric
Membranes	Optical
Enzymes	Calorimetric
Enzyme components	Acoustic
Receptors	Mechanical
Antibodies	'Molecular' electronic
Nucleic acids	
Organic molecules	

examined in an attempt to pave the way for future developments in this evolving science.

Biosensors will develop as a result of effort on several fronts. Configurations reported to date have relied largely on effecting novel partnerships between independent approaches which were in themselves conventional. Increasingly, attention will have to be paid to engineering both the components and the whole device to meet specific requirements. New biochemical reactions will either be unearthed or will have to be engineered using genetic manipulation or chemical techniques. These will be designed with a suitable detector in mind rather than relying on fortuitous availability from prior investigations. New materials for constructing transducers or effecting links between the components of a sensor is an exciting avenue for research. In addition, the plummetting price of some hardware such as lasers will make available low cost versions of sophisticated laboratory instrumentation. The construction of the sensor as a whole should not be neglected. The fundamental properties of the device must be understood both in terms of its constituents and in the complexities of their interrelationships in order to optimize critical criteria such as response time, selectivity, and stability. Immobilization technologies and new membrane materials may profoundly affect the end performance of a particular sensor.

The study of biosensors has been motivated by a strong practical instinct with clear applications always in sight. Much of the impetus of work has come from medical requirements. Instant analysis of clinical samples has an obvious appeal to physicians and patients alike, although some national health services are finding it difficult to incorporate this philosophy. Perhaps more exciting is the possibility of continuous *in vivo* monitoring of metabolites, drugs, and proteins using miniature, highly portable systems. The cardinal clinical example is the glucose sensor for diabetes which has become a classic subject for study in the field of biosensors. In this condition there is a requirement for both *in vitro* and *in vivo* monitoring with the possibility of managing the disease in a totally automated fashion via the insulin infusion pump. Implantable sensors share the hurdles facing other applications with the additional serious problem of the need for biocompatibility.

In recent years there has been a growing appreciation of the other possible uses of biosensors. Clinical research is spinning off into related veterinary areas and animal husbandry. The food industry is increasingly concerned about quality and has long recognized the value of rapid methods for estimating shelf life, deterioration, and contamination. The rise of biotechnology has stimulated investigations into fermentation monitoring and control with possibilities for process control also arising. Concern for both the industrial and natural environment has led to research on sensors for pollutants such as carbon monoxide and herbicides; while the ubiquitous military interest is focusing on specialized needs including biological and chemical defence.

The aim of this book is to provide the first advanced and comprehensive treatise on the subject of biosensors. A multiauthor approach was chosen to do full justice to the individualistic approaches that have characterized the history of the area. The contentious and fluid nature of some aspects of the field are expounded by their main proponents; each argument is made in a clear and concise style amenable to scientists of many disciplines with the overall conclusion being left to the reader. It is uncertain exactly which direction will predominate in the next decade, but there is little doubt that the biosensor will impinge on the lives of an increasing number and wide range of scientists.

Cranfield   A. P. F. T.
June 1986

Contents

xii   *Contents*

Contributors

W. JOHN ALBERY Department of Chemistry, Imperial College, London SW7 2AY, UK

K. G. M. M. ALBERTI The Medical School, University of Newcastle, Newcastle upon Tyne, UK

MARK A. ARNOLD Department of Chemistry, University of Iowa, Iowa City, Iowa 52242, USA

W. J. ASTON Genetics International (UK) Inc., 38 Nuffield Way, Abingdon, Oxfordshire OX14 1RL, UK

S. A. BARKER Department of Chemistry, University of Birmingham, Birmingham, UK

P. N. BARTLETT Department of Chemistry, University of Warwick, Coventry CV4 7AL, UK

H. PETER BENNETTO Bioelectrochemistry and Biosensors Group, King's College, University of London, Kensington Campus, Campden Hill Road, London W8 7AH, UK

BARRIE C. BLAKE-COLEMAN Biosensor Group, Microbial Technology Laboratory, Centre for Applied Microbiology and Research, Porton Down, Wiltshire, SP4 OJG, UK

GARY F. BLACKBURN Fundamental Research Laboratory, GTE Laboratories Inc., 40 Sylvan Road, Waltham, MA 02254, USA

JONATHAN BOX Bioelectrochemistry and Biosensors Group, King's College, University of London, Kensington Campus, Campden Hill Road, London W8 7AH, UK

ROBERT G. W. BROWN Royal Signals and Radar Establishment. Malvern, Worcs. WR14 3PS, UK

MICHAEL R. CALDER Biosensor Group, Microbial Technology Laboratory, Centre for Applied Microbiology and Research, Porton Down, Wiltshire, SP4 0JG, UK

M. F. CARDOSI Bioelectronics Divisions, Biotechnology Centre, Cranfield Institute of Technology, Cranfield, Bedfordshire, MK43 0AL, UK

ROBERT J. G. CARR Biosensor Group, Microbial Technology Laboratory, Centre for Applied Microbiology and Research, Porton Down, Wiltshire, SP4 0JG, England

ANTHONY E. G. CASS Centre for Biotechnology, Imperial College of

Science and Technology, London SW7 2AZ, UK

JAMES CASTNER Biomedical Division, E. I. du Pont de Nemours Co., Wilmington, Delaware, 19898, USA

DENZIL J. CLAREMONT Division of Chemical Pathology, United Medical and Dental Schools, Guy's Hospital Campus, London SE1 9RT, UK

LELAND C. CLARK, JR Children's Hospital Research Foundation, Elland and Bethesda Avenues, Cincinnati, Ohio 45229, USA

DAVID J. CLARKE Biosensor Group, Microbial Technology Laboratory, Centre for Applied Microbiology and Research, Porton Down, Wiltshire SP4 0JG, UK

DEREK H. CRASTON Department of Chemistry, Imperial College, London SW7 2AY, UK

CLAUS DÄHNE Battelle Geneva Research Centres, 7 Route de Drize, 1227 Carouge/Geneva, Switzerland

BENGT DANIELSSON Pure and Applied Biochemistry, Chemical Centre, University of Lund, P.O. Box 124, S–221 00 Lund, Sweden

KAY E. DAVIES Nuffield Department of Clinical Medicine, John Radcliffe Hospital, Oxford OX3 9DU, UK

GRAHAM DAVIS Integrated Ionics Inc., 2235 State Route 130, Dayton, New Jersey 08810, USA

GERARD M. DELANEY Bioelectrochemistry and Biosensors Group, King's College, University of London, Kensington Campus, Campden Hill Road, London W8 7AH, UK

SVEN–OLOF ENFORS Department of Biochemistry and Biotechnology, The Royal Institute of Technology, S–100 44 Stockholm, Sweden

MONIKA J. GREEN Genetics International, 11 Nuffied Way, Abingdon, Oxfordshire OX14 1RL, UK

G.G. GUILBAULT Department of Chemistry, and University of New Orleans, New Orleans, Louisiana 70148, USA

P.D. HOME The Medical School, University of Newcastle, Newcastle-upon-Tyne, UK

ISAO KARUBE Research Laboratory of Resources Utilization, Tokyo Institute of Technology, 4259 Nagatsuta, Midori-ku, Yokohama, Japan

RYUZO KAWAMORI First Department of Medicine, Osaka University Medical School, 1-1-50 Fukushima, Fukushima-ku, Osaka 553, Japan

DOUGLAS B. KELL Department of Botany and Microbiology, University College of Wales, Aberystwyth, Dyfed SY23 3DA, UK

ENDA KENNY Delta Biotechnology Ltd., Castle Court, 59 Castle Court, Boulevard, Nottingham NG7 1FO, UK.

DIETER KIRSTEIN Central Institute of Molecular Biology of the

Academy of Sciences of the GDR, Robert-Rössle-Str. 10, 1115 Berlin, GDR

S. S. KUAN Mycotoxin Research Center, Food and Drug Administration, 4298 Elysian Fields Avenue, New Orleans, Louisiana 70122, USA

JEREMY R. MASON Bioelectrochemistry and Biosensors Group, King's College, University of London, Kensington Campus, Campden Hill Road, London W8 7AH, UK

KLAUS MOSBACH Pure and Applied Biochemistry, Chemical Centre, University of Lund, P.O. Box 124, S-221 00 Lund, Sweden

JAMES MCCANN Genetics International (UK) Inc., 11 Nuffield Way, Abingdon, Oxfordshire OX14 1RL, UK

FRANK MCCAPRA The University of Sussex, School of Chemistry and Molecular Sciences, Falmer, Brighton BN1 9QJ, UK

JOHN M. OLD Nuffield Department of Clinical Medicine, John Radcliffe Hospital, Oxford OX3 9DU, UK

DOROTHEA PFEIFFER Central Institute of Molecular Biology of the Academy of Sciences of the GDR, Robert-Rössle-Str. 10, 1115 Berlin, GDR

JOHN C. PICKUP Division of Chemical Pathology, United Medical and Dental Schools, Guy's Hospital Campus, London SE1 9RT, UK

O. PROHASKA Case Western Reserve University, Department of Biomedical Engineering, 501 Wichender Building, Cleveland, Ohio 44106, USA

JOHN G. RARITY Royal Signals and Radar Establishment, Malvern, Worcs. WR14 3PS, UK

GERARD REACH Unité de Recherches sur le Diabète et la Nutrition chez l'Enfant, INSERM U-290, Hopital Saint Lazare, 107 rue du Fanbourg Saint Denis, 75010 Paris, France

GARRY A. RECHNITZ Department of Chemistry, University of Delaware, Newark, Delaware 19716, USA

REINHARD RENNEBERG Central Institute of Molecular Biology of the Academy of Sciences of the GDR, Robert Rössle-Str. 10, 1115 Berlin, GDR

SIBEL D. ROLLER Bioelectrochemistry and Biosensors Group, Kings College, University of London, Kensington Campus, Campden Hill Road, London W8 7AH, UK

FRIEDER W. SCHELLER Central Institute of Molecular Biology of the Academy of Sciences of the GDR, Robert-Rössle-Str. 10, 1115 Berlin, GDR

FLORIAN SCHUBERT Central Institute of Molecular Biology of the Academy of Sciences of the GDR, Robert-Rössle-Str. 10, 1115 Berlin, GDR

JEROME S. SCHULTZ Department of Chemical Engineering, University of Michigan, Ann Arbor, Michigan 48109, USA

W. RUDOLF SEITZ Department of Chemistry, University of New Hampshire, Durham, NH 03824, USA

MOTOAKI SHICHIRI First Department of Medicine, Osaka University Medical School, 1-1-50 Fukushima, Fukushima-ku, Osaka 553, Japan

ROBERT STERNBERG Laboratoire de Bioélectrochimie et d'Analyse du Milieu, U.E.R. de Sciences, U.A. 329 du C.N.R.S., Université Paris-Val de Marne, Ave. du Général de Gaulle, 94010 Créteil Cedex, France

JOHN L. STIRLING Bioelectrochemistry and Biosensors Group, King's College, University of London, Kensington Campus, Campden Hill Road, London W8 7AH, UK

RANALD M. SUTHERLAND Battelle Geneva Research Centres, 7 Route de Drize, 1227 Carouge/Geneva, Switzerland

THIERRY TALLAGRAND Laboratoire de Bioelectrochimie et d'Analyse du Milieu, U.E.R. de Sciences, U.A. 329 du C.N.R.S., Universite Paris-Val de Marne, Ave du Général de Gaulle, 94010 Créteil Cedex, France

DANIEL R. THÉVENOT Laboratoire de Bioélectrochimie et d'Analyse du Milieu, U.E.R. de Sciences, U.A. 329 du C.N.R.S., Université Paris-Val de Marne, Ave. du Général de Gaulle, 94010 Créteil Cedex, France

CHRISTOPHER F. THURSTON Bioelectrochemistry and Biosensors Group, King's College, University of London, Kensington Campus, Campden Hill Road, London W8 7AH, UK

A. P. F. TURNER Bioelectronics Division, Biotechnology Centre, Cranfield Institute of Technology, Cranfield, Beds. MK43 0AL, UK

GILBERTO D. VELHO Unité de Recherches sur le Diabète et la Nutrition chez l'enfant, INSERM U-290, Hopital Saint Lazare, 107 rue du Fanbourg Saint Denis, 75010 Paris, France

P. J. WARNER Biotechnology Centre, Cranfield Institute of Technology, Cranfield, Beds. MK43 0AL, UK

GEORGE S. WILSON Department of Chemistry, University of Arizona, Tucson, Arizona 85721, USA

LEMUEL B. WINGARD, JR. Department of Pharmacology, School of Medicine, University of Pittsburgh, Pittsburgh, Pennsylvania 15261, USA

FREDRIK WINQUIST University of Lund, Sweden

YOSHIMITSU YAMASAKI First Department of Medicine, Osaka University Medical School, 1-1-50 Fukushima, Fukushima-ku, Osaka 553, Japan

The biological component

1

The enzyme electrode

LELAND C. CLARK, JR.

Since life itself depends upon almost incomprehensibly balanced enzyme mediated substrate specific transfer of electrons, it may not be surprising that means to measure the vital biochemical cellular processes would involve sensors composed of the same substances. Like advances in the past, progress in the future will depend upon increased understanding and control of enzymes, probably synthesis of enzymes, a more sophisticated control of electron transfer, and a close interaction between electrochemistry and the physiology of living systems.

The key discovery by the Buchner brothers, that fermentation proceeded in the filtered juice of yeast cells destroyed by grinding with sand, was followed in 1926 by Sumner's success in crystallizing urease thus demonstrating that enzymes were merely proteins. Before that their supposedly magic role was believed to be intrinsically intertwined in the life process. Most thought enzymes should be treated as highly perishable, like fresh eggs, and stored in the cold until they could be measured or used.

By looking at enzymes as specific chemical transducers, translating an analyte into a substance capable of being detected by a chemically or physically sensitive detector, a new class of sensors, intrinsically responsive to biological compounds, has been conceived and developed. Combinations of enzymes, such as esterases, dehydrogenases, and oxidases and of detectors, such as polarographic, conductimetric, potentiometric, acoustic, and optical, offer promise to expand the selectivity, sensitivity, and versatility of these detectors. The first enzyme electrodes relied on enzymes physically entrapped on or very near the sensor's surface. Later on, chemical immobilization, insolubilization, or fixation techniques were adopted. Co-enzymes have also been physically and chemically affixed. Insolubilization as a means of enzyme life extension may have the advantage of avoiding the complications of colloid osmotic forces, especially when analytepermeable membranes are used in conjunction with an enzyme electrode. Ideally, enzyme-based biosensors should, like the revolutionary blood gas and pH electrodes, work directly in undiluted whole blood.

Glucose and lactate electroenzymatic systems are being widely used in biomedicine, especially where rapid on-the-spot analysis of small samples of blood are desired. Intravascular biosensors may find use in continuous monitoring of blood in pediatric and coronary intensive care units. The

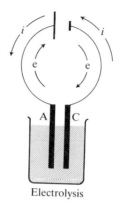

Electrolysis

Fig. 1.1 Electrolysis. At the anode (A) electrons are removed from the substrate and oxidation occurs. At the cathode (C) electrons (e) are added and reduction occurs. The applied potential controls the kind of reactions to some extent. Current (i), by convention, flows in the opposite direction.

future of implanted sensors, for example glucose electrodes, to control insulin pumps and lactate sensors to control cardiac pacemakers and defibrillators, depends largely upon finding means of stabilizing the needed enzymes when used at body temperature in contact with body fluids. A bright future for biosensors in biology and medicine seems intrinsic to their very nature.

In the evolutionary time scale of biosensors, we are just leaving the stage where we climbed down at dusk to hunt and entering the time when we cultivated the land in open sunshine. Enzymes are being harnessed for industrial use, in the analytical research laboratory, and in clinical monitoring. In a random selection of ten issues of *Analytical Electrochemistry* (CA Selects) for 1985, out of about 1500 abstracts, around 600 deal with enzyme electrodes.

Polarography depends upon electrolysis (Fig. 1). The beginnings of the polarographic enzyme electrode can be found in the dropping mercury electrode (Fig. 1.2) of Heyrovsky (1960), for in the years between the two wars he elucidated the electrochemical nature of the interface between this metal, the applied potential, and the chemical reactions. This was worked out in air-free solutions because oxygen was a considerable nuisance to polarography, as this new science was called, using the mercury electrode. There has been a continuous effort by chemists to increase the versatility and specificity of this electrochemical method. From an analytical viewpoint, the salient advantages of the dropping mercury electrode were its theoretical appeal, its reproducibility and its analytical capabilities, especially in pretreated samples in the laboratory. The workable but complex instrumentation required to adapt mercury polarography to the measurement of enzymes is shown in Fig. 1.3. But because liquid mercury was potentially toxic and cumbersome to use in biology the wonderful advantages inherent in a shiny new stirred

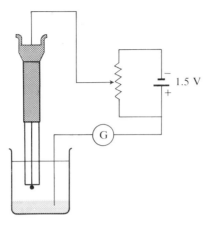

Fig. 1.2 The Heyrovsky dropping mercury electrode (Heyrovsky 1960). It is most useful in the range of + 0.4 to − 2.6 V applied voltage. Platinum electrodes can be used between + 0.9 and − 0.8 V.

mercury electrode every few seconds could not be used in many situations. For the many gains to be made in physiology by oxygen measurement, biologically inert solid anode and cathode surfaces seemed vastly preferable. Many kinds of solid electrodes were (and are still being) tested. Platinum was usually selected, partly because it could be sealed into and insulated with glass. But this solid unrenewable unstirred platinum surface was easily contaminated by the myriad of substances present in blood and living tissues. These problems have been reviewed by Davies (1962). Clark's cellophane covered platinum oxygen cathode (Clark, *et al.* 1953) overcame many of these problems but it was not until both platinum cathode and silver reference electrode were placed in their own electrically conductive micro-environment behind an electrically non-conductive gas-only permeable polyethylene membrane (Clark 1956) that a new, reproducible way to measure oxygen tension in tissues, liquids, and gases resulted. Because oxygen was the main concern in biology, and not the quantitation of a number of ions and organic substances, the potential could be held constant when oxygen was measured with a platinum electrode. Many biosensors combine the Clark oxygen electrode measurements with enzymes fastened on the electrode's membrane.

The cathode largely performs irreversible reduction of oxygen and the anode performs irreversible oxidation of its substrate, let's say, hydrogen peroxide and ascorbic acid. Unlike optical methods, though, the applied potential determines, as Heyrovsky showed, the kind of chemistry, while the current shows the amount. Thus the pressure of electrons controls and the flow measures.

Biosensors, meaning sensors which incorporate biological material in their structure (Fig. 1.4) were first described in 1962 at a New York Academy of Sciences symposium (Clark and Lyons 1962). In that presentation the use of

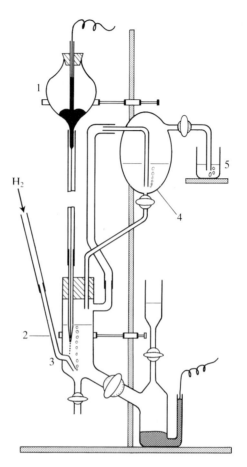

Fig. 1.3 Apparatus for following enzyme action (From Knoblock, E. *Chem Listy*, **38**, 193 (1944)).

enzyme transducers as membrane enclosed sandwiches was described to make electrochemical sensors (pH, polarographic, potentiometric, or conductimetric) more intelligent. They became specific for certain substrates by detection of a product of an enzyme catalysed reaction or a drop in a substance used in the reaction. For example, the combination of glucose oxidase with a Clark pO_2 electrode to measure glucose by detecting the drop in oxygen when glucose was converted to gluconic acid and hydrogen peroxide was described.

So basically, there are two kinds of polarographic enzyme electrode sensors. In one, the analyte consumes oxygen in the presence of an enzyme and the measurement depends upon a change in oxygen tension. In the other, the enzyme converts the analyte to a substance to which the sensor is sensitive. The purpose of the enzyme is to transduce the substance being

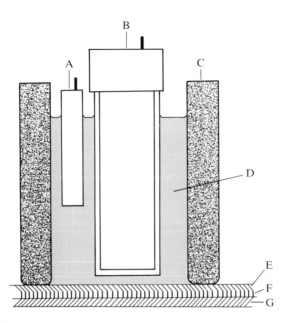

Fig. 1.4 The first enzyme electrode (Clark and Lyons, 1962).

measured, from one to which the sensor is not responsive, to one to which it is responsive. For this reason, the enzyme layer was originally referred to as a transducer. Perhaps the enzyme-formed substance, the product of interest, should be called a 'transformate'. The substrate, the analyte, would be changed to the 'transformate', in the milieu of either the 'catholyte' or the 'anolyte' in the enzyme layer.

If the classical amperometric oxygen electrode polarity is reversed so that the anode is about 0.6 V positive, the electrode is completely insensitive to oxygen but responds to hydrogen peroxide which is oxidized to water. The platinum anode also oxidizes ascorbic acid but not many other substances are found in animal juices in sufficient quantity to effect a current anywhere near the corresponding cathodic current for the oxygen electrode. The sensitivity of the anode to hydrogen peroxide was intriguing but since catalase is nearly everywhere it seemed that a biosensor to measure peroxide would be next to worthless, except perhaps to measure catalase or peroxidase. Heretofore, proteins were regarded as something which contaminated the platinum surface. My first use of platinum cathodes, for example, was motivated by the perceived need to keep blood proteins and cells away from the platinum surface. I suppose it was thinking about how to keep catalase away from the platinum anode that began the process that ended up by using the same membrane to keep catalase away, and since all enzymes are big protein molecules, to keep other enzymes near the platinum, at the same time. In the first enzyme electrode, the enzyme was shown as a sandwich, because one was still nervous about contaminating the platinum surface with proteins and coenzymes. But I also added enzyme to the electrolyte forming the path from the anode to the cathode, and the electrode worked well to measure glucose.

By 1963 I was working primarily with anodic polarography to measure H_2O_2 formed by reactions catalysed by the oxygen oxidoreductases. With the peroxide sensor, whole blood could be used, eliminating the need for centrifugation and permitting continuous monitoring of substrates such as glucose *in vivo* or in a flowing stream *in vitro*. When using oxygen electrodes the red cells and their oxygen-carrying hemoglobin had to be removed and only the serum or plasma used.

By 1965 or so, I was measuring glucose in the diluted blood of post-operative patients with a hand-held electrode in a beaker. I was still measuring lactate by the Barker–Summerson method and wishing that some-how a lactate oxidase that generated peroxide could be found. A patent applied for in 1965 (Clark 1970) covered the use of one or more enzymes to convert various substrates ultimately to hydrogen peroxide. It described the use of two electrodes to enable subtraction of current from an electrode without enzyme from current of an electrode with enzyme to eliminate inter-fering currents. By 1969 I had convinced the Yellow Springs Instrument Company to undertake the development of a dedicated glucose analyser for the direct measurement of glucose in 25 microlitre samples of whole blood. And by 1974 the Model 23 YSI analyser, after some faltering steps, appeared on the market.

It must be kept in mind that both the enzyme used and the polarized electrode itself generate products, by-products if you will, which are not necessarily wanted and which may impede the desired reaction. For example phenol, when oxidized, produces a black shiny deposit on the electrode surface which alters its chemical reactivity and may also produce an electrically insulating layer. It is also important that the by-products must not affect the activity of the enzyme. It is best when the products of the reaction are water soluble and can diffuse away. In the case of the glucose oxidase-based anode, the products are hydrogen peroxide, gluconolactone, gluconate, water, and oxygen, all of which are very soluble and diffusable.

One solution to interfering polarographically active substances in the sample, is to construct membranes which prevent the unwanted substances from reaching the platinum surface. This necessitates two membranes, the inner one preventing permeation of any unwanted substance, the outer one permitting passage of the substrate into the enzyme layer, and usually the interfering substance as well. A number of such proprietary combination membranes have been developed and several are on the market. The YSI glucose and lactate electrodes, for example, use a cellulose acetate and poly-carbonate Nuclepore combination.

The advance of polarographic techniques from the early two-electrode to three-electrode systems, to pulse polarography, to differential pulse polarography, and so on, has increased sensitivity and accuracy. It is important to keep in mind that the application of potentials in various schema not only affects the electrochemistry on the surface of the electrode but may also influence the nature and activity of the enzyme used. Signal amplification by enzyme recycling offers new avenues of increasing the sensitivity of enzyme based sensors (Scheller *et al.* 1985).

Of the many substrates that have been measured by the use of oxygen oxidoreductases are included glucose, lactate, pyruvate, galactose, alcohol, cholesterol, glycerol, hypoxanthine, xanthine, oxalate, and fructose. The ingenious use of ferrocene to mediate electron transfer in an oxidase based sensor to measure glucose is worthy of note (Cass *et al.* 1984; Aston, this Volume, Chapter 16; Cardosi and Turner, this Volume, Chapter 15).

New oxygen oxidoreductases, found in primitive forms of life such as fungi, are being discovered each year, but many more dehydrogenases have been found, usually in higher life forms of plants and animals. Racine *et al.* (1975) have coupled ferrocyanide/ferricyanide with lactic dehydrogenase in a lactate sensor.

The biosensor measurement of activity of a large number of enzymes in blood is also possible. Measurement of 'cardiac' enzymes, such as aspartate amino-transferase, creatine kinase, and creatine kinase MB, has proven clinically useful in judging infarct size. Stat measurement of these enzymes, together with lactate and glucose, could prove to be valuable in deciding therapeutic courses for patients with potentially lethal arrhythmias in the pre-hospitalization phase of acute myocardial infarction. Stat amylase measurements in pediatric patients may be valuable.

Rapid glucose measurement capabilities should be a part of every pediatric unit. Such round the clock availability of glucose measurements, among other things, could protect children from dangerous hypoglycaemia before surgery. Lactate and possibly pyruvate measurements should be available. Pediatric residents and nurses should learn to calibrate biosensor-based instrumentation so that glucose and lactate can be run at the same time or on the same samples used for blood gases and pH.

Conjunctival oxygen tension measurements have been pioneered by Fatt. The unique character of the palpebral circulation which make continuous pO_2 (as well as CO_2 and perhaps pH) monitoring possible could prove to be of value for glucose monitoring. A biosensor under the eyelid may be between 'invasive' and 'non-invasive'. Perhaps continuous recording of conjunctival lactate will become possible. Continuous monitoring of blood glucose would be valuable in labour and delivery by pregnant diabetics.

Enzyme micro-electrodes have a promising future. For the measurement of cellular intermediary metabolites it is difficult to imagine a method which could be more specific and elegant. Silver (1976) was the first to measure intracellular glucose. The Austrian scientists (Geibel *et al.* 1984) have measured volume fluxes and glucose in isolated perfused tubule segments using a platinum galactose oxidase electrode having a tip diameter of 15–30 μm. The galactose oxidase electrode is sensitive to raffinose, used in the latter studies, as well as to galactose, glycerol, fructose, and dihydroxyacetone. The nature of this enzyme electrode is related to internal solution potential in an interesting way (Johnson *et al.* 1982). There are several interesting ways to couple oxidase activity to other substrates (Hopkin 1985).

For use in undiluted blood or for implanted electrodes it must be remembered that the oxygen oxidoreductases ('oxidases') require oxygen and often their rate of oxidation of the substrate is a function of the pO_2. Without oxygen they will not normally function because the transformate will not be generated by the enzyme. Enfors (1983; Cleland and Enfors, 1983) has provided oxygen by anodic generation of oxygen in the enzyme layer, measuring the fermentation analyte according to the oxygen current required to keep the oxygen pressure steady (Fig. 1.5). The need for *in situ* fermentation biosensors parallel those for surgical implantation. Clark and Sachs (1968) had previously used a similar oxystat principle but the oxygen was added from a saturated solution by a servo system. Recently, it has been shown (Clark *et al.* 1986b) that sufficient gaseous oxygen can be supplied from an implanted Silastic drum to make an integral glucose sensor which is *glucose dependent* and essentially pO_2 independent. Gough and Leypoldt (1981) have described means of supplying oxygen to glucose sensors.

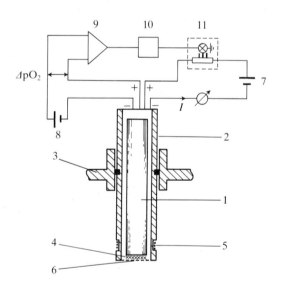

Fig. 1.5 Oxidase-based electrode supplied with electrolytic oxygen (from Enfors 1983).
1. Oxygen electrode; 2, electrode housing; 3, fermenter lid; 4, Pt-gauze with immobilized enzymes; 5, Pt-coil (cathode); 6, semipermeable membrane; 7, electrolysis voltage source; 8, reference voltage; 9, differential amplifier; 10, PID-controller; 11, electrolysis current controller; I, electrolysis current.

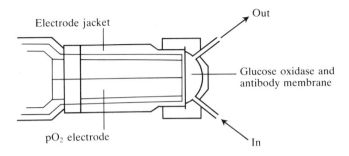

Fig. 1.6 Immunosensor based on the Clark pO_2 electrode (From Boitieux, J. L. *et al.* (1984). *Clinica Chimica Acta* **136**, 19).

Various combinations of antibody membrane and enzyme electrodes may provide new automatable sensors for antigens. Such biosensors, coupled perhaps with sensors for 'liver enzymes', could provide rapid reliable means of screening blood supplies. Figure 1.6 is based upon the measurement of oxygen consumption in the presence of glucose oxidase and glucose for quantitation of hepatitis B surface antigen antibodies. Other electroenzymatic methods for immunological research have been published and many more can be expected (Green, this Volume, Chapter 4).

Enzyme electrodes seem particularly well suited for instrumentation for physicians' offices and home monitoring, since such biosensors could be readily mass-produced from relatively inexpensive and stable components. An inexpensive device to monitor blood alcohol, perhaps through the skin, could be devised. Emergency medicine has specialized needs where rapid results can be life saving.

But perhaps the greatest future for enzyme electrodes will be as biosensors in or on the body. Sensors, as for lactate and glucose, would be made exceedingly small and incorporated in intravascular catheters for monitoring critically ill patients (Clark *et al.* 1986a; Clark and Duggan 1982). The importance of blood lactate as a measure of the adequacy of tissue oxygenation, or cardiac output, cannot be overemphasized. There is evidence, too, that a high maternal lactate during labour may have a deleterious effect on the newborn. Hypoxanthine may prove to be a valuable integrator of hypoxia. Implantable glucose sensors will almost certainly be devised capable of controlling insulin pumps (Clark *et al.* 1986a). This use in diabetes alone would justify the enormous effort in combining enzymes and electrochemistry.

References

Cass, A. E. G., Davis, G., Francis, G. D., Hill, H. A. O., Aston, W. J., Higgins, I. J., Plotkin, E. V., Scott, L. D. L. and Turner, A. P. F. (1984). Ferrocene-mediated enzyme electrode for amperometric determination of glucose. *Anal. Chem.* **56**, 667–71.

Clark, L. C., Jr. (1956). Monitor and control of blood and tissue oxygen tensions. *Trans. Am. Soc. Artif. Intern. Organs* **2**, 41–8.

—— (1970). Membrane polarographic electrode system and method with electrochemical compensation. U.S. Patent No. 3 539 455.

Clark, L. C., Jr. and Duggan, C. A. (1982). Implanted electroenzymatic glucose sensors. *Diabetes Care* **5**, 174–80.

Clark, L. C., Jr. and Lyons, C. (1962). Electrode systems for continuous monitoring in cardiovascular surgery. *Ann. NY Acad. Sci.* **102**, 29–45.

Clark, L. C., Jr. and Sachs, G. (1968). Bioelectrodes for tissue metabolism. *Ann. NY Acad. Sci.* **148**, 133–53.

Clark, L. C., Jr., Noyes, L. K., Grooms, T. A. and Moore M. S. (1984). Rapid micromeasurement of lactate in whole blood. *Crit. Care Med.* **12**, 461–4.

Clark, L. C., Jr., Wolf, R., Granger, D. and Taylor, Z. (1953). Continuous recording of blood oxygen tensions by polarography. *J. Appl. Physiol.* **6**, 189–93.

Clark, L. C., Jr., Noyes, L. K., Spokane, R. B., Sudan, R. and Miller, M. L. (1986*a*). Long term implantation of voltammetric oxidase/peroxide glucose sensors in the rat peritoneum. *Methods in Enzymology (Immobilized Enzymes and Cells)*. In Press.

—— (1986*b*). Design and long-term performance of surgically implanted electroenzymatic glucose sensors. *Ann. NY Acad. Sci.* In Press.

Cleland, N. and Enfors, S.-O. (1983). Control of glucose-fed batch cultivation of *E. coli* by means of an oxygen stabilized enzyme electrode. *Eur. J. Appl. Microbiol. Biotechnol.* **18**, 141–7.

Davies, P. W. (1962). The oxygen cathode. In *Physical techniques in biological research* (ed. W. L. Nastuk) Vol. 4, pp. 137–79. Academic Press, New York.

Enfors, S-O. (1983). Oxygen stabilized enzyme electrode. U.S. Patent No. 4 374 013.

Geibel, J., Volkl, H. and Lang, F. (1984). A microelectrode for continuous recording of volume fluxes in isolated perfused tubule segments. *Pflugers Arch.* **400**, 388–92.

Gough, D. A. and Leypoldt, J. K. (1981). Theoretical aspects of enzyme electrode design. *Appl. Biochem. and Bioeng.* **3**, 175–206.

Heyrovsky, J. (1960). Trends in polarography. Nobel Laureate Lecture, *Science* **132**, 123–30.

Hopkin, T. R., (1985). A multipurpose enzyme sensor based on alcohol oxidase. *Am. Biotechnol. Lab.*, Sept/Oct. 13.

Johnson, J. M., Halsall, H. B. and Heineman, W. R. (1982). Galactose oxidase enzyme electrode with internal solutions potential control. *Anal. Chem.* **54**, 1394–9.

Racine, P., Engelhardt, R., Higelin, J. C. and Mindt, W. (1975). An instrument for the rapid determination of L-lactate in biological fluids. *Med. Instrum.* **9**, 11–14.

Scheller, F., Renneberg, R. and Schubert, F. (1985). Coupled enzyme reactions. In *Intelligent sensors*. Engineering Foundation VIIIth Int. Conf. on Enzyme Eng., Helsingor, Denmark, Sept. 22–27, 1985. Prog. and Abstracts p. 49.

Silver, I. A. (1976). An ultra micro glucose electrode, In *Ion and enzyme electrodes in biology and medicine* (eds. M. Kessler, L. C. Clark, Jr., D. W. Lubbers, I. A. Silver, and W. Simon), pp. 189–92. Urban and Schwarzenberg, Munchen.

2

Micro-organism based sensors

ISAO KARUBE

2.1 Introduction

The industrial application of biochemical and microbiological processes in fields such as the production of pharmaceuticals, food manufacturing, wastewater treatment, and energy production is on the increase. Fermentation plays a very important role in such biotechnological processes, therefore a monitoring of raw materials, cell population, and products is necessary to achieve an effective system. Spectrophotometry and chromatography can be used for the determination of organic compounds, but they are not suitable for on-line measurement. Electrochemical determination of such compounds has distinct advantages: for example, samples can be measured over a wide concentration range without pretreatment and do not need to be optically clear. Recently, many biosensors have been developed for the determination of organic compounds. Enzyme sensors are highly specific for the substrate of interest, but the enzymes employed are generally expensive and unstable. Microbial sensors are composed of immobilized micro-organisms and an electrochemical device and are suitable for the on-line control of biochemical processes (Chang 1977; Guilbault 1976; Aizawa *et al.* 1977; Satoh, *et al.* 1977*a*, *b*). The microbial sensors developed by the author involve the assimilation of organic compounds by the micro-organisms, change in respiration activity, or the production of electroactive metabolites; these being monitored directly by an electrochemical device. This chapter describes several microbial sensors currently being developed in Japan.

2.2 Assimilable sugar sensor

In the cultivation of micro-organisms in cane molasses, which contains various sugars, determination of the total assimilable sugars in the broth is important for the control of the fermentation process. For example, catabolite repression occurs at high sugar concentration, causing an inhibition of cell growth. Reduced sugars and sucrose in culture broths are determined by the ferricyanide method (Technicon 1972). This method, however, is not completely reliable because unassimilable substances can interfere with the determination.

Assimilation of organic compounds by micro-organisms can be deter-

13

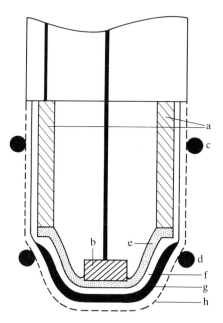

Fig. 2.1 Scheme of the microbial electrode for total assimilable sugars. a, Silver anode; b, platinum cathode; c, d, rubber rings; e, electrolyte gel; f, Teflon membrane; g, micro-organisms retained on nylon net; h, cellophane membrane.

mined from their respiratory activity, which can be directly measured using an oxygen electrode.

A microbial sensor consisting of immobilized living whole cells of *Brevibacterium lactofermentum* and an oxygen electrode was constructed for the continuous determination of total assimilable sugars (glucose, fructose, and sucrose) in a fermentation broth (Hikuma *et al.* 1980*b*). *Brevibacterium lactofermentum* was immobilized in a strip of nylon net (1 cm × 1 cm, 20 mesh) and attached to the oxygen electrode (Figs. 2.1 and 2.2). Total assimilable sugars were estimated from oxygen consumption by the immobilized micro-organisms. Addition of a glucose aliquot to the sensor system resulted in an increased oxygen consumption by the micro-organisms. This lowered the dissolved oxygen concentration of the solution causing the electrode current to decrease markedly with time until steady state was reached. The response time was 10 min using a steady state determination and 1 min by the pulse method. A linear relationship was found between the decrease in current and the concentration of glucose (1 mM), fructose (1 mM), and sucrose (0.8 mM) respectively. Sensitivity of the microbial sensor to glucose, fructose, and sucrose existed in a ratio of 1.00:0.80:0.92. The decrease in current was reproducible to within 2% of the relative standard deviation when a sample solution containing glucose (0.8 mM) was employed for the

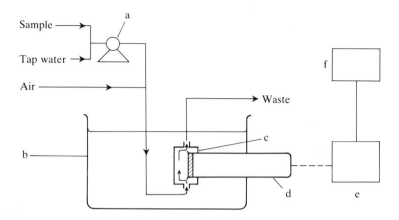

Fig. 2.2 Schematic diagram of the sensor system. a, Peristaltic pump; b, water bath; c, flow cell; d, microbial electrode; e, transmitter; f, recorder.

experiments. Total assimilable sugar was calculated by a summation of the responses of glucose, fructose, and sucrose, the difference between the observed and calculated concentrations being within 8%. The microbial sensor was applied in a fermentation broth for glutamic acid production, where it operated reliably for more than ten days and 960 assays.

2.3 Glucose sensor

A microbial sensor consisting of immobilized whole cells of *Pseudomonas fluorescens* and an oxygen electrode was developed for the determination of glucose (Hikuma, *et al.* 1980; Karube, *et al.* 1979*b*) (Fig. 2.3).

The microbial sensor was inserted into a sample solution and the sample solution was saturated with dissolved oxygen and stirred magnetically while measurements were taken.

Figure 2.4 shows typical response curves of the sensor. The theory of this sensor was the same as that of the assimilable sugar sensor. The steady state current was attained within 10 min at 30 °C. The exact time depended on the concentration of glucose added.

When the sensor was removed from the sample and placed in a glucose free solution, the current of the microbial sensor gradually increased and returned to the initial level within 15 min at 30 °C.

The sensor responded slightly to fructose, galactose, mannose, and saccharose, but no response was observed in the case of amino acids. Therefore, the selectivity of the microbial sensor for glucose was considered satisfactory.

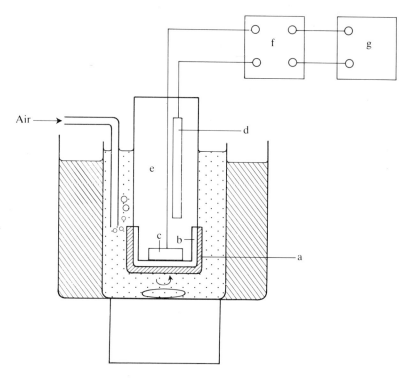

Fig. 2.3 Scheme of the microbial electrode sensor for glucose. a, Bacterial collagen membrane; b, Teflon membrane; c, platinum cathode; d, lead anode; e, electrolyte (KOH); f, ammeter; g, recorder.

A linear relationship was observed between the current and the concentration of glucose below 20 mg l^{-1} by a steady state determination and the minimum detectable concentration of glucose was 2 mg l^{-1}. The current was reproducible to within $\pm 6\%$ when a sample solution containing 10 mg l^{-1} of glucose was employed. The standard deviation was 6.5 mg l^{-1} over 20 experiments.

The microbial glucose sensor was applied to molasses broth and glucose was determined with an average relative error of $\pm 10\%$. The concentration of glucose was also determined by an enzymatic method (Karube *et al.* 1979*b*) for comparison, which gave correlation with the electrochemical method.

The reusability of the microbial sensor was examined. No decrease in current output was observed over a two week period and 150 assays.

2.4 Acetic acid sensor

When micro-organisms are grown on acetic acid as the carbon source, excess acetic acid inhibits growth and hence, the optimal concentration must be

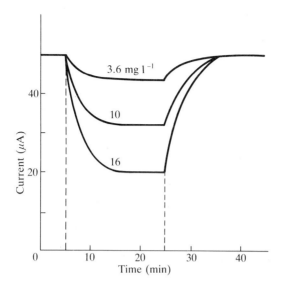

Fig. 2.4 Response curve of the microbial electrode sensor.

maintained by on-line monitoring. A microbial sensor comprising of immobilized yeast (*Trichosporon brassicae*), a gas-permeable Teflon membrane, and an oxygen electrode has been investigated for the continuous determination of acetic acid in fermentation broths (Hikuma *et al.* 1979a).

A porous membrane bearing the immobilized *T. brassicae* was attached to the surface of the oxygen electrode Teflon membrane and covered with a second gas-permeable Teflon membrane: thus the micro-organisms were trapped between the two porous membranes. The microbial sensor system consisted of a jacketed flow cell, a magnetic stirrer, a peristaltic pump, an automatic sampler, and a current recorder.

The principle of this microbial sensor was similar to that described above. The sample was kept at a pH well below the pK value for acetic acid (4.75 at 30 °C) because acetate ions cannot pass through the membrane. Figure 2.5 shows the response curves obtained for acetic acid concentrations of 18, 36, 54, and 72 mg l^{-1}.

The calibration graphs obtained showed linear relationships between the current decrease and the concentration of acetic acid up to 72 mg l^{-1}. The minimum concentration which could be determined was 5 mg l^{-1}. The current difference was reproducible within ± 6% for an acetic acid sample containing 54 mg l^{-1} and the standard deviation was 1.6 mg l^{-1} over 20 experiments.

With regard to the selectivity of the microbial sensor for acetic acid, it did not respond to volatile compounds such as formic acid and methanol, or to

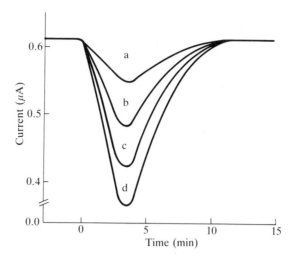

Fig. 2.5 Response curve of the acetic acid sensor. Sample solution (2.4 ml) was passed into the flow cell for 3 min. Acetic acid concentrations were a, 18 mg l^{-1}; b, 36 mg l^{-1}; c, 54 mg l^{-1}; d, 72 mg l^{-1}.

involatile nutrients such as glucose and phosphate ions. Although *Trichosporon brassicae* does utilize propionic acid, *n*-butyric acid, and ethanol, these are generally not present in fermentations, or are present in concentrations too low to affect the measurement of acetic acid.

The concentration of acetic acid in a fermentation broth for glutamic acid production was determined by the microbial sensor and also by gas chromatography: good agreement between the two was achieved, the regression coefficient being 1.04 for 26 experiments. The current output (0.29–0.25 μA) of the sensor was constant (within $\pm$ 10% of the original value) for more than three weeks and 1500 assays. This microbial sensor for acetic acid is now commercialized in Japan.

2.5 Alcohol sensor

On line measurements of methanol and ethanol concentrations in culture broths are necessary in the fermentation industries. In the cultivation of micro-organisms using alcohols as a carbon source, the concentration of alcohols must be maintained at the optimal level in order to avoid substrate inhibition. It is well known that many micro-organisms utilize alcohols as carbon sources. Therefore it is possible to construct a microbial sensor for alcohol using alcohol-utilizing micro-organisms (Hikuma, *et al.* 1979*b*).

The ethanol sensor consisted of immobilized *Trichosporon brassicae* and an oxygen electrode. The immobilization of the cells and electrode construction was the same as for the glucose sensor.

A long time is required for the determination using the steady state method. Therefore, the pulse method was employed for the determination, providing a response within six minutes. A linear relationship was observed between the current decrease and the ethanol concentration up to a maximum concentration of 22.5 mg l^{-1} and minimum concentration of 2 mg l^{-1}. The current difference was reproducible to within $\pm 6\%$ of the relative error when a sample solution containing 16.5 mg ethanol l^{-1} was employed. The standard deviation was 0.5 mg l^{-1} over 40 experiments.

The sensor did not respond to volatile compounds such as methanol, formic acid, acetic acid, propionic acid, and other non-volatiles such as carbohydrates, amino acids, and ions (Table 2.1). As the microbial sensor was covered with a gas permeable membrane, only volatile compounds can penetrate through the membrane.

Table 2.1 Response of the microbial electrode sensor to various compounds

Immobilized micro-organisms	Composition of sample*		Current decrease (μA)	Remarks
Trichosporon	Ethanol	30 ppm	0.13	
brassicae	Methanol	30 ppm	0	
	Acetic acid	100 ppm	0	
	Formic acid	100 ppm	0	
	Propionic acid	100 ppm	0	pH > 6
	Glucose	1 %	0	
	Saccharose	1 %	0	
	KH_2PO_4	5 %	0	

* Original concentration, diluted 2.8 times in the flow cell.

The selectivity of the microbial sensor for ethanol was therefore found to be satisfactory.

The microbial ethanol sensor was applied to yeast fermentation broths. The concentration of ethanol was also determined by gas chromatography, which gave satisfactory comparative results to the microbial sensor. The correlation coefficient was 0.98 over 20 experiments. The current output of the sensor in an ethanol concentration of 5.5–22.3 mg l^{-1} remained almost constant for more than three weeks and 2100 assay. This ethanol sensor is now commercialized in Japan.

An unidentified bacterium AJ3993 was also employed for a methanol sensor using the same configuration as for the ethanol sensor. The methanol concentration had a linear relationship to the current decrease up to 25 mg l^{-1}.

2.6 Formic acid sensor

Formic acid commonly occurs as an intermediate of cellular metabolism and is found in culture media, urine, blood, and gastric juices, also being a product of many chemical reactions. Selective spectrophotometric enzyme assays involving formate dehydrogenase, malate dehydrogenase, and tetrahydrofolic acid synthetase are not suitable for on-line monitoring.

Several anaerobic bacteria such as *Escherichia coli, Citrobacter freundii,* and *Rhodospirillum rubrum* produce hydrogen from formic acid. The reactions are summarized as follows:

$$\text{Formic acid} \xrightarrow{\hspace{3cm}} \text{Ferredoxin}_{\text{reduced}} + CO_2$$

$$\text{Ferredoxin}_{\text{reduced}} \xrightarrow{\text{Hydrogenase}} \text{Ferredoxin}_{\text{oxidized}} + H_2$$

$$\text{Formic acid} \xrightarrow{\substack{\text{Formate} \\ \text{dehydrogenase}}} \text{Cytochrome } c_{\text{reduced}} + CO_2$$

$$\text{Cytochrome } c_{\text{reduced}} \xrightarrow{\text{Hydrogenase}} \text{Cytochrome } c_{\text{reduced}} + H_2$$

Therefore, determination of formic acid is possible by using *C. freundii* and a fuel cell-type electrode. The principle of this microbial sensor is illustrated in Fig. 2.6. Such a specific microbial sensor, comprising immobilized *C. freundii*, two gas-permeable Teflon membranes and a fuel-cell type electrode has been investigated (Matsunaga *et al.* 1980). A linear relationship was obtained between the steady state current and the formic acid concentration up to a maximum of 1000 mg l^{-1} and a minimum 10 mg l^{-1}. The currents were reproducible with an average relative error of $\pm 5\%$ at a concentration of 200 mg l^{-1}. The standard deviation was 3.4 mg l^{-1} over 30 experiments. This sensor did not respond to non-volatile nutrients such as glucose, pyruvic acid, and phosphate ions. Although volatile compounds such as acetic acid, propionic acid, n-butyric acid, methanol and ethanol can

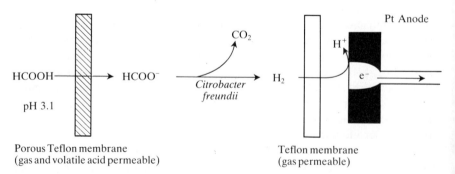

Porous Teflon membrane
(gas and volatile acid permeable)

Teflon membrane
(gas permeable)

Fig. 2.6 Principle of the microbial sensor.

permeate through the porous Teflon membrane, no current was obtained with these compounds because *C. freundii* cannot utilize them for H_2 production. The microbial sensor, and also gas chromatography, were used to determine the formic acid concentration in *Aeromonas formicans* culture medium. Good agreement was obtained between these methods, the regression coefficient being 0.98 for ten experiments. To study the stability of the immobilized *C. freundii* in the sensor, it was stored in 0.1 M phosphate buffer at 5 °C and used for formic acid (200 mg l^{-1}) determination over five-day intervals. The current output obtained from each assay remained constant for 20 days.

2.7 Methane sensor

World wide interest has arisen in the production of methane by fermentation of biomass. Methane is an attractive energy source and a main component of the natural gases used for fuel. Rapid methods for the detection and determination of methane in air are required, for example in the field of coal mining, because it forms an explosive mixture with air (5–14%). A methane sensor consisting of immobilized methane-oxidizing bacteria and an oxygen electrode has been developed (Karube *et al.* 1982).

The system is comprised of two oxygen electrodes, two reactors, an electrometer, and a recorder (Fig. 2.7). The reactors both contain culture media, one with and one without the immobilized bacterium *Methylomonas flagellata*. The electrodes were fixed inside custom-made Teflon flow-through cells, connected using glass and Teflon tubing. Two vacuum pumps were used, one to evacuate the gas-sample tube and the other to transport the sample gas through the system. The flow rate of the sample gas through the reactors was controlled (80 ml min^{-1}) using glass valves. A cotton filter removed other micro-organisms in the gas samples, preventing contamination of the reactors and gas lines. The latter were designed to maintain symmetry between the measuring and reference flows.

When sample gas containing methane was passed into the reactor, methane was assimilated by the immobilized micro-organisms with consumption of oxygen causing the current from the oxygen electrode to decrease to a minimum steady state. As the system contained two oxygen electrodes, the maximum difference between the currents depended on the concentration of methane in the sample gas. When pure air was again passed through the reactors, the current returned to its initial level within 60 s. The response time for the determination of methane was less than 60 s, and the total time required for methane assay was two minutes.

Calibration graphs for the system were perfectly linear for methane concentrations in the range 0–6.6 mmol, the current difference ranging from 0 to 0.35 μA and the minimum determinable concentration being 5 μmol.

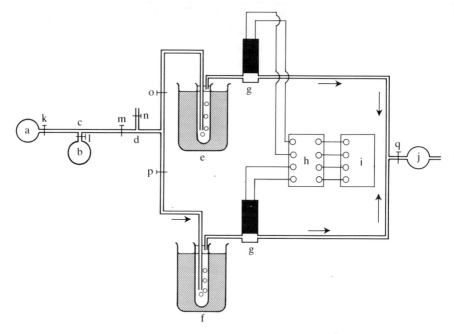

Fig. 2.7 Diagram of microbial sensor system for methane. a, Vacuum pump; b, sample gas bag; c, gas sample line; d, cotton filter; e, control reactor; f, methane-oxidizing bacteria reactor; g, oxygen electrode; h, amplifier; i, recorder; j, vacuum pump; k–q, glass stopcocks.

The current difference of a 0.66 mmol sample was reproducible to within ± 5% (S.D. 9.40 nA) over 25 experiments.

Analysis by conventional gas chromatography, over the range 0.2–3.5 mmol methane in air, gave a good correlation with the electrochemical method (correlation coefficient 0.97). The minimum measurable concentration of methane is 3 mmol by gas chromatography using a flame ionization detector, and 5 mmol with the microbial sensor. The sensor employing *M. flagellata* therefore warrants further development for rapid on-line determination of methane.

2.8 Glutamic acid sensor

Glutamic acid is produced by a fermentation process (being used as a seasoning for foods). A rapid and automatic method was required for determination of its concentration. Enzyme based auto-analysers can be used, but enzyme costs are prohibitive. The selectivity of this sensor to various amino acids was examined. The sensor responded to glutamic acid and glutamine and very slightly to some other amino acids. The response to glutamine can be decreased, if necessary, using acetone-treated *E. coli*. The microbial sensor did not respond under anaerobic conditions to organic substances such as glucose (7800 mg l^{-1}) and acetic acid (9200 mg l^{-1}) and the influence of inorganic ions on the response was negligible.

When this sensor was used to determine known concentrations of glutamic acid in a fermentation broth, satisfactory recovery data were obtained (99–103%) which were in good agreement with auto-analyzer determinations. The sensor was considered to be highly selective, stable, and reproducible.

Glutamate decarboxylase catalyses the decarboxylation of glutamic acid producing carbon dioxide and amine, but the enzyme is expensive and unstable. Certain micro-organisms, however, contain glutamate decarboxylase.

Consequently a microbial sensor for glutamic acid has therefore been devised incorporating immobilized *Escherichia coli* (as a source of glutamate decarboxylase activity) in conjunction with a CO_2-sensing electrode (Hikuma *et al.* 1980c). Preliminary experiments have shown that *E. coli* does not evolve carbon dioxide under anaerobic condition in the absence of glutamic aicd. Any carbon dioxide produced by these bacteria under such conditions results from the glutamate decarboxylase reaction. Nitrogen gas was passed through the flow cell in order to remove any dissolved oxygen from the buffer and sample solution. When a sample solution containing glutamic acid was injected into the system, glutamic acid permeated through the membrane to the immobilized micro-organisms and was metabolized by to produce carbon dioxide. The enzyme reaction was carried out at pH 4.4, which was sufficiently below the pk_a value (6.34 at 25 °C) of carbon dioxide. As a result, the potential of the CO_2-sensing electrode increased with time. The assay can be performed using an injection period of 1–3 min and measuring the maximum potential, with little loss of sensitivity.

A plot of the maximum potential *vs.* the logarithm of the glutamic acid concentration was linear in the range 100–800 mg l^{-1}. When replicates of a glutamic acid solution (400 mg l^{-1}) were measured, the standard deviation was 1.2 mg l^{-1} (20 experiments).

2.9 Cephalosporin sensor

Antibiotics are usually determined by microbioassay based on a turbidimetric or titrimetric method, but these methods require complicated procedures and are not suitable for a rapid determination.

It was found that *Citrobacter freundii* produced cephalosporinase, which catalyses the following reaction of cephalosporin with liberation of hydrogen ions:

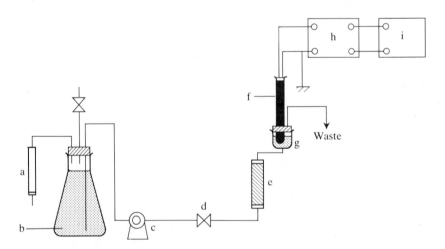

Cephalosporinase is, however, very unstable and as a result it is difficult to utilize it in the preparation of an enzyme sensor. Immobilized whole cells of *Citrobacter freundii* were employed for the cephalosporin sensor being immobilized in a collagen membrane. This bacteria-collagen membrane was then inserted into a membrane reactor.

The system used for continuous determination of cephalosporins is illustrated in Fig. 2.8. The reactor is a membrane type with a spacer located in the centre. The pH change caused by the enzymatic reaction was measured using a combined glass electrode and displayed on a recorder.

Sample solutions containing various amounts of cephalosporins were inserted into the reactor, causing the electrode potential difference to increase with time until a maximum was reached. The minimum response time depended on the flow rate and activity of the bacteria-collagen membrane. For a flow rate of 2 ml min^{-1}, the maximum potential difference was reached after 10 min.

A linear relationship was obtained between the logarithm of the

Fig. 2.8 Immobilized whole cell-based flow-type sensor for cephlosporins. a, Soda lime; b, buffer reservoir; c, peristaltic pump; d, sample inlet; e, immobilized whole cell reactor; f, combined glass electrode; g, sensing chamber; h, amplifier; i, recorder.

cephalosporin concentration and the maximum potential difference. 7-Phenyl-acetylamidodesacetoxy-sporanic acid (phenyl-acetyl-7ADCA), cephaloridine, cephalothin, and cephalosporin C were determined by the cephalosporin sensor.

The stability of the microbial sensor was examined with a solution containing 125 μg ml^{-1} of phenylacetyl-7ADCA. The cephalosporin determination was carried out several times a day, giving no change in the observed potential difference response after one week.

The system was applied to the determination of cephalosporin C in a broth of *Cephalosporium acremonium*, and was compared with a method based on high-pressure liquid chromatography (HPLC). The relative error of the determination by the microbial system was 8%. Accordingly, the method is suitable for continuous analysis of cephalosporins in fermentation broths.

2.10 BOD sensor

The biochemical oxygen demand (BOD) is one of the most widely used tests in the measurement of organic pollution. The conventional BOD test requires, however, a five day incubation period. Therefore, a more rapid and reproducible method is required for assessing BOD.

Trichosporon cutaneum, which is used for waste water treatment, was used for the BOD sensor (Karube *et al.* 1977). The sensor configuration is the same as previously described.

Phosphate buffer solution (0.01 M, pH 7) saturated with dissolved oxygen was transferred to the flow cell at a flow rate of 1 ml min^{-1}. When the current reached a steady state value, a sample was injected into the flow cell at a rate of 0.2 ml min^{-1}.

The steady state current was dependent on the BOD of the sample solution. Then the current of the microbial sensor gradually returned to the initial level. The response time of the microbial sensor (time required for the current to reach steady state) depended on the nature of the sample solution used.

A linear relationship was observed between the current difference (between initial and steady state currents) and the five-day BOD assay of the standard solution (glucose and glutamate solution) up to 60 mg l^{-1}. The minimum measurable BOD was 3 mg l^{-1}. The current was reproducible within $\pm$ 6% of the relative error when BOD 40 mg l^{-1} was employed over ten experiments.

The microbial sensor was applied to the estimation of 5-day BOD for untreated waste waters from a fermentation factory. The 5-day BOD of the waste waters was determined by a JIS method (Japanese Industrial Standard Committee). Good correlation was obtained between BOD estimated by the microbial sensor and those determined by the JIS method. (Regression coefficient was 1.2 over 17 experiments) and the ratios (BOD estimated by the

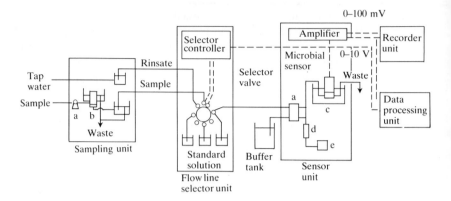

Fig. 2.9 Schematic diagram of continual measuring system for BOD. a, pump; b, filter; c, incubator; d, flow meter; e, air pump.

microbial sensor/5-day BOD determined by JIS method) were in the range from 0.85 to 1.36. This variation might have been caused by a change in composition of the organic waste water. The BOD of various kinds of untreated industrial waste waters were estimated by the sensor, and the response was found to depend on compounds present in the waste waters. The BOD sensor system shown in Fig. 2.9 has now been commercialized in Japan.

2.11 Ammonia sensor

The determination of ammonia is important in clinical and industrial process analysis. Several ammonia sensors based on potentiometry have been developed for the determination of ammonia, but interference by metal ions and volatile amines can occur. Therefore, an ammonia sensor based on amperometry is desirable for the determination of ammonia.

Nitrifying bacteria utilize ammonia as the sole energy source, the respiratory consumption of oxygen being as follows:

$$NH_3 + 1.5O_2 \xrightarrow{\textit{Nitrosomonas} \text{ sp.}} NO_2^- + H_2O + H^+$$

$$NO_2^- + 0.5O_2 \xrightarrow{\textit{Nitrobacter} \text{ sp.}} NO_3^-$$

Therefore, oxygen uptake by the bacteria can be directly determined by immobilizing the bacteria to an oxygen electrode.

An ammonia sensor consisted of immobilized bacteria, a gas permeable Teflon membrane, and an oxygen electrode (Hikuma *et al*, 1980a; Ohada *et al.* 1983). A linear relationship was observed between the current decrease and the ammonia concentration up to a maximum concentration of

42 mg l^{-1}, the minimum determinable concentration being 0.1 mg l^{-1}. The current decrease was reproducible to within $\pm 4\%$ of the relative error when a sample solution containing 21 mg l^{-1} of ammonium hydroxide was employed. The standard deviation was 0.7 mg dl^{-1} over 20 experiments.

The sensitivity of the microbial sensor was approximately equal to that of a glass electrode.

The sensor did not respond to volatile compounds such as acetic acid, ethanol and amines or nonvolatile nutrients such as glucose, amino acids and metal ions. The current output of the sensor was stable for more than ten days and 200 assays.

The determination of ammonia in human urine was performed using the microbial sensor and a conventional method. Good comparative results were obtained between ammonia concentrations determined by both methods, the microbial sensor possessing good long term ability.

2.12 Other microbial sensors

Various other microbial sensors have been developed by our group (Karube *et al.* 1979*a*; Matsunaga *et al.* 1978*a*, *b*; 1979). The characteristics of these microbial sensors are summarized in Table 2.2 (see over).

Table 2.2 Characteristics of micro-organism based sensors

Sensor	Immoblized Micro-organisms	Device	Response time (min)	Range (mg dm^{-3})
Assimilable sugars	*Brevibacterium lactofermentum*	O$_2$-probe	10	10 – 200
Glucose	*Pseudomonas fluorescens*	O$_2$-probe	10	2 – 2 × 10
Acetic acid	*Trichosporon brassicae*	O$_2$-probe	10	3 – 60
Ethanol	*Trichosporon brassicae*	O$_2$-probe	10	2 – 25
Methanol	Unidentified bacteria	O$_2$-probe	10	5 – 2 × 10
Formic acid	*Citrobacter freundii*	fuel cell	30	10 – 10^3
Methane	*Methylomonas flagellata*	O$_2$-probe	2	0 – 6.6^a
Glutamic acid	*Escherichia coli*	CO$_2$-probe	5	8 – 800
Cephalosporin	*Citrobacter freundii*	pH electrode	10	10^2 – 5 × 10^2
BOD	*Trichosporon cutaneum*	O$_2$-probe	15	3 – 60
Lysine	*Escherichia coli*	CO$_2$-probe	5	10 – 10^2
Ammonia	Nitrifying bacteria	O$_2$-probe	10	0.05 – 1
Nitrogen dioxide	Nitrifying bacteria	O$_2$-probe	3	0.51 – 255^b
Nystatin	*Saccharomyces cerevisiae*	O$_2$-probe	1(h)	0.5 – 54^c
Nicotinic acid	*Lactobacillus arabinosis*	pH electrode	1(h)	10^{-5} – 5
Vitamin B$_1$	*Lactobacillus fermenti*	fuel cell	6(h)	10^{-3} – 10^{-2}
Cell population	—	fuel cell	15	10^8 – 10$^{9\ d}$
Mutagen	*Bacillus subtilis* Rec$^-$	O$_2$-probe	1(h)	1.6 – 2.8 × 10^3

^{a} mmol, ^{b} ppm, ^{c} Units cm^{-3}, ^{d} Number cm^{-3}

References

Aizawa, M., Karube, I. and Suzuki, S., (1974). A specific bioelectrochemical sensor for hydrogen peroxide. *Anal. Chim. Acta*, **69**, 431.

Chang, T. M. S. (ed.)(1977) *Biomedical applications of immobilized enzymes and proteins*, Vol. 2 Plenum, New York.

Guilbault, G. G. (1976). *Handbook of enzymatic methods of analysis*. Marcel Dekked, New York.

Hikuma, M., Kubo, T., Yasuda, T., Karube, I. and Suzuki, S. (1979a). Amperometric determination of acetic acid with immobilized *Trichosporon brassicae*. *Anal, Chim. Acta* **109**, 33.

—— (1979b). Microbial electrode sensor for alcohols. *Biotechnol. Bioeng.* **21**, 1845.

—— (1980a). Ammonia electrode with immobilized nytrifying bacteria. *Anal. Chem.* **52**, 1020.

—— Obana, H., Yasuda, T., Karube, I., Suzuki, S., (1980b). Amperometric determination of total assimilable sugars in fermentation broths with use of immobilized whole cells, *Enzyme Microb. Technol.* **2**, 234.

—— (1980c). 'A potentiometric microbial sensor based on immobilized *Escherichia coli* for glutamic acid,' *Anal. Chim. Acta* **116**, 61.

Karube, I., (1984). Microbial sensor for screening mutagens. *Trends in Anal. Chem.* **3**, 40.

Karube, I., Matsunaga, T. and Suzuki, S., (1979a) Microbioassay of nystatin with a yeast electrode. *Anal. Chim. Acta* **109**, 39.

—— Mitsuda, S. and Suzuki, S., (1979b) Glucose sensor using immobilized whole cells of *Pseudomonas fluorecens*. *Europ. J. Appl. Microbiol. Biotechnol.* **7**, 343.

—— Okada, T. and Suzuki, S., (1982). A methane gas sensor based on oxidizing bacteria. *Anal. Chim. Acta* **135**, 61.

—— Mitsuda, S., Matsunaga, T. and Suzuki, S., (1977) A rapid method for estimation of BOD by using immobilized microbial cells. *J. of Fermentation Technology* **55**, 243.

Matsunaga, T., Karube, I. and Suzuki, S., (1978a). Rapid determination of nicotinic acid by immobilized *Lactobacillus arabinosus*. *Anal. Chim. Acta* **99**, 233.

—— (1978b). Electrochemical microbioassay of vitamin B1. *Anal. Chim. Acta* **98**, 25.

—— (1979) Electrode system for the determination of microbial population. *Appl. Envir. Microb.* **37**, 117.

—— (1980). A specific microbial sensor for formic acid. *Europ. J. Microbiol. Biotechnol.* **10**, 235.

Okada, T., Karube, I. and Suzuki, S., (1983). NO_2 sensor which use immobilized nitrite oxidizing bacteria, *Biotechnol. Bioeng.*, **25**, 1641.

Satoh, I., Karube, I. and Suzuki, S., (1977a). Continuous neutral lipid determination with lipase-collagen membrane reactor. *J. Solid-Phase Biochem.* **2**, 1.

—— (1977b). Enzyme electrode for free cholesterol, *Biotechnol. Bioeng.* **19**, 1095.

Technicon Industrial Systems, No. 142-71A, (1972).

3

Biosensors based on plant and animal tissue

MARK A. ARNOLD and GARRY A. RECHNITZ

Tissue materials from plant and mammalian sources have been successfully employed as the biocatalytic component for the construction of biosensors. This class of biocatalytic materials simply maintains the enzyme of interest in its natural environment which results in a considerable stabilization of the desired enzymatic activity. In many cases, tissue based biosensors have been found to have much improved useful lifetimes in comparison to the corresponding isolated enzyme based biosensor. In addition, tissue materials have been shown to provide sufficiently high specific activities for the construction of certain biosensors where isolated enzymes have failed. These advantages have been obtained without sacrificing overall selectivity in most cases. For those situations where interfering processes are present in the tissue material, a selectivity enhancement strategy has been developed. In this chapter the relative merits of tissue based biocatalysts are presented by considering individually each tissue biosensor that has been developed. Moreover, several biosensors based on related types of biocatalytic materials such as subcellular fractions of mammalian cells are reviewed. Finally, several possible models for the transport of substrate and product into, within, and out from the immobilized tissue cells are proposed for the first time.

From an historical point of view, tissue biosensors were introduced after the development of isolated enzyme and bacterial biosensors (Arnold 1983; Arnold and Meyerhoff 1984; Guilbault 1984; Meyerhoff and Fraticelli 1982; Rechnitz 1981, 1982). The concept of employing a whole section of mammalian tissue as a biocatalytic layer was first demonstrated with the fabrication of an arginine sensor (Rechnitz 1978). In this first case, a thin slice of bovine liver and an aliquot of the enzyme urease were co-immobilized at the surface of an ammonia gas-sensing probe. The reactions catalysed at the sensor tip are shown below.

$$\text{Arginine} \xrightarrow{\text{Bovine liver}} \text{Urea} + \text{Ornithine}$$

$$\text{Urea} \xrightarrow{\text{Urease}} 2NH_3 + CO_2$$

This first bovine liver probe opened the way for the development of several practical tissue biosensors.

Table 3.1 Biosensors based on tissues and related materials

Substrate	Biocatalytic material	Sensing element
Glutamine	Porcine kidney cells	NH_3-sensor
Adenosine	Mouse small-intestine mucosal cells	NH_3-sensor
Adenosine 5'-monophosphate	Rabbit muscle	NH_3-sensor
Adenosine 5'-monophosphate	Rabbit muscle acetone powder	NH_3-sensor
Guanine	Rabbit liver	NH_3-sensor
Hydrogen peroxide	Bovine liver	O_2-sensor
Glutamate	Yellow squash	CO_2-sensor
Pyruvate	Corn kernel	CO_2-sensor
Urea	Jack bean meal	NH_3-sensor
Phosphate/fluoride	Potato tuber/glucose oxidase	O_2-sensor
Dopamine	Banana pulp	O_2-sensor
Tyrosine	Sugar beet	O_2-sensor
Cysteine	Cucumber leaf	NH_3-sensor
Glutamine	Porcine kidney mitochondria	NH_3-sensor

Table 3.1 summarizes the tissue biosensors and related systems which have been reported since the first bovine liver based arginine electrode. Related systems include the use of sub-cellular fractions, mammalian organ acetone powders, plant seed meals, and entire plant leaves and fruits as the bio-catalytic component. The next section of this chapter will detail these biosensor systems individually with a particular interest in enhancements of the analytical response owing to the biocatalyst of interest.

3.1 Glutamine biosensor

A thin slice of porcine kidney cortex cells has been immobilized at the surface of an ammonia gas-sensing probe. A high concentration of the enzyme glutaminase, which catalyses the reaction shown below, is known to be located within these cells. By utilizing this biocatalytic activity in combination with an ammonia probe, a sensor for glutamine can be constructed.

$$\text{Glutamine} + H_2O \rightleftharpoons \text{Glutamate} + NH_3$$

Immobilization of the porcine kidney is accomplished by physically retaining the tissue material using a monofilament mesh of nylon with a pore size of 149 μm. To protect the gas permeable membrane of the ammonia probe from the various cellular components of the tissue slice, a thin cellulose

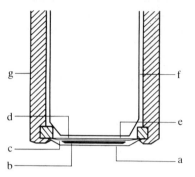

Fig. 3.1 Configuration of porcine kidney biosensor for glutamine. a, Nylon support membrane; b, porcine kidney slice; c, inner dialysis membrane; d, Teflon gas-permeable membrane; e, internal electrolyte; f, combination glass pH electrode; and g, outer body (components d–g represent the ammonia gas sensor).

diacetate membrane is positioned between the kidney section and the Teflon membrane. Figure 3.1 shows the arrangement of layers used for this biosensor.

As glutamine from the bulk solution interacts with the immobilized bio-

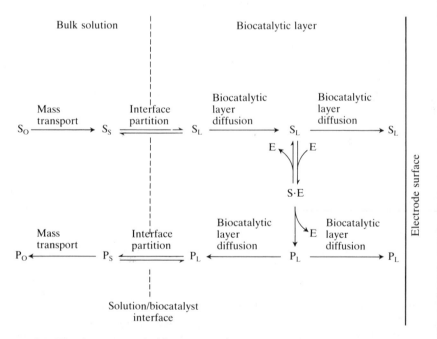

Fig. 3.2 Kinetic processes in biosensor response.

catalytic layer, ammonia is generated by the action of glutaminase. A steady state concentration of ammonia is eventually reached as the production of ammonia is counterbalanced by the depletion of ammonia at the probe surface. Simple diffusion of ammonia back into the bulk solution is mainly responsible for ammonia depletion (Arnold and Rechnitz 1982*b*, Carr and Bowers 1980). Figure 3.2 shows schematically the various kinetic processes which contribute to the sensor response. Because the ammonia probe is a potentiometric device, the resulting sensor response is related to bulk glutamine concentrations in a logrithmic fashion.

Figure 3.3 presents a typical glutamine calibration curve. For the porcine kidney glutamine biosensor, a typical response slope of 50 mV per concentration decade is observed over a linear range which extends from approximately 0.1 to 10 mM. A detection limit, as defined by IUPAC recommendations (IUPAC Analytical Chemistry Division 1976), of 0.01 mM has been established. Measured response times range from 7 to 5 minutes over the linear range of the sensor using a 0.1 M phosphate, pH 7.8 buffer. Longer response times are obtained at lower glutamine concentrations as is expected for this type of sensor (Carr and Bowers 1980; Kobos 1980).

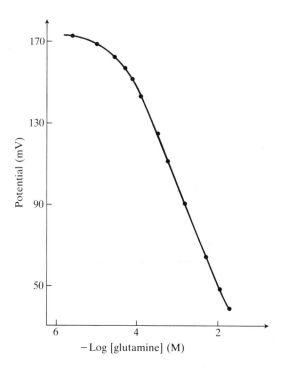

Fig. 3.3 Glutamine calibration curve using porcine kidney biosensor.

Of course, the selectivity of a biosensor based on whole tissue cells must be considered in detail owing to the large number of suspected biocatalytic activities within these cells. The selectivity properties of the porcine kidney biosensor have been examined and found to be suitable for glutamine determinations in complex biological matrixes. The following compounds have been specifically tested as possible interferents but no significant response has been observed: urea, L-alanine, L-arginine, L-histidine, L-valine, L-serine, L-glutamate, L-asparagine, L-aspartate, D-alanine, D-aspartate, glycine, and creatinine. Sensor response to various D-amino acids and glycine has been examined because high concentrations of D-amino acid oxidase are known to be located in porcine kidney cells (Dixon and Kleppe 1965). This enzyme catalyses the oxidative deamination of several D-amino acids in the presence of oxygen and water. Under the specified operating conditions of the glutamine biosensor, however, no response to the tested D-amino acids has been detected. Most likely this lack of interfering activity is due to the absence of flavin adenine dinucleotide (FAD) in the buffer system (Guilbault and Hrabankova 1971).

In order to obtain such a high degree of selectivity, it is necessary to include an anti-microbial agent in order to prohibit bacterial contamination of the tissue slice. Without the addition of a suitable agent, bacterial growth on the tissue material results in unwanted biocatalytic activities at the probe surface which drastically alters the sensor's selectivity pattern. For the glutamine sensors, 0.02% sodium azide is added as a preservative.

Selectivity of the tissue-based glutamine biosensor has been further established by application of the sensor to the quantification of glutamine in cerebrospinal fluid (CSF) control samples (Arnold and Rechnitz 1980a). After treatment of CSF samples with a cation exchanger to remove background ammonia-nitrogen which would interfer with the biosensor response, glutamine measurements can be made with good precision and accuracy over the clinically important range. For these glutamine measurements, however, iodoacetamide must be added to the working buffer to prohibit an interfering process which involves glucose. Apparently, glycolysis within the kidney cells generates an acid from glucose which alters the potential of the pH sensitive ammonia probe. Iodoacetamide is an established inhibitor of glycolysis and has been found to be effective in suppressing the glucose response of the glutamine biosensor. Glutamine determination in CSF samples can be made over the concentration range of 2.2×10^{-5} to 1.29×10^{-3} M with an average relative standard deviation of 5.6%. Such a sensor might prove valuable in studies involving Reye's syndrome where elevated glutamine levels have been proposed as a diagnostic tool.

An interesting feature of the tissue based glutamine biosensor is its extended lifetime in comparison to that of a similar biosensor based on the

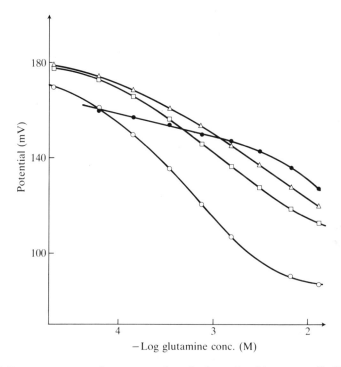

Fig. 3.4 Response curves for enzyme based glutamine biosensor. ○, Day one; □, day two; △, day three; and ●, day four.

isolated enzyme. In the case of the isolated enzyme system, glutaminase is immobilized at the ammonia sensor surface using a thin cellulose diacetate membrane. Calibration curves with the enzyme system have been found to degrade quite rapidly after sensor construction. Figure 3.4 shows several glutamine response curves using isolated glutaminase as the biocatalytic component. It can be seen that in a matter of days the response is essentially unusable owing to the loss of a large portion of the enzymatic activity. On the other hand, the tissue glutamine sensor has been found to be usable for up to 28 days with essentially no change in the steady-state and dynamic response properties of the biosensor (Rechnitz *et al.* 1979). This tremendous enhancement in the useful lifetime of the sensor has been attributed to a stabilization of the enzymatic activity by maintaining the enzyme in the tissue matrix. We are simply taking advantage of the optimal environment that nature has provided for the use of this particular enzyme. For these lifetime studies, biosensors were simply stored between use in the working buffer at room temperature; hence, no elaborate conditions or equipment are required for effective storage of the tissue biosensor.

Table 3.2   Response characteristics of glutamine biosensors

	Enzyme	Mitochondria	Bacteria	Tissue
Slope (mV/decade)	33–41	53	49	50
Detection limit (M)	6.0×10^{-5}	2.2×10^{-5}	5.6×10^{-5}	2.0×10^{-5}
Linear range (mM)	0.15–3.3	0.11–5.5	0.1–10	0.064–5.2
Response time (min)	4–5	6–7	5	5–7
Lifetime (days)	1	10^a	20^a	30^a

[a]Minimum value

The glutamine biosensor is unique in the sense that several types of biocatalytic materials have been employed and examined for its construction. Specifically, the isolated enzyme glutaminase, mitochondria from porcine kidney cells (see below), whole sections of porcine kidney tissue, and intact bacterial cells of the strain *Sarcina flava* have been studied as possible bio-catalytic materials and they have been directly compared in order to determine their relative merits (Arnold and Rechnitz 1980*b*).

Tables 3.2 and 3.3 summarize the most important properties of glutamine sensors based on each type of biocatalytic material. Table 3.2 lists the various

Table 3.3   Operation and preparation requirements for glutamine biosensors

Electrode Type	Operating medium	Preparation needs
Enzyme electrode	0.1 M phosphate buffer, pH 7.8, 0.02% NaN$_3$	Enzyme suspension held between dialysis membranes; store at room temperature in buffer.
Tissue electrode	0.1 M phosphate buffer, pH 7.8, 0.02% NaN$_3$	Tissue sliced and supported on nylon net; store in working buffer at room temp.
Mitochondrial electrode	Complex buffer system at pH 8.5; 120 mM KCl, 20 mM Tris-HCl, 40 mM Tris-H$_3$PO$_4$, 5 mM succinate, 1 g/1.5 ml rotenone, 0.02% NaN$_3$	Isolation of mitochondrial fraction, suspension of fraction between dialysis membranes. Condition in working buffer.
Bacterial electrode	0.1 M Tris-HCl, 0.01 M MnCl$_2$, pH 7.5	Culture bacterial strain under sterile conditions; washed cell suspension held between dialysis membranes.

analytical response characteristics of the sensors and the operation and preparation requirements are summarized in Table 3.3. These sensor properties have been attained under optimal conditions for the particular biosensor of interest.

From Table 3.2 it can be seen that values for the respective sensitivities, linear ranges, limits of detection, and response times are similar except for the poorly reproducible enzyme sensor. Hence, these response properties offer no compelling basis for selecting one type of biocatalyst over the other. From consideration of sensor lifetime (see Table 3.2), however, partial differentation of the biocatalyst types can be made. The isolated enzyme has simply too short a useful lifetime to be considered practical. The mitochondrial, bacterial, and tissue biosensors possess significantly longer lifetimes than the isolated enzyme because the enzymatic activity is housed in its natural environment.

After consideration of the preparation and operation requirements for the bacterial and mitochondrial biosensors, it becomes evident that the tissue biosensor is the system of choice for glutamine measurements. The bacterial sensor must be constructed under sterile conditions and the purity of the cell line must be maintained to ensure proper response properties. In addition, mitochondrial fractions must be isolated and maintained for consistant operation of the mitochondrial biosensor. Although isolation of mitochondria is relatively easy in comparison to purification of an enzyme, the required procedure is much more involved then that required to obtain a thin section of porcine kidney tissue. The bacterial biosensor might be the system of choice in cases where a phosphate buffer is unsuitable.

From this comparison study, it can be concluded that the biocatalytic material of choice for glutamine measurements is the porcine kidney slice. However, this conclusion can not be generalized to other types of biosensor systems. Indeed, more comparisons of this type are needed before any general statements can be made concerning biocatalytic materials.

3.2 Adenosine biosensor

Whereas the glutamine biosensor based on a slice of porcine kidney tissue has been demonstrated to possess a high degree of selectivity for glutamine over other biomolecules, it must be realized that tissue biosensors will rarely be highly selective for a given substrate because most tissue materials contain numerous enzymes and are capable of sustaining multiple metabolic pathways. Indeed, a biosensor for adenosine which involves the immobilization of mouse small intestinal mucosal cells at the surface of an ammonia gas-sensing probe displays a considerable response to adenosine-base nucleotides. A selectivity enhancement strategy has been developed for such tissue systems. This strategy involves experimental identification of the interfering

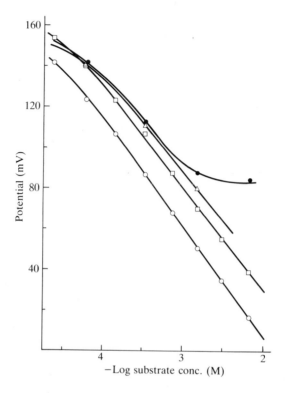

Fig. 3.5 Initial response of mouse small-intestine biosensor. ○, Adenosine; □, AMP; △, ADP; and ●, ATP.

pathway and selective repression of a key enzymatic activity within this pathway. This selectivity exhancement strategy is demonstrated with the mouse small intestine-based adenosine biosensor.

Adenosine electrodes are constructed by maintaining a suspension of mouse small-intestine mucosal cells at the surface of an ammonia gas-sensing probe. This immobilization is accomplished by entrapping the cells in a bovine serum albumin (BSA)-glutaraldehyde matrix on the gas-permeable membrane of the ammonia probe (Arnold and Rechnitz 1981a). The activity of the enzyme adenosine deaminase is employed.

Figure 3.5 shows the response observed for adenosine, adenosine mono-phosphate (AMP), adenosine diphosphate (ADP), and adenosine triphosphate (ATP), using the mouse small-intestine biosensor. These response curves are obtained using a working buffer of 0.2 M Tris-HC1 and 0.02% sodium azide at pH 8.2. It can be seen that adenosine containing nucleotides elicit a significant response which would severely interfere with adenosine measurements. To enhance the sensor selectivity, it is desirable to

Table 3.4 Possible interfering schemes for adenosine sensor

Scheme I:

$$AXP + H_2O \xrightarrow{\text{Non-specific deamination}} IXP + NH_3$$

Scheme II:

$$AMP + H_2O \xrightarrow{\text{AMP deaminase}} IMP + NH_3$$

Scheme III:

$$AMP + H_2O \xrightarrow{\text{Alkaline phosphatase}} Adenosine + Phosphate$$

$$Adenosine \xrightarrow{\text{Adenosine deaminase}} Inosine + NH_3$$

optimize the adenosine deaminating activity and to repress the nucleotide deaminating activity. The most effective method of repressing this activity depends on the metabolic pathway responsible for the interfering deamination.

Reports of the presence of AMP deaminase (Dixon and Webb 1964) and alkaline phosphatase (Conway and Cooke 1939) in mouse small-intestinal mucosal cells have led to three possible schemes for the interfering activity which are shown in Table 3.4. Scheme I represents the case where a single, nonspecific enzyme is present that catalyses the deamination of AMP, ADP, and ATP. Scheme II represents the situation where three specific deaminating enzymes are present for each of the substrates. Finally, Scheme III involves the combined activities of alkaline phosphatase and adenosine deaminase, in which the adenosine-containing nucleotides are converted to adenosine via the first enzyme and then deaminated by the second enzyme which results in the interference.

By examining the effects of various activators and inhibitors on the interfering activity, attempts can be made to distinguish which, if any, of the above mentioned schemes accurately describes the interfering activity. Reports have shown that phosphate ions inhibit the enzymatic activity of both alkaline phosphatase (Fernley and Walker 1967) and AMP deaminase (Ronca-Testoni *et al.* 1970). Also glycerophosphate is known to inhibit AMP deaminase (Sammons *et al.* 1970) and it is acted upon by alkaline phosphatase (Macfarlane *et al.* 1934). In the latter case, substrate specificity is such that at high concentrations of glycerophosphate the action of alkaline phosphatase on AMP is negligible. Figure 3.6 shows the effect of phosphate and glycerophosphate on the AMP and adenosine deaminating activities of

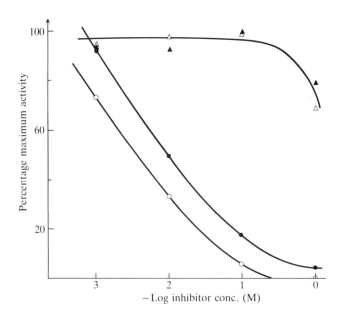

Fig. 3.6 Effect of glycerophosphate (solid characters) and phosphate (open characters) on the deamination of ○, ●, AMP and △, ▲, Adenosine.

the tissue-based adenosine electrode. It can be seen that high concentrations of each substance result in a drastic decrease in the AMP deaminating activity with only a slight decrease in the adenosine deaminating activity.

It is known that AMP deaminase is dependent on the presence of potassium ions for its activity (Zielke and Suelter 1960). A study of the effect of potassium ions on the mouse small-intestinal mucosal cell deamination of AMP reveals that there is no such dependence in terms of the interfering activity. On the other hand, the activity of intestinal alkaline phosphatase is reported to be stereospecifically inhibited by L-phenylalanine (Fishman 1963; Ghosh and Fishman 1966). The effect of L-phenylalanine on the response for AMP reveals an inhibition of the AMP deaminating activity at a concentration of 0.1 M L-phenylalanine. As a result virtually no response for AMP is detectable by the electrode system in the presence of L-phenylalanine.

The reported pH optima for the enzymes under consideration are approximately 6.5 for AMP deaminase (Conway and Cooke 1939) and from 7.0 to 9.0 for alkaline phosphatase (Kay 1932). The pH optimum for the AMP deaminating activity of the mouse small intestinal mucosal cells is 8.2 which is within the optimum pH range of alkaline phosphatase. A pH range from 9.0 to 9.4 has been found to be optimal for the adenosine deaminating activity.

High activity of AMP deaminase is commonly found in muscle tissues (Conway and Cooke 1939); whereas, alkaline phosphatase is found in high levels in intestinal mucosal cells of various mammalian species (Kay 1932).

Previously reported distribution patterns of these enzymes and the results presented above, including the inhibitory effects of glycerophosphate, phosphate, and L-phenylalanine, the lack of activation by potassium ions, and the pH optimum of the interfering activity, provide strong evidence that the coupling of alkaline phosphatase and adenosine deaminase is principally responsible for the interfering activity of the mucosal cell biocatalytic layer.

On the basis of the above results, a buffer system containing phosphate ions at pH 9.0 should effectively repress the interfering activity of the tissue-based adenosine electrode while optimizing the desired biocatalytic activity. Figure 3.7 shows the selectivity for adenosine which is obtained with a buffer system of 0.1 M Tris-HCl, 0.2 M K_2HPO_4, and 0.02% NaN_3 at pH 9.0. Under these conditions no response is observed for AMP, ADP, or ATP. Other possible interferents which have been tested and found to give no response include 3'-AMP, cAMP, adenine, guanosine, and guanine.

Although selectivity for adenosine is not an inherent characteristic of the tissue-based adenosine electrode, it is possible to enhance the selectivity of

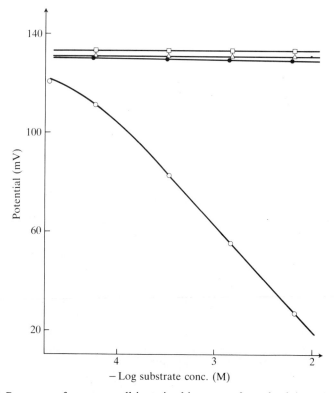

Fig. 3.7 Response of mouse small-intestine biosensor after selectivity enhancement. ○, Adenosine; □, AMP; △, ADP; and ●, ATP.

the electrode system by determining the metabolic pathway responsible for the interfering activity and by repressing this activity with an effective inhibitor. This technique of enhancing selectivity has proven valuable in the development of other tissue-based membrane electrodes.

3.3 AMP biosensor

Aside from the enhancement of biosensor lifetimes, tissue materials have been demonstrated to provide a large concentration of a particular biocatalytic activity. Because of the restricted surface area of the ammonia gas-sensing probe, limited amounts of an enzyme preparation can be immobilized at the sensor surface. Therefore, if the specific activity of the enzyme preparation is too low, small amounts of immobilized enzyme will result which leads to poor analytical response characteristics. An example of this low enzyme concentration effect is the AMP enzyme electrode (Papastathopoulos and Rechnitz 1976). The isolated enzyme for this sensor is commonly available only at low specific activities and, as a result, AMP biosensors with low slopes and short useful lifetimes are obtained. By employing a thin layer of rabbit muscle tissue, however, an AMP biosensor with considerable improvement in slope and lifetime is possible. Improvement in response can be directly attributed to a five-fold increase in the amount of biocatalytic activity at the probe surface.

Both the enzyme and tissue biosensors for AMP use the catalysed reaction shown below at the surface of an ammonia gas-sensing probe.

$$AMP + H_2O \rightleftharpoons IMP + NH_3$$

The isolated enzyme is immobilized at the probe surface using a cellulose diacetate membrane and the tissue biosensor holds a thin section of rabbit muscle tissue at the probe surface with a 37 μm nylon mesh. AMP biosensors of both types are stored at room temperature between use in a working buffer which consists of 0.1 M Tris-HCl, 0.1 M KCl, and 0.02% sodium azide at pH 7.5. The tissue biosensor must be conditioned for 2 to 4 hours after construction to remove background ammonia.

Various experimental parameters have been optimized with respect to the response of the tissue-based AMP sensor. These parameters include pH, potassium concentration, temperature, and tissue thickness. Optimal conditions have been found to be pH 7.5 with 0.1 M potassium at 25 °C. The effect of tissue thickness has been examined and the results are presented in Fig. 3.8. Increases in tissue thickness result in longer electrode response times with unusable response times being observed when the tissue thickness is greater than 0.81 mm. On the other hand, tissue slices less than 0.5 mm are difficult to handle and reproduce. For these reasons, tissue thicknesses ranging from 0.5 to 0.8 mm are typically used for sensor construction and

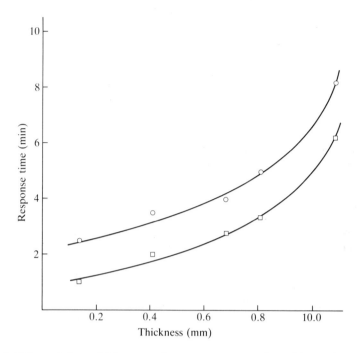

Fig. 3.8 Effect of tissue thickness on biosensor response time. Change in substrate concentration; ○, from 0.14 to 0.34 mM and □, from 3.0 to 6.6 mM.

can be conveniently prepared with a sharp razor blade.

A 0.5 mm rabbit muscle slice contains approximately five international units (IU) of AMP deaminating activity (Arnold and Rechnitz 1981*b*). This compares to only 0.1 IU of activity from a comparable volume (25 μl) of the commercially available enzyme. This small amount of activity results in enzyme biosensors with poor analytical response. In fact, before immobilization the isolated enzyme must be concentrated using a 16-hour filtration process which results in 0.9 IU of activity at the electrode surface (Papastathopoulos and Rechnitz 1976). Even after this concentration procedure, nearly five times greater activity can be supplied using the tissue slice. Table 3.5 summarizes the response characteristics for AMP sensors based upon each of these biocatalytic materials. Higher amounts of activity using the tissue section results in excellent response characteristics including a slope of 58 mV per concentration decade and a lifetime of at least 28 days. In contrast, the enzyme system displays a slope of only 46 mV per concentration decade and a lifetime of just four days. This study shows the effectiveness of using tissue slices over isolated enzymes in situations where the latter have insufficient biocatalytic specific activity.

In certain cases, it is difficult to locate a reliable supplier of a particular

Table 3.5 Comparison of AMP biosensor response characteristics

Response characteristic	Isolated enzyme	Tissue slice	Acetone powder
Slope (mV/Decade)	46	58	57
Linear range ($\times\ 10^4$, M)	0.8–150	1.4–100	3.3–130
Detection limit ($\times\ 10^5$, M)	6.0	4.8	4.0
Response time (min)	2–6	2.5–8.5	2.5–8.0
Lifetime (days)	4	28	25

mammalian species in order to obtain a specific tissue material. In these cases, it might be more convenient to employ an acetone powder of the desired tissue material as the biocatalytic component. The first such attempt has been reported in the construction of an AMP biosensor in which a slurry of rabbit muscle acetone powder is physically retained at the surface of an ammonia probe (Arnold and Fiocchi 1984).

The rabbit muscle acetone powder slurry is prepared by dispensing 300 μl of a 0.1 M Tris-HCl, 0.1 M KCl, 0.02% sodium azide, pH 7.9 buffer into a 1 ml plastic vial. A 100 mg portion of frozen acetone powder is added to this vial and the mixture is agitated on a vortex mixer for thirty seconds. This treatment produces a homogeneous slurry of the biocatalyst of which the desired amount (generally 10 mg) is placed on the Teflon membrane of the ammonia probe. A cellulose diacetate membrane is placed over the slurry and the electrode cap is screwed in position which holds the slurry in place. The finished biosensor must be allowed to condition overnight in the previously mentioned buffer solution to remove background ammonia from the biocatalytic layer.

Table 3.5 summarizes the response characteristics of the rabbit muscle acetone powder biosensor for AMP. In comparison to the other AMP biosensors, the acetone powder system matches very closely the response characteristics of the tissue biosensor. Both are superior to the isolated enzyme case, particularly with respect to slope and lifetime. Because the acetone powder is generally more readily available at lower cost it is most likely the biocatalytic material of choice for many AMP measurements.

3.4 Guanine biosensor

As more tissue type biosensing probes are developed, the need for an effective optimization strategy for tissue biocatalysts becomes increasingly evident. Such a strategy has been proposed in which the biochemical processes and membrane phases involved in biosensor response are specifically considered (Arnold and Rechnitz 1982a). This strategy is illustrated through the optimization of a guanine biosensor which employs a section of rabbit liver with an ammonia gas sensor. The important biocatalytic activity is shown below.

$$\text{Guanine} + \text{H}_2\text{O} \rightleftharpoons \text{Xanthine} + \text{NH}_3$$

Guanine biosensors are prepared by placing a 0.5 mm slice of rabbit liver between two cellulose dialysis membranes. The liver section is then positioned on the gas-permeable membrane of the ammonia probe and the sensor is assembled as normal. Freshly prepared sensors are conditioned overnight in a pH 8.0, 0.2 M borate buffer containing 0.02% sodium azide. Guanine sensors are stored in this buffer at room temperature between measurements.

Optimization of a tissue biosensor must include experimental characterizations of various sensor parameters. Typically, the method of tissue slice immobilization, effects of pH, activators, and inhibitors, biosensor lifetime, and overall selectivity must be considered in detail. Several methods of tissue slice immobilization are available based either on physical retainment with an appropriate membrane or entrappment in a crosslinked protein matrix. Many tissue materials can be effectively immobilized with relative ease using a mesh of nylon owing to the connective properties of most tissue sections. For the guanine biosensor, the rabbit liver is held at the electrode surface using a cellulose diacetate membrane because this liver material does not have the required mechanical integrity to permit the use of a large pore nylon mesh.

The effects of pH and activator as well as inhibitor concentrations on a tissue biosensor are generally important to consider. Biocatalytic activities and gas-sensing membrane electrodes are both dependent on solution pH. In addition, activators can often be added to enhance a desired activity and inhibitors can be employed to suppress an interfering activity. A convenient method for studying these effects is the initial rate measurement where the rate of product generation at the start of a biocatalysed reaction is directly related to the effective biocatalytic activity (Guilbault *et al.* 1968). Although this method can only supply relative information, it is quick and convenient for comparisons of various solution conditions. It is important to realize, especially during pH studies, that the initial rate of a biosensing probe is a function of both the catalytic and the sensing components. Therefore, measurements of this type allow for a simultaneous optimization of conditions with respect to each. For the guanine sensor, maximal rate of ammonia production is obtained using pH 9.5; however, based on biocatalyst stability and electrode lifetime considerations, pH 8.0 is more practical even though only 50 percent of the maximal activity is obtained.

The useful lifetime of a biosensor is frequently limited by the stability of the biocatalytic component (Arnold 1982*a*). For this reason, addition of stabilizing agents and optimization of storage conditions must be considered

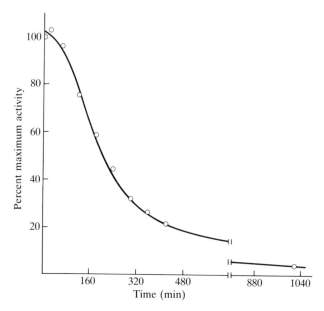

Fig. 3.9 Instability of guanase activity at pH 9.5.

for maximal lifetimes. The importance of proper storage conditions is exemplified nicely by the rabbit liver guanine sensor where the optimal pH for action of the biocatalyst is not the pH optimum for biocatalyst stability. Figure 3.9 shows the instability of the guanase activity at pH 9.5 which is the optimal pH for the catalysed reaction. The rapid decline in activity clearly indicates that biosensors stored at this pH would be short lived. Similar results are obtained at pH 9.0 and 8.5, but a stable biosensor results when a pH 8.0 storage solution is used.

Besides the stability of the immobilized tissue material, the lifetime of the bulk organ from which numerous biosensors can be prepared must be considered. Table 3.6 summarizes the storage conditions and minimal lifetime of several tissue materials. Excellent storage times and inherent low cost can make tissue slices the most economical type of biocatalyst for the construction of many biosensing probes.

Of course, any optimization scheme for tissue-based biosensors must give special attention to selectivity, because of the numerous metabolic paths typically found in tissue materials. The main type of interfering activities which are likely to occur include the generation of the measured product from a substrate other than the principal substrate and the utilization of a substrate whose reaction changes the pH at the electrode surface. The first of these is more common and more difficult to eliminate. A strategy for eliminating this type of interference has been reported (see above; Arnold

Table 3.6 Storage conditions of selected bulk organs

Substrate	Biocatalytic material	Storage conditions	lifetime[a] (months)
Glutamine	Porcine kidney	− 25 °C	6
AMP	Rabbit muscle	− 25 °C	7
Guanine	Rabbit liver	− 25 °C	7
Adenosine	Mouse small intestine	− 25 °C in 100% glycerol	2
Glutamate	Yellow squash	+ 4 °C	1
Pyruvate	Corn kernel	+ 4 °C	2

[a] minimum values

and Rechnitz 1981*a*) and involves determining the specific enzyme or enzymes responsible for the interfering activity followed by repression of that activity with the use of specific inhibitors. A major concern in this strategy is to ensure that the added inhibitor has no adverse effect on the desired biocatalytic activity. The second type of interference is best minimized by employing a working solution with high buffer capacity.

Selectivity for the mouse liver guanine biosensor has been found to be excellent in the presence of 1 mM magnesium (II) to inhibit adenosine deaminase and in the absence of phosphate to prohibit the action of guanosine phosphorylase (Arnold and Rechnitz 1982*a*). The resulting sensor displays no response to millimolar concentrations of inosine, adenine, GMP, IMP, creatinine, creatine, asparagine, serine, urea, glutamine, glutamate, ornithine, threonine, lysine, valine, glycine, and arginine.

The combination of fine-tuning the biochemical process and the appropriate selection of membrane materials, tissue thickness, and immobilization process represent the essential elements of the best optimization strategy currently available for tissue biosensors.

3.5 Hydrogen peroxide biosensor

Up to this point each of the tissue sections of interest have been coupled with a potentiometric ammonia membrane electrode. The first amperometric-based tissue biosensor has been reported by Mascini *et al.* (1982) where a slice of bovine liver has been immobilized on an oxygen sensitive probe for the measurement of hydrogen peroxide. This liver contains a large concentration of the enzyme catalase which catalyses the following reaction:

$$2H_2O_2 \longrightarrow O_2 + 2H_2O$$

Oxygen production is monitored amperometrically.

Tissue based peroxide sensors are prepared using a 0.1 mm thick section of bovine liver which is held at the oxygen electrode by a nylon mesh. Livers from a variety of species have been found to be suitable and measurements are obtained in a nitrogen purged buffer of 0.05 M phosphate and 0.2% sodium azide at pH 6.8. A conditioning period of two hours is required after construction.

Hydrogen peroxide response curves reveal a linear response from the bovine liver biosensor down to the 10 μM level. Curves are linear for approximately one order of magnitude and response as well as recovery times are quite fast being less than two minutes at moderate concentrations. This sensor displays remarkable selectivity for hydrogen peroxide with large concentrations of likely interferents such as glucose, alcohol, L-amino acids, and lactate giving no response.

In comparison to an isolated enzyme biosensor, the tissue sensor displays less susceptibility to changes in solution pH and temperature. Moreover, the tissue system is show to have a considerably longer lifetime than the isolated enzyme system, presumably, due to a stabilizing effect of the tissue matrix.

3.6 Glutamate biosensor

The first tissue biosensor involving a slice of plant material has been reported for glutamate measurements (Kuriyama and Rechnitz 1981). A thin layer of yellow squash is immobilized at the surface of a carbon dioxide gas-sensing probe. The reaction shown below is catalysed by the action of glutamate decarboxylase which is know to be present in high concentrations in yellow squash.

$$\text{Glutamate} \rightleftharpoons \text{4-Aminobutyrate} + CO_2$$

The section of squash material is immobilized by entrappment in a BSA-glutaraldehyde matrix and 0.002% chlorhexidine diacetate is used as the preservative.

Optimal response of the yellow squash glutamate biosensor requires a 0.1 M phosphate, pH 5.5 buffer which includes 40% glycerol and 0.3 mM pyridoxal-5'-phosphate (PLP). Under these conditions a Nernstian response to glutamate is obtained from 4.4×10^{-4} to 4.7×10^{-3} M with a slope of 48 mV per concentration decade and a detection limit of 2×10^{-4} M. Response times in the range of ten minutes are common, and the probe remains active over a seven day period. Most importantly, the selectivity for this sensor is excellent with no response to a wide variety of other biologically important compounds (Kuriyama and Rechnitz 1981).

Overall the tissue glutamate biosensor compares favorably to the isolated enzyme system which demonstrates the feasibility of employing plant materials as the biocatalytic component.

3.7 Pyruvate biosensor

As with certain mammalian tissue based biosensing electrodes, a plant tissue pyruvate biosensor shows an extended lifetime over the corresponding isolated enzyme system (Kuriyama *et al.* 1983). This enhancement in sensor lifetime is achieved with no loss of selectivity and is attributed to stabilization of the biocatalytic activity by the plant tissue matrix.

Corn kernels are known to possess high concentrations of the enzyme pyruvate decarboxylase which catalyses the following reaction:

$$\text{Pyruvate} + H_2O \rightleftharpoons \text{Acetaldehyde} + CO_2$$

By coupling this biocatalytic activity with a carbon dioxide gas sensor, pyruvate measurements can be made. Pyruvate sensors have been prepared by physically retaining a thin layer of corn kernel at the carbon dioxide electrode surface with a common dialysis membrane and by entrappment in a BSA-glutaraldehyde matrix. Similar immobilization schemes have been used in the fabrication of pyruvate sensors based on the isolated enzyme.

Response characteristics for the corn kernel tissue and isolated enzyme pyruvate sensors are tabulated in Table 3.7. The corn kernal biocatalyst results in superior response with respect to slope, linear range, and limit of detection. The enzyme system, on the other hand, displays better response times. An attempt to quicken the response time of the tissue electrode has been made by fractionating the corn kernel and immobilizing only the active components. Unfortunately, this strategy is not effective in this case because the biocatalytic activity is evenly distributed throughout much of the kernel.

As summarized in Table 3.7, the useful lifetime of the corn kernel electrode is significantly better than that for the isolated enzyme based sensor. In fact, the response slope of the enzyme system continually declines from about 35 to 12 mV per concentration decade over a three day period; whereas, the tissue system shows minimal changes over a seven day period. This extended lifetime is achieved without sacrificing selectivity, as the tissue system shows no response to a wide variety of compounds tested as possible interferents (Kuriyama *et al.* 1983).

Table 3.7 Response characteristics of pyruvate biosensors

	Enzyme	Corn kernel
Slope (mV/decade)	35	47
Detection limit (M)	1.6×10^{-4}	8.0×10^{-5}
Linear range (mM)	0.74–4.3	0.25–3.0
Response time (min)	4–10	10–25
Lifetime (days)	1	7

3.8 Urea biosensor

A biosensor for the measurement of urea has been reported in which a layer of jack bean meal is employed as the biocatalytic component (Arnold and Glazier 1984). This meal naturally contains a high amount of the enzyme urease which catalyses the following reaction:

$$\text{Urea} + H_2O \longrightarrow 2NH_3 + CO_2$$

This biocatalytic material has been found to be an effective alternative to the isolated enzyme system.

Jack bean meal urea biosensors are prepared by removing the outer layer of the whole jack bean and pulverizing the treated seed with a mortar and pestle. Generally, 7 mg of the freshly ground meal is placed on the surface of an ammonia gas sensor and a paste is made by adding a small volume of buffer (0.2 M Tris-HCl, pH 8.5, 0.1 mM EDTA). After the paste is spread evenly over the membrane, glutaraldehyde is added to crosslink the proteins which results in a stable biocatalytic layer. Urea response curves are obtained in the Tris-HCl, EDTA buffer at 25 °C and biosensors are conveniently stored in this same buffer at room temperature.

Response characteristics for the bean meal urea sensor compare favorably with an isolated enzyme-based urea sensor. Table 3.8 summarizes the important response characteristics for each of these sensors. Moreover, the bean meal has been found to possess an impressive selectivity for urea over a wide range of tested possible interferents (Arnold and Glazier 1984). The jack bean meal has the advantages of lower cost and more convenient storage conditions over the isolated enzyme. Purified urease is moderately expensive and must be stored at or below freezing temperatures. The bean meal, on the other hand, is considerably less expensive and can be effectively stored at room temperature. Overall, jack bean meal is a suitable alternative to purified urease for the construction of urea biosensors.

Table 3.8 Comparison of jack bean meal and urease biosensors

Response characteristic	Jack bean meal	Urease
Slope (mV/Decade)	58	55
Linear range ($\times 10^5$, M)	3.4–150	3.0–500
Detection limit ($\times 10^6$, M)	2.1	1.0
Response time (min)	1–5	1–5
Lifetime (days)	94	60

3.9 Phosphate–fluoride sensor

A hybrid biosensor based on a thin layer of potato tuber and a solution of glucose oxidase has been described for the quantification of phosphate and/or fluoride. The following reactions are catalysed at the surface of an oxygen sensor where the potato tuber provides the enzymatic activity of acid phosphatase:

$$\text{Glucose-6-phosphate} + H_2O \xrightarrow{\substack{\text{Potato} \\ \text{tuber}}} \text{Glucose} + \text{Phosphate}$$

$$\text{Glucose} + O_2 \xrightarrow{\substack{\text{Glucose} \\ \text{oxidase}}} \text{Gluconolactone} + \text{Peroxide}$$

A steady state current is attained from a set glucose-6-phosphate concentration in the external solution. Phosphate and fluoride are well known inhibitors of acid phosphatase (Schubert *et al.* 1984); therefore, the addition of either anion will slow the rate of glucose generation which can be measured as a decrease in the consumption of oxygen. Typically, a steady-state current is established, corresponding to a particular rate of oxygen consumption. The sample or standard containing either phosphate or fluoride is then added and the increase in current is determined from a first derivative recording of a current *vs.* time curve.

Because phosphate is a competitive inhibitor of acid phosphatase, a linear relationship is observed between phosphate concentrations and the reciprocal of the maximum rate of current change. A linear range has been reported from 25 μM to 1.5 mM phosphate. On the other hand, fluoride calibration curves are not linear because of the complicated nature of the non-competitive type of inhibition this anion imposes on acid phosphatase. A workable curve from 0.2 mM to 6 mM fluoride can be obtained, however, Measuring times for both anions are on the order of five minutes and the hybrid sensor remains active for at least 24 days when stored at 4 °C between measurements.

As one might expect for a sensor dependent on inhibition of an enzymatic activity, the potato-based hybrid biosensor suffers from interferences by a variety of acid phosphatase inhibitors. Compounds such as nitrate, borate, molybdate, and organic phosphates are the most noteworthy. Also, glucose and glucose-6-phosphate must be considered interferents as their presence can alter the rate of oxygen production. With appropriate sample pretreatment, however, accurate measurements of both phosphate and fluoride concentrations can be obtained.

3.10 Dopamine biosensor

A tissue biosensor with selective response to dopamine has been developed in which a thin layer of banana pulp is physically immobilized at the surface of an amperometric oxygen electrode (Sidwell and Rechnitz 1985). Figure 3.10

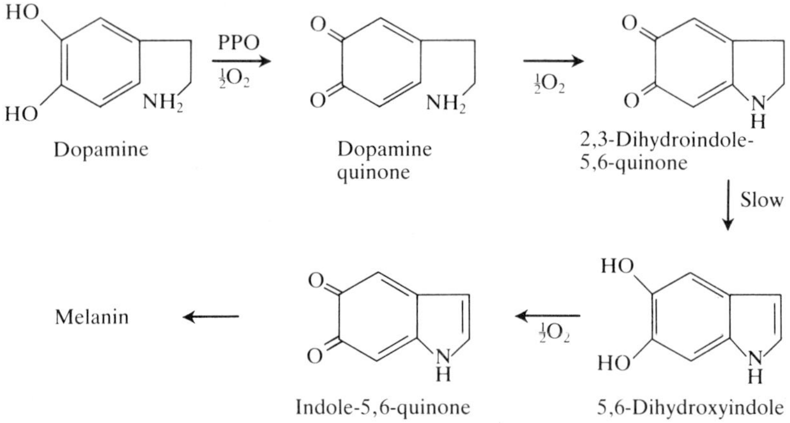

Fig. 3.10 Reactions in the catalytic oxidation of dopamine. PPO represents polyphenol oxidase.

shows the reactions that occur at the electrode surface. Oxygen consumption during this reaction sequence is monitored and the resulting current is related to dopamine concentrations.

Calibration curves based on steady-state currents have been obtained using a 0.1 M, pH 6.5 phosphate buffer at 25 °C. These response curves are linear over a dopamine concentration range from 0.2 to 1.2 mM and sensor response times are on the order of one to three minutes. These electrode response characteristics remain unchanged for at least one week when the electrode is stored in buffer.

The development of this dopamine sensor suggests that by careful selection of appropriate plant materials, tissue sensors for catacholamine neurotransmitters are possible.

3.11 Tyrosine biosensor

An amperometric tyrosine biosensor has been reported in which a slice of sugar beet (*Beta vulgaris altissima*) is immobilized at the surface of an oxygen sensing probe (Schubert *et al.* 1983) This sensor employs the activity of tyrosinase which is located within the beet structure and oxygen consumption is monitored. The beet slice is maintained on the probe surface using a common dialysis membrane and response curves are obtained using a pH 7.0 phosphate buffer at 25 °C.

Response to tyrosine is linear from 0.1 to 0.4 mM and a useful response up to 0.9 mM is achieved. The sensor is stable for at least eight days and its response times are on the order of several minutes. Selectivity is marginal for tyrosine with other materials eliciting a significant response such as dihydro-xyphenylalanine, 2,4-dichlorophenol and *p*-chlorophenol.

3.12 Cysteine biosensor

Yet another type of plant material has been demonstrated to be applicable for the construction of biosensors. Modified cucumber leaves have been immobilized at the surface of an ammonia sensor for the measurement of cysteine. Plant leaves offer a particularly attractive structural arrangement for possible use as biocatalysts. Many leaves have a multilayer structure consisting of a waxy coating (cuticle) at the outer surface, a layer of epidermal cells, followed by a third layer (spongy mesophyll) directly under the epidermis, with the same arrangement repeated in reverse on the other side of the leaf. The cuticle is hydrophobic in nature but permits the passage of gases; gas exchange takes place through small surface openings called stomata. The spongy mesophyll layer is the most active in metabolic processes involving gases. For the construction of biocatalytic membrane electrodes, the cuticle can be detached from either the upper or lower epidermal layer and the remaining leaf structure fixed at the surface of a gas sensing potentio-metric electrode with the exposed epidermal layer contacting the sample and the gas permeable waxy cuticle facing the internal elements of the sensor.

The principle has been demonstrated (Smit and Rechnitz 1984) with the use of cucumber leaves at an NH_3 sensor to construct a probe for L-cysteine. Such leaves have biocatalytic activity involving the enzyme L-cysteine desulfhydro-lase according to

$$\text{L-Cysteine} + H_2O \longrightarrow \text{Pyruvate} + H_2S + NH_3$$

Thus, sensors can be constructed using either NH_3 or H_2S gas-sensing electrodes, but the NH_3 case is preferable on chemical grounds.

The technique is quite simple. Cucumber plants (*Cucumis saturis*) are grown from seed in Fertilite seed starter soil. Mature leaves are detached when needed and soaked in water for 45 minutes; this soaking softens the cuticle and permits ready removal to expose the biochemically active epidermis. This procedure is necessary because the substrate, L-cysteine, cannot readily diffuse through the waxy cuticle layer. Leaf discs are then cut to fit the gas-sensor tip and held there with a dialysis membrane. Such a biosensor gives a response to L-cysteine in pH 7.6 phosphate buffer between approximately 10^{-3} to 10^{-5} M with a slope of about 35 mV per decade. The relatively poor slope and fairly long response times of this sensor show that further development is needed, but the long useful lifetime (up to four weeks) and extremely low cost of the biocatalyst suggest that leaf materials could be attractive alternatives to immobilized enzymes or cells.

3.13 Mitochondria based biosensor

Besides whole slices of mammalian tissue, effective biosensors can be prepared by fractionating the tissue cells and immobilizing just the subcellular component that is richest in the biocatalytic activity of interest. Such a strategy might prove fruitful to increase the amount of immobilized activity or to improve sensor selectivity by eliminating an interfering activity which is present in another compartment of the cell. Indeed, subcellular fractions have been demonstrated to be useful as analytical reagents with the use of rat liver microsomes for the determination of throxine (Meyerhoff and Rechnitz 1979). The first successful subcellular based biosensor has been developed for glutamine measurements in which the mitochondrial fraction from porcine kidney cortex cells is immobilized at an ammonia gas sensor (Arnold and Rechnitz 1980*b*). Two isozymes of glutaminase are known to exist in mitochondria (Crompton, McGivan, and Chappell 1973), and this activity is utilized in the glutamine probe.

The mitochondrial fraction of porcine kidney cels is isolated according to a standard procedure involving differential centrifugation (Johnson and Lardy 1967). The glutamine sensor is prepared by immobilizing the resulting mitochondrial fraction with a common cellulose diacetate type dialysis membrane. Completed biosensors are stored in a buffer composed of 0.120 M potassium chloride, 0.02 M Tris-chloride, 0.04 M Tris-phosphate, 0.005 M succinate, 1 μg/1.5 ml rotenone, and 0.02% sodium azide at pH 8.5. Sensors are stored and operated at room temperature.

Table 3.2 summarizes the analytical response characteristics which are obtained from the mitochondria electrode. These response characteristics compare very well to the tissue and bacterial electrode systems and are superior to the isolated enzyme case. The selectivity for the mitochondria-based glutamine sensor has been measured to be very good (Arnold and Rechnitz 1980*b*).

Successful fabrication of this mitochondria biosensor demonstrates that subcellular materials can be effective biocatalytic components. Although it is not necessary in the case of a glutamine biosensor, subcellular factions may be useful in improving sensor response and selectivity when the entire tissue section lacks the necessary properties.

3.14 Mechanism of tissue biosensor response

The response mechanism for plant and animal tissue electrodes has not yet been determined. In fact, no fundamental studies have been reported concerning the transport mechanism of substrate and product molecules within a tissue slice biocatalytic layer. Determination of the transport mechanism involved is important for the overall development of tissue materials as analytical reagents.

Because tissue cells serve to house the enzyme of interest, the substrate must be transported within the biocatalytic layer in such a way as to make contact with the enzyme. It is reasonable that substrate must be transported into the immobilized cells before contact with the enzyme. Moreover, transport of the electrode measurable product from the cells must be considered. To further complicate matters, the principal enzyme can be located within a specific subcellular organelle which requires additional mechanisms for the transport of substrate and product into, within, and from the organelle of interest. In the light of experimental (Arnold and Rechnitz 1982*b*) and theoretical (Carr and Bowers 1980) observations concerning the dependency of biosensor response characteristics on substrate diffusion processes within the biocatalytic layer, the transport mechanisms in question have important implications with respect to the analytical properties of tissue-based biocatalysts.

Several models can be proposed to describe the interaction between substrate and enzyme within a tissue slice biocatalyst. Figure 3.11 shows these various models schematically.

Model I represents the case where cells on the outer surface of the tissue slice completely break down structurally releasing the principal enzyme at the sensor surface. As the electrode ages, cellular debris diffuses away from the electrode surface which exposes a fresh layer of cells and generates a fresh supply of enzyme. This model eliminates the complications of substrate entrance into the cells. Of course the rate of enzyme release must be constant to be consistant with the excellent reproducibility observed for tissue electrodes and it must be slow to ensure sufficient amount of enzyme over extended periods (i.e. 30 days).

The structural integrity of porcine kidney tissue cells has been estimated in preliminary studies (Arnold 1982*b*). For this study a slice of porcine kidney was suspended in a small volume of a phosphate buffer (0.1 M, pH 7.8) with 0.02% sodium azide. After this material was incubated overnight at room temperature, the solution was centrifuged and the cells collected. The

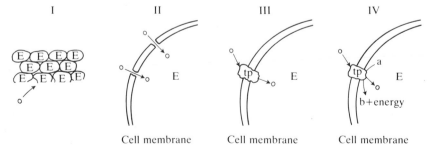

Fig. 3.11 Schematic representations of proposed models for substrate-enzyme interaction. o, substrate, E, active enzyme; and, tp, transport protein.

resulting supernatant was analysed for glutaminase activity which is the enzymatic activity that is employed in the glutamine biosensor. A small amount of glutaminase activity was found in this supernatant. The resulting pellet of kidney cells was resuspended in fresh buffer. This mixture was again incubated at room temperature overnight and centrifuged as before. The second time, no glutaminase activity was found in the supernatant, but considerable activity was found in the kidney cells themselves.

The above mentioned results, suggest that the integrity of the cells is maintained at least during initial use of kidney cells as a biocatalyst. The small amount of glutaminase in the first supernatant is most likely from cell fragments generated during the initial cutting of the tissue slice from the bulk organ.

Model II presents the possible case where the immobilized cells break down sufficiently to allow free diffusion of substrate and product molecules in and out of the tissue cells but not so completely that the principal enzyme can diffuse away from the electrode surface. Recent research in the area of permeabilized cells show how such channels can develop in the outer membranes of both prokaryotic and eukaryotic cells by treatments such as osmotic shock and freeze–thaw cycling (Felix 1982). It might be the case that such channels develop in immobilized tissue slices during electrode construction either by water washing of the tissue layer or by thawing of the previously frozen tissue material.

Models III and IV represent the cases where the immobilized tissue cells remain intact at the electrode surface. Model III requires that presence of transport proteins specific for the substrate of interest to aid in taking this substrate across the cell membrane. Besides requiring a transport protein, model IV requires a sources of energy from within the tissue cell to aid in the transport process. The requirement of an energy source for model IV renders this model quite unlikely, since cell viability in these systems is very seriously in doubt.

At this point, little information is available concerning any of these proposed mechanisms. We offer these models as a starting point for investigations into the response mechanism of tissue based sensors.

As is presented in this chapter, considerable progress has been made in the advancement of tissue-based biosensing probes. Future research in this area looks promising with the development of new probes for different biomolecules. The application of novel tissue classes, such as insects and aquatic plants, have yet to be investigated. Moreover, fundamental studies concerning the structure of tissue slice biocatalytic layers are most certainly needed. Finally, the application of tissue biocatalysts with other types of analytical transducers must be considered. Indeed, the major advantages of providing stable and large amounts of a desired biocatalytic activity should benefit other types of biocatalysis based analyses.

References

Arnold, M. A. (1983). An introduction to biocatalytic membrane electrodes. *Amer. Lab.* **15**, 34–40.

—— (1982*a*), *Tissue-based biocatalytic membrane electrodes*. Ph.D. Dissertation, University of Delaware, Section I.

—— (1982*b*), *Tissue-based biocatalytic membrane electrodes*. Ph.D. Dissertation, University of Delaware, Section II.

—— and Fiocchi, J. A. (1984). Rabbit muscle acetone powder as biocatalyst for adenosine 5'-monophosphate biosensor. *Anal. Lett.* **17**, 2091–109.

—— and Glazier, S. A. (1984). Jack bean meal as biocatalyst for urea biosensors. *Biotech. Lett.* **6**, 313–18.

—— and Meyerhoff, M. E. (1984). Ion-selective electrodes. *Anal. Chem.* **56**, 20R–48R.

—— and Rechnitz, G. A. (1980*a*), Determination of glutamine in cerebrospinal fluid with a tissue-based membrane electrode. *Anal. Chim. Acta.* **113**, 351–4.

—— (1980*b*). Comparison of bacterial, mitochondrial, tissue and enzyme biocatalysts for glutamine selective membrane electrodes. *Anal. Chem.* **52**, 1170–4.

—— (1981*a*). Selectivity enhancement of a tissue-based adenosine sensing membrane electrode. *Anal. Chem.* **53**, 515–8.

—— (1981*b*). High activity membrane electrode for adenosine 5'-monophosphate using rabbit muscle tissue as biocatalyst. *Anal. Chem.* **53**, 1837–42.

—— (1982*a*). Optimization of a tissue-based membrane electrode for guanine. *Anal. Chem.* **54**, 777–82.

—— (1982*b*). Substrate consumption by biocatalytic potentiometric membrane electrodes. *Anal. Chem.* **54**, 2315–17.

Carr, P. W. and Bowers, L. D. (1980). *Immobilized enzymes in analytical and clinical chemistry*. Wiley, New York.

Conway, E. J. and Cooke, R. (1939). The deaminases of adenosine and adenylic acid in blood and tissues. *Biochem. J.* **33**, 479–92.

Crompton, M., McGivan, J. D. and Chappel, J. B. (1973), The intramitochondrial location of the glutaminase isoenzymes in pig kidney. *Biochem. J.* **132**, 27–34.

Dixon, M. and Kleppe, K. (1965). D-amino acid oxidase; II. specificity, competitive inhibition, and reaction sequence. *Biochim. Biophys. Acta* **96**, 368–82.

—— and Webb, E. C. (1964). *Enzymes* (2nd ed.). Academic Press, New York.

Felix, H. (1982). Permeabilized cells. *Anal. Biochem.* **120**, 211–34.

Fernley, H. H. and Walker, P. G. (1967). Studies on alkaline phosphatase; inhibition by phosphate derivatives and the substrate specificity. *Biochem. J.* **104**, 1011–18.

Fishman, W. H., Green, S. and Inglis, N. I. (1963). L-phenylalanine: an organ specific, stereospecific inhibitor of human intestinal alkaline phosphatase. *Nature, London* **198**, 685–86.

Ghosh, N. K. and Fishman, W. H. (1966). On the mechanism of inhibition of intestial alkaline phosphatase by L-phenylalanine; I. Kinetic studies. *J. Biol. Chem.* **241**, 2516–22.

Guilbault, G. G. (1984). *Analytical uses of immobilized enzymes*, Marcel Dekker, New York.

—— and Hrabankova, E. (1971). New enzyme electrode probes for D-amino acids and asparagine. *Anal. Chim. Acta* **56**, 285–90.

—— Smith, R. K. and Montalvo, J. G., Jr. (1968). Use of ion selective electrodes in enzymic analysis; cation electrodes for deaminase enzyme systems. *Anal. Chem.* **41**, 600–605.

IUPAC Analytical Chemistry Division (1976). Recommendations for nomenclature of ion-selective electrodes. *Pure Appl. Chem.* **48**, 127–32.

Johnson, D. and Lardy, H. (1967). Isolation of liver or kidney mitochondria. In *Methods in Enzymology* (eds. R. W. Estabrook, and M. E. Pullman) Vol. X. Academic Press, New York.

Kay, H. D. (1932). Phosphatase in growth and disease of bone. *Physiol. Rev.* **12**, 384–442.

Kobos, R. K. (1980). Potentiometric enzyme methods In *Ion-selective electrodes in analytical chemistry* (ed. M. Freiser) Vol. II, Chapter 1. Plenum. New York.

Kuriyama, S. and Rechnitz, G. A. (1981). Plant tissue-based biocatalytic membrane electrode for glutamate. *Anal. Chim. Acta* **131**, 91–6.

—— Arnold, M. A. and Rechnitz, G. A. (1983). Improved membrane electrode using plant tissue as biocatalyst. *J. Membr. Sci.* **12**, 269–78.

Macfarlane, M. G., Patterson, L. M. B. and Robison, R. (1934). The phosphatase activity of animal tissue. *Biochem. J.* **28**, 720–24.

Mascini, M., Jannelle, M. and Palleschi, G. (1982). A liver tissue-based electrochemical sensor for hydrogen peroxide. *Anal. Chim. Acta* **138**, 65–9.

Meyerhoff, M. E. and Fraticelli, Y. M. (1982). Ion-selective electrodes. *Anal. Chem.* **54**, 27R–44R.

—— and Rechnitz, G. A. (1979). Microsomal thyroxine measurements with iodide selective membrane electrode. *Anal. Lett.* **12**, 1339–46.

Papastathopoulos, D. S. and Rechnitz, G. A. (1976). Highly selective enzyme electrode for 5'-adenosine monophosphate. *Anal. Chem.* **48**, 862–4.

Rechnitz, G. A. (1978). Biochemical electrodes uses tissue slice. *Chem. Eng. News* **56** (Oct. 9), 16.

—— (1981), Bioselective membrane electrode probes. *Science* **214**, 287–91.

—— (1986), *Bioselective membrane electrodes using tissue materials as biocatalysts. Methods in enzymology.* In press.

—— Arnold, M. A. and Meyerhoff, M. E. (1979). Bio-selective membrane electrode using tissue slices. *Nature (London)* **278**, 466–7.

Ronca-Testoni, S. Raggi, A. and Ronca, G. (1970). Muscle AMP aminohydrolase; III. A comparative study on the regulatory properties of skeletal muscle enzyme from various sources. *Biochem. Biophys. Acta* **198**, 101–12.

Sammons, D. W., Henry, H. and Chilson, D. P. (1970). Effect of salts on inhibition of chicken muscle adenosine monophosphate deaminase by phosphate esters and inorganic phosphate. *J. Biol. Chem.* **245**, 2109–13.

Schubert, F., Rennebarg, R., Scheller, F. W. and Kirstein, L. (1984). Plant tissue hybride electrode for determination of phosphate and fluoride. *Anal. Chem.* **56**, 1677–82.

—— Wallenberger, U. and Scheller, F. (1983). Plant tissue-based amperometric tyrosine electrode. *Biotech. Lett.* **5**, 239–42.

Sidwell, J. S. and Rechnitz, G. A. (1985). Bananatrode — an electrochemical biosensor for dopamine. *Biotech. Lett.* **7**, 419–22.

Smit, N. and Rechnitz, G. A. (1984). Leaf-based biocatalytic membrane electrodes. *Biotech. Lett.* **6**, 209–14.

Valle-Vega, P., Young, C. T. and Swaisgood, H. E. (1980). Arginase-urease electrode for determination of arginine and peanut maturity *J. Food. Sci.* **45**, 1026–30.

Zielke, C. L. and Suelter, C. H. (1960). Purine, purine nucleoside, and purine nucleotide aminohydrolases. *The Enzymes* (3rd edn.; ed. P. D. Boyer) Vol. 4, Chapter 3. Academic Press, New York.

4

New approaches to electrochemical immunoassays

MONIKA J. GREEN

When Yalow and Berson (1959, 1960) published their work on the detection of plasma insulin by radioimmunoassay they provided a revolutionary new method for the accurate and specific measurements of low levels of hormones, enzymes, drugs, viruses, tumour antigens, bacterial antigens, and many proteins and organic substances that had hitherto been difficult or impossible to detect.

Immunoassays are fundamentally simple and are based on the interaction of the analyte or ligand (Ag) in question with its specific binding partner or antibody (Ab) (eqn. 4.1)

$$\text{Ab} + \text{Ag} \rightleftharpoons \text{AbAg} \tag{4.1}$$

to form an antibody/antigen (AbAg) complex. An equilibrium is reached and the equilibrium or affinity constant K is defined as

$$K = [\text{AgAb}]/[\text{Ag}][\text{Ab}]. \tag{4.2}$$

So for a fixed concentration of antibody, the ratio of bound-to-free antigen at equilibrium is quantitatively related to the total amount of ligand present. This forms the basis for all immunoassays. Thus if a fixed amount of labelled antigen is introduced into the assay the concentration of the unknown antigen can then be determined. Unknown concentration of antibodies can be determined by using labelled antibodies. 'Labelling' agents such as radioisotopes, enzymes, red cells, fluorescent probes, chemiluminescent probes, or metal tags may be used to label either an antibody or an antigen. In radioimmunoassay (RIA) and enzyme immunoassays (EIA) the antigen is labelled. In immunoradiometric (IRMA) and immunoenzymometric assays (IEMA) antibodies are labelled. Most immunoassay techniques require a separation step to discriminate between the bound and unbound labelled antigen or labelled antibodies; this makes the technique somewhat cumbersome and time consuming.

The growing trend away from radioimmunoassays and the increasing number of enzyme-linked immunoassays, coupled with the wide range of low detection limits of electroanalytical methods, has resulted in a proliferation of papers in the last decade trying to link immunoassays to electrochemical means of detection. Amperometric and potentiometric methods have both been used with varying degrees of success. This review will limit itself to these methods. The differences between these two electrochemical techniques is clearly defined elsewhere in this book, (Kuan and Guilbault, Chapter 9; Wilson, Chapter 11) and it should suffice for the distinction to be made that amperometric assays measure current and a linear relationship exists between the current and the concentration of electroactive species that is either oxidized or reduced at the electrode; potentiometric assays measure the change in potential and a logarithmic relationship exists between potential and concentration with an idealized change in potential of $59/n$ mV per decade.

Current published electrochemical immunoassays can be further classified (see Fig. 4.1).

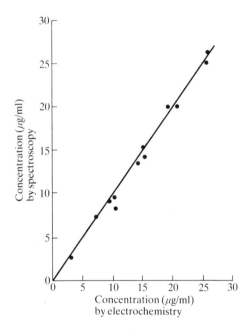

Fig. 4.1 Correlation plot of spectroscopic assay results against electrochemical results for serum samples from patients on phenytoin maintenance therapy (from Eggers *et al.* 1982).

a) Amperometric immunoassays developed around the Clark electrode. These employ enzymes that can either consume or produce oxygen in the presence of suitable substrates.
b) Amperometric enzyme immunoassays that employ both an enzyme

and electrochemically detect product of that enzyme.

c) Amperometric immunoassays that do not employ enzymes but utilize either an antibody or antigen that is labelled with an electroactive species.

d) Potentiometric immunoassays that are based on a change in potential that occurs when either an antibody or antigen is immobilized on an electrode and its specific binding partner binds to it.

e) Potentiometric immunoassays where the method of detection is a more conventional potentiometric electrode, e.g. ion selective electrode, CO_2 electrode, ammonia electrode, or pH electrode.

Examples of all five types of immunoassays will be given below.

4.1 Amperometric immunoassays based on the Clark electrode

The use of the Clark oxygen electrode to detect either the loss or formation of oxygen as a consequence of an enzymic reaction was an interesting progression for enzyme immunoassays. The two most commonly used enzyme labels were glucose oxidase and catalase.

Aizawa *et al.* in 1979 constructed an enzyme linked immunoassay to monitor human chorionic gonadotropin (hCG) using catalase labelled hCG. They immobilized an antibody on to a pre-cast cellulose membrane, the membrane was then placed over the teflon membrane of the oxygen electrode.

$$2H_2O_2 \longrightarrow 2H_2O + O_2 \tag{4.4}$$

Both labelled and non-labelled hCG were allowed to compete for the antibody in the membrane. The membrane was washed to remove bound from free hCG — and the electrode exposed to hydrogen peroxide solution. The hydrogen peroxide solution in the presence of catalase disproportionates to yield oxygen and water. The rate of increase in oxygen tension is monitored, a calibration plot suggests that the sensor can monitor between 0.02 and 100 I U ml^{-1} of hCG. Unfortunately using one antibody the assay was prone to cross reactivity due to lutenizing hormones. However the existance of good monoclonal antibodies against the α and β subunits of hCG and the use of a sandwich type ELISA assay — using not labelled hCG but labelled second antibody, could form the basis of an improved biosensor for hCG. Another Japanese group (Itagaki *et al* 1983) have more recently used catalase labels in

date, all of which cut DNA at DNA sequence-specific sites generating fragments of reproducible size. The digested DNA sample (usually 5 or 10 μg)
is then loaded into a well of an 0.8% agarose gel and subjected to
electrophoresis in a horizontal gel apparatus. DNA fragments are negatively
charged and migrate towards the anode according to their size, the smallest
fragments travelling the furthest. The gel is soaked in ethidium bromide solution so that the DNA can be visualized and photographed under ultraviolet
light and then soaked in alkali to make the DNA fragments single-stranded.
After neutralization in strong buffer, the gel is set up for the transfer of the
DNA fragments out of the gel onto a nitrocellulose or nylon filter. This is
achieved by laying the filter on top of the gel and covering the filter with dry
paper towels which blot the fragments out of the gel in the same positions to
which they had migrated. The fragments are fixed permanently to the filter
by baking (if nitrocellulose filters are used) and then the filter (Southern blot)
is ready for hybridization to a radioactively labelled DNA probe.

The hybridization reaction is usually carried out in a polythene bag, made
by sandwiching the filter between two sheets of thick polythene and heat-
sealing three sides. the fourth side is heat-sealed after a few millilitres of
presoak buffer have been added and the filter is then incubated at the temperature of hybridization for a short period, a step which is necessary to
reduce the background hybridization signal to a minimum. After presoaking,
the buffer is squeezed out of the bag, 1–2 ml of hybridization buffer plus the
single-stranded ^{32}P labelled probe added, and the bag resealed. When the
hybridization reaction is complete, the filter is removed from the bag and
washed under stringent conditions (0.1 $\times$ SSC, 0.1% SDS at 65 °C) to
remove all the unhybridized probe. The filter is then finally subjected to autoradiography to localize the complementary DNA fragments which have
hybridized to the probe. These appear as dark bands on the developed X-ray
film. By running marker DNA fragments of known molecular weight, the
sizes of the hybridizing fragments can be estimated by the distance they have
travelled in the agarose gel.

5.3 DNA probes in detecting human genetic disease

5.3.1 Carrier detection in genetic disease

The haemoglobinopathies are the most extensively studied group of genetic
disorders and many methods of carrier detection based on the technique of
restriction enzyme have been developed. The different approaches can be
divided into those that detect the genetic disorder directly and the indirect
approach of using linked DNA polymorphisms. The direct approaches
usually require the isolation of gene specific probes and the determination of
the molecular basis of the genetic disorder. Even then, in many cases, a direct
approach may not be possible and an indirect method has to be used. For

genetic disorders such as Duchenne muscular dystrophy, where the mutant gene is as yet unidentified, the indirect method is the only approach for carrier detection and prenatal diagnosis (Harper *et al.* 1983; Pembrey *et al.* 1984).

5.3.1.1 Direct detection If a genetic disorder results from a deletion of DNA sequence, genomic DNA probes or cDNA probes can be used to detect the defect directly. If a large deletion is involved, removing all the DNA sequence complementary to the appropriate DNA probe, the probe will fail to hybridize to DNA from an affected individual on a Southern blot. For example, α°-thalassaemia results from DNA deletions which remove both of the α-globin genes and the homozygous condition can be diagnosed by the absence of any α-globin gene fragments hybridizing to an α-gene probe. However the detection of heterozygotes for such gene deletions is not so straightforward as the probe will hybridize to DNA fragments from the normal chromosome giving an identical band pattern to that from normal DNA, except that the intensity of the bands on the autoradiograph will be only a half that from normal DNA (provided that equal amounts of normal and heterozygous DNA are compared). However, detecting dosage differences on a Southern blot is often technically difficult. For genetic disorders located on the X chromosome, the absence of hybridization of a specific probe can be used to detect males affected by a gene deletion (Old *et al.* 1984) but again, the detection of females carrying the disorder depends on detecting only half the hybridization signal generated by an equal amount of normal DNA.

For small gene deletions, or in cases where the DNA probe sequence spans the start or end of the gene deletion, the disorder can be detected by the identification of a characteristic abnormal DNA fragment on a Southern blot. An individual carrying the disorder will have both normal and abnormal bands and an affected individual only abnormal bands. α°-Thalassaemia can be detected this way by using a ς-globin gene probe which hybridizes to DNA sequences adjacent to the start of the DNA deletion. Small deletions involving only a few hundred base pair can be detected by the presence of an abnormal band which is smaller than the normal restriction fragment. A type of β°-thalassaemia found only in Asian Indians can be detected in this manner (Fig. 5.1).

Genetic disorders which result from DNA deletions or insertions of just a few nucleotides cannot be detected by the above method because the resolution between bands on a Southern blot is not good enough. Also many genetic disorders are caused by point mutations which often do not cause any change of length of restriction fragments. However, if the mutation either creates or abolishes a restriction enzyme recognition site, the mutation will be detectable directly by restriction enzyme analysis, provided that the required DNA

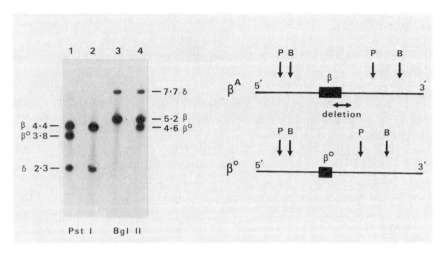

Fig. 5.1 The direct detection of a type of β^0-thalassaemia which is caused by a deletion of 617 base pairs at the 3' end of the β-globin gene. The β^0 gene can be detected directly by using Pst I (P) or Bgl II (B), which have recognition sites on either side of the normal and mutant β genes, and therefore the β^0 gene DNA fragments are 0.6 kb smaller than the normal ones. The autoradiograph shows normal DNA (tracks 2 and 3) and DNA from an individual heterozygous for this type of β-thalassaemia (tracks 1 and 4). DNA fragments containing cross-hybridizing δ-globin gene fragments are also observed.

fragments are sufficiently large enough to be detected on a Southern blot (fragments smaller than 500 base pairs are not so easily detected). Sickle cell anaemia is a good example of such a genetic disorder. It results from a single base change of A to T in codon 6 of the β-globin gene and this mutation abolishes three slightly different recognition sites present in the normal β-gene sequence. The first two to be discovered, Mnl I and Dde I, produced DNA fragments too small to be detected easily and therefore were not used in preference to the previously established method of linkage analysis using the nearby Hpa I polymorphic site (see later). However the third enzyme site to be discovered at the sickle cell mutation locus, Mst II, generated easily detectable DNA fragments and this approach is now the standard method of prenatal diagnosis even though the sickle point mutation has been shown to be directly detectable by yet another method, the oligonucleotide probe technique.

Oligonucleotide probes are synthetic single-stranded DNA molecules of approximately 20 bases in length which can be used to detect single point mutations. A pair of such oligonucleotide probes are required, one complementary to the normal DNA sequence and the other to the mutant sequence. The probes are hybridized to restriction enzyme digested DNA, either on a Southern blot or in a dried-down agarose gel, and then the filter or gel washed under such conditions that the mismatched DNA hybrids are destabilized in relation to the perfectly matched hybrids and thus removed from the filter. This approach has been used to detect sickle cell anaemia, β-thalassaemia, and α-1 antitrypsin deficiency (Conner *et al.* 1983; Orkin *et al.* 1983; Kidd *et al.* 1983). Although β-thalassaemia has been shown to be caused by at least thirty different point mutations, only a few mutations are found in any particular population and in some populations, such as in Sardinia, one mutation accounts for the vast majority of cases of β-thalassaemia and such a population has proved very suitable for the use of oligonucleotide probes for prenatal diagnosis of β-thalassaemia. However for genetic disorders with a high frequency of new mutations such as haemophilia and Duchenne muscular dystrophy, the oligonucleotide approach is not suitable and an indirect approach using linked DNA polymorphisms has to be used.

5.3.1.2 Indirect detection   The discovery that natural variations in DNA sequence occur randomly throughout the genome has led to the most applicable method for the carrier detection of genetic disorders. This approach depends on demonstrating linkage of a DNA polymorphism to the mutant gene under study. DNA polymorphisms occur because variations in DNA sequence result in the loss of an existing restriction enzyme recognition site or the creation of a new one. A polymorphic restriction site will produce DNA fragments of different lengths in different people depending on whether the site is present or absent. The polymorphic fragments are inherited in a simple Mendelian fashion and can be used as markers for chromosomes carrying either normal or mutant genes, provided that the polymorphism is sufficiently close to the mutant gene so that the chance of DNA recombination between the polymorphic site and the mutant gene is very low (Kan and Dozy 1978); Botstein *et al.* 1980). Such DNA polymorphisms are referred to as restriction fragment length polymorphisms (RFLPs), and an example is shown in Fig. 5.2.

More than 17 different polymorphic restriction sites have been discovered in the β-globin gene cluster since the first report by Kan and Dozy in 1978 of a Hpa I polymorphic site and its usefulness for diagnosing sickle cell anaemia by linkage analysis. Many of these polymorphic sites have proved very useful for the detection and prenatal diagnosis of β-thalassaemia, HbS, HbE, and HbC, even though such studies require the investigation of DNA from not just the couple at risk but also from previously born children and/or grandparents and lateral relatives in order to assign the linkage of RFLPs (as the majority of RFLPs do not exist in linkage disequilibrium). Many other genetic disorders can now be diagnosed by using linked RFLPs, even in cases where the biochemical defect is unknown such as Duchenne muscular

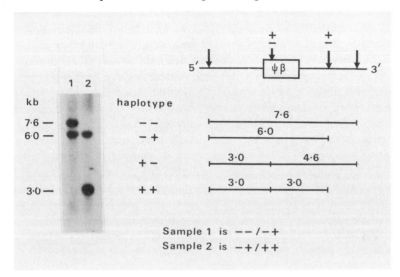

Fig. 5.2 A restriction fragment length polymorphism used for diagnosing β-thalassaemia by linkage analysis. The diagram shows the location of two Hind II polymorphic sites (±) in and near the β-globin pseudogene (ψβ). Four polymorphic fragments can be detected with a ψβ-gene probe, depending on the combination of the presence of absence of each site (haplotype). The haplotypes of two normal individuals are shown.

dystrophy (for a review, see Davies (1985). A list of genetic disorders for which DNA probes are available is shown in Table 5.1.

5.3.2 Prenatal diagnosis

5.3.2.1 Source of fetal DNA   Fetal DNA for DNA analysis can be obtained by either amniocentesis or chorionic villus sampling. Amniocentesis is a well established procedure which is usually carried out at 15–16 weeks' gestation. As soon as the techniques for the detection of haemoglobinopathies by restriction enzyme analysis were developed in 1978, prenatal diagnosis was shown to be possible using fetal DNA from cultured amniocytes. A large amount of fetal DNA (20–45 μg) is obtained from a flask of confluent amniocytes but it takes 2–3 weeks for the cells to grow to confluency. Alternatively DNA can be prepared from amniotic fluid cells without culturing, but a large amount of amniotic fluid is required to obtain enough live cells to provide sufficient DNA for a diagnosis (5 or 10 μg). This is obtained from 40 ml of amniotic fluid, which has been found by the authors to yield from 3 μg to 25 μg DNA, with an average yield of 14 μg.

Fetal DNA can also be obtained from a chorionic villi sample which is obtained at 9–11 weeks' gestation and permits a first trimester diagnosis. Such a diagnosis has many major advantages over the midtrimester approach

Table 5.1   Diagnosis of disease using DNA probes

Disease	Gene probe
Haemoglobinopathies	α, β, γ-Globin (Old 1985)
Collagen disorders	Collagen (Prockop and Kivirikko 1984) (Sykes 1983)
Dwarfism	Human growth hormone (Moore *et al.* 1982)
Emphysema	α-1 Antitrypsin (Kidd *et al.* 1983)
Lesch–Nyhan syndrome	HPRT (Yang *et al.* 1984)
Phenylketonuria	Phenylalanine hydroxylase (Woo *et al.* 1983)
Christmas disease	Factor IX (Choo *et al.* 1982)
Haemophilia A	Factor VIII
Glucose-6-phosphate dehydrogenase deficiency	G-6PD (Persico *et al.* 1981)
Ornithine transcarbamylase deficiency	OTC (Old *et al.* 1984)
Antithrombin-3 deficiency	Antithrombin-3 (Bock and Levitan 1983)
Cholesterol metabolism/ heart disease	LDL receptor (Russell *et al.* 1983), HMG coreductase (Chin *et al.* 1982), Apolipoproteins (Tolleshaug *et al.* 1983)
Duchenne muscular dystrophy	Linked RFLPs (Bakker *et al.* 1985)
Huntington's chorea	Linked RFLP (Gusella *et al.* 1983)
Cystic fibrosis	Linked RFLPs

using amniotic fluid DNA, but the risks to the fetus from the chorionic villus sampling procedure have not yet been fully evaluated. Chorionic villi are a superb source of DNA and an average sized sample will yield between 25–40 μg of DNA, more than enough DNA for a prenatal diagnosis and therefore allowing in many cases a second and third restriction enzyme site polymorphism to be studied to confirm the diagnosis.

5.3.2.2 A practical example   A first trimester diagnosis of β-thalassaemia by linkage analysis of a restriction fragment length polymorphism is shown in Fig. 5.3. DNA from the father, mother, and their normal child was analysed first to determine if a prenatal diagnosis was possible using RFLPs. A complete diagnosis was shown to be feasible using a polymorphic Ava II site in the β-globin pseudogene ($\psi\beta$) approximately 15 kilobases (kb) from the β-thalassaemia mutation in the β-globin gene, and a prenatal diagnosis was subsequently performed using DNA from a chorionic villus sample.

Figure 5.3 shows the band pattern obtained by digestion of DNA with Ava II and hybridization of the Southern blot to a ^{32}P labelled plasmid containing the human β-globin DNA sequence. If the Ava II site is present (+) on both

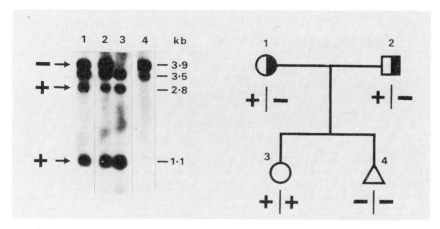

Fig. 5.3 First trimester diagnosis of β-thalassaemia by linkage analysis using an Ava II polymorphic site in the β-globin pseudogene. The autoradiograph shows that in tracks 1 and 2 the mother and father, both heterozygous for β-thalassaemia (half-shaded symbols) were $+ / -$; in track 3 the normal child (open circle) was $+ / +$; in track 4 the fetus (triangle) was $- / -$, and therefore diagnosed as homozygous for β-thalassaemia.

chromosomes, three fragments containing β-globin gene sequences are detected; with sized of 1.1 kb, 2.8 kb, and 3.5 kb. If the site is missing (–) on both chromosomes, only two fragments are observed, a 3.5 kb and a 3.9 kb fragment. Therefore the 3.5 kb is a constant band and the 3.9 kb fragment results from the sum of the two smaller fragments. An individual heterozygous for the polymorphic site has all four bands, as seen in the DNA from the father and mother in tracks 1 and 2. DNA from the normal child in track 3 contained only the 1.1 kb, 2.8 kb, and 3.5 kb fragments indicating that the polymorphic site was present (+) on both of the normal chromosomes in the child and therefore in each of the parents (assuming that DNA recombination has not taken place between the polymorphic site and the b-globin gene). Thus the polymorphic site is absent on both the chromosomes carrying the β-thalassaemia gene in this family and can be used as a marker for prenatal diagnosis. DNA from a chorionic villus sample was than analysed (Old 1986) and found to contain only the 3.5 kb and 3.9 kb bands (track 4). Therefore both fetal chromosomes carried the (–) RFLP indicating that it had inherited both β-thalassaemia genes and was affected.

5.4 Future prospects for non-radiometric detection

Clearly the method of choice at the monent for labelling DNA probes is to use ^{32}P-nucleotides of the highest specific activity. There are many disadvantages to ^{32}P-labelling such as the potential health hazard of radioactivity, but perhaps the most important disadvantage is that the half-life of ^{32}P is only 14 days and therefore probes have to be labelled fresh every one to two weeks. The use of non-radioactive methods of labelling DNA probes will overcome many of these disadvantages and should permit the development of diagnostic kits for detection of DNA sequences of abnormal genes, viruses, micro-organisms, etc.

Although many different methods of non-radioactive DNA labelling are being developed, two approaches have already met with limited success and are being marketed at the time of writing. The first approach is to substitute the incorporation of ^{32}P-nucleotide into the DNA probe with a chemically-modified nucleotide such as a biotinylated dUTP, an analogue of dTTP. The modified nucleotides are incorporated in the standard way e.g. by nick-translation but at a slower rate. The hybridized biotinylated DNA probe is then detected by its interaction with biotin-binding protiens such as avidin or streptavidin complexed with colour-producing enzymes such as horseradish perioxidase, acid phosphotase, or alkaline phosphotase or by a double antibody system using an anti-biotin antibody followed by a fluorescent secondary antibody. The second approach is to chemically modify the DNA probe in a way which does not affect its hybridization properties, such as by sulphonation. The modified DNA probe is then detected with a specific monoclonal antibody and then by a secondary antibody conjugated to peroxidase or alkaline phosphotase. Kits for DNA labelling by the two approaches are on the market (Enzo Biochem Inc. and Orgenics Ltd.) but the sensitivity of these systems is still not quite sufficient for restriction enzyme analysis of DNA in which the detection of less than 1 pg of single copy gene sequences is the goal. However such systems will detect 5–10 pg of DNA by dot blotting and therefore can be used in genetic engineering experiments for Southern blotting, plaque and colony hybridization for detection of viral DNA in cells and in tissue sections of clinical samples, and for *in situ* hybridization of DNA probes to chromosomes.

Acknowledgements

We would like to thank Rachel Kitt for patiently typing the manuscript. We are grateful to The Medical Research Council, The Muscular Dystrophy Group of Great Britain, and The Muscular Dystrophy Association of America for financial support.

References

Bakker, E., Hofker, M. H., Goorl, N., Mandel, J. L., Davies, K. E., Kunkel, L. M., Willard, H. F., Fenton, W. A., Sandkuyl, L., Majoor-Krakauer, D., Van Essen, A., Jahoda, M., Sachs, E. S., Van Ommen, G. J. B. and Pearson, P. L. (1985).

Prenatal diagnosis and carrier detection of Duchenne muscular dystrophy with closely linked RFLPs. *Lancet* **1**, 655–8.

Bock, S. C. and Levitan, D. J. (1983). Characterisation of an unusual DNA length polymorphism 5' to the human antithrombin III gene. Nucl. Acids Res. **11**, 8569–82.

Botstein, D., White, R. L., Scolnick, M. H. and Davis, R. W. (1980). Construction of a genetic linkage map in man using restriction fragment length polymorphisms. *Am. J. Hum. Genet.* **32**, 314–31.

Chin, D. J., Luskey, K. L., Faust, J. R., MacDonald, R. J., Brown, M. S. and Goldstein, J. L. (1982). Molecular cloning of a 3-hydroxyl-methylglutamyl coenzyme A reductase and evidence for regulation of its mRNA. *Proc. Natl. Acad. Sci. USA* **79**, 7704–8.

Choo, K. H., Gould, K. G., Rees, D. J. G. and Brownlee, G. G. (1982). Molecular cloning of the gene for human anti-haemophilic factor IX. *Nature* **299**, 178–80.

Conner, B. J., Reyes, A. A., Morin, C., Itakura, K., Teplitz, R. L. and Wallace, R. B. (1983). Detection of sickle cell β^s-globin allele by hybridization with synthetic oligonucleotides. *Proc. Natl. Acad. Sci. USA* **80**, 278–82.

Davies, K. E. (1985). Molecular genetics of the human X chromosome. *J. Med. Genet.* **22**, 243–9.

Feinberg, A. P. and Vogelstein, B. (1983). A technique for radiolabelling DNA restriction endonuclease fragments to high specific activity. *Anal. Biochem.* **132**, 6–13.

Gusella, J. F., Wexler, M. S., Conneally, P. M., Naylor, S. L., Anderson, M. A., Tanzi, R. E., Watkins, P. C., Ottina, K., Wallace, M. R., Sakaguchi, A. Y., Young, A. B., Shoulson, I., Bonilla, E. and Martin, J. B. (1983). A polymorphic DNA marker genetically linked to Huntington's disease. *Nature* **306**, 234–9.

Harper, P. S., O'Brien, T., Murray, J. M., Davies, K. E., Pearson, P. L. and Williamson, R. (1983). The use of linked DNA polymorphisms for genotype prediction in families with Duchenne muscular dystrophy. *J. Med. Genet.* **20**, 252–4.

Kan, Y. W. and Dozy, A. M. (1978). Polymorphism of DNA sequence adjacent to human β-globin structural gene: Relationship to sickle mutation. *Proc. Natl. Acad. Sci. USA* **75**, 5631–5.

—— Golbus, M. S. and Dozy, A. M. (1976). Prenatal diagnosis of α-thalassaemia: Clinical application of molecular hybridization. *N. Engl. J. Med.* **295**, 1165–7.

Kidd, V J., Wallace. R. B., Itakura, K. and Woo, S. L. C. (1983). α_1-antitrypsin deficiency detection by direct analysis of the mutation in the gene. *Nature* **304**, 230–4.

Lawn, R. M., Fritsch, E. F., Parker, R. C., Blake, G. and Maniatis, T. (1978). The isolation and characterization of linked δ and β-globin genes from a cloned library of human DNA. *Cell* **15**, 1157–74.

Leary, J. J., Brigati, D. J. and Ward, D. C. (1983). Rapid and sensitive colorimetric method for visualising biotin-labelled DNA probes hybridised to DNA or RNA immobilised on nitrocellulose: bio-blots. *Proc. Natl. Acad. Sci. USA* **80**, 4045–9.

Moore, D. D., Conkling, M. E. and Goodman, H. M. (1982). Human growth hormone: multigene family. *Cell* **29**, 285–286.

Old. J. M. (1985). Prenatal diagnosis of the haemoglobinopathies. In *Genetic disorders of the fetus*, (2nd edn., ed. A. Milunksy). In press. Plenum, New York.

—— (1986). Fetal DNA analysis, In *Genetic analysis of human Diseases: a practical approach* (ed. K. E. Davies). IRL Press Oxford.

—– and Higgs, D. R. (1983). Gene analysis. Methods in hematology, In *The Thalas-saemias* (ed. D. J. Weatherall), Vol. 6, pp. 74–102. Churchill Livingstone, Edinburgh.

—— Briand, P. L., Purvis-Smith, S., Howard, N. J., Wilcken, B., Hammond, J., Pearson, P., Cathelineau, L., Williamson, R. and Davies, K. E., (1984). Prenatal diagnosis of OTC deficiency by direct gene analysis. *Lancet* **1**, 73–5.

Orkin, S. H. and Kazazian, H. H. (1984). The mutation and polymorphism of the human β-globin gene and its surrounding DNA. *Ann. Rev. Genet.* **18**, 131–71.

—— Markham, A. F. and Kazazian, H. H. (1983). Direct detection of the common Mediterranean β-thalassaemia gene with synthetic DNA probes: an alternative approach for prenatal diagnosis. *J. Clin. Invest.* **71**, 775–9.

Pembrey, M. E., Davies, K. E., Winter, R. M., Elles, R. G., Williamson, R., Fazzoni, T. A. and Walker, C. (1984). The clinical use of DNA markers linked to the gene for Duchenne muscular dystrophy. *Arch. Dis. Child.* **59**, 208–16.

Persico, M. G., Toniolo, C., Nobile, C., D'Urso, M. and Luzzatto, L. (1981). cDNA sequences of human glucose 6-phosphate dehydrogenase cloned in pBR322. *Nature* **294**, 778–80.

Prockop, D. J. and Kivirikko, K. I. (1984). Heritable diseases of collagen. *N. Engl. J. Med.* **311**, 376–86.

Rigby, P. J. W., Dieckmann, M., Rhodes, C. and Berg, P. (1977). Labelling deoxyribonucleic acid to high specific activity *in vitro* by nick-translation with DNA polymerase. *J. Mol. Biol.* **113**, 237–51.

Russell, D. W., Yamamoto, T., Schneider, W. J., Slaughter, C. J., Brown, M. S. and Goldstein, J. L. (1983). cDNA cloning of the bovine low density lipoprotein receptor: feedback regulation of a receptor mRNA. *Proc. Natl. Acad. Sci. USA* **80**, 7501–5.

Southern, E. M. (1975). Detection of specific sequences among DNA fragments separated by gel electrophoresis. *J. Mol. Biol.* **98**, 503–17.

Sykes, B. (1983). A high frequency Hind III restriction site polymorphism with a collagen gene. *Disease Markers* **1**, 141–6.

Tolleshaug, H., Hobgood, K. K., Brown. M. S. and Goldstein, J. L. (1983). The LDL receptor locus in familial hypercholesterolaemia: multiple mutations disrupt transport and processing of a membrane receptor. *Cell* **32**, 941–51.

Wilson, J. T., Wilson, L. B., DeRiel, J. K., Villa-Komaroff, L., Efstratiadis, A., Forget, B. G. and Weissman, S. M. (1978). Insertion of synthetic copies of human globin genes into bacterial plasmids. *Nucl. Acids Res.* **5**, 563–81.

Woo, S. L. C. , Lidsky, A. S., Guttler, F., Chandra, T. and Robson, K. J. H. (1983). Cloned human phenylalanine hydroxylase gene allows prenatal diagnosis and carrier detection of classical phenylketonuria. *Nature* **306**, 151–5.

Yang, T. P., Patel, P. I., Chinault, A C., Stout, J. T., Jackson, L. G., Hilderbrand, B. M. and Caskey, D. T. (1984). Molecular evidence for new mutation at the hprt locus in Lesch–Nyhan patient. *Nature* **310**, 412–4.

6

Immobilization of the biological component of biosensors

S. A. BARKER

6.1 Applications to sensors

If we pose the problem: 'what is required of immobilization methods in biosensors?', then adaptability, reliability, and an option to bond the biological component to the sensor via molecules that conduct electrons figure high on the list. Although only minute quantities of the biological component (e.g. enzyme or antibody) are required, the purer it is the more reliable it will be. Obviously it must not contain either other substances which might interfere with the assay or other enzymes which catalyse reactions producing products detectable by the electrode chosen. Other elements of reliability require (1) a high degree of specificity to be exhibited by the biological component; (2) a good stability to the temperature, ionic strength, pH, redox potential, and chemical composition to be encountered within the sample environment; (3) an inbuilt device or devices that limit contamination, biodegradation of the biological component, and/or its mode of attachment; and (4) where the user is a patient then infection must be avoided often by a disposable component approach.

Adaptability includes immobilization methods applicable to enzymes, multiple enzymes and cofactors, micro-organisms, antibodies, lectins, and other immunoreaction components as well as organelles, tissue slices, and liposomes. The test is whether these biological components retain activity and stability when attached to the support matrix in the biosensor.

There is often a need for electrons to pass from an enzyme based biological component to the amplifier or microprocessor component. Ferrocene represents only the first of many potential ways of solving this problem (see Chapter 15). The cell in its natural state provides many examples of such transmission, e.g. cytochromes which are hemoproteins whose principal biological function is electron and/or hydrogen transport by valency change of their heme iron. The key development in the Yellow Springs Instrument Company sensor (Grooms et al. 1980; Chapter 1) was a device to prevent interference from other electroactive species in blood. This was accomplished by a cellulose acetate membrane which is used with a Nucleopore polycarbonate membrane to form an enzyme sandwich. When such a membrane had only bovine serum albumin between the layers and no enzyme, virtually no current was recorded in fresh whole blood, plasma, or serum and it was insensitive to uric acid, ascorbic acid, biluribin, molecular oxygen, and many drugs.

6.2 Introduction

In the immobilization of the biological component of the sensor we are particularly concerned with those methods which are applicable generally to a range of surfaces. This permits the choice of support surface to be as wide as possible and ensures that no refabrication of the support is required. Thus many surfaces have hydroxyl groups attached to them whether adjacent to carbon, silicon, or other atoms. Hence a method such as surface treatment with titanium tetrachloride, washing with water, and contacting with the biological component is of very wide applicability and provides a titanium sandwich chelate between support and biological component which is non-biodegradable and resistant to a wide range of physiological pHs within which biological components will exhibit their activity. It has the additional advantage that it can also be applied to support surfaces having $-NH_2$ and other groups amenable as ligands to the titanium atom. The initial surface treatment with titanium tetrachloride is the activation step and the activated surface can be dried at this stage if required. Once this surface is washed with water and the chloride ligands thereby replaced, it cannot be dried and should be immediately contacted with the biological component (Barker *et al.* 1971). Perhaps overiding all other considerations is the necessity for the biological component to exhibit maximum activity in its immobilized micro-environment i.e. to exhibit unit activity comparable with that in solution. Many early procedures gave dismal efficiences of 1–5% compared with the greater than 50% achievable by the titanium procedure with many enzymes.

Under some circumstances it may be desirable to replate the surface with the biological component. This can always be achieved by the titanium procedure. Other advantages often eagerly sought are (a) an ability for the biologically active component to operate at a wider pH range than in solution or at a different pH range than in solution, (b) attainment of greater stability by the immobilization procedure, (c) an ability to dispense with its co-enzyme, or (d) the ability to co-immobilize more than one biologically active component. No one method can yet provide all these but typically the titanium procedure affords (a)(b) and (d) with many enzymes.

Where pH changes are required, then the micro-environment created on the surface of the sensor after immobilization can often act as an insoluble 'buffer'. Thus free amine groups enable the enzyme range to be extended downwards while free carboxyl groups permit its upward extension but never by more than 2 pH units.

True mating of the sensor and the biological component is essential and has recently been achieved (Higgins *et al.* 1983; Chapters 15 & 16) by the use of mediator sandwich molecules between the sensor and biological component (e.g. with ferrocene). This approach has the additional advantage of enabling the enzyme quinoprotein glucose dehydrogenase to be used thus dispensing with the need for coenzyme (D'Costa *et al.* 1986). Here the nature of the bonding between sensor support (carbon felt electrodes) and enzyme are probably in the nature of electron transition complexes. The famous example of this taught to students is the interaction between benzene and hexafluo-robenzene. Thus the aromatic or hetero-aromatic residues in protein enzymes, antigens, or antibodies would be the expected target of such bonding.

Overloading of the surface support with the biological component should be avoided since, while activity increases with loading initially, this can decrease with high loading because of restricted access particularly where the biological component is interacting with another macromolecule. One method for partially overcoming this is to have a porous surface on the support (Kennedy *et al.* 1973). Much success has been gained by this ploy with immobilized glucamylase acting on starch or immobilized trypsin acting on casein. This feature is particularly important in immuno-biosensors where interaction is often between antibody and an antigen macromolecule.

In biosensors it is vital that leakage of the biological components does not occur to any extent during use of the biosensor. Methods of entrapment of enzymes or other biological components would be suspect in this aspect except where the biologically active component is a microbial cell.

6.3 Immobilization procedures

Entrapment in a gel matrix is a favoured method of immobilization par-ticularly for enzymes having small substrates which then have greater ease of access than a large substrate. Numerous matrices have been employed but recently the most favoured have been alginate and gelatin /collagen/cross-linked protein. With alginate, cross-linking the linear chains with Ca^{++} ions is generally employed. The Na alginate can be sterilized by autoclaving at 121 °C for 15 minutes and then, after mixing with the biological component, e.g. *Aspergillus* cells (Kuek and Armitage 1985), injected into 0.1 M $CaCl_2$ and the beads allowed to harden for 30 minutes. Observation after prolonged use showed that loss of surface calcium alginate was lowest where agitation was least vigorous. Improvement of inulinase stability was noted for calcium alginate immobilized *Kluyveromyces marxianus* cells following surface treat-ment with hardening agents. Stability doubled after glutaraldehyde treat-ment and was increased six fold for hexamethylenediamine/glutaraldehyde or polyethyleneimine/glutaraldehyde compared with unhardened cells (Bajpai and Margaritis 1985).

With the need to produce surface coatings, simple procedures like those employed for immobilizing *Arthrobacter simplex* cells on glass are much sought after (e.g. Fig. 6.1). Here the support was treated with colloidal particles of hydrous alumina or alternatively the cells were pretreated with aluminium ions (Mozes and Rouxhet 1984) Both glass beads of glass wool could be employed with a single layer comprising $3 \times 10^7 - 7 \times 10^7$ cells cm^{-2} for cortisol–prednisolone transformation.

Mere precipitation of lipase (triacylglycerol acylhydrolase) from solution with chilled acetone was sufficient to immobilize the enzyme on diatomaceous earth, Hyflo Supercel giving the highest interesterification activity (Wisdom *et al.* 1984) when employed in an organic phase of petroleum spirit.

Attachment of glucamylase to porous silica was achieved via pretreatment with titanium tetrachloride and then reaction of the dried support with 1, 6-diaminohexane in carbon tetrachloride. After washing, contacting with glutaraldehyde was used to anchor the enzyme to the surface (Cabral, *et al.* 1984).

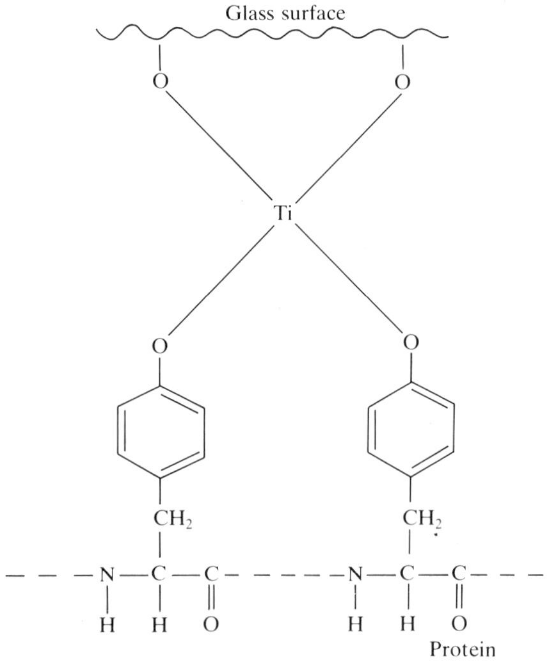

Fig. 6.1 Proposed enzyme-glass complex.

Table 6.1 Immobilization procedures used in enzyme electrodes and thermistors

Procedure	Enzyme	Reference
1. Irreversible adsorption onto graphite	D-Glucose oxidase	Ikeda *et al.* (1984)
2. Co-immobilisation with FAD on Teflon bonded carbon black	D-Glucose oxidase	Sonawat *et al.* (1984)
3. Glutaraldehyde mediated cross-linking with bovine serum albumin onto a Pd–Pd O electrode	Urease	Szuminsky *et al.* (1984)
4. Glutaraldehyde mediated cross-linking with bovine serum albumin onto platinum	D-Glucose Oxidase	Wingard *et al.* (1984)
5. Dimethylsuberimidate mediated reaction with insoluble collagen	D-Glucose oxidase	Ngo and Lenhoff (1983)
6. Entrapment in a gelatin support	L-Lysine oxidase	Romette *et al.* (1983)
7. Co-immobilization	D-Glucose oxidase and catalase	Cleland and Enfors (1983)
8. Co-immobilization via glutaraldehyde mediated crosslinking with bovine serum albumin on Pt foil	D-Glucose oxidase and catalase	Wingard *et al.* (1983)
9. Adsorption on $CaCO_3$ particles	Nitrite oxidising bacteria	Okada *et al.* (1983)
10. Urease immobilized membrane dipped in ethylene diamine or polylysine	Urease	Tokinaga *et al.* (1984)
11. Glutaraldehyde for cross-linking the enzyme with a porous polycarbonate film.	Glucose oxidase	Matsushita (1984*a*)
12. Trapped between Pt plate and polyethylene phthalate film subsequently irradiated	Glucose oxidase	Matsushita (1984*b*)
13. Direct O-alkylation of Nylon 6	Urease	Begum and Mottolo (1984)

Table 6.1 *Continued*

Procedure	Enzyme	Reference
14. Entrapment between cellophane dialysis membrance and NH_3 gas permeable membrane	Asparaginase	Nikolelis (1984)
15. Co-immobilization on activated collagen strip supports	Luciferase and FMN-oxido reductase	Blum and Coulet (1984)
16. Co-immobilization by adsorption on medium porosity glassy carbon	FAD and glucose oxidase	Miyawaki and Wingard (1984)
17. Reaction with concanvalin A prereacted with cyanogen bromide activated agarose	Ascorbic acid oxidase, β-fructofuranosidase in enzyme thermistor	Mattiasson and Danielsson (1982)
18. Glutaraldehyde mediated reaction with controlled pore glass	β-D-Galactosidase, D-galactose oxidase in enzyme thermistor	Mattiasson and Danielsson (1982)
19. Glutaraldehyde mediated reaction with gelatin onto a CO_2 gas sensitive electrode	L-Lysine decarboxylase	Tran *et al.* (1983)
20. Glutaraldehyde mediated co-immobilization on Clark type electrode	Alcohol oxidase, catalase	Verdyuyn *et al.* (1983)
21. Immobilization via coating enzyme loaded on *p*-benzoquinone-C paste electrode with a nitrocellulose film	Glucose oxidase	Ikeda *et al.* (1985)
22. Co-immobilization on unwoven nylon cloth of enzyme with electron acceptor K ferricyanide	Glucose oxidase	Kawaguri *et al.* (1984)
23. Enzyme on membrane over a platinum electrode	Uricase or glucose oxidase	Tokyo Elec. (1985)
24. Co-immobilization on arylaminated controlled pore glass	β-Fructofuranosidase /mutarotase	Masoom and Townshend (1985)

Table 6.1 *Continued*

Procedure	Enzyme	Reference
25. Enzyme immobilized at electrode surface with glutaraldehyde	Adenosine deaminase	Bradley and Rechnitz (1985)
26. Enzyme immobilized on a porous polycarbonate membrane	Alcohol oxidase	Clark *et al.* (1984*a*)
27. Enzyme immobilized between two membranes of cellulose ester using buffered glutaraldehyde	Oxalate oxidase	Clark *et al.* (1984*b*)
28. Enzyme immobilized on porous side of a cellulose acetate membrane	L(+) Lactate oxidase	Tsuchida *et al.* (1985)

Yeast cells (negatively charged surface) can adhere to glass (negatively charged surface) or polycarbonate without the use of chemical reagents. Only storage of the cells in pure water (Van Haecht *et al.* 1984) is required prior to adhesion. During this phase the cells are starved and the cell wall modified in such a way as to promote adhesion.

Radiation mediated grafting of polyacrolein onto poly (methyl methacrylate) microspheres was shown to activate the particles for subsequent chymotrypsin immobilization at pH 8.3 (Clark *et al.* 1984).

If dextran is periodate oxidized and the product reacted with glycine and then sodium borohydride, coupling with N^{6-} (N^- (2 aminoethyl) propionamide)-NAD^+ affords a dextran bound co-enzyme NAD^+ derivative (coupling agent 1-ethyl-3-(3-dimethylamino propyl)- carbodiimide) with an activity almost equal to that of free NAD^+ for the ADH and LDH catalysed reactions (Adachi *et al.* 1984).

Genetics International (1984*a*) used ferrocene absorbed on an electrode as the support for their glucose oxidase electrode. Earlier (1984*b*) they stipulated mediator compounds comprising at least two organic rings on electrodes of carbon particle paste or solid carbon.

The above examples serve to illustrate the four main approaches to enzyme immobilization (Fig. 6.2).

1. Physical adsorption at a solid surface
2. Entrapment in polymeric gel or within microcapsules.
3. Cross-linking by means of bifunctional reagents often in combination with 1 or 2.
4. Covalent binding to a reactive insoluble support.

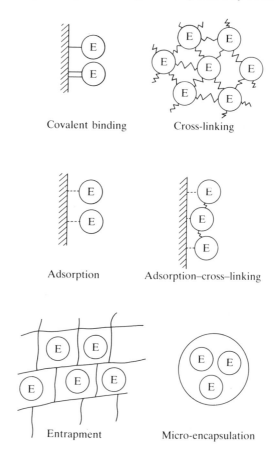

Fig. 6.2 Methods of enzyme immobilization.

6.3.1 Adsorption

Substances such as alumina, charcoal, clay, cellulose, kaolinite, collodion, silica gel, glass, hydroxyapatite, and collagen are known to adsorb enzymes. Obviously this list can be extended to ion exchangers such as DEAE cellulose, CM-cellulose, DEAE-Sephadex, Dowex 50, and a variety of phenolic resins. The great advantage of adsorption is that usually no reagents are required and only a minimum of activation or 'clean-up' steps. Adsorption tends to be less disruptive to enzyme protein than chemical methods of attachment (3 and 4 above). Binding forces are due to hydrogen bonds, multiple salt linkages, Van der Waal's forces, and the formation, where appropriate, of electron

Table 6.2 Immobilization procedures in other devices

Procedure	Objective	Reference
1. Reaction of concanavalin with cyanogen bromide activated agarose	Topographic probe for protein–protein interactions with D-galacto-syltransferase	Wong *et al.* (1983)
2. Reaction with activated thiol-agarose and anti (immunoglobulin G) antibody via thiol-disulphide interchange	Development of a screening method for detection of monoclonal antibodies in growing cultures	Kimura *et al.* (1984)
3. Glucose oxidase used as a label in enzyme immunoassay — active film with enzyme coated directly on the gas selective membrane of the pO_2 electrode	A computerized automatic system for determination of hepatitis B surface antigen (H Bs Ag) in biological fluids	Romette and Boitieux (1984)
4. Immobilization of immunoglobulins on silica surfaces wherein reactive groups introduced by chemical vapor deposition of silane. Also compared with IgG immobilized by thiol-disulphide exchange	Use in an immunosensor	Jonsson *et al.* (1985)

Immunosensors are biosensors that embody antibodies as their selective binding components. They include enzyme immunosensors, optical fibre based fluoresence immunosensors, piezoelectric systems, immunoFET systems (field effect transistors), optical systems, evanescent wave systems, surface plasmon resonance devices, and conformation sensitive transducers and have been reviewed by North (1985).

transition complexes. Unfortunately, except for the last named, the binding forces are more susceptible to change in pH, temperature, ionic strength, or even the presence of the enzyme substrate.

6.3.2 Entrapment

If a polymeric gel is prepared in a solution containing an enzyme, the enzyme becomes trapped within the forming gel matrix. With due attention to the degree of cross-linking employed, this method of preparation can be applied to any enzyme since the protein molecule is trapped within a three

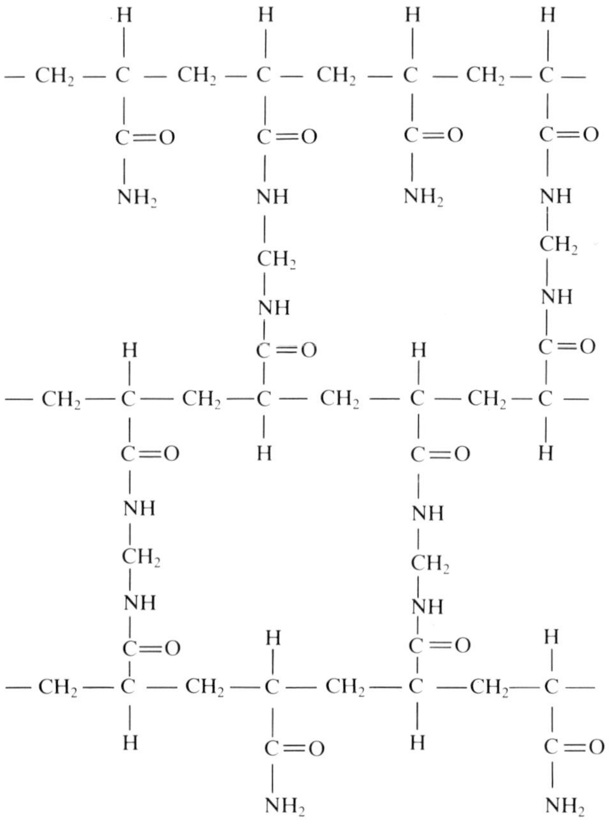

```
        H              H              H              H
        |              |              |              |
— CH₂ — C — CH₂ — C — CH₂ — C — CH₂ — C —
        |              |              |              |
        C=O            C=O            C=O            C=O
        |              |              |              |
        NH₂            NH             NH₂            NH
                       |                             |
                       CH₂                           CH₂
                       |                             |
                       NH                            NH
        H              |              H              |
        |              C=O            |              C=O
— CH₂ — C — CH₂ — C — CH₂ — C — CH₂ — C —
        |              |              |              |
        C=O            H              C=O            H
        |                             |
        NH                            NH
        |                             |
        CH₂                           CH₂
        |                             |
        NH                            NH
        |              H              |              H
        C=O            |              C=O            |
— CH₂ — C — CH₂ — C — CH₂ — C — CH₂ — C —
        |              |              |              |
        H              C=O            H              C=O
                       |                             |
                       NH₂                           NH₂
```

Fig. 6.3 Major structural features of the acrylamide N, N-methylene bis-acrylamide copolymer.

dimensional lattice (see Fig. 6.3 — the structure of a polyacrylamide gel used in the early developments of an enzyme electrode). Besides the example already given starch gels, nylon, and silastic gels can be employed.

Unfortunately this method suffers from two major drawbacks, (1) large diffusional barriers to the transport of substrate and product leading to reaction retardation particularly with high molecular weight substrates, e.g. ribonuclease, trypsin, and dextranase, and (2) continuous loss of enzyme activity since some pore sizes permit escape of the enzyme. Nevertheless, crosslinking entrapped protein with glutaraldehyde can often overcome the latter problem.

6.3.3 Cross-linking

Bifunctional agents that induce intermolecular cross-linking (see Fig. 6.4) can bind enzymes to solid supports. Cross-linking an enzyme to itself is both

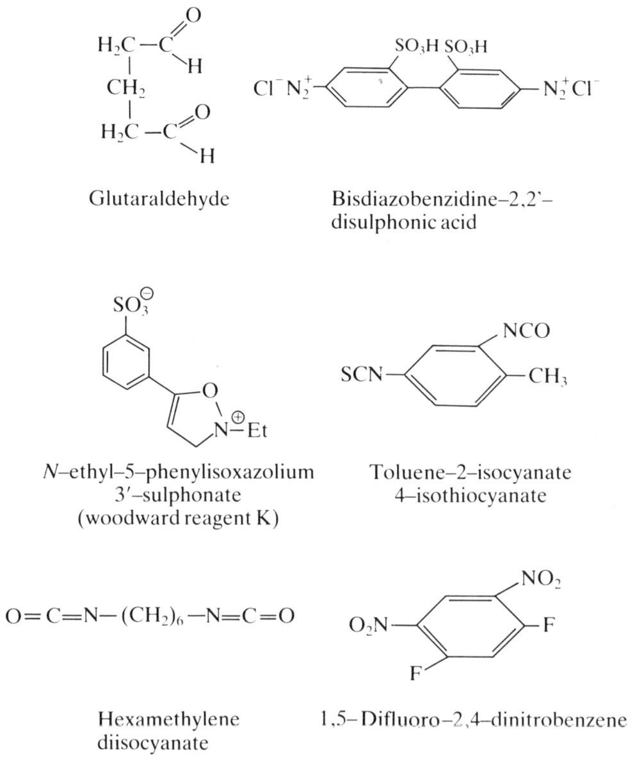

Fig. 6.4 Some common bifunctional reagents for cross-linking protein.

expensive and inefficient as some of the protein material will inevitably be acting mainly as a support resulting in relatively low enzymic activity. Other disadvantages include diffusional limitations and lack of rigidity or mechanical strength. However bifunctional reagents are widely used in stabilizing physically adsorbed enzymes by cross-linking. Glutaraldehyde will often react with the lysine amino groups in an enzyme and in the case of trypsin will largely prevent self-digestion at the peptide bond adjacent to the point of attachment. Such reactions must be optimized and the pH values for the most rapid insolublization of lysozyme and papain are nearly the same as their isoelectric points.

6.3.4 Covalent bonding

Common reactions for covalent bonding are shown in Fig. 6.5. Covalent bonding between the enzyme and support matrix is accomplished through functional groups in the enzyme which are not essential for its catalytic activity. Use is made of nucleophilic functional groups present in amino acid

a. The cyanogen bromide technique

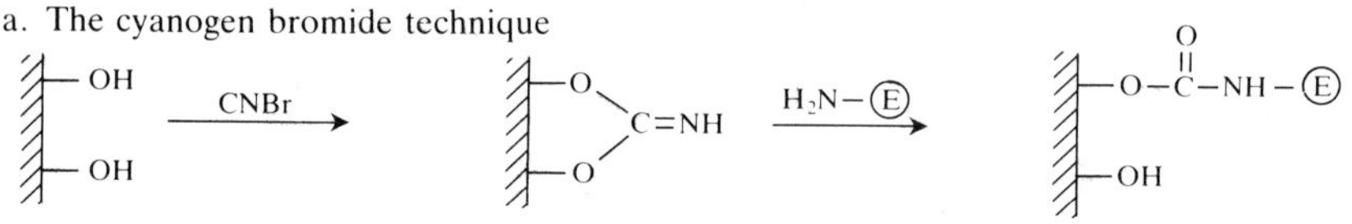

b. The Carbodi-Imide method

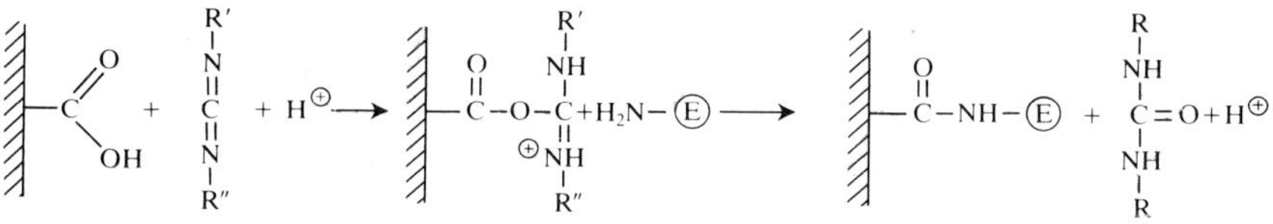

c.   Via acyl groups by treatment of hydrazides with nitrous acid

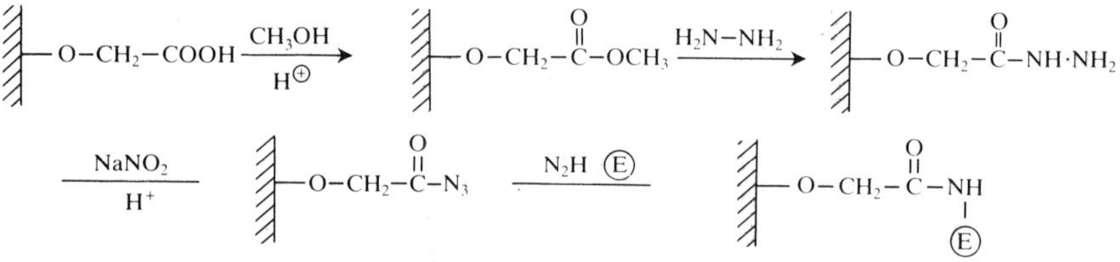

d.   Coupling using cyanuric chloride

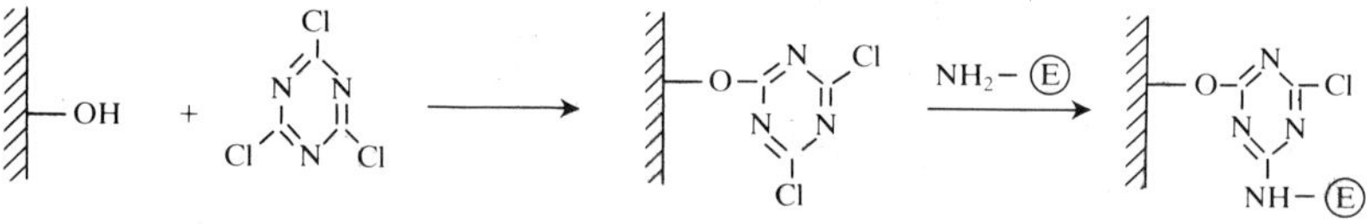

e.   Coupling through diazonium groups from aromatic amino groups

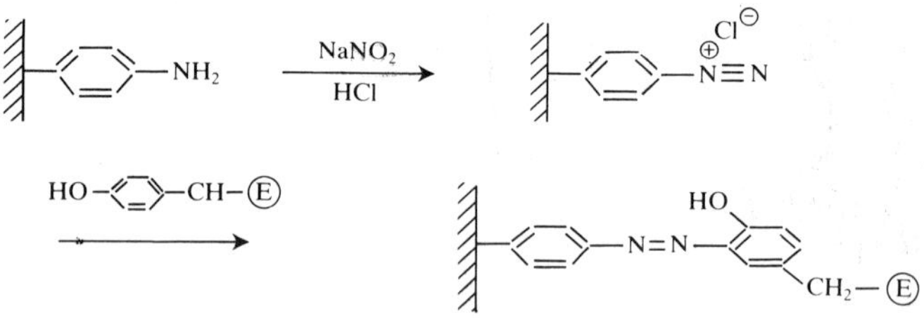

f.   Coupling via thiol groups

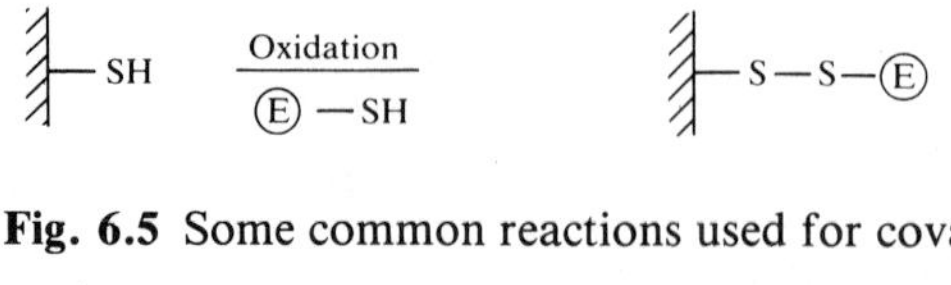

Fig. 6.5 Some common reactions used for covalent binding.

side chains of proteins for coupling. These are as diverse as amino, carboxylic acid, hydroxyl, phenolic, imidazole, and thiol groups. Coupling preferably takes place at low temperature, low ionic strength, and within the physiological pH range. Often coupling is done in the presence of the enzyme substrate to protect its active site. Covalent bonding has the great advantage that the enzyme is unlikely to be released during use from the optimum support matrix chosen (e.g for porosity, non-biodegradability, etc). The diversity of methods permits the avoidance of the active site in the process of linking. The efficiency of coupling should always be studied particularly the relative efficiency of a given amount of the enzyme acting in solution compared with its activity in the immobilized state. It is a useful parameter to determine choice of coupling procedure and support before the whole sensor is assembled. Mosbach's (1978) review article affords a good starting point for those new to the field and in particular covers the important area of immobilization of co-enzymes and their recycling. Specific examples of their application in enzyme electrodes are given.

References

Adachi, S., Ogata, M., Tobata, H. and Hashimoto, K. (1984). Effects of molecular weight of dextran and NAD density on coenzyme activity bound to dextran. *Enz. Microb. Technol.* **6**, 259-62.

Bajpai, P. and Margaritis, A. (1985). Improvement of inulinase stability of calcium alginate immobilized K. marxianus cells. *Enz. Microb. Technol.* **7**, 34-6.

Barker, S. A., Emery, A. N., Novais, J. W. (1971) Enzyme reactors for industry. *Proc. Biochem.* **6** (Oct), 11-13.

Begum, K. D. and Mottolo, H. A., (1984) Nylon shavings enzyme reactor for batch determination of urea. *Anal. Biochem.* **142**, 1-6.

Blum, L. J., and Coulet, P. R., (1984). Coimmobilisation of luciferase and FMN oxidoreductase in an enzyme electrode. *Anal. Chim. Acta* **161**, 355-8.

Bradley, C. R. and Rechnitz, G. A. (1985). Immobilisation barrier effects on the dynamic response characteristics of potentiometric adenosine deaminase enzyme electrodes — membrance thickness effect etc. *Anal. Chem.* **57**, 1401-4.

Cabral, J. M. S., Cardosa, J. P., Novais, J. M. and Kennedy, J. F. (1984). A simple kinetic model for the hydrolysis of α-D-glucans using glucamylase immobilised on porous silica. Enz. Microb. Technol. **6**, 365-70.

Clark, D. S., Bailey, J. E., Yen, R. and Rembaum, A. (1984). Enzyme immobilisation on grafted polymeric microspheres. *Enz. Microb. Technol.* **6**, 317-20.

—— Noyes, L. K., Grooms, T. A. and Moore, P. E. (1984a). Direct rapid electro-enzymatic sensor for measuring alcohol in whole blood and fermentation products-enzyme electrode using Hansenula polymorpha immobilized alcohol oxidase. *Ann. N. Y. Acad. Sci.* **434**, 515-19.

—— (1984b). Oxalate sensing enzyme electrode using immobilised barley seedling oxalate oxidase. *Ann. N. Y. Acad. Sci.* **434**, 512-14.

Cleland, N. and Enfors, S. O. (1983). Control of glucose fed batch cultivations of

E. coli by means of an oxygen controlled stabilized enzyme electrode containing immobilised glucose oxidase and catalase. *Eur. J. Appl. Microbiol. Biotechnol.* **18**, 141–7.

D'Costa, E. J., Higgins, I. J., and Turner, A. P. F. (1986) Quinoprotein glucose dehydrogenase and its application in an amperometric glucose sensor. *Biosensors* **2**, 71–89.

Genetics International (1984*a*). Analytical equipment and sensor electrodes therefore. European Patent 127958.

—— (1984*b*) Measurement of enzyme catalysed reactions. European Patent 125137.

Grooms, T. A., Clark, L. C. and Weiner, B. J. (1980). The design of peroxide enzyme membrane polarographic sensors for clinical and industrial analysis. In *Enzyme Engineering* (Eds. H. H. Weetall and G. R. Royer) Vol. **5**, 217–29. Plenum Press, New York.

Higgins, I. J., Hill H. A. O. and Plotkin, E. V. (1984). Measurement of enzyme catalysed reactions. European Patent 125137. 14th Nov.

Ikeda, T., Hamada, H., Miki, K. and Senda, M. (1985) Glucose oxidase immobilised benzoquinone-carbon paste electrode as a glucose sensor. *Agric. Biol. Chem. (Japan)* **49**, 541–3.

—— Katasho, I., Kamei, M., and Senda, M. (1984). Electrocatalysis with a glucose oxidase immobilized graphite electrode. *Agric. Biol. Chem. (Japan)* **48**, 1969–76.

Jonsson, U., Malmqvist, M. and Ronnberg, I. (1985). Immobilization of immuno globulins in silica surfaces: stability for use as immunosensor and in affinity chromatography. *Biochem. J.* **227**, 363–71.

Kawaguri, M., Nankai, S., Iijima, T. (1984). Biosensor. PCT Int. App. WO 84 03562. 13 Sept.

Kennedy, J. F., Barker, S. A. and Rosevear, A. (1973). Preparation of water insoluble trans-2, 3-cyclic carbonate derivative of macroporous cellulose and its use as a matrix for enzyme immobilisation. *J. Chem. Soc. Perkin*, 2293–9.

Kimura, S., Hayano, T. and Kato, K. (1984). Properties and applications to immunoassay of monoclonal antibodies to neuron specific γγ enolase. *Biochem. Biophys. Acta* **799**, 252–9.

Kuek, C. and Armitage, T. M. (1985). Scanning electronmicroscopic examination of calcium alginate beads immobilizing growing mycelia. *Enz. Microb. Technol.* **7**, 121–5.

Masoom, M. and Townshend, A. (1985). Simultaneous determination of sucrose and glucose in mixtures by flow injection analysis with immobilized enzymes — invertase/mutarotase column and glucose oxidase column. *Anal. Chim. Acta* **171**, 185–94.

Matsushita (1984*a*). Biosensor. Japan Kokai Tokkyo Koho JP 59 67, 452 17th April.

—— (1984*b*). Biosensor. Japan Patent 011896. 4th August.

Mattiassin, B. and Danielsson, B. (1982). Calorimetric analysis of sugars and sugar derivatives with aid of an enzyme thermistor. *Carb. Res.* **102**, 273–82.

Miyawaki, O. and Wingard, L. B. (1984). FAD and glucose oxidase immobilised on carbon. *Ann. N. Y. Acad. Sci.* **434**, 520–2.

Mosbach, K. (1978). Immobilized coenzymes in ligand affinity chromatography and their use as active coenzymes. *Advances in Enzymology*, **46**, 205–78.

Mozes, N. and Rouxhet, P. G. (1984) Dehydrogenation of cortisol by *Arthrobacter simplex* immobilized as supported monolayer. *Enz. Microb. Technol.* **6**, 497–502.

Ngo, T. T. and Lenhoff, H. M. (1983). Amperometric assay for collagenase. Amplification by use of GOD conjugated to insoluble collagen. *Appl. Biochem. Biotechnol.* **8**, 407–14.

Nikolelis, D. P. (1984). Construction of an immobilised asparaginase sensor and determination of asparagine in blood serum. *Anal. Chim. Acta* **161**, 343–8.

North, J. R. (1985). Immunosensors: antibody based biosensors — comparison of construction methods and devices. *U. K. Trends Biotechnol.* **3**, 180–6.

Okada, T., Karube, I. and Suziki S. (1983). NO$_2$ sensor which uses immobilized nitrite oxidising bacteria. *Biotechol. Bioeng.* **25**, 1641–51.

Romette, J. L. and Boitieux J. L. (1984). Oxidase enzyme: enzyme and immunoenzyme sensor — computerized automatic system development: glucose oxidase application. *Ann. N. Y. Acad. Sci.* **434**, 533–5.

—— Yang, J. S., Kusakabe, H. and Thomas, D. (1983). Enzyme Electrode for specific determination of L-lysine. *Biotechnol. Bioeng.* **25**, 2557–66.

Sonawot, H. M., Phadke, R. S. and Govil, G. (1984). Covalent immobilization of FAD and glucose oxidase on carbon electrodes studies using cyclic voltammetry. *Biotechnol. Bioeng.* **26**. 1066–70.

Szuminsky, N. J., Chen, A. K. and Liu, C. C. (1984). A miniature Palladium — Palladium oxide enzyme electrode for urea determination. *Biotechnol. Bioeng.* **26**, 642–5.

Tokinaga, D., Kobayashi, T., Katori, A. and Karasawa, Y. (1984). Urease immobilised urea electrode and process for preparing the same U.S. Patent 4, 476, 005. Oct. 9th. Hitachi Ltd.

Tokyo Elec. (1985). Enzyme electrode containing immobilised glucose oxidase or uricase with enzyme store for supplementation JP 224055. 24th June.

Tran. N. D., Romette, J. L. and Thomas, D. (1983). An enzyme electrode for specific determination of L-lysine. A real time sensor. *Biotech. Bioeng.* **25**, 329–40.

Tsuchida, T., Takasugi, H., Yoda, K. Takizawa, K., and Kobayashi, S. (1985). Application of L-lactate electrode for clinical analysis and monitoring of tissue culture medium — an enzyme electrode for L-lactic acid determination. *Biotechnol. Bioeng.* **27**, 837–41.

Verdyuyn, C., Van Dijken, J. P., and Scheffers, W. A. (1983). A simple sensitive and accurate alcohol electrode. *Biotechnol. Bioeng.* **25**, 1049–55.

Van Haecht, J. L., De Bremaeker, M. and Rouxhet, P. G. (1984). Immobilization of yeast by adhesion to a support without use of a chemical agent. *Enzym. Microbiol. Technol.* **6**, 221–7.

Wingard, L. B., Cantin, L. A. and Castner, J. F. (1983). Effect of enzyme matrix composition on potentiometric response to glucose using glucose oxidase immobilised on Platinum. *Biochim. Biophys. Acta* **748**, 21–7.

—— Castner, J. F., Yao, S. J., Wolfson, S. K., Drash, A. L. and Liu, C. C. (1984). Immobilised glucose oxidase in the potentiometric detection of glucose. *Appl. Biochem. Biotechnol.* **9**, 95–104.

Wisdom, R. A., Dunnill, P., Lilly M. D. and McCrae, A. (1984). Enzyme interesterification of fats: factors influencing the choice of support for immobilised lipase. *Enzym. Microbiol. Technol.* **6**, 443–6.

Wong, S. S., Malorie, T. E. and Lee, T. K. (1983). Use of Concanavalin A as a Topographical Probe for Protein–Protein interaction. Lactose Synthase. *Biochim. Biophys. Acta,* **745**, 90–6.

7

Genetic engineering

P. J. WARNER

7.1 Introduction

This chapter is concerned with the impact genetic manipulation is likely to have on sensor technology. During the last ten years, four discoveries made during the nineteen seventies have revolutionized genetics. These discoveries were restriction endonucleases, plasmids (initially in bacteria), nucleic acid hybridization, and methods for sequencing DNA. They have allowed genes from diverse origins to be transferred to and expressed in different organisms, usually bacterial cells. The state of the art of recombinant DNA technology is outlined briefly below.

How, then, can use be made of this technology in the development of sensors? The purpose of this chapter is to answer this question, with the use of specific examples, where appropriate.

Recombinant DNA technology will have a role in improvement of the biological component of enzyme based and whole cell biosensors. This will allow both improvement of these sensors for existing roles, for example by optimizing the enzymes employed and also permit their applications to be broadened. It may also be instrumental in reducing cost through providing a readily available sources of an enzyme that would otherwise be difficult to obtain in quantity.

7.2 Recombinant DNA technology

It is outside the scope of this book to provide the reader with a detailed account of methods of genetic engineering. The reader will however find that an excellent introduction is given by Old and Primrose (1985). Only a brief account of the techniques involved is given here.

7.2.1 Molecular cloning

An outline of a typical molecular cloning experiment is given in Fig. 7.1. Firstly it involves the isolation of the nucleic acid encoding the functions of interest from its natural host. In bacteria and other prokaryotes the DNA of interest can often be isolated directly. For higher plants and animals the procedure is slightly different because the DNA includes sequences, known

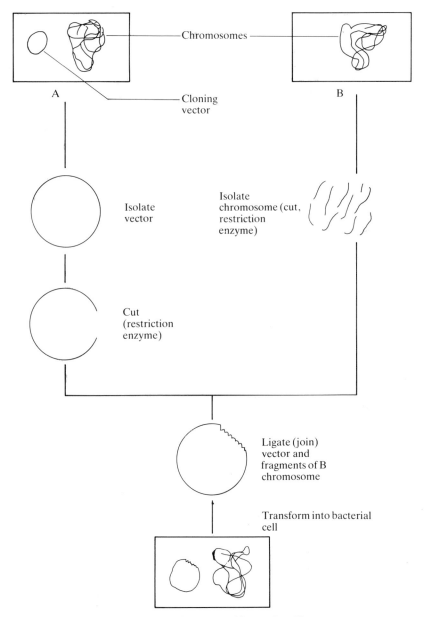

Chromosomes

A

Cloning
vector

B

Isolate
vector

Isolate
chromosome (cut,
restriction
enzyme)

Cut
(restriction
enzyme)

Ligate (join)
vector and
fragments of B
chromosome

Transform into bacterial
cell

Bacterium contains recombinant plasmid

Fig. 7.1 An example of a cloning experiment showing the role of the cloning vector.

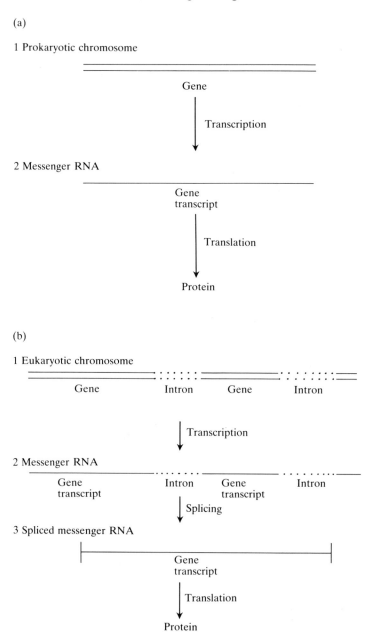

Fig. 7.2 The flow of genetic information in (a) prokaryotes and (b) eukaryotes. In the former, the DNA is transcribed to messenger RNA (mRNA) and translated to give the protein. In eukaryotes the genes include intervening sequences (introns), which are

as introns. These are intervening sequences within genes, which are subjected to elimination from the messenger RNA (a process known as splicing) after transcription, but before translation (Fig. 7.2). In order that the genes of interest can be expressed in prokaryotes it is necessary to eliminate these (Fig. 7.3). To facilitate this, the messenger RNA (mRNA) is isolated. This is achieved by using cells in which the product of the gene of interest is likely to be induced; that is conditions under which the mRNA of interest is a substantial proportion of the total mRNA present. Messenger RNA can be readily isolated from eukaryotes, because unlike other types of RNA, its ends consist of poly-adenine (polyA) tails, which will associate with poly-thymine (polyT) in a suitable affinity column. Once isolated, the mRNA is subjected to reverse transcription *in vitro* (using a viral enzyme called reverse transcriptase), which produces DNA which does not include introns. This is known as complimentary DNA (cDNA).

Once a DNA fragment likely to be expressed in a bacterium has been obtained the following procedure is followed. The DNA is then cut using restriction endonucleases (Kessler *et al.* 1985). These are enzymes which cut DNA wherever a specific recognition sequence is found, to leave short overhangs on either fragment. A small autonomously replicating piece of DNA termed a plasmid is similarly treated and then the two fragments of DNA from diverse origins are joined using an enzyme termed DNA ligase. The recombined molecule is then transferred to a bacterium. This is usually achieved by genetic transformation, in which under certain conditions the bacterium will take up the naked DNA, which is then replicated. We now have a recombinant molecule maintained within a new host. The plasmids used as cloning vectors have selectable genetic markers such as antibiotic resistance, and so their presence can be selected for, after transformation. If the foreign DNA is cloned into the middle of one of these genes, the recombinants will have then lost one of these markers, unlike molecules which have just recircularized after they have been cut by restriction endonuclease. They will therefore be recognizable as organisms sensitive to one particular antibiotic. This procedure is termed insertional inactivation, and is shown in Fig. 7.4. The 'foreign genes' may or may not be expressed; this means that the bacterium may or may not display the characteristics encoded by the cloned genes. If the latter is the case, the genes of interest can be re-cloned into plasmids specially designed to promote expression of cloned genes. As an alternative to a bacterial plasmid, some bacteriophages (bacterial viruses)

---

faithfully transcribed. The components of the genes themselves are known as exons. The introns are removed from the mRNA before transcription. Therefore if the DNA is cloned directly into prokaryotes the introns will not be recognized and will remain in the mRNA at translation, preventing production of an active protein. This problem has been overcome by use of the strategy shown in Fig. 7.3.

1 Isolate spliced messenger RNA

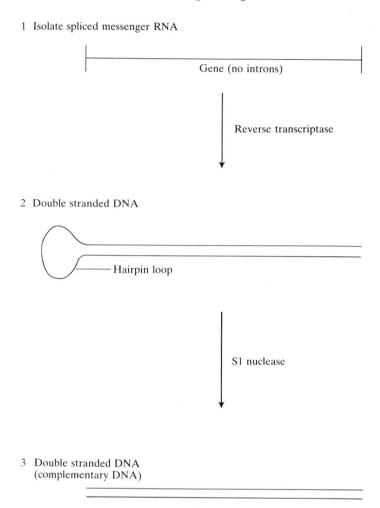

2 Double stranded DNA

3 Double stranded DNA
   (complementary DNA)

Fig. 7.3 Molecular cloning of eukaryotic DNA. The messenger RNA encoding the required product is isolated first, because it contains no introns (Fig. 7.2). This is then treated with a viral enzyme called reverse transcriptase, which generates an intron-free DNA sequence. A double stranded sequence is typically obtained, which includes single stranded regions at one end, which are removed by a single strand specific DNA degrading enzyme (S1 nuclease). This leaves a DNA sequence, known as complementary DNA (cDNA) suitable for cloning in a prokaryotic host (bacterium).

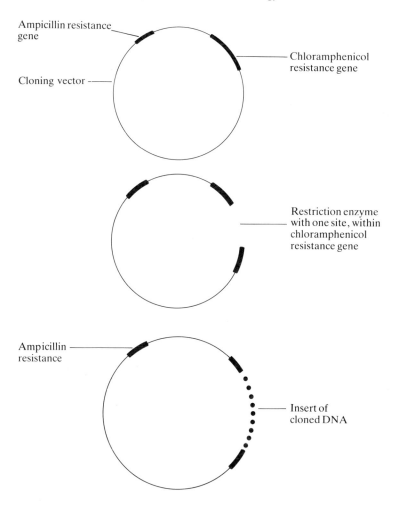

Fig. 7.4 Use of insertional inactivation to identify recombinant molecules. A unique site on the plasmid for a particular restriction enzyme lies within the chloramphenicol resistance gene and it is here that the foreign DNA is inserted. Organisms which have acquired recombinant molecules will be recognized, since they are chloramphenicol sensitive (the insertion has interfered with the structural integrity of the chloramphenicol resistance gene) but retain ampicillin resistance.

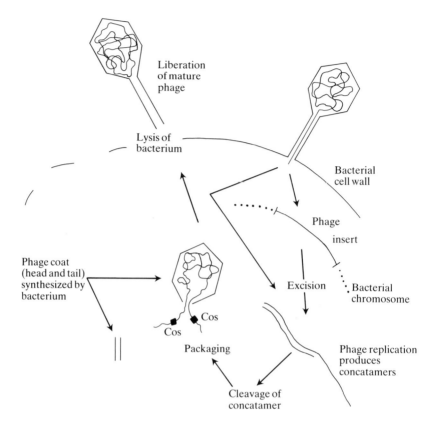

Fig. 7.5 The life cycle of bacteriophage Lambda. On infecting the host bacterium, the phage can either undergo the lytic cycle or become incorporated into the bacterial chromosome, with which it replicates (the lysogenic state). At some stage in the future the phage may once again become lytic — this process can be induced by irradiation of lysogens with UV light. The lytic cycle is a vegetative process, at the end of which the host cell lyses, releasing large numbers of phage. The 'cos' sites are responsible for packaging replicated DNA into phage coats.

have also been developed for use as cloning vectors. The life cycle of bacteriophage lambda of *Escherichia coli*, the best known example of a phage cloning vector from which many cloning vectors have been developed (Brammar 1982), is shown in Fig. 7.5. The techniques used are similar to those for cloning using plasmids, but recombinants are usually isolated as plaques of bacteriophage, rather than intact bacterial cells. Plaques are circular regions of clearing in a lawn of bacteria grown on a plate, resulting from infection of a single bacterium with one phage, which has lysed to provide many thousand copies of itself, which then infect surrounding cells.

Whilst *Escherichia coli* is the best developed system to use for DNA cloning, similar systems are being developed for a range of bacteria, both Gram-positive and Gram-negative. These include *Pseudomonas, Bacillus*, and *Streptomyces*. The above cloning techniques also are possible in yeasts and similar experiments are becoming possible in cells from higher animals and plants.

7.2.2 Nucleic acid hybridization

This topic will not be dealt with in any detail here, since the technology has been described elsewhere in this volume (Chapter 5). I shall merely remind the reader that the technique allows the similarity of fragments of two pieces of DNA (southern blotting: Southern 1975) and pieces of RNA and DNA (northern blotting: Adams *et al.* 1979) to be established. The relevence of the technique to this chapter is discussed below.

7.2.3 DNA sequencing

DNA sequencing technology has been available for about the last eight years. Two methods have been developed, a chemical method (Maxam and Gilbert 1977) and a method which relies on inhibition of the polymerase reaction leading to a halt being placed on DNA synthesis at specific points (Sanger 1977).

7.2.3.1 Maxam and Gilbert method In this method a defined fragment of DNA generated by restriction endonuclease digestion is used. The sequence is labelled at one end with ^{32}phosphate. Reagents are then used which alter one of the four bases present in DNA such that it can be removed and the strand can be cleaved, using certain chemical reagents (Table 7.1). If only partial reaction is allowed to occur a set of end labelled fragments of different lengths is generated. Each of the reactions detailed in Table 7.1 are used and the sequence information is then determined on a high resolution polyacrylamide gel.

Table 7.1 Reagents used in Maxam and Gilbert sequencing

Base specificity	Base reaction	Altered base removal	Strand cleavage
Guanine	dimethyl sulphate	piperidine	piperidine
Guanine + adenine	acid	acid-catalysed depurination	piperidine
Thymine + cytosine	hydrazine	piperidine	piperidine
Cytosine	hydrazine + NaCl	piperidine	piperidine
Adenine cytosine	NaOH	piperidine	piperidine

7.2.3.2 Sanger sequencing   This is the most widely used method of DNA sequencing, since it generally allows larger fragments of DNA to be analysed, with less chance of error. The DNA to be sequenced is first cloned into a single stranded bacteriophage vector which can be used in *E. coli*. Phage M13 and its derivatives are most commonly used. (Messing *et al.* 1981). The single stranded DNA is then used as a substrate for DNA polymerase which faithfully copies the first strand. However, if the normal deoxynucleoside phosphate is substituted by the dideoxy nucleoside phosphate, although this analogue can be incorporated, it will halt further activity of the polymerase, thus inhibiting any further chain elongation. Initiation of the process is achieved using a chemically synthesized universal nucleotide primer. The reaction is carried out in the presence of the four dNTPs one of which is labelled with ^{32}P, and there are four reaction mixes, each with a low concentration of the analogues. One therefore ends up with a mixture of radiolabelled DNA fragments, with one end in common, but of variable length and a base specific opposite end. The DNA from each mix, after incubation, is converted to the single stranded form and electrophoresed on a polyacrylamide gel. The sequence can be read directly from the gel. This method allows between 250 and 500 base pairs to be sequenced in one set of reactions and the data is then analysed, frequently with the assistance of a computer.

7.2.4 Site specific mutagenesis

Once the sequence of a piece of DNA has been determined, the technology now exists to make site-specific changes to the sequence, so that the effect of specific amino acid changes in a protein can be investigated (Dalbadie-McFarland *et al.* 1982; Zoller and Smith, 1982). This technique is known as site-specific mutagenesis. Single stranded DNA is again the substrate and a synthetic oligonucleotide, in which one base pair has been changed and hence a specific mutation with known effect introduced, is used as the primer. DNA polymerase is used to reform a duplex and the resulting molecule (plasmid) with two slightly different strands, is transformed into a bacterial host. Mutant clones may in some cases be able to be phenotypically selected or screened for, but otherwise they can be detected by differences in their ability to hybridize with the synthetic oligonucleotide. This technique is the corner stone of DNA mediated protein engineering and a more thorough account of this can be found in this volume (Chapter 8).

Above I have attempted to outline some of the techniques used in genetic engineering which may be applicable to the development of biosensors. I shall now move on to describe the type of improvements we can expect to see them bring about in this field.

7.3 Applications to sensor technology

7.3.1 Improved yield of enzyme

An obvious application of recombinant DNA technology is for cases when the enzyme to be used in a biosensor is present in small amounts or difficult to isolate. An example of the latter problem in our laboratory has been the isolation of glucose dehydrogenase (GDH) (Duine *et al.* 1982). This enzyme is of potential use in a glucose sensor, since it would show greater sensitivity than glucose sensors based on glucose oxidase (GOD), and unlike GOD sensors, would have no requirement for oxygen (Turner and Pickup 1985; D'Costa *et al.* 1986). The source of GDH for our studies has been the bacterium *Acinetobacter calcoaceticus*. The yield of the enzyme from this organism has, however, been poor (Ameyama *et al.* 1981) since it appears to be present at very low levels. Its role in this organism is unclear, but it is probably concerned with energy metabolism. Glucose dehydrogenase consists of an apoenzyme and also a cofactor, PQQ, which serves as a cofactor for several other dehydrogenase enzymes in a range of organisms. Molecular cloning of the genes which encode the apoenzyme, and expression in an alternative organism, such as *E. coli*, would allow easier isolation of GDH. It offers the ability to improve production of the enzyme in three ways:

1. The gene encoding GDH can be cloned into a multi-copy plasmid vector. These plasmids are present in up to 50 copies per cell and hence the gene of interest is present in many copies and a large amount of the product may be produced.
2. The gene of interest can be cloned into a plasmid such that it is close to a strong promoter (for the host organism). A promoter is the site at which ribosomes bind for translation of messenger RNA into protein and so the use of a so called expression vector of this type permits efficient transcription and translation which will lead to greater production of the protein. A number of plasmids have been engineered such that they contain sites for restriction enzymes which allow insertion of foreign DNA 'downstream' of an efficient promoter.
3. For some systems plasmids known as secretion vectors have been developed and these enable the product of the cloned gene to be secreted into the culture supernatant. This has obvious advantages when one is concerned with isolation and purification of an enzyme.

The cofactor PQQ has been found to be associated with several enzymes, incluing methanol dehydrogenase, the enzyme which allows methylotrophic bacteria to oxidize methanol (Duine and Frank 1981). It can be readily isolated from these organisms and hence cofactor isolation is not a problem. Furthermore the PQQ from these alternative sources, when combined with the GDH apoenzyme, has been shown to result in an active holoenzyme. It is therefore only necessary, in this instance, to clone the gene which encodes the apoenzyme.

Above I have used an enzyme from a prokaryotic organism as an example. However, this technique is particularly appropriate to sensors which would employ enzymes from higher animals and plants. Often such enzymes are expensive to produce, because they are present at low concentrations and because the growth of cells from higher organisms under laboratory culture is technically difficult and relatively slow.

7.3.2 *Improvement of enzyme properties*

A second application of molecular biology to sensor development relies on modern specific methods of mutagenesis which allow one to undertake enzyme engineering (see Chapter 8). This will permit alteration to the active site of an enzyme, so that it may have a faster turnover rate for a particular substrate. Alternatively the range of substrates attacked by an enzyme may be modified by this process. In this way the enzyme would be made more suitable for the task in hand. A prerequisite for this kind of work is a knowledge of the three dimensional structure of the enzyme. This is usually determined by X-ray crystalography and will be necessary, in order that a prediction of the region of the protein which forms the active site can be made. One can than make specific base pair changes in the DNA, which result in a change of a specific amino acid residue in the protein chain. The first stage in this procedure would be to clone the gene of interest on to a small plasmid, and transform the clone into *E. coli*. Using the procedures outlined above it would then be possible to sequence this gene and subsequently make specific base pair changes to the DNA sequence. These changes could then be examined to determine the effect on the properties of the enzyme. This technique would be applicable to almost any enzyme for which sufficient structural information is available.

7.3.3 *Genetic manipulation of whole organisms for use in sensors*

The use of whole organism sensors has been implicated for certain applications in which it is difficult to use cell-free enzyme systems. An example of this is the use of whole organisms of a methanotrophic bacterium in a sensor designed to detect methane (Chapter 2). The sensor uses the enzyme methane monooxygenase, which oxidizes methane to methanol (Dalton *et al.* 1984). In this case it has so far not been possible to use the enzyme in a cell-free system, because it has been difficult to obtain a pure stable preparation of the enzyme *in vitro* and because other components of the bacterial cell are required to maintain its activity. These include the presence of co-enzymes and the ability of the host organism's metabolism to generate sufficient reducing power. Although attempts have been made to provide reducing power for the enzyme electrochemically, no immediate solution to either problem is likely, and the alternative is to use immobilized whole organisms rather than the required enzyme alone. However these whole organism systems can be subjected to genetic manipulation and some examples follow. The level of the enzyme required for the sensor can be increased such that it is a higher proportion of the cell protein. Another possibility is to provide the organism with an improved uptake system for the substrate, so that it can be brought into contact with the enzyme more readily and thus improve the response and sensitivity of the sensor. It may also be possible to alter the cellular location of the enzyme of interest, so that, for example in the case of bacteria, it is located in the periplasmic space and again the substrate can gain access more readily. A final possibility involves modification of the genes encoding the cell wall of the organisms employed, so that they attach more readily to the surface of the sensor, or show improved electron transfer to it. This idea is at present somewhat speculative, since it is difficult to envisage the specific genetic changes that would be necessary. As with protein engineering, this application requires prior knowledge of the physiology and genetics of the particular organism and is therefore probably best suited to species which are well characterized in these ways, or to well characterized organisms to which the genes of interest have been introduced and expressed by genetic manipulation.

7.4 Conclusions

It is without doubt that genetic manipulation will have a role to play in the development of biosensors, as it is doing in many other areas of bio-technology. However in this field it seems likely that once the commercial exploitation of these devices has been realized, that biosensors whose performance results from the application of genetic manipulation will be of importance in the development of a second generation of sensing devices, financed by the profits obtained from those shortly to be marketed.

References

Adams, S. L., Alwine, J. C., De Crombugghe, B. and Postan, I. (1979). Use of recombinant plasmids to characterise collagen RNAs in normal and transformed chick embryo fibroblasts. *J. Biol. Chem.* **254**, 4935–8.

Ameyama, M., Shinagawa, E., Matsushita, K. and Adachi, O. (1981). D-Glucose dehydrogenase of *Gluconobacter suboxydans*. Solubilisation, purification and characterization. *Agricultural and Biological Chemistry* **45**, 851–61.

Barth, P. T. (1979). RP4 and R300B as wide host range plasmid cloning vehicles. In *Plasmids of medical, environmental, and commercial importance* (eds. K. N. Timmis and A. Puhler). Elsevier, North Holland.

Bolivar, F. (1979). Molecular cloning vectors derived from the Col El type plasmid, pMBl. *Life Sciences* **25**, 807–17.

Brammar, W. J. (1982). Vectors based on bacteriophage lambda. In *Genetic Engineering*, (ed. R. Williamson), Vol 3, 53–80. Academic Press, New York.

Dalbadie-McFarland, G., Gohen, L. W., Riggs, A. D., Morin, C., Itakura, K. and Richards, J. H. (1982). Oligonucleotide-directed mutagenesis as a general and powerful method for studies of protein functions. *Proc. Natl. Acad. Sci. USA* **79**, 6409–13.

Dalton, H., Prior, S. D., Leak, D. J. and Stanley, S. H. (1984). Regulation and Control of Methane Monooxygenase. In *Microbial growth on C_1 compounds* (eds. R. L. Crawford and R. S. Hanson) pp. 75–82. ASM, Washington.

D'Costa, E. J., Higgins, I. J. and Turner, A. P. F. (1986). Quinoprotein glucose dehydrogenase and its application in an amperometric glucose sensor. *Biosensors* **2** (accepted).

Duine, J. A. and Frank J. (1981). Methanol dehydrogenase: A quinoprotein. In *Microbial growth on C_1 compounds.* (ed. H. Dalton) pp. 31–41. Heyden, London.

Duine, J. A., Frank, J. and Van der Meer, R. (1982). Different forms of quinoprotein aldolase-(gluclose-) dehydrogenase. *Archives of Microbiology* **31**, 27–31.

Kessler, C., Neumaier, T. S. and Wolf, W. (1985). Recognition sequences of restriction endonucleases and methylases — a review. *Gene* **33**, 1–102.

Maxam A. M. and Gilbert, W. (1980). Sequencing end-labelled DNA with base specific chemical cleavages. In *Nucleic acids*, Part 1. Methods in Enzymology 65, (eds. L. Grosman and K. Moldave) pp. 499–560. Acad. Press, New York.

Messing, J. and Vieira, J. (1982). A new pair of M13 vectors for selecting either DNA strand of double digest restriction fragments. *Gene* **19**, 269–76.

Old, R. W. and Primrose, S. B. (1985). *Principles of genetic engineering* (3rd edn). Blackwell Scientific, Oxford.

Sanger, F., Nicklen, S. and Coulson, A. R. (1977). DNA sequencing with chain terminating inhibitors. *Proc. Natl. Acad. Sci. USA* **74**, 5463–7.

Southern, E. M. (1975). Detection of specific sequences among DNA fragments separated by gel electrophoresis. *J. Mol. Biol.* **98**, 503–17.

Turner, A. P. F. and Pickup, J. C. (1985). Diabetes mellitus: Biosensors for research and management. *Biosensors* **1**, 85–115.

Zoller, M. J. and Smith, M. (1982). Oligonucleotide directed mutagenesis using M13 derived vectors: An efficient and general procedure for the production of point mutations in any fragment of DNA. *Nucl. Acids Research* **10**, 6487–500.

8

Protein engineering and its potential application to biosensors

ANTHONY E. G. CASS and ENDA KENNY

8.1 Introduction

In this chapter on the potential application of protein engineering to bio-sensors we take protein engineering in its broad sense to imply the modification of the covalent structure of a protein by addition, substitution, or deletion of groups such that the chemical properties of the molecule are different from those found in the native state. Chemical properties included in this definition could range from catalysis of a completely different reaction by an enzyme through a shift in substrate specificity to an increase in the lifetime of the native biological activity under a particular set of conditions.

The mechanisms that can be used to effect such changes vary from modifying the nucleotide sequence of the DNA that codes for the protein of interest so that a defined change in amino acid sequence results; through to the incorporation of the native enzyme into the final biosensor in such a way that the properties of the enzyme are modified by its interaction with the other components of the device. Before we consider the kinds of changes that might be useful in adapting proteins to biosensor applications it might be appropriate to consider some of the relevant properties of proteins that affect their performance in biosensors.

The kinetic parameters k_{cat} and K_M are obviously important in determining the properties of the sensor. In general, biosensors contain relatively high loadings of enzyme activity and hence a high k_{cat} (turnover number) means that only small amounts (in milligrams) of enzyme are needed. In the specific, but important, case of membrane sensors a high k_{cat} would tend to result in a device limited by membrane transport and thus to one relatively insensitive to variations in enzyme loading or loss of enzyme activity.

When we turn to the Michaelis constant K_M, its effect on the sensor appears in the linear range of the device. Ideally there should be a linear relationship between the output signal and the analyte concentration and in general terms this is reflected in the K_M (or apparent K_M) of the enzyme. Inspection of the Michaelis–Menten equation shows that this condition holds for concentrations up to about 0.2 K_M although other factors such as immobilization or the presence of a membrane will also be important. A parameter derived from the above two is the specificity constant, k_{cat}/K_M, of the enzyme and it is generally desirable to have a high value for the analyte of interest compared to other potential substrates.

The effect of temperature on the performance of the biosensor is often composed of several different and competing processes. As in any chemical reaction the rate of the enzymatic reaction will increase with increasing temperature and thus the response of the device will also be temperature dependent, the magnitude of this effect reflecting the activation energy of the rate limiting step. Enzymes also undergo thermal inactivation and the rate of this will depend on the activation energy for the unfolding of the protein and the temperature. Finally even if the enzyme is stable the device may show a biphasic response if there is a change in rate determining step. In addition to temperature there are a number of other causes of protein denaturation that can lead to loss of activity, and an increase in the general 'robustness' of the biological component would enhance the practical application of biosensors.

pH is another environmental variable that affects the response of biosensors when the enzyme's activity is controlled by ionizing groups. A shift in pH optimum and a broadening of the optimum range may be necessary to make the sensor compatible with the analytical matrix. Proteins are also denatured by extremes of pH and this may be particularly important in food and drink analyses where the samples are often rather acidic.

Finally where the biological component needs to be immobilized it may be that the residues involved in immobilization are also important for activity and an alternative method is needed. Table 8.1 summarizes some of the potential targets for protein engineering for biosensors.

In this chapter we will survey the many different approaches to modifying proteins starting at the level of DNA sequence and working upwards. The examples we discuss will not be concerned with biosensors *per se* but they will serve to illustrate some of the results that have been achieved in altering the properties of proteins.

At the outset it should be made clear that the engineering, i.e. directed modification, of proteins can generally only be made within the framework

---

Table 8.1   Some potential targets for protein engineering for biosensors

---

1. Improved turnover Number.
2. Shift in or removal of pH dependence.
3. Change in linear response range to substrate concentration.
4. Improved stability during storage and operation.
5. Reduction in susceptibility to interfering substances.
6. Widening or narrowing of substrate specificity.
7. Change in cofactor requirement.

---

of a detailed body of information about the protein. Ideally this would include a three-dimensional structure at sufficient resolution to locate the individual residues. Unfortunately, for many proteins used in biosensors this kind of information is either absent or incomplete; for example probably the most widely used enzyme in this area is glucose oxidase yet despite being readily available in a highly purified form in substantial quantities we still know remarkably little about the molecule. There is no published amino acid sequence and no crystal structure. The kinetic properties of the enzyme are well understood (Bright and Porter 1975) but there is no structural skeleton on which to 'hang' this information. Lack of knowledge at this level means that we are often handicapped in being able to truly engineer molecules or even to rationalize the effects of changes made empirically.

With this caveat in mind we nonetheless feel that the engineering of protein molecules for biosensor applications is sufficiently important to warrant discussion. After all protein molecules evolved to fulfill a specific biological need and not to provide the components of man-made devices. Although some of the biological properties can be exploited to our own ends, it is not surprising that others are more or less incompatible with the final application.

Bearing these points in mind we shall now commence with our survey of the ways and means of protein engineering.

8.2 Modification at the DNA level

Since the early 1970s when it was first shown that DNA could be cleaved and rejoined *in vitro* recombinant DNA technology has become an important tool in molecular biology (Cohen *et al.* 1973). The techniques of genetic engineering now allow us to isolate, propagate, and sequence any gene of interest be it from plant, animal, or micro-organism. The knowledge of the DNA sequence of the gene then allows us to derive the amino acid sequence of the protein that it codes for, and conversely we can create nucleotide sequences corresponding to any desired polypeptide chain. In the case of fairly small peptides the chemical synthesis of the gene *in vitro* has been achieved (Edge *et al.* 1981) and hence there is no theoretical barrier to the construction of genes encoding novel activities. The difficulties arise in the effective synthesis of long polynucleotides in reasonable yield, free from byproducts of similar sequence, and in actually designing the polypeptide sequence that has the desired activity. We still know very little about the determinants of protein folding. Accordingly, at present, we are limited to the modification of existing proteins by introducing base changes at specific locations in the gene.

The advantages of effecting these changes at the level of DNA rather than protein are several. Firstly, because DNA is the genetic material and is faithfully replicated during growth only a single manipulation is required. Modification at the level of protein will need repeated application as stocks are consumed. Secondly a single genetic change leads to a single product whereas chemical modification of the protein often leads to mixtures of products. Finally any amino acid may be changed by genetic manipulation whereas there may be steric or reactivity barriers to chemically modifying residues in the protein. In its current state *in vitro* mutagenesis aims to effect point mutations at one or a limited number of sites in the gene and to observe the effect of this on the resulting protein.

Chemical mutagenesis has been used to change cytosine to thymine by treatment with sodium bisulphite where, under appropriate conditions, this can be targeted to a specific region of the DNA (Shortle and Nathans 1978). Techniques have also been developed that render relatively specific regions in a DNA sequence single stranded which, after resynthesizing the gap, force a mismatched or misincorporated base to be included (Shortle *et al.* 1982). In these methods, however, the position of the point of mutation cannot be exactly predetermined and thus a number of mutants must be screened to find an appropriate one. Oligonucleotide directed mutagenesis has circumvented these problems and has opened the way to introducing specific point mutations into DNA.

In 1978 two reports demonstrated how precise changes in DNA could be effected with oligonucleotides by introducing mutations into the genome of the bacteriophage ϕX174. This phage's DNA exists as a single stranded form in the mature virus particle but upon infection converts to a double stranded or replicative form (RF) prior to the generation of new phages. Hutchinson *et al.* (1978) and Razin *et al.* (1978) used synthetic oligonucleotides complementary to the viral (+) strand as primers for the *in vitro* synthesis of the opposite (–) strand, forming a closed circular RF molecule incorporating the priming oligonucleotide. If the primers contained a mismatched base the RF DNA still formed satisfactorily but now the progeny were of two types containing either the wild type DNA or that from the mismatched primer. The latter were detected by screening for the mutant gene. Subsequently several other mutations were introduced into ϕX174 using this method (Gillan and Smith 1979).

Since these initial observations two developments have tremendously accelerated the use of oligonucleotide directed mutagenesis. The first has been in the synthesis of the oligonucleotide primers (Sproat and Gait 1984). Automated, semi-automated, and manual solid phase synthetic protocols are available and the protected, activated precursors are supplied by a number of chemical companies, thus the production of primers is now a routine process. The second advance has been the standardization of the methodology using M13 bacteriophage cloning vectors (Zoller and Smith 1983). M13 is like ϕX174 in possessing both single and double stranded forms thus enabling the

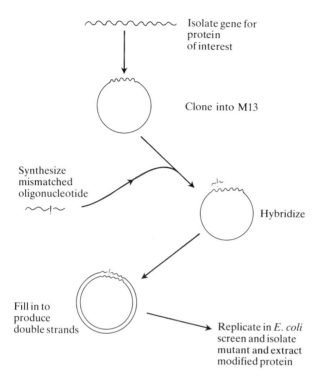

Fig. 8.1 Scheme for oligonucleotide directed mutagenesis. The basic steps involved in using this method in the bacteriophage M13 are shown. For more details on the methodology the reader should consult the references given in the text.

cloning of the gene of interest in the RF and the mutagenesis in the single stranded form. M13 is of particular use in this regard as it has been specifically developed as a cloning vehicle for the isolation of DNA fragments for sequencing by the chain-termination method of Sanger *et al.* (1977) and there are several unique cloning sites (Messing 1983). The scheme for mutagenesis in M13 is shown in Fig. 8.1.

Wallace *et al.* (1981) showed that the mutagenesing oligonucleotide could also be used as a hybridization probe to screen for the mutant DNA. To do this the oligonucleotide is radioactively labelled with ^{32}P and as it is obviously more homologous to the mutant than wild type DNA it will hybridize more strongly to the former. Mutant clones can then be identified by autoradiography.

Once the mutated DNA has been identified it can be excised from the RF, recloned into a suitable host/vector system for maximizing expression, and the resulting protein isolated. Multiple application of this method can be used to introduce a number of changes.

Within the framework of the above strategy a number of enzymes have been modified and the properties of the mutant enzymes investigated (Ackers and Smith 1985).

Tyrosyl tRNA synthetase is one of the most intensively studied examples as both its structure and kinetics are well understood (Fersht *et al.* 1984). The enzyme catalyses the aminoacylation of tRNA^{tyr} by tyrosine in a two step reaction:

Enzyme + Tyrosine + ATP $\longrightarrow$ Enzyme.adenyltyrosine + PPi
Enzyme.adenyltyrosine + tRNA $\longrightarrow$ Enzyme + Tyrosyl.tRNA + AMP

Initial results (Winter *et al.* 1982) showed that when cysteine-35 was altered to a serine there was a 4.5 fold increase in the K_M for ATP. Similarly the introduction of a glycine residue at this position also resulted in an enzyme of lower activity (Wilkinson *et al.* 1983). It is known from the crystallographic work that cysteine-35 makes a hydrogen bond contact with the ribose ring of ATP and so it is not surprising that the introduction of a glycine residue results in a lower activity. At first sight the results with serine seem odd as it might be expected that the stronger hydrogen bonding ability of the hydroxyl as compared to the sulphydryl group would result in enhanced binding. However in the unliganded enzyme the hydrogen bonding is to a water molecule, and the different steric requirement for sulphydryl versus hydroxyl groups means that in the mutant enzyme the binding of ATP results in the exchange of a strong hydrogen bond by a much weaker one with the observed consequences for binding and catalysis (Wilkinson *et al.* 1983).

The introduction of different residues into the enzyme does not necessarily result in the loss of some of the catalytic activity, for example the replacement of threonine-51 by a proline resulted in both a decrease in K_M and an increase in k_{cat} leading to an overall increase in k_{cat}/K_M of 25 fold (Wilkinson *et al.* 1984). In attempting to understand and predict the effects of amino acid replacements in mutant enzymes it is necessarily to be able to distinguish between the direct interaction of the residue with substrate and concomitant structural changes that alter contacts elsewhere in the molecule. The result described above in replacing a threonine residue by a proline is a case in point. One approach used in trying to resolve this point has been to study the effects of double mutants. If the effect of the two mutations is the same as the sum of their individual contributions then it is likely that the role of the amino acid residues is purely a local one. Conversely any deviation from this implies a more diffuse role; Carter *et al.* (1984) have termed this 'coupling' and have shown that in the threonine/proline case the enhanced activity is due to a structural change, improving the contact of histidine-48 with ATP. This interaction of the histidine residue with ATP has been further probed by introducing mutations into position 48. When the histidine is replaced by an asparagine the resulting enzyme is as active as the wild type, in contrast the introduction of a glutamine residue gives a much less active product (Lowe *et al.* 1985). This result implies that the histidine residue is hydrogen bonded through its N and rules out any electrostatic interaction.

Further fine structure analysis of the mutants at position 51 has been carried out by replacing the threonine with alanine, cysteine, or proline (Fersht *et al.* 1985*a*). Detailed kinetic analyses of the mutants has shown that each exhibits a maximum activity depending on the ATP concentration. As it is known that this residue is variable in tyrosyl tRNA synthetases from different sources it appears that the different enzymes have evolved to maximize their activity at the prevailing intracellular ATP concentration.

Recently the role of hydrogen bonds in the specificity of tyrosyl tRNA synthetase has been probed by comparing the properties of a number of mutants of the enzyme (Fersht *et al.* 1985*b*). By systematically varying the residues the authors were able to assess the contribution of hydrogen bonds to the binding of and specificity for ATP and tyrosine. The conclusions from this work are that removal of a residue that hydrogen bonds to an uncharged group on the substrate only destabilizes the latter's binding energy by 2–6 kJ mol^{-1} whilst if the hydrogen bond is to a charged group then a much larger effect, up to 16 kJ mol^{-1}, is observed. In a later paper Wells and Fersht (1985) were able to show that hydrogen bonds are also important in the preferential binding of the transition state of the substrate over the ground state.

Although most of the mutations that have been made in this enzyme have been at the active site the interaction between the subunits has also been investigated. Native tyrosyl tRNA synthetase is a homodimer that exhibits half of the sites reactivity, and the crystal structure reveals that phenylalanine 164 is important in subunit contacts. If this residue is replaced by an aspartate then steady state kinetics, active site titration, and equilibrium binding studies reveal that at high pH, in the absense of tyrosine or ATP as ligands, and at low enzyme concentration the dimer dissociates (Jones *et al.* 1985). The authors propose that it is the ionization of the aspartate residue that induces dissociation whilst the ligands only bind appreciably to the dimer. tRNA has no effect on the monomer/dimer equilibrium suggesting that it shows no differential binding to either form.

β-Lactamase catalyses the hydrolysis of penicillins and is the basis of a number of sensors for β-lactam antibiotics. The gene for this enzyme is a common marker and is carried by the vector pBR322 (Bolivar *et al.* 1977). Dalbadie–McFarland *et al.* (1982) used a doubly mismatched oligonucleotide to invert the serine/threonine dipeptide at the active site resulting in the loss of activity. If the active site serine is replaced by cysteine the mutant protein is still active though at a lower level than the wild type, and is sensitive to inhibition by sulphydryl reagents (Sigal *et al.* 1982). Thiol lactamase does however have some favourable properties compared to the native enzyme, it is more resistant to trypsin and is not inhibited by boric acid (Sigal *et al.* 1984).

An important goal in improving enzymes is to try and increase the temperature stability and one approach to this is to introduce intramolecular cross-links. This has been attempted with dihydrofolate reductase and with T4 lysozyme. Preliminary results suggest that disulphide bridges can be mutated into both these proteins. In the case of the dihydrofolate reductase proline-39 was replaced by a cysteine and it appears that a disulphide bridge was formed between this residue and the cysteine at position 85 leading to a dependence of the activity on oxidation state (Villafranca *et al.* 1983). T4 lysozyme had isoleucine-3 replaced by a cysteine and peptide mapping revealed that the newly introduced residue formed a disulphide with cysteine-97. Neither the amino acid replacement nor the formation of the bridge affected the activity though there was an effect on the initial rate of thermal denaturation with the mutant showing a slower decay in activity than the wild type. Interestingly though, the difference appears to be due not to the disulphide bridge *per se* but rather is a function of the thiol group of cysteine 54 (Perry and Wetzel 1984).

The pH optimum of an enzyme can be shifted by the mutagenesis of surface charged groups as illustrated by the protease subtilisin. Replacement of a surface aspartate residue by serine resulted in a shift in the activity linked pK_a from 7.17 in the wild type enzyme to 6.88 in the mutant (Thomas *et al.* 1985). As expected for an electrostatic effect the shift was only observed at low ionic strength. Another protease recently investigated by oligonucleotide mutagenesis is carboxypeptidase A (CPA). In this example the aim was to probe the postulated role of tyrosine-248 in catalysis (Gardell *et al.* 1985). A mutant enzyme with this residue replaced by phenylalanine has essentially the same k_{cat} as the wild type but exhibits a higher K_M (6 fold) and a much higher inhibitor constant with potato CPA inhibitor (70 fold).

These examples serve to illustrate how we are beginning to be able to modify the sequences and hence properties of proteins by manipulation of their genes. Undoubtedly at present the lack of both structural data and the relevant cloned genes that is the major impediment to the application of this technique to biosensors. The power of the method along with the opportunity to obtain large amounts of material by cloning for overproduction will mean that genetic engineering will have as large an impact in the area of biosensors as it has already had in many other areas of biotechnology (see also Chapter 7).

8.3 Modification of the polypeptide chain

There are many reagents that are available to modify the various reactive side chains found in proteins and some of these are collected in Table 8.2.

Table 8.2 Typical chemical modifications on proteins

Residue	Modifiers
Lysine	Arylating agents e.g. trinitrobenzenesulphonate
	Acid anhydrides e.g. maleic, succinic
	Isoureas and imidates
Arginine	α, β-Diketones
Histidine	Diethylpyrocarbonate
	Alkylating agents e.g. chloroketones
Cysteine	Alkylating agents e.g. iodoacetate, *N*-ethylmaleimide,
	Ethyleneimine
Tyrosine	Tetranitromethane
	Acylating agents e.g. acetic anhydride, acetylimidazol
	Iodinating agents e.g. iodide + lactoperoxidase
Glutamic and	Carbodimides + amines
aspartic acids	Diazo compounds

Chemical modification studies have been of importance in elucidating the structure and mechanism of many proteins and for labelling the protein with 'reporter' groups. At best these reagents are selective for a particular amino acid residue, and in favourable cases environmental factors may render one or two residues of a particular type significantly more or less reactive than the rest. Targeting the reagent to the active site can be achieved by using a close structural analogue of the substrate that also carries the modifying group. A further elegant refinement of this approach is to 'uncover' the reactive group during catalysis and thus produce a suicide substrate. In most of these modifications the resulting protein is completely devoid of biological activity so this approach is less than suitable for our needs! However there have also been less drastic modifications and we will now consider some of these.

8.3.1 Modifications that increase the activity

These modifications are relatively rare, as might be expected, and at first sight it may appear strange that the activity of an enzyme subject to millions of years of evolutionary pressure can be improved upon. However it must be remembered that the enzyme has evolved to work in a specific cellular environment and thus improvements in activity can occur under conditions that are rather different from this. As an illustration of this the work of Plapp (1970) on alcohol dehydrogenase showed that modification of the lysine residues with methylpicolinimidate:

resulted in a derivative 19 times more active than the native enzyme when assayed at high substrate concentration. After modification the enzyme still showed an ordered bi-bi mechanism characteristic of the native enzyme in which co-enzyme dissociation is rate limiting in both directions. It is this observation that provides a clue to the rationale for the observed effects. The Michaelis and product inhibition constants for the modified enzyme are some 12–53 times greater than in the native form whereas the turnover numbers are 12–30 times larger. Apparently the enhanced activity at high substrate concentration is due to an increase in the off-rates for the co-enzymes. When the substrate concentrations are decreased the native and modified species approach one another in activity.

Another example of a modified enzyme with improved activity is provided by dihydrofolate reductase from chicken liver, although in this case the molecular basis for the change is not understood. A variety of reagents that react with cysteine-11 cause a 5–10 fold increase in activity (Barbehenn and Kaufman 1980 and references therein) with the physiological substrates NADPH and dihydrofolate. In this case though a price has to be paid for the improvement in terms of a much reduced thermal stability of the modified enzyme. Finally we also mention the enhancement in ATPase activity of 14S and 30S dynein after modification of the amino groups with trinitrobenzene-sulphonate (Shimizu 1979).

8.3.2 Modifications that alter surface properties

The examples discussed in the previous section although of interest, and in some cases capable of *post hoc* rationalization, were not predicted and hence are of little use in attempting to 'engineer' a protein in a specific fashion. One class of chemical modification that can be predicted based upon some knowledge of the protein and a little judicious physical chemistry is that which attempts to alter the surface properties of the molecule. Amongst these kinds of modifications the simplest to perform and interpret are those based upon altering the surface charge. Typical changes are shown in Fig. 8.2 where the charge is either removed or reversed. Using this type of chemistry the pKa of chymotrypsin was shifted ± 1 pH unit from the native value of 7 (Valenzuela and Bender 1971). As expected the conversion of a positive charge to negative increased the pKa whilst a negative to positive decreased it. The succinylated chymotrypsin also showed an increased k_{cat} and decreased K_M for hydrolysis of ester substrates whilst the enzyme modified with ethylenediamine showed no change in k_{cat}. In the latter case K_M was found to be strongly pH dependent; unlike the native enzyme where K_M did not vary with pH.

Acetylation of trypsin also led to an enhancement of activity although in this case it was the *O*-acetylation of an exposed tyrosine residue that is critical (Spomer and Wotton 1971). Modification of the lysine residues with acetyl groups had no effect. The cause of the improved activity was ascribed to an

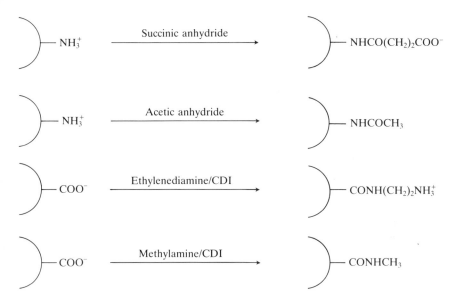

Fig. 8.2 Some typical chemistries for neutralizing or reversing the charge of surface amino or carboxyl groups in proteins. CDI is a water soluble carbodiimide.

increased rate of formation of the acyl enzyme in ester and amide hydrolyses.

Sometimes the attachment of charged groups can be used as an alternative to the addition of cations to the reaction medium as in the example of plastocyanin. The reaction of this blue copper electron transfer protein with $P700^+$ in the chloroplast usually requires the presence of magnesium ions to 'screen' the negative charges of the carboxyl groups on the plastocyanin. Burkey and Gross (1982) were able to achieve the same effect and also to shift the midpoint potential by $> + 40 \, \text{mV}$ by modifying the protein with ethylenediamine.

Even when the surface charge is maintained, favourable effects can sometimes be achieved as shown by the work of Cupo *et al.* (1980). These authors converted the lysine residues to homoarginine by treating several proteins (chymotrypsin, ribonuclease, lysozyme, α-lactalbumin, cytochrome *c*, carbonic anhydrase, and bovine serum albumin) with *O*-methylisourea:

$$\text{NH}_2-\overset{\displaystyle \overset{\text{NH}}{\|}}{\text{C}}-\text{OCH}_3$$

It was argued that the bulky guanidino group was less likely than the amino group to move into the hydrophobic regions of the protein and so the

$CH_3-O-(CH_2)_2-O-(CH_2)_2-O-(CH_2)_2-O-(CH_2)_2CO--$ (I)
$CH_3 CH_2 (CH_2)_2-O-(CH_2)_2-O-(CH_2)_2-O-(CH_2)_2CO--$ (II)
$CH_3 CH_2 (CH_2)_2 CH_2 (CH_2)_2-O-(CH_2)_2-O-(CH_2)_2CO--$ (III)
$CH_3 CH_2(CH_2)_2 CH_2(CH_2)_2 CH_2 (CH_2)_2-O-(CH_2)_2CO--$ (IV)
$CH_3 CH_2(CH_2)_2 CH_2(CH_2)_2 CH_2 (CH_2)_2 CH_2 (CH_2)_2CO--$ (V)

Fig. 8.3 Various groups attached to the surface lysines of thermolysin, by Urabe *et al.* (1978). The hydrophobicity of the modifying groups increases from I to V and has a differential effect on the thermal stability of the resulting derivatives.

substitution of the latter by the former should stabilize the structure. Exchange of tritium out of the protein into water was indeed consistent with a less flexible structure for the modified proteins.

A considerable improvement in the thermal stability of thermolysin was achieved by acylating 6–7 of the amino groups of lysine residues with long chain fatty acids containing different numbers of ether groups (Urabe *et al.* 1978) as shown in Fig. 8.3. The hydrophobic nature of the chain decreases from V to I and derivatives of I had essentially full activity ($>90\%$ of the native enzyme) and showed a much improved thermal stability. In contrast derivatives of V were insoluble in water.

Stabilization of the protein may also be achieved by coupling it to a water soluble polymer as for example in the case of adenosine deaminase (Rosemeyer *et al.* 1982). Attachment of the enzyme to cyanogen bromide activated dextran resulted in a derivative that was only 13% as active as the native material with an increased K_M and a decreased k_{cat}. However the half time for loss of activity at 60 °C was increased from 1 to 2 hours.

8.3.3 Modifications that alter specificity

Changes in the substrate specificity of an enzyme can be bought about by a variety of modifications and these have been recently reviewed by Kaiser *et al.* (1985).

Proteases often have an associated esterase activity and when carboxypeptidase A is acetylated at 2 of its tyrosines there is an apparent 6-fold enhancement in its esterase action with concomitant virtually complete abolition of proteolytic activity. Pancreatic ribonucleases (RNase) has been subjected to many chemical modifications and one interesting one involves the dimerization of the enzyme using the cross-linking agent dimethylsuberimidate. The native enzyme is a monomer with little activity towards double stranded RNA but after cross-linking the product shows an enhanced (78–440 fold) hydrolytic action with the double stranded form. Esterase activity has also been introduced into this enzymes by cross-linking in the presence of the inhibitor indolepropionic acid. Introduction of activity under these conditions is assumed to arise by cross-linking in an unusual conformation of the enzyme.

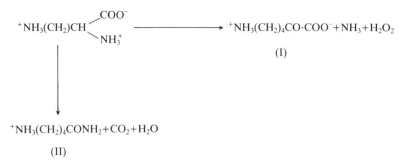

$$^+NH_3(CH_2)CH\begin{array}{c}COO^-\\NH_3^+\end{array} \longrightarrow {}^+NH_3(CH_2)_4CO\cdot COO^- + NH_3 + H_2O_2$$

(I)

$$^+NH_3(CH_2)_4CONH_2 + CO_2 + H_2O$$

(II)

Fig. 8.4 The reactions of lysine monooxygenase acting as either an oxidase (I) or a monooxygenase (II). The latter is the physiological reaction but the former reaction may be induced by modifying the lysine residues in the enzyme.

Enzymes involved in oxidative reactions can often have their specificity altered under appropriate conditions; for example interconversion of mono-oxygenase and oxidase reactions of lysine monooxygenase can be achieved by treatment of the enzyme with agents that react with the thiol groups as shown in Fig. 8.4. In the case of monoamine oxidase the type of reaction remains the same but the modification results in a loss of activity with the natural substrate tyramine and an enhanced activity with histamine. Flavoprotein dehydrogenases can, on modification, have their acceptor specificity relaxed so that the range of compounds reducible by these enzymes is widened from $NAD(P)^+$ to include dyes and dioxygen. In effect the enzymes have been converted from dehydrogenases to oxidases, an examples of this is xanthine dehydrogenase/oxidase (Kaminski and Jezewska 1979). Glutathione reductase catalyses the reaction

$$GSSG + NADPH + H^+ \longrightarrow 2GSH + NADP^+$$

and modifying the lysine residues with trinitrobenzenesulphonate results in a protein with substantial NADPH oxidase activity and no glutathione reductase activity (Carlberg and Mannervik 1980).

8.3.4 Coenzyme attachment

One interesting and potentially useful modification of an enzyme is to attach a normally freely diffusing co-enzyme to the polypeptide chain. This has been described for the combination of an NAD analogue and alcohol dehydro-genase (Mansson *et al.* 1978). The resulting conjugate contained approxi-mately one co-enzyme per active site and had some 20% of the activity of the enzyme/soluble coenzyme combination. In a second publication (Mansson *et al.* 1979) the authors further demonstrated that this conjugate could be linked to the turnover of a second (lactate) dehydrogenase. This type of approach could obviously be extended to ADP/ATP, pterin, and folate dependent enzyme systems. It has the great advantage that biosensors utilizing these would be independent of added co-enzymes.

8.3.5 New enzyme activities

The possibility of introducing a completely new activity into a protein has been achieved in a few instances. The strategy here is to attempt to enhance the weak catalytic activity of an organic molecule by covalently attaching it to a protein chain to take advantage of the latter's ability to bind the substrate. One of the best examples of this approach is flavopapain (Kaiser *et al.* 1980). Papain is a plant protease that contains a catalytically active thiol group. Treating papain with bromo-isoalloxazines results in the covalent attachment of the redox group to the thiol (Levine *et al.* 1977) as shown in Fig. 8.5. These molecules are devoid of proteolytic activity but now have oxidase activity. A derivative of papain made by alkylating the active site cysteine residue showed a low activity in oxidizing dithiols (Fried and Kaiser 1981) and dihydronicotinamides (Levine *et al.* 1977, Levine and Kaiser 1978). Only modest enhancements were observed for dithiol oxidations compared to the isoalloxazine moiety alone; typical rate enhancements were 4–17 fold with k_{cat}/K_M values of 4–21 M^{-1} s^{-1} (Fried and Kaiser 1981). Model building studies suggested that another derivative should be a better catalyst in dihydronicotinamide oxidations and this indeed proved to be so. Rate enhancements compared to the uncomplexed group ranged from 4 to 621 depending upon the dihydronictinamide and for the best substrate the value of k_{cat}/K_M was 5.7×10^5 M^{-1} s^{-1} a value comparable to native flavoenzymes (Levine and Kaiser 1978). In addition the derivative did show some typical enzymatic properties including saturation kinetics and a stereochemical preference for the 4A hydrogen atom in the oxidation of NADH (Levine and Kaiser 1980).

Modifications at the active site are not the only way that new enzyme activities can be generated. Margalit *et al.* (1983) labelled three surface histidine residues in myoglobin with pentammineruthenium groups. After

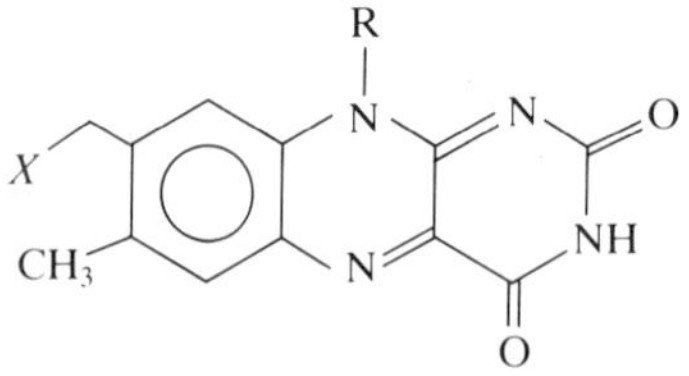

(I) 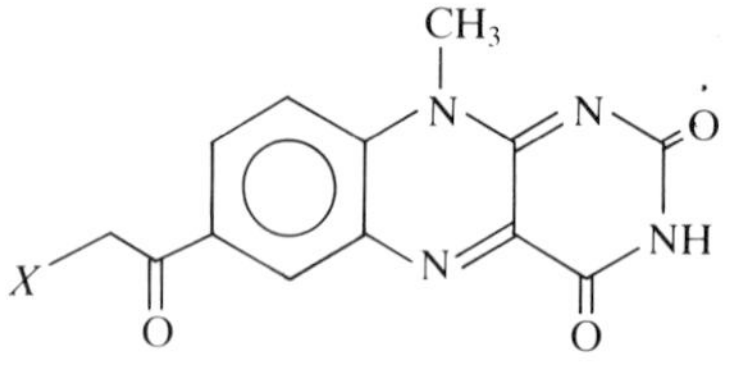   (II)

Fig. 8.5 Two flavin derivatives used in the semi-synthesis of flavopapain.
   X is Br or S-Papain.
The derivative (I) (where *X* = S-Papain) is a much less active enzyme than (II).

modification the haem centre exhibited stronger anion binding. More interestingly the haem also had good oxygen dependent ascorbate and duro-hydroquinone oxidase activities.

8.3.6 Semisynthesis

The use of semisynthesis of substitute proteins with naturally occuring amino acids has been superceded by the use of oligonucleotide directed mutagenesis (*vide supra*). Chemical methods may still be appropriate when substitution by an unusual amino acid is desired. The review by Chaiken (1981) and the book by Offord (1979) cover this area.

8.3.7 Modification by immobilization

The immobilization of proteins on many different supports using a wide variety of chemistries has been extensively reviewed in the books by Chibata (1978), Zaborsky (1973), and Mosbach (1976), see also Chapter 6. Analytical applications have been described by Carr and Bowers (1980). In the space available we cannot do justice to all of the work that has been carried out and the reader is urged to consult the sources cited above for specific details and references to the original literature. In this section we will just point out some of the typical effects that immobilization can have.

8.3.7.1 Apparent activity Often the apparent activity of an enzyme is reduced after immobilization. This may be due to a number of factors; sometimes the immobilization chemistry leads to modification of an active site residue that is important for catalytic function. Such a process might be anticipated as many active site residues have an enhanced reactivity, although they may also be sterically protected. If this type of inactivation does occur then either an alternative coupling chemistry should be sought or conditions chosen to suppress reaction at the active site, e.g. by performing the immobilization in the presence of substrate, product, or inhibitor.

Even when the immobilization does not directly interfere with the enzyme–substrate reaction the nature of the support may give rise to diffusional barriers. For example in the work of Schaefer and Wilson (1983) on the reactivity of cytochrome *c* immobilized on a bead formed agarose support the authors found that although they could preserve much of the activity of the cytochrome *c* with both oxidase and, to a lesser extent reductase, only the cytochrome bound on the surface of the bead reacted. The submitochondrial particles used as the substrate were excluded from the majority of the cytochrome *c* which was inside the porous beads. Similarly it has been found that immobilized hydrolases show a higher apparent activity with small substrates than with macromolecules. In general bead formed supports show less diffusional restriction than fibrous ones and response times for reactions occuring at planar surfaces tend to be faster than those in porous materials.

In contrast to these observations under some circumstances, particularly with coupled enzyme systems, the immobilized preparation may show an apparently higher overall activity than the soluble one. Under these conditions substrate channeling occurs and the co-immobilization results in a shorter diffusion path between the enzymes, or expressed another way, a higher local concentration of the intermediate product results in an apparently increased activity.

Careful choice of support and coupling chemistry are therefore needed to optimize activity and response time. Also the choice of immobilization method must be compatible with the final configuration and ease of manufacture of the sensor. Finally even if the support and coupling reactions are appropriate the very act of immobilization may reduce the conformational mobility and hence activity of the protein.

8.3.7.2 Stability   There is a general feeling that immobilization leads to an improvement in stability of the bound protein towards physical and chemical stresses. Chibata (1978) reports that of 50 enzyme immobilizations 60% showed an increase in stability, 16% showed a decrease, and 24% were unaffected. However having said that, it must be appreciated that stability towards thermal denaturation, proteolytic degradation, pH extremes, or chemical denaturants may each reflect quite different aspects of protein unfolding. Similarly operational and storage stabilities may rely on quite different physical or chemical processes. At present the best approach is again empirical and it may be necessary to identify the causes of activity loss in order to guide an appropriate immobilization strategy.

8.3.7.3 Partitioning   Although it is often necessary for the immobilization matrix to simply be an inert support for the active biological material there may be instances were a more active role can also be assumed. Under such circumstances the matrix can provide a micro-environment that is different from the bulk solution. This effect is closely akin to the protein surface modifications discussed earlier in this chapter. A positively charged matrix will tend to exclude protons so an enzyme in this matrix will exhibit an apparent optimum pH lower than its normal value. Similarly a hydrophobic substrate will tend to partition into a hydrophobic matrix and thus lower the apparent K_M for that substrate. Conversely the matrix may be designed to exclude interfering substances present in the analyte mixture. Such effects are relatively easy to predict and are likely to become more important as attempts are made to produce biosensors to fulfill more stringent operational criteria.

Finally in this section on immobilization we should mention co-enzyme immobilization (Mossbach 1976). Biosensors using freely diffusing co-enzymes suffer from a potential problem due to loss of the co-enzyme from the sensor. One solution to this is to immobilize the coenzyme to a support, either soluble or insoluble, in order to retain it.

8.4 Conclusions

In this chapter we have sought to describe the many different ways that are available for altering the properties of proteins and thus render them potentially more suitable for application in biosensors. The most powerful and versatile of these techniques is undoubtedly that of oligonucleotide directed mutagenesis; however the amount of background information necessary to use it in specific applications is substantial and may not be available for the particular enzyme of interest. Indeed it is true to say that at present none of the important enzymes in biosensors is being subjected to this techṇique. Tailoring surface properties is another approach that should be widely applicable and is capable of predictive use even in the absense of crystallographic data.

We can summarize this chapter by confidently predicting that the engineering of proteins for biosensors, though far less developed than for other applications at present, is likely to become important in the next generation of these devices.

References

Ackers, G. K. and Smith, F. R. (1985). Effects of site specific amino acid modification of protein interaction and biological function. *Ann. Rev. Biochem.* **54**, 597-629.

Barbehenn, E. K. and Kaufman, B. T. (1980). Alteration of the properties of chicken liver dihydrofolate reductase as a result of modification by tetrathionate. *J. Biol. Chem.* **255**, 1978-84.

Bolivar, F., Rodriguez, R. L., Greene, P. J. Betlach, M. C., Heyner, H. L., Boyer, H. W., Crosa, J. H. and Falkow, S. (1977). Construction and characterisation of new cloning vehicles. II. A multipurpose cloning system. *Gene* **2**, 95-113.

Bright, H. J. and Porter, D. J. T. (1975). Flavoprotein oxidases *The Enzymes* **XII**, 421-511.

Burkey, K. O. and Gross, E. L. (1982). Chemical modification of spinach plastocyanin: separation and characterization of four different forms. *Biochemistry (USA)* **21**, 5886-90.

Carlberg, I. and Mannervik, B. (1980). Oxidative activity of glutathione reductase effected by 2, 4, 6,-trinitrobenzenesulfonate. *FEBS Lett.* **115**, 265-8.

Carr, P. W. and Bowers, L. D. (1980). *Immobilised enzymes in analytical and clinical chemistry.* Wiley, New York.

Carter, P. J., Winter, G., Wilkinson, A. J. and Fersht, A. R. (1984). The use of double mutants to detect structural changes in the active site of the tyrosyl-tRNA synthetase (*Bacillus stearothermophilus*). *Cell* **38**, 835-840.

Chaiken, I. M. (1981). Semi-synthetic peptides and proteins. *Crit. Rev. Biochem.* **11**, 255–301.

Chibata, I. (1978). *Immobilised enzymes.* Wiley, New York.

Cohen, S. N., Chang, A. C. Y., Boyer, H. W. and Helling, R. B. (1973). Construction of biologically functional bacterial plasmids *in vitro. Proc. Natl. Acad. Sci. (USA)* **70**, 3240–4.

Cupo, P., El–Deiry, W., Whitney, P. L. and Awad, W. M. (1980). Stabilization of proteins by guanidination. *J. Biol. Chem.* **255**, 10828–33.

Dalbadie–McFarland, G., Cohen, L. W., Riggs, A. D., Morin, D., Itakura, K. and Richards, J. H. (1982). Oligonucleotide-directed mutagenesis as a general and powerful method for studies of protein function. *Proc. Natl. Acad. Sci. (USA)* **79**, 6409–13.

Edge, M. D., Greene, A. R., Heathcliffe, G. R., Meacock, P. A., Schuck, W., Scanlon, P. B., Atkinson, T. C., Newton, C. R. and Markham, A. F. (1981). Total synthesis of a human leukocyte interferon gene. *Nature* **292**, 756–62.

Fersht, A. R., Shi, J. P., Wilkinson, A. J., Blow, D. M., Carter, P., Waye, M. M. Y. and Winter, G. P. (1984). Analysis of enzyme structure and activity by protein engineering. *Angew. Chem. (Int. Ed.)* **23**, 467–73.

——, Wilkinson, A. J., Carter, P. J. and Winter, G. (1985*a*) Fine structure-activity analysis of mutations at position 51 of tyrosyl t-RNA synthetase. *Biochemistry (USA)* **24**, 5858–61.

——, Shi, J. P., Knill-Jones, J., Lowe, D. M., Wilkinson, A. J., Blow, D. M., Brick, P., Carter, P., Waye, M. M. Y. and Winter, G. (1985*b*). Hydrogen bonding and biological specificity analyzed by protein engineering. *Nature* **314**, 235–8.

Fried, H. E. and Kaiser, E. T. (1981). Oxidation of dithiols by flavopapain. *J. Amer. Chem. Soc.* **103**, 182–4.

Gardell, S. J., Craik, C. S., Hilvert, D., Urdea, M. S. and Rutter, W. J. (1985). Site-directed mutagenesis shows that tyrosine 248 of carboxypeptidase A does not play a crucial role in catalysis. *Nature* **317**, 551–5.

Gillam, S. and Smith, M. (1979). Site-specific mutagenesis using synthetic oligo-deoxyribonucleotide primers: I. Optimum conditions and minimum oligodeoxy-ribonucleotide length. *Gene* **8**, 81–97.

Hutchinson, C. A., Phillips, S., Edgell, M. H., Gillam, S., Jahnke, P. and Smith, M. (1978). Mutagenesis at a specific position in a DNA sequence. *J. Biol. Chem.* **253**, 6551–60.

Jones, H. D., McMillan, A. J., Fersht, A. R. and Winter, G. (1985). Reversible dissociation of dimeric tyrosyl-tRNA synthetase by mutagenesis at the subunit interface. *Biochemistry (USA)* **24**, 5852–7.

Kaiser, E. T., Levine, H. L., Otsuki, T. and Fried, H. E. (1980). Studies on the mechanism of action and stereochemical behaviour of semisynthetic model enzymes. *Adv. Chem. Ser.* **191**, 35–48.

Kaiser, E. T., Lawrence, D. S. and Rokita, S. E. (1985). The chemical modification of enzymatic specificity. *Ann. Rev. Biochem.* **54**, 565–95.

Kaminski, Z. W. and Jezewska, M. M. (1979). Intermediate dehydrogenase-oxidase form of xanthine oxidoreductase in rat liver. *Biochem. J.* **181**, 177–82.

Levine, H. L., Nakagawa, Y. and Kaiser, E. T. (1977). Flavapapain: Synthesis and properties of semisynthetic enzymes. *Biochem. Biophys. Res. Commun.* **76**, 64–70.

Levine, H. L. and Kaiser, E. T. (1978). Oxidation of Dihydonicotinamides by Flavopapain. *J. Amer. Chem. Soc.* **100**, 7670–7.

—— (1980). Stereospecificity in the oxidation of NADH by flavopapain. *J. Amer. Chem. Soc.* **102**, 343–5.

Lowe. D. M., Fersht, A. R., Wilkinson, A. J., Carter, P. and Winter, G. (1985). Probing histidine-substrate interactions in tyrosyl-tRNA synthetase using asparagine and glutamine replacements. *Biochemistry (USA)* **24**, 5106–9.

Mansson, M.-O., Larrsson, P.-O. and Mosbach, K. (1978). Covalent binding of an NAD analogue to liver alcohol dehydrogenase resulting in an enzyme-coenzyme complex not requiring exogenous coenzyme for activity. *Eur. J. Biochem.* **86**, 455–63.

—— (1979). Recycling by a second enzyme of NAD covalently bound to alcohol dehydrogenase. *FEBS Lett* **98**, 309–13.

Margalit, R., Pecht, I. and Gray, H. B. (1983). Oxidation-reduction catalytic activity of a petaamineruthenium (III) derivative of sperm whale myoglobin. *J. Amer. Chem. Soc.* **105**, 301–2.

Messing, J. (1983). New M13 vectors for cloning. *Meth. Enzymol.* **101**, 20–78.

Mosbach, K. (1976). Immobilised enzymes. *Meth. Enzymol.* **XLIV**.

Offord, R. E. (1979). *Semisynthetic proteins.* John Wiley, Chichester.

Perry, L. J. and Wetzel, R. (1984). Disulfide bond engineered into T4 lysozyme: Stabilization of the protein towards thermal inactivation. *Science* **226**, 555–7.

Plapp, B. V. (1970). Enhancement of the activity of horse liver alcohol dehydrogenase by modification of amino groups at the actives sites. *J. Biol. Chem.* **245**, 1727–35.

Razin, A., Hirose, T., Itakawa, K. and Riggs, A. D. (1978). Efficient correction of a mutation by use of chemically synthesised DNA. *Proc. Natl. Acad. Sci. (USA)* **75**, 4268–75.

Rosemeyer, H., Kornig, E. and Seela, F. (1982). Adenosine deaminase covalently linked to soluble dextran. The effect of immobilisation on thermodynamic and kinetic parameters. *Eur. J. Biochem.* **122**, 375–80.

Sanger, F., Nicklen, S. and Coulson, A. R. (1977). DNA sequencing with chain terminating inhibitors. *Proc. Natl. Acad. Sci. (USA)* **74**, 5463–7.

Schafer, M. A. and Wilson, G. S. (1983). Spectral and electron transfer properties of sepharose 6MB-immobilized cytochrome *c*. *J. Biol. Chem.* **258**, 12835–41.

Shimizu, T. (1979). Enhancement of 14S and 30S dynein adenosine triphosphatase activities by modification of amino groups with trinitrobenzenesulfonate. A comparison with modification of SH groups. *J. Biochem. (Tokyo)* **85**, 1412.

Shortle, D. and Nathans, D. (1978). Local mutagenesis: a method for generating viral mutants with base substitutions in preselected regions of the viral geonome. *Proc. Natl. Acad. Sci. (USA)* **75**, 2170–4.

——, Grisafi, P., Benkovic, S. J. and Botstein, D. (1982). Gap misrepair mutagenesis: efficient site directed induction of transition, transversion and frameshift mutations *in vitro*. *Proc. Natl. Acad. Sci. (USA)* **79**, 1588–92.

Sigal, I. S., Harwood, B. G. and Arentzen, R. (1982). Thiol-β-lactamase: Replacement of the active site serine of RTEM β-lactamase by a cysteine residue. *Proc. Natl. Acad. Sci. (USA)* **79**, 7157–60.

——, DeGrado, W. F., Thomas, B. J. and Petteway, S. R. (1984). Purification and properties of thiol β-lactamase. *J. Biol. Chem.* **259**, 5327–32.

Slama, J. T., Orugati, S. R. and Kaiser, E. T. (1981). Semisynthetic enzymes. Synthesis of a new flavopapain with high catalytic efficiency. *J. Amer. Chem. Soc.* **103**, 6211–3.

Spomer, W. E. and Wotton, J. F. (1971). The hyrolysis of α'-*N*-benzoyl-L-argininamide catalysed by trypsin and acetyltrypsin. Dependence on pH. *Biochim. Biophys. Acta* **235**, 164–171.

Sproat, B. S. and Gait, M. J. (1984). Solid-phase synthesis of oligodeoxyribonu-cleotides by the phosphotriester method. In *Oligonucleotide synthesis — a practical approach* (ed. M. J. Gait) pp. 83–115. IRL Press, Oxford.

Thomas, P. G., Russell, A. J. and Fersht, A. R. (1985). Tailoring the pH dependence of enzyme catalysis using protein engineering. *Nature* **318**, 375–6.

Urabe, I., Yamamoto, M., Yamada, Y. and Okada, H. (1978). Effect of hydrophobicity of acyl groups on the activity and stability of acylated termolysin. *Biochim. Biophys. Acta* **524**, 435–41.

Valenzuela, P. and Bender, M. L. (1971). Kinetic properties of succinylated and ethylenediamine-amidated δ-chymotrypsins. *Biochim. Biophys. Acta* **250**, 538–48.

Villafranca, J. E., Howell, E. E., Voet, D. H., Strobel, M. S., Ogden, R. C., Abelson, J. N. and Kraut, J. (1983). Directed mutagenesis of dihydrofolate reductase. *Science* **222**, 782–8.

Wallace, R. B., Schold, M., Johnson, M. J., Dembek, P. and Itakura, K. (1981). Oligonucleotide directed mutagenesis of the human α-globin gene: a general method for producing point mutations in cloned DNA. *Nucleic Acid Res.* **9**, 3647–56.

Wells, T. N. C. and Fersht, A. R. (1985). Hydrogen bonding in enzymatic catalysis analyzed by protein engineering. *Nature* **316**, 656–7.

Wilkinson, A. J., Fersht, A. R., Blow, D. M. and Winter, G. (1983). Site-directed mutagenesis as a probe of enzyme structure and catalysis: tyrosyl-tRNA synthetase cysteine 35 to glycine 35 mutation. *Biochemistry (USA)* **22**, 3581–6.

——, Carter, P. and Winter, G. (1984). A large increase in enzyme-substrate affinity by protein engineering. *Nature* **307**, 187–8.

Winter, G., Fersht, A. R., Wilkinson, A. J., Zoller, M. and Smith, M. (1982). Redesigning enzyme structure by site-directed mutagenesis: Tyrosyl t-RNA synthetase and ATP binding. *Nature* **299**, 756–8.

Zaborsky, O. R. (1973). *Immobilised enzymes* CRC Press, Ohio.

Zoller, M. J. and Smith, M. (1983). Oligonucleotide-directed mutagenesis of DNA fragments cloned into M13 vectors. *Meth. Enzymol.* **100**, 468–500.

Bioelectrochemistry
(a) Potentiometric sensors

9

Ion-selective electrodes and biosensors based on ISEs

S. S. KUAN and G. G. GUILBAULT

9.1 Introduction

pH is one of the most commonly made measurements in the chemical laboratory. The glass electrode, selective for hydrogen ion, a reference electrode, and a pH meter combine to form an extremely useful analytical tool. The advantages of this measuring system, are speed, sensitivity, cost, reliability, and the sample is not destroyed or consumed in the process. The same advantages apply to other ion-selective electrodes which have become available in the past few years. At this time, ion-selective electrodes which are sensitive to particular cations and anions can be purchased or constructed at moderate cost. The analytically useful range of these sensors is generally from 10^{-1} M to 10^{-5} M although there are many sensors which are useful at even lower concentrations. Since the response of ion-selective electrodes is logarithmic, the precision of measurements is constant over their dynamic range.

Ion-selective electrodes are finding many applications in biological studies. Particularly useful applications are in the field of clinical chemistry where a large number of samples, and the need for a rapid method of analysis, rule out many slower, more involved methods.

Enzyme electrodes represent the most recent advance in analytical chemistry. These devices combine the selectivity and sensitivity of enzymatic methods of analysis with the speed and simplicity of ion-selective electrode measurements. The result is a device that can be used to determine the concentration of a given compound in solution quickly and a method that requires a minimum of sample preparation. Enzyme electrodes for the determination of glucose, urea, L-amino acids, penicillin, and other substances of clinical importance have been developed.

9.2 Ion-selective electrodes

The hydrogen-selective or pH electrode, the best known ion-selective electrode, traces its discovery to Cremer (1906) and Haber and Klemensiewicz (1909) who found that certain glasses respond to hydrogen ion activity. The response of the glass electrode was commonly believed to be a result of migration of hydrogen ions through the thin glass membrane. The studies carried out by Karreman and Eisenman (1962) and the work of Stephanova *et al.* (1963) provided the insight necessary for the development of new ion-selective electrodes. At present, ion-selective electrodes for Na^+, K^+, Mg^{++}, Ca^{++}, Cd^{++}, Cu^{++}, Ag^+, NH_4^+, S^-, I^-, Br^-, Cl^-, CN^-, SCN^-, F^-, NO_3^-, ClO_4^-, BF^-, as well as H^+, are available. The electrodes are available from many manufacturers and as newer methods of preparation of ISEs have been developed, several kits for the preparation of different electrodes using a common body or housing have been introduced.

An ion-selective electrode may be defined as a device that develops an electrical potential proportional to the logarithm of the activity of an ion in solution. The term 'specific' is sometimes used to describe an electrode. This term indicates that the electrode responds to only one particular ion. Since no electrode is truly specific for one ion, the term ion-selective is recommended as more appropriate.

The response of an ion-selective electrode to an ion, i, of activity a_i and charge z, is given by the Nickolski equation:

$$E = \text{constant} + \frac{2.303\,RT}{zF} \log [a_i + k_{ij}(a_j)^{z/y}] \tag{9.1}$$

in which E is the measured potential, R is the gas constant and is equal to 8.314 joules deg^{-1}, T is the absolute temperature in °Kelvin, F is the Faraday constant equal to 96 487 coulombs equiv^{-1}, k_{ij} is the selectivity coefficient, and j is any interfering ion of charge y and activity a_j. The sign of the second term on the right-hand side of eqn (9.1) is positive for cations and negative for anions.

The selectivity coefficient is a numerical description of the preferential response of an ion-selective electrode to the major ion, i, in the presence of the interfering ion j. The lower the numerical value of k_{ij} for a particular ion-selective electrode the greater concentration of j can be tolerated before causing errors in the measurement. Values of k_{ij} can be calculated from:

$$\pm \frac{E_2 - E_1}{2.303\,RT/zF} = \log k_{ij} + \left(\frac{z}{y} - 1\right)\log a_i \tag{9.2}$$

in which E_1 and E_2 are the measurements of separated solutions of the principle ion and interfering ion, respectively, at the same activity. Or, more realistically, k_{ij} may be obtained by making measurements of the potential of an ion-selective electrode in solutions of constant interferent activity, a_j, and changing primary ion activity, a_i. Then k_{ij} may be determined by

$$a_i = k_{ij}(a_j)^{z/y}. \tag{9.3}$$

The value of a_i is taken at the point where serious deviation from Nernstian response is noted (Moody and Thomas 1972).

At present, ion-selective electrodes can be divided into several categories according to the composition of their sensor membranes.

1. Glass electrodes are ion-selective electrodes in which the sensing membrane is a very thin membrane of glass usually in the shape of a bulb. The composition of the glass determines the selectivity of the membrane. Glass electrodes are available which are sensitive to H^+ (pH electrodes) and to cations in the order $Ag^+ > H^+ > K^+ > NH_4^+ > Na^+ > Li^+$, Ca^{++}, Mg^{++} over a concentration range 10^{-1} to 10^{-5} M.

2. Solid-state electrodes are ion-selective electrodes in which the sensor is a thin layer of a single or mixed crystal or precipitate which is an ion conductor. Two classes of these electrodes are distinguished: homogeneous and heterogenous. Homogeneous electrodes refer to those electrodes in which the membrane is a pellet prepared from a precipitate, mixture of precipitates, or a single crystal. In the heterogeneous electrodes a precipitate or mixture or precipitates is dispersed in an inert supporting matrix such as silicone rubber or poly (vinyl chloride) (PVC).

3. Liquid ion-exchange electrodes are prepared by dissolving an organic ion exchanger in an appropriate solvent. The solution is held in an inert matrix. Ion exchangers at present used in the preparation of these electrodes may be a ligand association complex such as those formed by the transition metals with derivatives of 1,10-phenanthroline, quarternary ammonium salts, organic-phosphate complexes, and antibiotics. In some cases the exchanger and solvent are entrapped in an inert polymer matrix such as PVC or poly (methyl methacrylate) and coated on a platinum wire or graphite rod.

4. There are special electrodes which employ a coating over the membrane of an ion-selective electrode. The coating may be a gas-permeable membrane in which case electrodes sensitive to CO_2 or NH_3 are the result. The gas diffuses through the membrane and alters the pH of an internal filling solution. The pH change is measured with a glass electrode and is proportional to the concentration of gas which enters the membrane. Another coating, which has been used successfully, contains an enzyme which converts a substrate to an ion which is detected by an ion-selective electrode.

These electrodes will be discussed in some detail in the second part of this paper.

When using an ion-selective electrode to make potentiometric measurements of the activity of a given ion in solution, it is important to remember that the device is affected by the activity of the ion. Therefore, species which may complex the ion of interest and lower its activity must either be removed or masked. It is often necessary to use a buffer solution to control ionic strength, pH, and to prevent changes in the activity of the ion being measured by oxidation, reduction, or complexation.

There have been a large number of reports of applications and progress in the design and manufacture of ion-selective electrodes in the literature. An important development has been the use of PVC in the preparation of ion-selective electrodes. Electrodes manufactured with PVC are much lower in cost, they have essentially the same response characteristics and usually can be used for longer period of time than previous electrode assemblies. Moody *et al.* (1970) constructed a calcium-selective electrode using a liquid ion exchanger incorporated in a PVC matrix. The optimum concentration of calcium exchanger used in preparation was described by Griffiths *et al.* (1972). The electrode constructed in this manner gave a near-Nerstian response (30 mV per pC a unit) over the range 2.6×10^{-2} to 6.0×10^{-5} M in $CaCl_2$ solution. Davies *et al.* (1972) prepared nitrate ion-selective electrodes by incorporating commercially available liquid ion exchangers in PVC. These electrodes overcome the problem of leakage that is associated with other liquid ion exchange assemblies.

Pick *et al.* (1973) have used valinomycin in a variety of neutral carriers to prepare ion-selective electrodes for potassium. The response time of this type of electrode is usually less than 3 s and the useful range of the electrodes is 10^{-1} to 10^{-5} M. This electrode prepared from this material is exceptional in that there is very little or no drift in potential over a three-day period. As the working characteristics of electrodes are improved and new electrodes are introduced many new applications of these devices can be expected.

The use of ion-selective electrodes for the determination of the calcium content of biological materials has been investigated vigorously since calcium is one of the most important electrolytes in human physiology (Moore 1969). The electrode most commonly used in these studies has been a liquid ion-exchanger of the calcium salt of didecyl phosphoric acid in didecyl-phenyl phosphonate. Such an electrode has a working range of 10^0 to 10^{-5} M in calcium. The electrode responds to ionized calcium and if the total calcium content of a sample is to be measured, calcium must be freed from ligands or chelates prior to measurement.

The normal values of calcium in serum range from 8.5 to 10.5 mg/100 ml in elders to 9.0 to 11.0 mg/100 ml in children (Tietz 1970). Of this, 30 to 55% is present as protein-bound calcium, 5 to 10% is present in the form of complexes and chelates and the remainder is ionized calcium (Moore 1969). Studies of apparent ionized serum calcium have been carried out by Hattner *et al.* (1970) and by Li and Piechoki (1971). In the case of serum measurements, standards are prepared using solutions with sodium content (150 mM) that approximates the sodium concentration of serum samples. A new calcium-selective electrode based on a neutral carrier has been developed by

Ammann *et al.* (1972). This electrode is reported to have superior selectivity for calcium over sodium and magnesium.

The family of electrodes prepared from silver sulphide alone or mixed with halogen salts of silver are well characterized (Pungor 1967; Rechnitz 1967). The precipitates are used either in the form of a pellet or mixed in an inert supporting matrix such as silicon rubber. When silver sulfide is used alone, the electrode responds to sulfide and silver ions over the concentration range 10^0 to 10^{-7} M. The sulfide content of natural waters and low levels of silver have been determined with this electrode.

When a particular silver halide is mixed with silver sulphide to form a sensor membrane, the membrane behaves as though it was composed of the halide salt alone. Electrodes for iodide, bromide, and chloride have been prepared in this manner. The iodide electrode also responds to cyanide. An electrode for thiocyanate can be prepared by mixing silver thiocyanate with silver to form a sensor membrane. The selectivity coefficients of the halide and pseudo-halide electrodes can be estimated by:

$$k_{ij} = \frac{\text{Solubility product of Ag}_i}{\text{Solubility product of Ag}_j}. \tag{9.4}$$

Liquid ion-exchange electrodes which are sensitive to nitrate, perchlorate, fluoroborate, and chloride generally have a useful working range of 10^{-1} to 10^{-5} M. The liquid ion-exchange electrode for chloride is not as seriously affected by the presence of sulphide and the halogens as the solid-state chloride electrode. Therefore, it can be used for many assays in which the interference caused by sulphide or the halogens is not negligible. The perchlorate and fluoroborate electrodes have limited applications in analysis. However, the nitrate electrode has been used to directly determine nitrate in many types of samples.

The glass electrodes for determination of monovalent and divalent cations have been used in a variety of clinical and environmental studies. Garrels (1967) used a potassium/sodium glass electrode for measuring these cations in sea water. Parts-per-billion quantities of sodium in water were measured by Budd and Jones (1963) and Annino (1967) used a sodium ion-selective electrode to measure the sodium content of urine. There are many other applications of glass electrodes in the areas of environmental and clinical chemistry. The text edited by Eisenman (1967) and the chapter of the N.B.S. publication written by Khuri (1969) are recommended to those who are interested in these areas (see also Chapter 20).

Antibiotics and similar compounds have been used successfully to prepare cation-selective electrodes. The calcium ion-selective electrode developed by Ammann *et al.* (1972) has been mentioned earlier. Pioda *et al.* (1967) have studied the properties of the antibiotic nonactin for use as a sensor membrane. An electrode prepared from this material in an inert matrix is sensitive to NH_4^+ with linear near-Nernstian response of 51 mV per decade change over the concentration range 10^{-1} to 10^{-4} M NH_4^+. This electrode responds poorly to Li^+ ion activity and the selectivity for NH_4^+ over K^+ and Na^+ was reported to be superior to glass electrodes sensitive to ammonium ion. The nonactin electrode has been used in an enzyme system and will be discussed in the second part of this review. Valinomycin-based potassium ion-selective electrodes have been studied (Eyal and Rechnitz 1971). The antibiotic may be used in a suitable organic solvent or an inert matrix (Pick *et al.* 1973) and electrodes prepared in this manner have been used to measure the potassium content of serum (Frant and Ross 1970). Greater concentrations of sodium can be tolerated with the antibiotic electrode than with the sodium glass electrode. For a more detailed account of the neutral carrier ion-selective electrodes, the chapter by Eisenman (1967) in the N.B.S. proceedings is recommended.

The final electrodes to be considered are the gas sensing type prepared by placing a gas-permeable membrane over a housing which contains a pH electrode and internal filling solution. Electrodes of this type are available for ammonia, carbon dioxide, and hydrogen sulphide. The CO_2 electrodes have found most use in the determination of blood P_{CO_2} (Haake 1975; Winters 1981.) Ammonia in natural waters and solids has been determined directly using an ammonia electrode and the measurement of the ammonia or ammonium content of a wide variety of samples is feasible since only gases which diffuse through the membrane would interfere with the operation of the device.

9.3 Enzyme electrodes

The classic potentiometric enzyme electrode is a combination of an ion-selective electrode base sensor with an immobilized (insolubilized) enzyme, which provides a highly selective and sensitive method for the determination of a given substrate. Some of the ion-selective electrodes useful in construction of enzyme electrodes are presented in Table 9.1. Advantages of such potentiometric sensors are simplicity of instrumentation (only a pH meter is needed, not a polarographic system as required for amperometric based probes), low cost, and easy availability of a large number of good, reliable base ISEs.

Clark and Lyon (1962) first introduced the concept of the 'soluble' enzyme electrode (Chapter 1), but the first working electrode was reported by Updike and Hicks (1971) using glucose oxidase immobilized in a gel over a polarographic oxygen electrode to measure the concentration of glucose in biological solutions and tissues. These are both voltammetric or amperometric probes, i.e. the current produced upon application of a constant applied voltage is measured. The first potentiometric (no applied voltage, the voltage

Table 9.1 Possible ISE sensors useful in construction of enzyme electrode

Potentiometric sensors	Useful for
NH_3	Urea, amino acids, glutamine, glutamic acid, nitrate, nitrite, creatinine, lyase, and deaminase enzymes.
CO_2	Urea, amino acids, decarboxylative enzyme systems.
pH	Penicillin, RNA, DNA, glucose, enzyme reactions giving pH change.
I^-	Glucose, amino acids, cholesterol, alcohols.
CN^-	Amygdalin.

produced is monitored) enzyme electrode was described by Guilbault and Montalvo for urea in 1969. Since this, over one hundred different electrodes have appeared in the literature; a summary of these can be found in a recent book (Guilbault 1984).

In enzyme electrodes, the enzyme is usually immobilized, thus reducing the amount of material required to perform a routine analysis, and eliminating the need for frequent assay of the enzyme preparation in order to obtain reproducible results. Furthermore, the stability of the enzyme is often improved when it is incorporated in a suitable gel matrix. An electrode for the determination of urea prepared by covering an ammonium ion selective electrode with chemically bound urease has been used for over 300 days, for example (Guilbault 1984).

Of the two methods used to immobilize an enzyme: (a) the chemical modification of the molecules by the introduction of insolubilizing groups and (b) the physical entrapment of the enzyme in an inert matrix, such as starch or polyacrylamide (Chapter 6), the technique of chemical immobilization is the best to make electrode probes.

An enzyme electrode operates via a five-step process: (i) the substrate must be transported to the surface of the electrode, (ii) the substrate must diffuse through the membrane to the active site, (iii) reaction occurs at the active site, (iv) product formed in the enzymatic reaction is transported through the membrane to the surface of the electrode, and (v) product is measured at the electrode surface. The first step, transport of the substrate, is most critically dependent on the stirring rate of the solution, so that rapid stirring will bring the substrate very rapidly to the electrode surface. If the membrane is kept very thin, using highly active enzyme, then steps 2 and 4 are eliminated or minimized; since step 3 is very fast, the response of an enzyme electrode should theoretically approach the response time of the base sensor. Many researchers have shown with experimental data that one can approach this behaviour by using a thin membrane and rapid stirring.

9.4 Preparation of a typical electrode

Take the base sensor (chosen from Table 9.1) and turn it upside down (Fig. 9.1b). Cover the sensor with a piece of pig intestine membrane (Universal Sensors, New Orleans, USA). Wet the membrane with 30 μl of 25% albumin solution, then add 10 units of enzyme, dissolving it in the albumin solution. Add 5 μl of 25% glutaraldehyde to complete the immobilization and let dry. Then cover with a piece of dialysis membrane (cellophane of 20–25 μm thick, Will Scientific, Arthur Thomas, Sigma, etc.) about twice the diameter of the size of the electrode sensor. Place a rubber O-ring, with a diameter that fits the electrode body snugly, around the cellophane membrane (Fig. 9.1b), and gently push the O-ring onto the electrode body, so that enzyme forms a nice uniform layer on top of the electrode surface. Place the electrode in buffer solution overnight to allow penetration of buffer

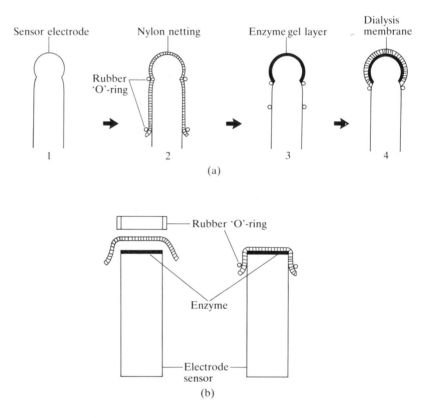

Fig. 9.1 Preparation of enzyme electrode probes
(a) using physically entrapped enzymes and
(b) using chemically attached enzymes.

into the enzyme and permit loss of entrapped air. Store the electrode in buffer (optimum for the enzyme system) in a refrigerator between use.

9.4.1 Apparatus

The enzyme electrode, once constructed, is used like any other ion-selective electrode. The potentiometric probes, e.g. urea, amino acids, penicillin, are plugged directly into a digital voltmeter (e.g. Orion, Corning, Sargent, Amel, etc.). The mV read for each concentration tested are then plotted *vs.* concentration in a linear-log plot.

A reference electrode, generally a calomel electrode, is used together with the enzyme electrode. Alternatively, the reference electrode can be combined as an integral part of the enzyme electrode, as is the case with the ammonia, carbon dioxide, or oxygen electrode base sensors used in the urea, amino acid, glucose, or alcohol probes.

Finally, the electrode must be kept in a solution with constant stirring rate, since it has been shown that a change in stirring rate will change the potential of the electrode measured.

9.5 Operational properties of electrodes

Table 9.2 gives a listing of some enzyme electrodes that have been prepared for analysis of common substrates together with the enzyme used, the sensor, the immobilization method, the stability of the probe, the response time of the electrode, the units (U) of enzyme used to make the electrode, and the range of concentrations determinable. (See Guilbault (1984) for a complete listing of electrodes available.)

In several cases, many different base sensors could be used. For example, for urea, one could use either a cation electrode, which measures the NH_4^+ ion formed in the urease catalysed hydrolysis of urea:

$$\text{Urea} \xrightarrow{\text{Urease}} NH_4^+ + HCO_3^- \tag{9.5}$$

or an NH_3 or CO_2 electrode to measure either the NH_3 (formed by adding ^-OH to $NH_4^+ \longrightarrow NH_3$) or the CO_2 (formed by adding H^+ to the $HCO_3^- \longrightarrow CO_2$). By far the best probe is the NH_3 electrode, because of its high specifity and low limit of detection (10^{-6} M compared to 5×10^{-5} M for the CO_2 electrode). The disadvantage of use of this electrode is slow response time (2–4 min) and long recovery time to return to the original base line (5–10 min). Guilbault and Mascini (1977), for example, showed that by chemically attaching urease to a polypropylene membrane, which is an integral part of the NH_3 gas membrane electrode, that 200–1000 assays can be performed on one electrode with a C.V of 2.5% over the range of 5×10^{-5} to 10^{-2} M. At least 20 assays/hr can be made with excellent correlation with the results obtained by the spectrophotometric diacetyl procedure.

Table 9.2 Typical electrodes and their characteristics

Type	Enzyme	Sensor	Immobilization[a]	Stability	Response time	Amount of enzyme (U)	Range (mol/l)[b]
1. Urea	Urease (EC 3.5.1.5)	Cation	Physical	3 weeks	30 s–1 min	25	10^{-2}–5×10^{-5}
		Cation	Physical	2 weeks	1–2 min	75	10^{-2}–10^{-4}
		Cation	Chemical	>4 months	1–2 min	10	10^{-2}–10^{-4}
		pH	Physical	3 weeks	5–10 min	100	5×10^{-3}–5×10^{-5}
		Gas(NH_3)	Chemical	4 months	2–4 min	10	5×10^{-2}–5×10^{-5}
		Gas(NH_3)	Chemical	20 days	1–4 min	0.5	10^{-2}–10^{-4}
		Gas(CO_2)	Physical	3 weeks	1–2 min	25	10^{-2}–10^{-4}
2. Glucose	Glucose oxidase	pH	Soluble	1 week	5–10 min	100	10^{-1}–10^{-3}
		I^-	Chemical	>1 month	2–8 min	10	10^{-3}–10^{-4}
3. L-Amino acids (general)[d]	L-AA oxidase (EC 1.4.3.2)	Cation	Physical	2 weeks	1–2 min	10	10^{-2}–10^{-4}
		NH_4^+	Chemical	>1 month	1–3 min	10	10^{-2}–10^4
		I^-	Chemical	>1 month	1–3 min	10	10^{-3}–10^{-4}
L-Tyrosine	L-Tyrosine decarboxylase (EC 1.1.25)	Gas(CO_2)	Physical	3 weeks	1–2 min	25	10^{-1}–10^{-4}
L-Glutamine	Glutaminase (EC 3.5.1.2)	Cation	Soluble	2 days[c]	1 min	50	10^{-1}–10^{-4}
L-Glutamic acid	Glutamate dehydrogenase (EC 1.4.1.3)	Cation	Soluble	2 days[c]	1 min	50	10^{-1}–10^{-4}
L-Asparagine	Asparaginase (EC 3.5.1.1)	Cation	Physical	1 month	1 min	50	10^{-2}–5×10^{-5}

Table 9.2 *Continued*

Type	Enzyme	Sensor	Immobilization[a]	Stability	Response time	Amount of enzyme (U)	Range (mol/l)[b]
4. D-Amino acids (general)[e]	D-AA oxidase (EC 1.4.3.3)	Cation	Physical	1 month	1 min	50	10^{-2}–5×10^{-5}
5. Penicillin	Penicillinase (EC 3.5.2.6)	pH	Physical / Soluble	1–2 weeks / 3 weeks	0.5–2 min / 2 min	400 / 1000	10^{-2}–10^{-4} / 10^{-2}–10^{-4}
6. Amygdalin	β-Glucosidase (EC 3.2.1.21)	CN^-	Physical	3 days[f]	10–20 min	100	10^{-2}–10^{-5}
7. Nitrate	Nitrate reductase/ nitrite reductase (EC 1.9.6.1/ 1.6.6.4)	NH_4^+	Soluble	1 day	2–3 min	10	10^{-2}–10^{-4}
8. Nitrite	Nitrate reductase (EC 1.6.6.4)	Gas(NH_3)	Chemical	3–4 months	2–3 min	10	5×10^{-2}–10^{-4}

[a] 'Physical' refers to polyacrylamide gel entrapment in all cases; 'chemical' is attachment chemically to glutaraldehyde with albumin, to polyacrylic acid, or to acrylamide, followed by physical entrapment.

[b] Analytically useful range, either linear or with reasonable change if curvature is observed.

[c] Preparation lacks stability as evidence by constant decrease in signal each day.

[d] Electrode responds to L-cysteine, L-leucine, L-tyrosine, L-trytophan, L-phenylalanine, and L-methionine.

[e] Electrode responds to D-phenylalanine, D-alanine, D-valine, D-methionine, D-leucine, D-norleucine, and D-isoleucine.

[f] Time required for signal to return to base line before reuse.

The range of most enzyme electrodes is 10^{-2} to 10^{-4} M, with some extending up to 10^{-1} M (depending on the solubility of the substrate in the aqueous solution) and some extending down to 10^{-5} M, or lower, depending on the detection limit of the base sensor.

Deterioration of the enzyme electrode can be seen by three changes in the response characteristics: (1) with age the upper limit will decrease, from say 10^{-1} to 10^{-2} M, (2) the slope of the calibration curve of potential *vs.* log [concentration], originally 60 mV/decade, Nernstian, will drop to 50, 40 perhaps 30 mV/decade, or lower, and (3) the response time of the electrode, originally 30 s–4 min, (approximately the same as that of the base sensor), will become longer as the enzyme ages.

In construction of an enzyme electrode, it is important that a highly purified enzyme be used (at least 10 units/mg) so that only a small amount of enzyme need to be used in the construction of the electrode. This will ensure a fast response time, approaching that of the base probe. As can be seen in Table 9.1, at least 10 U (1 mg) of enzyme is generally used.

The stability of the electrode depends on the type of entrapment, chemically attached enzyme electrodes being the most stable (500–1000 runs/electrode), and a storage stability of about 6–14 months.

9.6 Examples of enzyme electrodes based on ISEs

9.6.1 Some commonly used enzyme electrodes

9.6.1.1 Urea (diagnostic indication for kidney function) The first urea electrode was prepared by Guilbault and Montalvo (1969), by immobilizing urease in a polyacrylamide matrix on nylon or dacron nets. These nets were then placed onto a Beckman cation selective electrode (which responds to ammonium ion). In later publications Guilbault and Montalvo (1970) described an improved electrode, covered with a cellophane membrane, that could be used for 21 days with no loss of activity.

In attempts to improve the selectivity of the urea determination, Guilbault and Nagy (1973) used a silicone rubber based nonactin ammonium-ion selective electrode as the base sensor, together with immobilized urease in a polyacrylic gel. Guilbault *et al.* (1973) used a three electrode system, which allowed dilution to a constant interference level. Four months electrode stability resulted.

Anfalt *et al.* (1973) polymerized urease directly onto the surface of an Orion ammonia gas membrane by means of glutaraldehyde. Sufficient ammonia was produced in the enzyme reaction layer, even at pH values as low as 7–8, to allow direct assay of urea in the presence of large amounts of Na^+ and K^+. A response time of 2–4 minutes was observed.

A urea electrode, using physically entrapped urease and a glass electrode to measure the pH change in the solution, was described by Nilsson *et al.* (1973).

The response time of the electrode to urea was about 7–10 minutes, and a linear range of 5×10^{-5} to 10^{-2} mol/l was obtained with a slope of 0.8 pH units per decade.

Still another possibility for a urea electrode is the use of a urease covered carbon dioxide sensor, to measure the second product of the urea-urease reaction, HCO_3^-. Guilbault and Shu (1972) showed that Na^+ and K^+ had no influence on this electrode and the linear range was 10^{-4} to 10^{-2} mol/l.

A coated wire urea electrode was described by Alexander and Joseph (1981), in which a pH sensing antimony metal wire was coated with a layer of urease. Response times of 1–2 minutes were obtained, with a linear range of 5×10^{-4} to 10^{-2} mol/l urea and a slope of 44 mV/decade. Later Joseph (1985) described a urea electrode based on a gas membrane, ammonia electrode, constructed of antimony metal. This microsensor responds from 10^{-4} to 10^{-2} mol/l of urea in 30–45 s. The ammonia sensor was reported to have a faster base line recovery than the commercial gas membrane electrodes, thus a distinct advantage.

Mascini and Guilbault (1977) described a highly specific and reproducible enzyme electrode for urea, using the enzyme urease chemically bound and attached to a new, improved Teflon membrane, which is an integral part of the ammonia gas membrane electrode. From 200–1000 assays could be performed on one electrode, with a coefficient of variance of 2.5%, over the concentration range 5×10^{-5} to 10^{-2} mol/l; at least 20 assays/hr can be performed.

Enzyme electrodes for urea, using glutaraldehyde attached urease and either a carbon dioxide or a cation selective glass electrode sensor, were described by Tran-Minh and Brown (1975). A range of $10^{-5} - 10^{-1}$ mol/l was obtained using the ammonia glass electrode as the base sensor.

9.6.1.2 Creatinine (a diagnostic indicator of kidney function)   Thompson and Rechnitz (1974) have described the use of unpurified creatininase with an ammonium probe for a creatinine electrode. Guilbault *et al.* (1980) used a similar system, albeit with purified creatininase immobilized onto alkylamine glass beads, packed into a stirrer, and an ammonia electrode as sensor. The residual ammonia level of blood serum was lowered using several removal techniques.

An improved direct-reading, specific electrode for creatinine was disclosed by Guilbault and Coulet (1983), using a highly specific creatininase from Carlo Erba. Linearity from 1–100 mg% was obtained. An enzyme electrode system for creatinine proposed by Tsuchida and Yoda (1983) utilized three enzymes: creatinine amidohydrolase (CA), creatine amidohydrolase (CI) and sarcosine oxidase (SO), co-immobilized onto the porous side of a cellulose acetate membrane. Two multi-enzyme electrodes were constructed using a hydrogen peroxide sensing electrode, one for creatinine plus creatine using a

CA/CI/SO membrane, and one for creatine using a CI/SO membrane. The response time of the electrodes was 20 s in the rate mode, with a detection limit of 1 mg/l.

More than 500 assays could be performed with one electrode, and no loss of activity was observed after nine months of storage at 4 °C.

Mascini *et al.* (1985) proposed an enzyme reactor system, consisting of soluble NADPH and α-ketoglutarate, with glutamate dehydrogenase immobilized onto nylon tubes, for the removal of 98% of the ammonia present in human blood and urine samples in 50 s. This abatement of ammonia permits the use of an ammonia probe, coupled with immobilized creatininase (Carlo Erba enzyme coil, the Clinibond), for the assay of creatinine at low levels in blood and urine. Only 200 μl of sample are required, and the entire process was carried out in a single flow stream.

9.6.1.3 Amino acids   Enzyme electrodes have been widely used for the assay of amino acids in clinical analysis since several amino acids (tyrosine, phenylalanine, tryptophan, methionine) are important diagnostic health indicators. The first of such analytical probes was described by Guilbault and Hrabankova (1970), who placed an immobilized layer of L-amino acid oxidase from snake venom over a monovalent cation electrode, which senses the ammonium ion formed in the enzyme catalysed oxidation of the amino acid. Gauilbault and Nagy (1973b) developed two different types of sensors for L-phenylalanine in blood: (a) an L-amino acid oxidase/peroxidase reaction layer in polyacrylamide, placed over an iodide selective electrode. This probe senses the decrease in the activity of iodide at the electrode surface, according to reactions 9.6 and 9.7:

$$\text{L-Phenylalanine} \xrightarrow{\text{Oxidase}} H_2O_2 \tag{9.6}$$

$$H_2O_2 + 2H^+ + 2I^- \xrightarrow{\text{Peroxidase}} I_2 + 2H_2O \tag{9.7}$$

the second electrode (b) used a silicone rubber based nonactin type ammonium ion electrode covered with L-amino oxidase in polyacrylamide gel. This electrode has a longer linear range and is more selective than electrode (a).

Guilbault and Shu (1972) evaluated the used of a base carbon dioxide sensor coated with tyrosine decarboxylase for assay of L-tyrosine in body fluids. A linear range of 2.5×10^{-4} to 10^{-2} mol/l was observed, with a slightly faster response time than that recorded for a similarly based urea electrode.

Guilbault and Shu (1971) described an enzyme electrode for glutamine, prepared by entrapping glutaminase on a nylon net held between a layer of cellophane and a cation electrode. The electrode responds to glutamine over the concentration range $0.1 - 10^{-4}$ mol/l, with a response of only 1–2 min.

A totally specific enzyme electrode for the assay of L-lysine was described by White and Guilbault (1978). No response was observed with any D- or L-amino acid, except for L-lysine. The electrode can be used for the assay of amino acid in complex matrices, without the necessity for extensive separations and extensive instrumentation (e.g. amino acid analyser). The electrodes are quite stable, with a linear range of L-lysine of 5×10^{-5} to 0.1 mol/l. The only limitation is the long response time (5–10 min).

Fung *et al.* (1979) have proposed a totally specific electrode for L-methionine, prepared by immobilizing L-methionine γ-lyase (EC 4.4.1.11) onto an ammonia specific electrode. The α, γ elimination of L-methionine proceeds with formation of α-ketobutyrate, methane thiol, and ammonia.

Only methionine reacts with purified enzyme, with a linear range of 10^{-2} – 10^{-5} mol/l observed.

A potentiometric L-tyrosine electrode for the direct determination of L-tyrosine in biological fluids was described by Havas and Guilbault. The sensor element of the probe is a carbon dioxide gas membrane electrode covered with a layer of immobilized apo L-tyrosine decarboxylase. A linear range of 2×10^{-3} to 4×10^{-5} mol/l is observed, with no interference from any other L-amino acids or from D-tyrosine.

9.6.1.4 Glucose and sugar electrodes   As mentioned previously, glucose assay is of extreme importance, used as a diagnostic monitor for diabetes.

Nagy *et al.* (1973) described a self-contained electrode for glucose based on an iodide membrane sensor:

$$\text{Glucose} + O_2 \xrightarrow{\text{Glucose oxidase}} \text{Gluconic acid} + H_2O_2 \quad (9.8)$$

$$H_2O_2 + 2I^- + 2H^+ \xrightarrow{\text{Peroxidase}} 2H_2O + I_2 \quad (9.9)$$

The highly sensitive iodide sensor monitors the decrease in the iodide activity at the electrode surface. The assay of glucose was performed both in a stream and at a stationary electrode. Pretreatment of the blood sample was required to remove interfering reducing agents, such as ascorbic acid, tyrosine, and uric acid.

Nilsson *et al.* (1973) described the use of conventional pH glass electrodes for the preparation of enzyme-pH electrodes by either entrapping the enzymes within polyacrylamide gels around the glass electrode, or as a liquid layer trapped within a cellophane membrane. In an assay of glucose, based on a measurement of the gluconic acid produced, the pH response was almost linear from 10^{-4} to 10^{-3} mol/l with a pH change of about 0.85 per decade. Electrodes of this type were also constructed for urea and penicillin. The ionic strength and pH were controlled using a weak (1 mmol/l) phosphate buffer, pH 6.9, and 0.1 mol/l sodium sulphate.

9.6.1.5 Penicillin   Another very important electrode described has been the penicillin electrode, now widely used to monitor for the penicillin content of fermentation broths. The electrode is based on use of a pH probe, coated with immobilized enzyme penicillinase.

$$\text{Penicillin} \xrightarrow{\text{Penicillinase}} \text{Penicilloic acid} \tag{9.10}$$

The response time is very fast (< 30 s) with a slope of 52 mV/decade over the range $5 \times 10^{-2} - 10^{-4}$ M (Nilsson *et al.* 1973).

9.7 Commercial availability of enzyme probes

Immobilized enzymes, together with ISE sensors, arc used in several instruments available commercially. Owens-Illinois (Kimble) has designed a urea instrument using immobilized urease and an ammonia electrode probe. Patent rights to this system have been purchased by Technicon, who markets the instrument in Europe.

Self-contained electrode probes are based on ISE's available from only Universal Sensors (P. O. Box 736, New Orleans, La. 70148 USA), which offers probes for urea, creatinine, amino acids, and others based glutaraldehyde immobilization.

References

Alexander, P. W. and Joseph J. P. (1981). *Anal. Chim. Acta* **131**, 103.
Ammann, D., Pretsch, E. and Simon, W. (1972). Calcium ion-selective electrode based on a neutral carrier. *Anal. Lett.* **5**, 843–50.
Anfalt, T., Granelli, A. and Jagner, D. (1973). Urea electrode based on the ammonia probe. *Anal. Lett.* **6**, 969–75.
Annino, J. S. (1967). Determination of sodium in urine by specific ion electrode. *Clin. Chem.* **13**, 227–32.
Budd, A. L. and Jones, R. H. (1963). *The Analyzer* **4**, 5.
Clark, L. and Lyons, C. (1962). Electrode systems for continuous monitoring in cardiovascular surgery. *Ann. N. Y. Acad. Sci.* **102**, 29–45.
Cremer, M. (1906). *Z. Biol.* **47**, 562.
Davies, J. E. W., Moody, G. J. and Thomas, J. D. R. (1972). Nitrate ion selective electrodes based on polyvinyl chloride matrix membranes. *Analyst (London)* **97**, 87–94.
Eisenman, G. (ed.) (1967). *Glass electrodes for hydrogen and other cations.* Marcel Dekker, New York.
—— G. (1969). In Ion-selective electrodes, Special Publication 314 (ed. R. A. Durst). National Bureau of Standards, Washington D.C.
Eyal, E. and Rechnitz, G. A. (1971). Mechanistic studies on the valinomycin-based potassium electrode. *Anal. Chem.* **43**, 1090–3.
Frant, M. S. and Ross, J. W. (1970). Potassium ion specific electrode with high

selectivity for potassium over sodium. *Science* **167**, 987–8.

Fung, K. W., Kuan, S. S., Sung, H. Y. and Guilbault, G. (1979). Methionine selective enzyme electrode. *Anal. Chem.* **51**, 2319–24.

Garrels, R. M. (1967). Ion sensitive electrodes and individual ion activity coefficients. In *Glass electrodes for hydrogen and other cations* (ed. G. Eisenman) Marcel Dekker, New York, pp. 344–61.

Griffiths, G. H., Moody, G. J. and Thomas, J. D. R. (1972). Optimum composition of polyvinyl chloride matrix membranes used for selective calcium-sensitive electrodes. *Analyst (London)* **97**, 420–7.

Guilbault, G. (1984). *Handbook of immobilized enzymes.* Marcel Dekker, New York.

—— and Hrabankova, E. (1970). L-amino acid electrode. *Anal. Letters* **3**, 53–7.

—— and Mascini, M. (1977). Urease coupled ammonia electrode for urea determination in blood serum. *Anal. Chem.* **49**, 795–8.

—— and Montalvo, J. (1969). *J. Am. Chem. Soc.* **91**, 2164.

—— (1970). *J. Am. Chem. Soc.* **92**, 2533.

—— and Coulet, P. R. (1983). Creatinine-selective enzyme electrodes. *Anal. Chim. Acta* **152**, 223–8.

—— and Nagy, G. (1973*a*). Improved urea electrode. *Anal. Chem.* **45**, 417–19.

—— (1973*b*). Enzyme electrodes for the determination of L-phenylalanine. *Anal. Lett.* **6**, 301–12.

—— and Shu, F. (1971). Electrode for the determination of glutamine. *Anal. Chim. Acta* **56**, 333–40.

—— (1972). Enzyme electrodes based on the use of a carbon dioxide sensor. *Anal. Chem.* **44**, 2161–6.

——, Chen, S. and Kuan, S. (1980). A creatinine specific enzyme electrode. *Anal. Letters* **13**, 1607–24.

——, Kuan, S. and Nagy, G., (1973). Improved electrode for the assay of urea in blood. *Anal. Chim. Acta* **67**, 195–201.

Haake (1975). Brinkman Instruments, Cantiague Rd., Westbury, New York, U.S.A.

Haber, F. and Klemensiewicz, Z. (1909). *Z. Phys. Chem.* **67**, 385.

Hattner, R. S., Johnson, J. W., Bernstein, D. S., Wachman, A. and Brackman, J. (1970). *Clin. Chim. Acta* **28**, 67.

Joseph, J. P. (1985). An enzyme microsensor for urea based on an ammonia gas electrode. *Anal. Chim. Acta* **169**, 249–56.

Karrenman, G. and Eisenman, G. (1962). *Bull. Math. Biophys.* **24**, 413.

Khuri, R. N. (1969). In *Ion-selective electrodes*, Special Publication 314 (ed. R. A. Durst). National Bureau of Standards, Washington D.C., p. 287.

Li., T. K. and Piechoki, J. T. (1971). *Clin. Chem.* **17**, 411.

Mascini, M., Fortunati, S., Moscone, D. and Palleschi, G. (1985). Ammonia abatement in an enzymic flow system for the determination of creatinine in blood sera and urine. *Anal. Chim. Acta* **171**, 175–84.

Moody, G. J. and Thomas, J. D. R. (1972). Development and publication of work with ion-sensitive electrodes. *Talanta* **19**, 623–39.

——, Oke, R. B. and Thomas, J. D. R. (1970). Calcium-sensitive electrode based on a liquid ion exchange in a polyvinyl chloride matrix. *Analyst (London)* **95**, 910–18.

Moore, E. W. (1969). In *Ion-selective electrodes*, Special Publication 314 (ed. R. A.

Durst). National Bureau of Standards, Washington D.C., p. 215.

Nagy, G., von Storp, H. and Guilbault, G. (1973). Enzyme electrode for glucose based on an iodide membrane sensor. *Anal. Chim. Acta* **66**, 443–55.

Nilsson, H., Akerlund, A. and Mosbach, K. (1973). Determination of glucose, urea and penicillin using enzyme pH electrodes. *Biochim. Biophys. Acta* **320**, 529–34.

Pick, J., Toth, K., Pungor, E., Vasak, M. and Simon, W. (1973). Potassium-selective silicone rubber membrane electrode based on a neutral carrier. *Anal. Chim. Acta* **64**, 477–80.

Pioda, L., Wachter, M., Dohner, R. and Simon, W. (1967). *Helv. Chim. Acta* **50**, 1373.

Pungor, E. (1967). Theory and application of anion selective electrodes. *Anal. Chem.* **39**, (13), 28A.

Rechnitz, G. A. (1967). Ion selective electrodes: a review. *Chem. Eng. News* June **12**, 146.

Stephanova, O. K., Shultz, M. M., Materova, E. A. and Nicolsky, B. P. (1963). *Vestn. Leningrad, Univ.* **4**, 93.

Thompson, H. and Rechnitz, G. (1974). Ion electrode based enzymic analysis of creatinine. *Anal. Chem.* **46**, 246–9.

Tietz, N. W. (1970). *Fundamentals of clinical chemistry* Saunders, Philadelphia, p. 637.

Tran-Minh, C. and Brown, G. (1975). Construction and study of electrodes using cross-linked enzymes. *Anal. Chem.* **47**, 1359.

Tsuchida, T. and Yoda, K. (1983). Multi-enzyme membrane electrodes for determination of creatinine and creatinine in serum. *Clin. Chem.* **29**, 51–5.

Updike, S. J. and Hicks, G. P. (1971). The enzyme electrode. *Nature* **214**, 986–8.

White, C. and Guilbault, G. (1978). Lysine specific enzyme electrode for determination of lysine in grains and food. *Anal. Chem.* **50**, 1481–5.

Winters, I. (1981). *Acid base physiology in medicine* The London Co. Cleveland, Ohio USA.

10

Potentiometric biosensors based on redox electrodes

LEMUEL B. WINGARD JR. and JAMES CASTNER

10.1 Introduction

The subject of potentiometric biosensors has been approached by many as an extension to the study of ion selective electrodes (ISE). The bases for this perception are two fold. First a majority of the high impedance electro-chemical biosensors described in the literature contain an ISE; and second, the purpose for developing these modified electrodes has been professed by many to be simply a desire to extend the analytical utility of the base probe. This utilitarian view has sharply focused the direction of research in the field.

The theory, types, and performance characteristics of biosensors based on ISE technology have been reviewed in the preceeding chapter. In this chapter, we will extend the discussion by considering another design: namely, bio-probes based on redox electrodes. Such a system has less specificity and thus

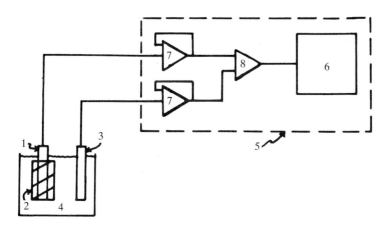

Fig. 10.1 General circuitry for measurement of potential at non-ISE type indicating electrode. The components are as follows: 1, indicating electrode; 2, biological material on indicating electrode; 3, reference electrode; 4, electrolyte containing material to be measured; 5, high impedance potentiometer; 6, display unit; 7, operational amplifier current follower; and 8, comparator circuit.

more general application. A comparison of these two potentiometric systems is presented in order to identify clearly the principles which distinguish the two approaches.

Both ISE and redox electrode based biosensors share a commonality of:

1) Analyte selectivity is dependent upon the biological activity associated with the material directly coupled to the indicating electrode.

2) The analytical signal, in this case the Emf, is measured under null current flow conditions, thus requiring high impedance instrumentation.

3) The potential at the indicating electrode is measured with respect to a stable reference electrode. This is shown schematically in Fig. 10.1.

The ISE and redox types of potentiometric biosensors are distinguished by the electrochemical reactions taking place at the respective sensing electrodes. ISEs operationally are permselective membrane sensors which track ion exchange events at the membrane/solution interfaces (see Fig. 10.2) (Irving 1976). Classical examples of permselective membranes are

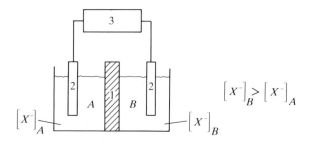

$$\left[X^- \right]_B > \left[X^- \right]_A$$

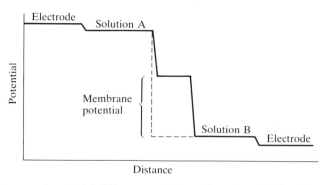

Fig. 10.2 Source of potential differences arising with an ion selective electrode. The components are as follows: 1, ion exchange membrane with fixed negative charges; 2, platinum electrodes; 3, potentiometer. Interfacial junction potentials are shown by the potential differences between the electrodes and the adjacent solution.

pH glass, lanthanium fluoride crystals, and ionophore doped PVC films. Redox electrodes typically, but not exclusively, are noble metal probes that exhibit Nernstian behaviour for changes in the concentration ratio of oxidized and reduced species in the sample solution. The selection of Pt, Au, or Pd for use as electrodes is based on the premise that these metals are good electrical conductors, while at the same time they are not chemically reactive. A corollary to the above statement is that the measured potentials for any redox couple should be independent of the electrode material. In practice this argument does not hold universally. Evidence of this is given by the warning of R. A. Adams about the use of noble metal electrodes (Adams 1969): 'One of the undisputed points with regard to platinum electrode methodology (most of the following discussion also applies to gold and noble metal electrodes in general) is that *reproducible* results are *almost* always obtained provided the general pretreatment of the electrode is duplicated each time.'

It is a common practice in reporting electrochemical measurements obtained via redox electrodes to provide the reader with procedural information about the condition of the indicating electrode. This includes (1) the method for cleaning the electrode surface, (2) the purity of the bulk material, and (3) the molecular morphology of the surface (i.e. poly *vs.* single crystalline material). An example showing how the type of platinum surface pretreatment influences the potentiometric response for a series of glucose oxidase redox electrodes is given in a later section. This pretreatment influence may be caused by the presence of electrochemically active functional groups on the surface of the noble metal or other electrode materials, e.g. glassy carbon. The presence of these moieties can impact upon the precision and the accuracy of the respective redox measurement.

The analytical integrity of redox electrodes also is influenced by the selection of reference electrode. However, this situation is not unique to redox probes but is shared by ISE probes as well. An in-depth treatment of this topic is beyond the scope of this section. The contribution played by the reference electrode is summarized schematically in Fig. 10.3. As shown in the figure, the sample solution is separated by a liquid junction from the reference electrode internal electrolyte. At this junction (usually through a fritted glass plug), a concentration gradient of ionic species can develop; and correspondingly, a potential difference can be generated. The magnitude of the potential will be transitory and dependent upon diffusional processes of the charged species. Control of the electrode junction potentials can be achieved experimentally in one of two ways. First, all of the ionic species on both sides of the junction can be of the same charge/mobility ratio; or second, the reference electrode can be calibrated with a standard sample solution. The theory of electrode junction potentials is covered in detail elsewhere (Bard and Faulkner 1980; Plambeck 1982 and references therein). In summary, biosensors based on redox electrodes are constrained in the same manner as ISE

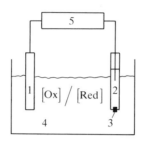

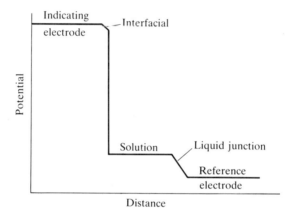

Fig. 10.3 Source of potential differences arising with a redox electrode. The components are as follows: 1, indicating electrode; 2, reference electrode with internal electrolyte solution; 3, porous plug (liquid junction); 4, redox material in solution (ratio of oxidized to reduced form establishes a potential); 5, potentiometer.

systems. However, with redox systems there is the added constraint of a lack of knowledge about the relationship between electrode surface chemistry and the observed potentials. On the other hand, redox electrodes can have faster potentiometric response times due to the absence of mass transfer across interfaces. In addition, the base redox electrode exhibits lower electrical resistance than the typical ISE electrode, therefore requiring less expensive instrumentation, i.e. lower impedance devices. Redox systems are less selective and thus have a broader range of applications.

10.2 Examples of biosensors based on redox electrodes

Conceptually, two approaches can be taken for the construction of potentiometric biosensors based on redox electrodes. They are (1) construction of a biocatalytic surface or (2) construction of a blocked interface. Examples of biocatalytic surfaces on redox electrodes include work with glucose oxidase (Castner and Wingard 1984; Wingard *et al.* 1983), glycerol dehydrogenase (Chen *et al.* 1982), and urease (Joseph 1984). The blocked interface system can utilize an antibody–antigen complex to mediate the potentiometric response due to changes in a given analyte concentration. These referenced systems have been characterized experimentally; but none have been brought into commercial practice as yet.

Of the above examples, the glucose oxidase redox electrode system probably is the one that has been most well characterized (Castner and Wingard 1984; Wingard *et al.* 1983; Proctor *et al.* 1985; Wingard *et al.* 1984). This enzyme catalyses the reaction of β-D-glucose plus O_2 to produce glucono-lactone plus hydrogen peroxide. As mentioned in the Introduction, biocatalytic enzyme redox electrodes involve the immobilization of an oxido-reductase enzyme on the electrode surface with the primary analyte in solution. Alternative schemes can involve (1) immobilization of an enzyme cofactor, such as a porphyrin or flavin, on the electrode surface with reliance on apoenzymes in the sample to catalyse the oxidation or reduction of the immobilized redox center or (2) immobilization of both the enzyme and a mediator molecule on the electrode surface. In our glucose oxidase work, the enzyme is immobilized on a noble metal or a carbon electrode. The redox potential of these electrodes is thought to be dependent on the glucose, oxygen, and hydrogen peroxide in the solution and on functional groups on the platinum or carbon surface. The procedures and results for the glucose oxidase redox electrode work are summarized below.

Glucose oxidase, alone or mixed with catalase, has been immobilized on platinum, porous graphite, and gold and has been shown to produce a direct potentiometric response in the presence of glucose solution at pH 7.4. For example, a mixture of catalase, lyophilized glucose oxidase from *A. niger*, bovine serum albumin, and glutaraldehyde is mixed in sodium phosphate buffer at pH 7.4. The mixture is poured into a mould that contains a disc of 0.05 mm thick platinum foil. The thickness of the cross-linked enzyme-albumin matrix can be controlled, for example from 0.05 cm to 0.32 cm by the use of spacers in the mould. Glutaraldehyde cross-linking of the protein takes place over a 2 hr period at room temperature. The cross-linked matrices are next washed with buffer for 1–2 days to remove loosely attached enzyme prior to testing for enzymatic activity or for potentiometric evaluation (Wingard *et al.* 1983).

A 0.32 cm thick cross-linked enzyme-albumin matrix contains about 8 μg of glucose oxidase (about 0.8 units of activity). The apparent activity of the immobilized enzyme can be determined quite conveniently by the o-dianisidine/peroxidase colorimetric procedure, using glucose and oxygen as the substrates. The apparent activity is only 0.0044 units or less than 1% of that

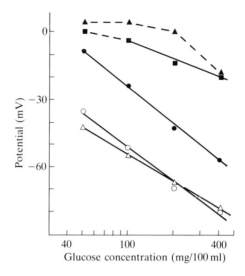

Fig. 10.4 Potentiometric response of glucose oxidase-platinum electrode to oxygenated glucose solution at pH 7.4 in 0.1 M sodium phosphate buffer. Potentials are the measured values minus the potential with plain buffer (no glucose). Potentials are with respect to Ag/AgCl (1 M KCℓ). Lines fitted by linear least squares. Symbols: △ and ○ measurements made with enzyme-platinum out of mould; ▲ (0.24 cm), ■ (0.16 cm), ● (0.05 cm) measurements made with enzyme-platinum in mould (numbers in parentheses indicate thickness of enzyme matrix).

expected for 8 μg of glucose oxidase. The low activity is attributed to diffusional constraints imposed by the cross-linked matrix. Therefore, a proportionally greater glucose oxidase activity would be expected with the thinner cross-linked enzyme-albumin matrices.

Direct potentiometric measurements are carried out by immersing the glucose oxidase electrode and a Ag/AgCl reference electrode in an oxygen-saturated solution of glucose, with the pH controlled at 6.0 ± 0.1 to 7.5 ± 0.1 using 0.1 M sodium phosphate buffer. The potentials can be measured using a suitable potentiometer, such as a Keithley 610C. Typical results are shown in Fig. 10.4 for a series of different thicknesses of enzyme matrix on one side of the platinum disc. With the enzyme-platinum disc removed from the mould, the enzyme matrix layer is very thin (*ca.* 0.02 cm). Whereas with the enzyme-platinum in the mould, the layer of enzyme matrix is 0.05–0.24 cm thick. It is evident from Fig. 10.4 that a Nernstian relationship is observed for glucose concentrations of 50–400 mg/100 ml. This is of interest for clinical glucose determination since normal blood glucose levels occur in the range 90–120 mg/100 ml.

Similar linear results are observed when the glucose oxidase matrix is

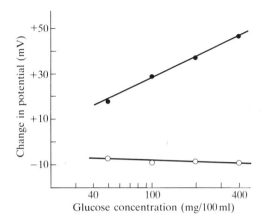

Fig. 10.5 Potentiometric response of glucose oxidase-porous graphite electrode to oxygenated glucose solution at pH 7.4 in 0.1 M sodium phosphate buffer. Symbols: ○ measurements made with bare graphite electrode; ● measurements made with glucose oxidase matrix coated graphite electrode.

placed on porous graphite instead of platinum (Fig. 10.5). However, in this case a positive potential versus log [glucose concentration] slope is obtained, as compared to a negative slope with the platinum based electrode (Wingard *et al.*, 1984). Possible mechanisms for these two cases are discussed next.

The source of the potentiometric response appears to involve the oxidation or reduction of electrode surface functional groups by hydrogen peroxide. This compound is generated as a product of the glucose oxidase catalysed oxidation of glucose. Therefore, the redox couple being measured is attached to the electrode surface instead of being free in solution as depicted in Fig. 10.3. The postulated mechanisms are summarized here, with the reader referred elsewhere for a more detailed discussion (Castner and Wingard 1984; Wingard *et al.* 1984). In the case of platinum (Fig. 10.4), the potential becomes more negative with increasing glucose concentration. This suggests a net reduction reaction is occuring on the platinum surface. The slope in Fig. 10.4 is about − 40 mV/decade of glucose concentration; although as discussed later this slope is dependent upon the method of pretreatment of the platinum surface (Castner and Wingard 1984). A slope of − 40 mV/decade is suggestive of greater than one-electron but less than two-electron transfer, and probably results from several reactions occuring in parallel or in series. The following reactions can occur with a net positive E^0; although other one-electron transformations very likely are present:

$$H_2O_2 = O_2 + 2H^+ + 2e^- \qquad\qquad E^0 = -0.68 \text{ V}$$
$$Pt(OH)_2 + 2H^+ + 2e^- = Pt + 2H_2O \qquad\qquad E^0 = 0.98 \text{ V}$$

In aqueous solution, platinum oxide formation is thought to begin with an oxidation in which OH groups attach reversibly to the surface layer of platinum atoms. At roughly monolayer coverage, the outer layers of platinum atoms undergo an irreversible rearrangement to allow OH groups to enter into the platinum lattice (Hoare 1974). Exactly which one-electron reactions are present is not known, but could involve the reduction of some of the platinum moieties through an intermediate $+1$ oxidation state. The influence of pH on the measured potentials was not tested directly since a change in the solution pH would have a major influence on the activity of the enzymes. However, varying the pH between 5.4 and 8.4 has no effect on the potential of a bare platinum electrode (i.e. no enzyme present). Obviously, a clear explanation of the source of the potential with platinum must await a better understanding of platinum-oxygen-water-hydrogen peroxide mechanistic chemistry.

In the case of carbon (Fig. 10.5), the positive slope of about 30 mV/decade is indicative of a two-electron oxidation reaction taking place on the electrode surface. Porous graphite electrodes contain aldehyde as well as hydroquinone functional groups (Evans and Kuwana 1979) that can undergo two-electron oxidations to carboxylic acid and quinone groups, respectively. However, a more detailed explanation of the source of the potentiometric response must await additional experimental work.

The magnitude of the potentiometric response is influenced by the type of pretreatment given to the platinum electrode surface. This is demonstrated by pretreating platinum electrodes as follows: (1) heating in gas flame, (2) electrochemical oxidation, (3) electrochemical reduction, (4) electrochemical neutral, and (5) electrochemical deposition of platinic chloride. The neutral, oxidation, and flamed pretreated electrodes exhibit a significant difference in the slopes of the potentiometric response to glucose between the bare platinum and the enzyme matrix coated platinum electrodes (Castner and Wingard 1984). The flamed and electrochemically pretreated bare platinum electrodes were studied further using ESCA (Proctor *et al.*, 1985). The thermally treated platinum contains less carbonaceous surface contamination than the electrochemically pretreated platinum; and surface oxidation is greater when done electrochemically than when done by flaming. Silicon contamination of the platinum surface, due to diffusion from within the bulk metal, is observed when the platinum is pretreated by flaming.

A present limitation with the glucose oxidase-platinum electrode concerns the reproducibility of the surface potentials. Any given platinum-glucose oxidase electrode produces a linear potentiometric response when plotted against the logarithm of the glucose concentration. However, upon repeated use, there sometimes is evidence of hysteresis when the direction of change in the glucose concentration is reversed. In addition the magnitude of the bare metal potentiometric response is difficult to maintain constant with repeated use of the electrode. Therefore, additional research is needed to establish methodology for more thorough characterization of platinum surface redox chemistry or for simple recalibration of the electrodes if potential drifting is a factor. Alternatively, a known redox couple could be attached to a potentiometrically inert electrode surface.

It probably will require considerable research before a potentiometric redox electrode can be incorporated into a viable sensor for *in vivo* use to regulate an insulin delivery system. The simplicity of design and of components also make a potentiometric redox electrode an attractive system for (1) monitoring of effluent systems or (2) monitoring and feedback control of certain fermentation reactors. However, in all of these systems where a significant quantity of substrate is reacted (i.e. glucose), a problem can develop if the supply of the second substrate (i.e. oxygen) is too low or if a mechanism for the regeneration of oxidized cofactor is not present.

Acknowledgement

This work was supported by a grant from the National Institutes of Health.

References

Adams, R. N. (1969). *Electrochemistry at solid electrodes* pp. 206–8. Marcel Dekker, New York.

Bard, A. J. and Faulkner, L. R. (1980). *Electrochemical Methods* pp. 62–72. Wiley, New York.

Castner, J. F. and Wingard Jr., L. B. (1984). Alterations in potentiometric response of glucose oxidase platinum electrodes resulting from electrochemical or thermal pretreatments of a metal surface. *Anal. Chem.* **56**, 2891–6.

Chen, A. K., Starzmann, J. A. and Liu, C. C. (1982). Potentiometric quantitation of glycerol using immobilized glycerol dehydrogenase. *Biotechnol. Bioeng.* **24**, 971–5.

Evans, J. F. and Kuwana, T. (1979). Introduction of functional groups onto carbon electrodes via treatment with radio-frequency plasmas. *Anal. Chem.* **51**, 358–65.

Hoare, J. P. (1974). In *Encyclopedia of electrochemistry of the elements*, (ed. A. J. Bard) pp. 210–38. Marcel Dekker, New York.

Irving, H. M. N. H. (1976). Recommendations for nomenclature of ion-selective electrodes. *Pure Appl. Chem.* **48**, 127–32.

Joseph, J. P. (1984). A miniature enzyme electrode sensitive to urea. *Mikrochim. Acta* **2**, 473–79.

Plambeck, J. A. (1982). *Electroanalytical chemistry: basic principles and applications* pp. 168–77. Wiley, New York.

Proctor, A., Castner, J. F., Wingard Jr., L. B. and Hercules, D. M. (1985). Electron spectroscopic (ESCA) studies of platinum surfaces used for enzyme electrodes. *Anal. Chem.* **57**, 1644–9.

Wingard Jr., L. B., Cantin, L. A. and Castner, J. F. (1983). Effect of enzyme-matrix composition on potentiometric response to glucose using glucose oxidase immobilized on platinum. *Biochim. Biophys. Acta* **748**, 21–7.

Wingard Jr., L. B., Castner, J. F., Yao, S. J., Wolfson Jr., S. K., Drash, A. L. and Liu, C. C. (1984). Immobilized glucose oxidase in the potentiometric detection of glucose. *Appl. Biochem. Biotechnol.* **9**, 95–104.

Bioelectrochemistry
(b) Amperometric sensors

11

Fundamentals of amperometric sensors

GEORGE S. WILSON

11.1 Introduction

Amperometric detection has found wide application to measurements in biological media. Under favourable conditions concentrations of 10^{-8} to 10^{-9} M can be detected and a dynamic range of three to four orders of magnitude can be readily achieved. In the context of biosensors, it is appropriate to examine some of the fundamental features of amperometry as they influence detector response.

The application of a potential between a reference and indicating electrode can give rise to a current which, in turn, may be related to the concentration of an electroactive analyte in solution. The measured current can be directly related to the rate of the electrochemical reaction occurring at the indicating (sensing) electrode. It is important, however, to identify and control the conditions which define the rate determining step of the overall electrolytic process. The rate of the heterogeneous electron transfer process (i_{CT}) occurring directly at an electrode can be controlled by variation of the applied potential according to the Butler–Vollmer equation (Bard and Faulkner 1980). Thus in many systems it is possible to choose a potential such that the current is not limited by heterogeneous electron transfer even if this process is electrochemically irreversible. If this condition is met, then the relevant rate determining step may be controlled by diffusion/mass transfer, adsorption, or chemical kinetic processes respectively. The overall sensor current, i_T, may be described by the generalized equation (11.1) below.

$$\frac{1}{i_T} = \frac{1}{i_{ID}} + \frac{1}{i_{ED}} + \frac{1}{i_{CT}} + \frac{1}{i_{AD}} + \frac{1}{i_K} + \dots \tag{11.1}$$

There are two diffusional terms, i_{ID} and i_{ED}, which define the rates of internal and external diffusion respectively. The latter relates to diffusion in bulk solution up to the electrode or a membrane/solution interface. Internal diffusion involves the movement of relevant species within a membrane or reaction layer. The overall response may be controlled by charge transfer (i_{CT}) or by the adsorption of reactants on a membrane or electrode surface (i_{AD}). The movement of analyte species from the solution to the sensor may be coupled to a chemical reaction which proceeds at a finite rate (i_K). It should be emphasized, however, that the terms in the above equation are not completely independent of each other.

11.2 Diffusion/mass transfer

Although the indicating electrode may assume a variety of different geometries, a planar configuration is illustrated schematically in Fig. 11.1. Under these conditions, a potential is applied such that species O is reduced at the electrode surface at a diffusion controlled rate. The sample concentration profile shown in Fig. 11.1 can be time dependent. Its shape will be governed both by the nature of the controlled potential perturbation of the electrode and by mass transfer through diffusion and convection. Fick's First Law,

$$- J_0(x, t) = D_0 \ \frac{\partial C_0(x, t)}{\partial x},\tag{11.2}$$

states that the flux J at the electrode surface to which the current is proportional is determined by the slope of the concentration gradient for species O at that point. This is a crucial property as it may ultimately be possible to relate this flux to solution analyte concentration.

A classical work (Levich, 1962) describes the flow of solution past surfaces and the fluxes generated through diffusion and convection. Probably the best defined and certainly the most useful configuration from the fundamental point of view is the rotating disk electrode. The simple expedient of

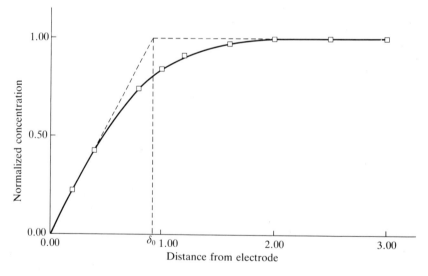

Fig. 11.1 Concentration profile for a potentiostatic experiment.

increasing the rotational speed of the electrode causes increased mass transfer and a thinner diffusion layer. The resulting steady-state current is given by the relationship

$$i_L = 0.62nFAD_0^{2/3}w^{1/2}\nu^{-1/6}C_0^b \qquad (11.3)$$

where D is the diffusion coefficient, F is the faraday (96480 $C\,mol^{-1}$), A is the electrode area, w is the rotation speed in s^{-1}, ν the kinematic viscosity in cm sec^{-1}, and C_0^b the bulk concentration. Equation 11.3 can be rewritten as

$$\frac{1}{i_T} = \frac{1}{i_N} + \frac{1}{i_L} \qquad (11.4)$$

The observed current is i_T which is partitioned between i_L, a mass transfer dependent current which varies with w, and i_N which is rotation speed independent. A plot of $1/i_T$ vs. $w^{-1/2}$ will yield an intercept of $1/i_N$. Thus the rotating disk facilitates *a priori* separations of i_N and i_L. It remains to determine the physical meaning of i_N. This approach has been used extensively for the characterization of electroactive polymer films (Andrieux *et al.* 1984).

The wall-jet electrode configuration has recently gained increasing attention and several presentations of theory have recently appeared (Dalhuijsen *et al.* 1985; Albery, 1985). This hydrodynamic configuration offers the potential advantages of improved sensitivity due to increased mass transfer efficiency and decreased sensitivity to the characteristics of the mobile phase in a flowing stream (Gunasingham 1984). The technique has been applied in HPLC (Gunasingham *et al.* 1985) and for bromine titration of proteins (Albery *et al.* 1984).

In practical applications stirring the solution increases mass transfer thus making the diffusion layer thinner and leading to higher sensitivity. This is advantageous as long as mass transfer can be reproducibly controlled. If simple diffusion is perturbed by coupled kinetic or other processes, then both the time and magnitude of the electrode response can be significantly affected. This point will be discussed further in connection with kinetic processes. Since the diffusion coefficient, D, appears in the expression for the flux, it follows that the resulting current from an electroactive biological molecule will depend on its size. The diffusion coefficient for a 'large' molecule of, for example, 150 k Daltons, is generally no less than a factor of 100 smaller than that of a typical 'small' molecule or ion. In many electro-chemical experiments the current has a fractional power dependence on D. Thus if all other factors are equal, the difference in current between a 'large' and a 'small' molecule should not be more than a factor of 10–20. Low observed currents for 'large' molecules have been attributed to diffusional effects when, in fact, they are often controlled by some other kinetic step.

Amperometric sensors are frequently covered with a protective membrane which is permselective to species of interest. The membrane serves to isolate the electrode from the biological fluid and to contain in a thin layer reagents such as enzymes essential to the detection system. Proteins from the biological medium which adsorb on the electrode and affect its response can be excluded. The membrane has two other important and not widely appreciated functions. First, it is possible for species to partition across the membrane/solution interface causing either a diminution or enhancement of response. This effect may be observed in addition to charge or molecular sieving effects. Second, the presence of a relatively thick membrane (50–1000 μm) creates a substantial diffusional barrier. If too thick, a slow response (5–10 min) can result. An advantage, however, is that the response of the sensor is unaffected by the motion (stirring) of the analyte solution because the external diffusion term of eqn 11.1 is much larger than the internal.

There is currently considerable interest in the properties of membranes which may be used to cover an electrochemical sensor. Traditionally the rate of transport of species across a membrane has been measured by placing it between two stirred solution compartments containing the component of interest at two different concentrations. From the resulting flux between the two compartments, the diffusivity may be calculated if the membrane thickness is known. Stirring conditions are often not well defined. Recently the properties of a membrane-covered rotating disk electrode (Gough and Leypoldt 1979, 1980*a*, *b*) have been used to measure membrane transport. By rotating the electrode, the ratio of the external to internal diffusion (permeability) rates can be varied. The steady-state flux across the membrane is measured by electrolysis of the diffusing species as it encounters an electrode in contact with the inner side of the membrane. The resulting current, i_d, is given by the relationship

$$i_d = i_L \left[\frac{1}{1 + P_s/P_M} \right] \tag{11.5}$$

where i_L is the current in the absence of the membrane. The permeability in the membrane phase $P_M = \alpha D_M/\delta_M$ and the permeability in the solution phase $P_s = D/\delta$ define the response. The ratio of the solution to membrane permeabilities (P_s/P_M) is called the Biot number. The mass transfer behaviour of the system is defined by the diffusion coefficients in the membrane and solution respectively, by the membrane thickness, and by the partition coefficient $\alpha = [s]_{mem}/[s]_{soln}$ of the electroactive species (s) between the membrane and solution. The rotating disk method in this form is limited to electroactive species, but in many cases these are the components of interest in biosensors. Negatively charged membrane-coated electrodes prepared by dip coating with a polymer solution such as cellulose acetate (Sittampalam and Wilson 1983; Wang and Hutchins 1985) or Nafion™

(Gerhardt *et al.* 1984; Nagy *et al.* 1985) have been shown to be effective in the selective retardation of anionic species. This is an important finding because it greatly facilitates the detection of hydrogen peroxide and positively charged neuroactive substances in the presence of large amounts of endogenous ascorbate or urate.

11.3 Heterogeneous electron transfer

In the last decade significant progress has been made in the utilization of amperometric techniques to enhance understanding of biologically relevant molecules. These include such small molecules as quinones, catecholamines, purines, flavins, thiols, and disulphides and proteins such as cytochromes, ferredoxins, and flavoproteins. All of these molecules are involved in biological redox reactions. The interested reader is referred to several monographs (Dryhurst 1977; Dryhurst, *et al.* 1982) for details. In aqueous solution pH 7, there will be an applied potential 'window' from about $+ 1.0$ to $- 0.6$ V *vs.* the normal hydrogen electrode (NHE) and if analytes are electroactive within this range, they may possibly be monitored. The major problems are electrode fouling by proteins and filming of the electrode by the product or products of the electron transfer reaction. Because of its importance as a substrate or cofactor in many enzymatic reactions of analytical interest, the oxidation of reduced nicotinamide adenine dinucleotide (NADH) has attracted considerable interest. The oxidation of this compound occurs only with difficulty and the product adsorbs on the electrode (Blankespoor and Miller 1984). For this and other systems, numerous attempts have been made to modify the electrode by heat treatment (Stutts *et al.* 1983; Wightman *et al.* 1984) by imbedding particulate metals in the surface (Kao and Kuwana 1984; Weisshaar and Kuwana 1984) or by adsorption or attachment of a chemical modifier to the surface (Stutts and Wightman 1983). It appears that the introduction of oxygen functionalities onto the surface facilitates electron transfer. Gorton *et al.* (1984) have reported that adsorption of meldola blue (7-dimethylamino-1, 2 benzophenoxazine) on graphite yields mediated electron transfer through the formation of a charge transfer complex. Lowered oxidation potentials are observed. Although results have been encouraging for the NADH system as well as others, the modified electrodes have not generally exhibited sufficient stability to be of practical utility. This area remains, nonetheless, an important one.

The case of electroactive proteins is somewhat more obscure. Under ordinary conditions, the vast majority of proteins exhibit no electroactivity even when electron transfer centres are known to be present in the molecule. There are perhaps three possible explanations for these observations. First, the protein may be irreversibly adsorbed on the electrode thus preventing further electron transfer from occurring. Second, the electroactive centre may be buried so that it cannot come in adequate contact with the electrode surface; and third, as noted above, the smaller diffusion coefficient of a macromolecule will lead to smaller currents. Strategies for direct ampero- metric detection of proteins must specifically address the first two problems. When the polyelectrolyte protein encounters the high field (10^4–10^6 V/cm) at the electrode solution interface, there is good reason to believe that the molecular structure will be significantly altered. This may result in partial or complete denaturation of the molecule. Thus reduction either of the protein or electrode surface charge should lower the energy of this interaction. Using this reasoning Armstrong *et al.* (1982) added Mg^{2+} to a solution of *Clostridium pasteurianum* ferredoxin generating a reversible wave. Apparently ion pair formation between the Mg^{2+} and the negatively charged protein lowers the overall effective molecular charge. Similar results have been observed for plastocyanin (Armstrong *et al.* 1985). In 1979 the Oxford group (Eddowes and Hill 1979) demonstrated that an electrode could be modified by adsorption of 4, 4'bipyridyl. Nearly reversible behaviour for cytochrome *c* was observed on such an electrode and subsequent studies showed that adsorption of the protein on the electrode prior to electron transfer was a requirement (Eddowes *et al.* 1981). The adsorption equilibrium is rapid and reversible and this is apparently the function of the bipyridyl electrode modifier. The bipyridyl is not electroactive at the potential of protein reduction. The third example is cytochrome c_3 (desulfovibrio vulgaris) (Niki *et al.* 1979; Hinnen *et al.* 1983; Niki *et al.* 1984). This four haem protein is irreversibly adsorbed on a bare electrode thus modifying it for further rapid and reversible electron transfer. The number of examples of rapid and direct electron transfer involving proteins is not great and therefore until suitable stable modified electrodes are available, the use of mediators appears to be the most promising approach.

Some years ago it was demonstrated that electrogenerated small molecular reactants could be used to couple biological redox couples to an electrode (Swartz and Wilson 1971; Ito and Kuwana 1971). The mediator serves to faci- litate a biological electron transfer which is favorable thermodynamically but not kinetically. This is accomplished according to the scheme

$M_O + e^- \rightleftarrows M_R$	Electrochemical	(11.6)
$B_O + e^- \rightarrow B_R$	Electrochemical	(11.7)
	(very slow reaction)	
$M_R + B_O \rightarrow M_O + B_R$	Chemical	(11.8)

where M_O and B_O are the oxidized forms and M_R and B_R are the reduced forms of the mediator and biological molecule respectively. The electrochemical process will occur at the characteristic potential of the mediator. This potential is such that reaction 11.7 would also occur were it not for unfavour- able heterogeneous electron transfer kinetics. Because M_O is regenerated close to the electrode surface as a consequence of reaction 11.8 it does not have to diffuse very far to again undergo electron transfer. Therefore a significant enhancement of the current can be observed for only a small amount of B_O present if the chemical reaction is rapid. The observed current may be related to the concentration of B_O present, and this approach has been widely employed in electro-analytical methods. The reactions of electrogenerated M_R are not very specific so care must be taken to exclude other potential oxidants which can compete with B_O. One might imagine immobilizing the mediator on the electrode or confining it in a layer near the surface.

In the development of biosensors, particularly those involving enzyme catalysed redox reactions, it would be useful to use the electrode as a 'cofactor'. The well-studied glucose oxidase system serves as an example to illustrate this point.

$$\beta\text{-D-Glucose} + E_O \rightarrow \text{Gluconic Acid} + E_R \quad (11.9)$$
$$E_R + C_O \rightarrow E_O + C_R \quad (11.10)$$

E_O and C_O are the oxidized forms and E_R and C_R the reduced forms of the enzyme and cofactor respectively. In homogeneous solution, C_O is ordinarily oxygen, C_R hydrogen peroxide. When the enzyme is immobilized to form a sensor, the objective, of course, is to obtain an amperometric response which is proportional to glucose concentration. In order for this condition to be fulfilled, reaction 11.9 must be the rate determining step. It has been demonstrated* that fluctuation in the ambient C_O (oxygen) level can significantly affect sensor response for both *in vivo* and *in vitro* measurements. If E_R could be oxidized rapidly and directly at the electrode, then oxygen variations would not be a problem. While there is some evidence that glucose oxidase can be oxidized at an electrode (Ianniello *et al.* 1982; Durliat and Comtat 1984) the rates in general appear to be neither sufficiently rapid nor reproducible to be the basis for a practical device. Kulys and co-workers (1980) first reported on the use of a conducting salt formed from the *N*-methylphenazinium (NMP$^+$) cation and the tetracyanoquinodimethane anion (TCNQ$^-$) as an electrode material for facilitating electron transfer of glucose oxidase. Recently Albery *et al.* (1985) have extended this work to include conducting salts of tetrathiafulvalene and quinoline with TCNQ. They report heterogeneous electron transfer rates of greater than 10^{-2} cm s^{-1} and electrodes which are stable for at least a month. It is argued that electron transfer is direct rather than mediated as previously suggested (Kulys *et al.* 1980). These findings are encouraging evidence that rapid direct electron transfer involving glucose oxidase is feasible. It is also possible to mediate the oxidation of E_R by electrogenerating C_O in a sequence analogous to reactions 11.9 and 11.10. The use of mediators for this purpose is the

*D. R. Thévenot (1985). Unpublished results.

subject of several other chapters in this monograph. (Davis, Chapter 14; Cardosi and Turner, Chapter 15; Aston, Chapter 16; Bennetto *et al.*, Chapter 17).

11.4 Theory of amperometric enzyme electrode response

In the optimization of electrode performance it is important to understand the factors which affect stability, dynamic range, and response time. An important consideration is the kinetic behavior of the immobilized enzyme. During the mid 1970s there was a great deal of discussion concerning the effects of immobilization on the intrinsic properties of the enzyme. If the catalytic activity of the enzyme is high, it is quite possible that the overall rate of the reaction is limited by mass transfer to the catalytic surface or layer. The parameter which describes this situation is referred to in the chemical engineering literature as the Damkoehler Number

$$D_a = \frac{V_{max}}{\left[\dfrac{D}{\delta}\right] K_M}$$

where V_{max} is the maximum rate of the homogeneous enzymatic reaction and K_M is the Michaelis constant (assuming that the enzyme obeys Michaelis–Menten kinetics). For $D_a \leqslant 0.1$ the reaction will be catalysis controlled while for $D_a \geqslant 10$ the reaction will exhibit mass transfer control. We demonstrated (Shu and Wilson, 1976) that the properties of the rotating disk electrode could be used to distinguish kinetic and mass transfer effects without having to resort to variation in enzyme loading. At a rotation speed of 1600 rpm essentially linear behaviour is observed for a Lineweaver–Burk plot suggesting that kinetic control defines the response with $D_a \approx 0.01$. K_M values similar to those for the soluble enzyme were obtained under conditions of constant (air saturated) oxygen levels. Mass transfer limitations cause the K_M values to increase, however increased oxygen concentrations result in increased K_M values for glucose. This is a consequence of the sequence given by reactions 11.9 and 11.10. The interplay between the enzyme kinetics and the fluxes of oxygen and glucose must be taken into account. Recent theoretical treatments have dealt with the importance of oxygen as a co-substrate (Leypoldt and Gough 1984; Albery and Bartlett 1985).

If an enzyme electrode were actually operated under kinetically controlled conditions, the current-concentration relationship would be non-linear and a useful range of less than one order of magnitude would be the result. However, as noted above, such sensors are operated with a membrane between the enzyme layer and the solution. This provides a barrier and a response proportional to the diffusional flux which is not limited by enzyme kinetics unless the activity of the enzyme becomes too low. This is the reason why the response of an amperometric electrode will remain constant for an extended period and then suddenly drop. As has been pointed out (Horvath and Engasser 1974), the response of the sensor will be independent of enzyme activity as long as the activity is high enough. However, the enzyme decays gradually and eventually reaches the point where the response becomes kinetically controlled. At this point, the sensor response no longer remains constant. For more detailed discussion of the theory of enzyme electrode response and the behaviour of immobilized enzymes, the reader is referred to published work (Leypoldt and Gough 1984; Albery and Bartlett 1985; Goldstein 1976; Carr and Bowers 1980). An ideal situation would be one in which a thin membrane is employed, having the properties of favouring oxygen transport over glucose so that oxygen remains in excess within the reaction layer. The development of membranes with such special properties will undoubtedly profoundly influence the development of biosensors of all types.

11.5 Electrodes and electrode geometry

Although classical electrochemical measurements of analytes in biological media were made using the dropping mercury electrode (Brezina and Zuman 1958), solid electrodes constructed of Pt, Au, and various forms of carbon have been the sensors of choice in recent years. A major limitation of solid electrodes has been the preparation of reproducible surfaces. Electrode pretreatment procedures involving polishing, heat treatment, and cycling of the electrode between several different potentials have helped both reproducibility and response. Most 'bare' electrodes, however, do not give reproducible response after extended (several hours) exposure to proteinaceous solutions. Oxygen is by far the most common analyte monitored with an amperometric biosensor, the Clark electrode is used for this purpose (Clark and Lyons 1962). The pioneering work of Adams (1969, 1976) has led to the development of *in vivo* monitoring techniques for catecholamines and other important neuroactive substances. Electrodes designed for monitoring transient neurotransmitter response in the caudate nucleus of a rat brain must not only give rapid response but must be miniaturized so that spatial resolution is possible. Wightman and co-workers (Kovach *et al.* 1985; Howell and Wightman 1984) have developed a range of micro-electrode probes constructed of carbon fibers and Pt or Au wire. Electrodes with diameters of less than 0.5 μm have been constructed. With such a small electrode area, measured currents are typically in the nanoampere range. Because the characteristic electrode area to diffusion layer thickness ratio is small, the voltammetric response differs significantly from that of larger electrodes. The resulting small currents make possible the convenient use of these electrodes for cyclic voltammetry at very high scan rates (10^3 to 10^4 V/s).

When inserted into living tissues as probes, such an electrode will sample the fluid in the 'pool' immediately surrounding the electrode.

Another extremely important electrode configuration is that of the flow through amperometric detector. The most commonly employed device consists of a thin-layer cell containing a planar electrode of Pt, Au, or glassy carbon. The counter electrode and reference electrode are located downstream. The cell resistance in this case can be quite high but again the currents are in the nanoampere range so that IR drops are usually insignificant. This configuration has been very successfully and widely employed as a detector in liquid chromatography (LCEC) (Krull *et al.* 1983). Picomole detection limits have been reported (Lin *et al.* 1984). There have been a number of fundamental investigations of the behaviour of this type of electrode with a view to optimization of response (Gunasingham and Fleet 1983; Weber, 1983). This configuration has been used primarily for *in vitro* sampling often accompanied by sample clean-up and a chromatographic separation. Thévenot and co-workers, however, have demonstrated the use of such an enzyme electrode in conjunction with an extracorporal shunt for real-time monitoring of blood glucose concentrations (see Chapter 22). The flow-through detector is normally operated at a constant DC potential although scanning is possible in some situations. The thin-layer detector is a kind of flow reactor and one can use combinations of electrodes at different potentials to selectively convert or monitor species initially present in the sample or generated electrochemically within the detector (Roston and Kissinger 1982). The detector response is flow rate dependent so it is important that this is carefully controlled, particularly at low detection limits. Pulsation of the solvent pump creates periodic variations in the signal. Under typical flow conditions 10–20% of the total electroactive material passing through the detector will be electrolysed. This usually produces a sharp peak whose height or area can be used as the basis for quantitation.

The sensitivity and selectivity of amperometric detection has made it well suited for immunoassays. This subject has been recently reviewed by Heineman and Halsall (1985). It is not generally feasible to directly detect antibodies electrochemically and thus it has been necessary to label the antibody or antigen (hapten) with an electroactive species. More commonly the activity of an enzyme, measured by determining the concentration of an electroactive product released in solution, forms the basis for an enzyme immunoassay. Because every mole of enzyme can produce in a reasonable time at least 10^3–10^4 moles of product, an amplification results. Subpicomole detection is accordingly feasible. Assays for hepatitis B surface antigen (Boitieux *et al.* 1984), α_1 acid glycoprotein (Doyle *et al.* 1984) and phenytoin (Eggers *et al.* 1982) have been reported. An *in situ* flow through immuno-reactor formed the basis for the femtomole detection of IgG (de

Alwis and Wilson 1985). This assay can be performed with a precision and accuracy of $\pm 3\%$ in less than 30 minutes.

Sensitivity of the enzyme immunoassay would be significantly enhanced if the immunosorbent were located as close to the amperometric sensor as possible. Unfortunately most immunological reactions have such large equilibrium constants that it is difficult to displace the antibody–antigen complex once formed. Ikariyama and co-workers (1985) have developed a clever system for displacement of the enzyme label from a membrane-covered electrode so that the high affinity reaction occurs in solution and not at the sensor surface. Immunosensor surfaces yielding rapid and repro-ducible response are still rare.

Many biosensors are operated at a fixed potential. This provides the significant advantage of instrumental simplicity. However, there will always be a background current which can become significant at low analyte con-centrations. Establishment of the background correction and *in vivo* calibra-tion of biosensors are two challenging problems in need of reliable solutions. Fluctuation in these parameters can be due to 'poisoning' of the electrode by components in the medium. Sensitivity and response time are both adversely affected. If the fluctuating baseline is due to variations in concentrations of endogenous electroactive interference, then a dual (differential) electrode system may be employed. This approach has been used with the glucose electrode where one electrode is coated with a glucose oxidase membrane, the other electrode membrane contains no enzyme. Electroactive impurities are presumed to diffuse through both membranes in the same fashion (Thévenot *et al.* 1979). In cases where the electrode becomes fouled by matrix contaminants or by the product of an electrode reaction, a multipulse potential step protocol has been employed (Lane and Hubbard 1976; Polta and Johnson 1983). This can serve the function of preconditioning the electrode including removal of accumulated films as well as establishing a baseline in a potential region where no electrolysis occurs. Various forms of pulse polarography have also proven useful. Cyclic or linear sweep voltammetry is particularly useful in two kinds of applications. Many of the neuroactive substances are oxidized at approximately the same potential thus making it difficult to distinguish them. The complete cyclic voltammogram reflects the chemistry of the electrolysis products which are different. This information serves as a qualitative fingerprint (Stamford *et al.* 1984) as well as a means for quantitating overlapping electrochemistry. It has been recently shown (Wang and Freiha 1984) that organic molecules of biological interest can be concentrated on a treated electrode surface. Using a linear scan the deposited analyte is stripped from the surface yielding a well-defined peak.

Amperometry provides a promising approach to the development of both *in vivo* and *in vitro* biosensors. Wide dynamic range (10^4 to 10^5) is possible thus making it generally more widely applicable than potentiometric detection. The challenge lies in efficient coupling of biospecific reactions to the electrode response. Such sensors must operate in extremely heterogeneous environments and, in the case of implantable sensors, at 37 °C.

References

Adams, R. N. (1969). *Electrochemistry at solid electrodes*. Marcel Dekker, New York.
—— (1976). Probing brain chemistry with electroanalytical techniques. *Anal. Chem.* **48**, 1126A–1138A.
Albery, W. J. (1985). The current distribution on a wall-jet electrode. *J. Electroanal. Chem.* **191**, 1–13.
—— and Bartlett, P. N. (1985). Amperometric enzyme electrodes Part I. Theory. *J. Electroanal. Chem.* **194**, 211–22.
—— and Craston, D. H. (1985). Ampèrometric enzyme electrodes Part II. Conducting salts as electrode materials for the oxidation of glucose oxidase. *J. Electroanal. Chem.* **194**, 223–35.
—— Svanberg, L. R. and Wood., P. (1984). The estimation and identification of proteins by ring-disc titration Part II. Application to liquid Chromatography. *J. Electroanal. Chem.* **162**, 45–53.
Andrieux, C. P., Dumas-Bouchiat, J. M. and Saveant, J. M. (1984). Kinetics of electrochemical reactions mediated by redox polymer films. *J. Electroanal. Chem.* **169**, 9–21.
Armstrong, F. A., Hill, H. A. O. and Walton, N. J. (1982). Direct electrochemical reduction of ferredoxin promoted by Mg^{2+}. *FEBS Lett.* **145**, 241–4.
—— Oliver, B. N. and Whitford, D. (1985). Direct electrochemistry of the photosynthetic blue copper protein plastocyanin. Electrostatic promotion of rapid charge transfer at an edge-oriental pyrolytic graphite electrode. *J. Am. Chem. Soc.* **107**, 1473–6.
Bard, A. J. and Faulkner, L. R. (1980). *Electrochemical Methods*. Wiley, New York.
Blankespoor, R. L. and Miller, L. L. (1984). Electrochemical oxidation of NADH kinetic control by product inhibition and surface coating. *J. Electroanal. Chem.* **171**, 231–41.
Boitieux, J. L., Thomas, D. and Desmet, G. (1984). Oxygen electrode-based enzyme immunoassay for the Amperometric determination of hepatitis B surface antigen, *Anal. Chim. Acta* **163**, 309–13.
Brezina, M. and Zuman, P. (1958). *Polarography in medicine, biochemistry and pharmacy*. Interscience, New York.
Carr, P. W. and Bowers, L. D. (1980). *Immobilized enzymes in analytical and clinical chemistry*. Wiley, New York.
Clark, L. C. and Lyons, C. (1962). Electrode systems for continuous monitoring in cardiovascular surgery. *Ann. N. Y. Acad. Sci.* **102**, 29–45.
Dalhuijsen, A. J., van der Meer, Th. H., Hoogendoorn, C. J. and van Bennekom, W. P. (1985). Hydrodynamic properties and mass transfer characteristics of

electrochemical flow-through cells of the confined wall-jet type. *J. Electroanal. Chem.* **182**, 295–313.

de Alwis, W. U. and Wilson, G. S. (1985). Rapid sub-picomole electrochemical enzyme immunoassay for immunoglobulin G. *Anal. Chem.* **57**, 2754–56.

Doyle, M. J., Halsall, H. B. and Heineman, W. R. (1984). Enzyme linked immunosorbent assay with electrochemical detection for α_1-acid glycoprotein. *Anal. Chem.* **56**, 2355–60.

Durliat, H. and Comtat, M. (1984). Amperometric enzyme electrode for the determination of glucose based on thin-layer spectroelectrochemistry of glucose oxidase. *Anal. Chem.* **56**, 148–52.

Dryhurst, G. (1977). *Electrochemistry of biological molecules.* Academic Press, New York.

—— Kadish, K. M., Scheller, F. and Renneberg, R. (1982). *Biological electrochemistry* Vol. I. Academic Press, New York.

Eddowes, M. J. and Hill, H. A. O. (1979). Electrochemistry of horse heart cytochrome *c*. *J. Am. Chem. Soc.* **101**, 4461–4464.

—— Albery, W. J., Hill, H. A. O. and Hillman, A. R. (1981). Mechanism of the reduction and oxidation reaction of cytochrome *c* at a modified gold electrode. *J. Am. Chem. Soc.* **103**, 3904–3910.

Eggers, H. M., Halsall, H. B. and Heineman, W. R. (1982). Enzyme immunoassay with flow amperometric detection of NADH, *Clin. Chem.* **28**, 1848–51.

Gerhardt, G. A., Oke, A. F., Nagy, G., Moghaddem, B. and Adams, R. N. (1984). Nafion-coated electrodes with high selectivity for CNS electrochemistry. *Brain Res.* **290**, 390–95.

Goldstein, L. (1976). Kinetic behaviour of immobilized enzyme systems. *Meth. Enzymol.* **44**, 397–450.

Gorton, L., Torstensson, A., Jaegfeldt, H. and Johansson, G. (1984). Electrocatalytic oxidation of reduced nicotinamide coenzymes by graphite electrodes modified with an adsorbed phenoxazinium salt, meldola blue. *J. Electroanal. Chem.* **161**, 103–20.

Gough, D. A. and Leypoldt, J. K. (1979). Membrane-covered, rotated disk electrode. *Anal. Chem.* **51**, 439–444.

—— (1980*a*). Rotated, membrane covered oxygen electrode. *Anal. Chem.* **52**, 1126–30.

—— (1980*b*). Transient studies of glucose, oxygen and hydroquinone at a membrane-covered rotated disk electrode, *J. Electrochem. Soc.* **127**, 1279–86.

Gunasingham, H. (1984). Large volume wall-jet cells as electrochemical detectors for high performance liquid chromatography. *Anal. Chim. Acta* **139**, 193–47.

—— and Fleet, B. (1983). Wall-jet electrode in continuous monitoring voltammetry. *Anal. Chem.* **55**, 1409–14.

—— Tay, B. T. and Ang, K. P. (1985). The electrolytic efficiency of amperometric detection on normal phase HPLC. *Anal. Chim. Acta* **176**, 143–50.

Heineman, W. R. and Halsall, H. B. (1985). Strategies of electrochemical immunoassay. *Anal. Chem.* **57**, 1321–31a.

Hinnen, C., Parsons, R. and Niki, K. (1983). Electrochemical and spectroreflectance studies of adsorbed horse heart cytochrome *c* and cytochrome c_3 (*D. vulgaris*, Miyazaki strain) at a gold electrode, *J. Electroanal. Chem.* **147**, 329–337.

Horvath, C. and Engasser, J. M. (1974). External and internal diffusion in hetero-geneous enzyme systems. *Biotechnol. Bioeng.* **16**, 909–23.

Howell, J. O. and Wightman, R. M. (1984). Ultrafast voltammetry and voltammetry in highly resistive solutions with microvoltammetric electrodes. *Anal. Chem.* **56**, 524–9.

Ianniello, R. M., Lindsay, T. J. and Yacynych, A. M. (1982). Differential pulse voltammetric study of direct electron transfer at glucose oxidase chemically modified graphite electrodes. *Anal. Chem.* **54**, 1098–1101.

Ito, M. and Kuwana, T. (1971). Spectroelectrochemical study of indirect reduction of triphosphopyridine nucleotide. *J. Electroanal. Chem.* **32**, 415–25.

Ikariyama, Y., Kunoh, H. and Aizawa, M. (1985). Sensitive bioaffinity sensor with metastable molecular complex receptor and enzyme amplifier. *Anal. Chem.* **57**, 496–500.

Kao, W. H. and Kuwana, T. (1984). Electrocatalysis of electrodeposited spherical Pt microparticles dispersed in a polymeric film electrode. *J. Am. Chem. Soc.* **106**, 473–6.

Krull, I. S., Bratin, K., Shoup, R. E., Kissinger, P. T. and Blank, C. C. (1983). LCEC for trace analysis: recent advances in instrumentation, methods and applications. *Am. Lab.* **15**, 57–65.

Kovach, P. M., Caudill, W. L., Peters, D. G. and Wightman, R. M. (1985). Faradaic electrochemistry at microcylinder, band and tubular band electrodes. *J. Electroanal. Chem.* **185**, 285–95.

Kulys, J. J., Samaline, A. S. and Svirmickas, G. J. S. (1980). Electron exchange between the enzyme active center and organic metal. *FEBS Lett.* **114**, 7–10.

Lane, R. F. and Hubbard, A. T. (1976). Differential double pulse voltammetry at chemically modified platinum electrodes for *in vitro* determination of catecho-lamines. *Anal. Chem.* **48**, 1287–93.

Levich, V. G. (1962). *Physiocochemical hydrodynamics*, Prentice-Hall, Englewood Cliffs. N. J. USA.

Leypoldt, J. K. and Gough, D. A. (1984). Model of a two-substrate enzyme electrode for glucose. *Anal. Chem.* **56**, 2896–2904.

Lin, P. Y. T., Bulawa, M. C., Wong, P., Lin, L., Scott, J. and Blank, C. L. (1984). The determination of catecholamines, indoleamines, metabolites, and related activities using three micron liquid chromatography columns. *J. Liq. Chrom.* **7**, 509–38.

Nagy, G., Gerhardt, G. A., Oke, A. F., Rice, M. E., Adams, R. N. and Moore, R. B., III, Szentirmay, M. N. and Martin, C. R. (1985). Ion exchange and transport of neurotransmitters in nafion films on conventional and microelectrode surfaces. *J. Electroanal. Chem.* **188**, 85–94.

Niki, K., Yagi, T., Inokuchi, H. and Kimura, K. (1979). Electrochemical behaviour of cytochrome c_3 of *Desulfovibrio vulgaris*, Strain Miyazaki, on the mercury electrode. *J. Am. Chem. Soc.* **101**, 3335–40.

—— Kobayashi, Y. and Matsuda, H. (1984). Determination of macroscopic standard potentials of a molecule with a reversible *n*-consecutive one electron transfer process. *J. Electroanal. Chem.* **178**, 333–41.

Polta, J. A. and Johnson, D. C. (1983). The direct electrochemical detection of amino acids at a platinum electrode in an alkaline chromatographic effluent. *J. Liq.*

Chromatogr. **6**, 1727–43.

Roston, D. A. and Kissinger, P. T. (1982). Series dual electrode detector for liquid chromatography/electrochemistry. *Anal. Chem.* **54**, 429–34.

Shu, F. R. and Wilson, G. S. (1976). Rotating ring-disk electrode for surface catalysis studies. *Anal. Chem.* **48**, 1679–1686.

Sittampalam, G. and Wilson, G. S. (1983). Surface modified electrochemical detector for liquid chromatography. *Anal. Chem.* **55**, 1608–10.

Stamford, J. A., Kruk, Z. L., Millar, J. and Wightman, R. M. (1984). Striatal dopamine uptake in the rat: *In-vivo* analysis by fast cyclic voltammetry. *Neurosci. Lett.* **51**, 133–8.

Stutts, K. J., Kovach, P. M., Kuhr, W. G. and Wightman, R. M. (1983). Enhanced electrochemical reversibility at heat-treated glassy carbon electrodes. *Anal. Chem.* **55**, 1632–4.

—— and Wightman, R. M. (1983). Electroanalysis of ascorbate oxidation with electrosynthesized surface-bound mediators. *Anal. Chem.* **55**, 1576–9.

Swartz, D. B. and Wilson, G. S. (1971). Small-volume coulometric redoxostat. *Anal. Biochem.* **40**, 392–400.

Thévenot, D. R., Sternberg, R., Coulet, P. R., Laurent, J. and Gautheron, D. C. (1979). Enzyme collagen membrane for electrochemical determination of glucose. *Anal. Chem.* **51**, 96–100.

Wang, J. and Freiha, B. A. (1984). Extractive preconcentration of organic compounds at carbon paste electrode. *Anal. Chem.* **56**, 849–52.

—— Hutchins, L. D. (1985). Thin-layer electrochemical detector with a glassy carbon electrode coated with a base-hydrolyzed cellulosic film. *Anal. Chem.* **57**, 1536–41.

Weber, S. G. (1983). The dependence of current on flow rate in thin-layer electrochemical detectors used in liquid chromatography. *J. Electroanal. Chem.* **145**, 1–7.

Weisshaar, D. E. and Kuwana, T. (1984). Electrodeposition of metal micro-particles in a polymer film on a glassy carbon electrode. *J. Electroanal. Chem.* **163**, 395–9.

Wightman, R. M., Deakin, M. R., Kovach, P. M., Kuhr, W. G. and Stutts, K. J. (1984). Methods to improve electrochemical reversibility at carbon electrodes. *J. Electrochem. Soc.* **131**, 1578–83.

12

Amperometric enzyme electrodes: theory and experiment

W. JOHN ALBERY and DEREK H. CRASTON

12.1 Introduction

Amperometric enzyme electrodes combine the advantages of the specificity of the enzyme for recognizing particular target molecules with the direct transduction of the rate of reaction into a current. The first generation of devices of this sort for instance the glucose electrode (Chapter 1; Clark and Lyons 1962; Guilbault and Lubrano 1973), relied on the natural enzymatic reaction:

$$\text{Glucose} + O_2 \xrightarrow{\text{GOD}} \text{Gluconolactone} + H_2O_2$$

where GOD is glucose oxidase [EC 1.1.3.4]. The electrode is merely used to measure the concentration of either the natural substrate O_2 or the product H_2O_2. This has to be a fairly complicated device with two membranes; furthermore the response of the device is affected by the ambient concentration of O_2.

More recently second generation systems have been developed (Chapters 15 and 16; Cass *et al.* 1984*a*, *b*) in which the enzyme performs the first redox reaction with its substrate, but is then reoxidized by a mediator as opposed to oxygen; the mediator in its turn is oxidized by the electrode:

$$\text{Glucose} + \text{GOD/FAD} \longrightarrow \text{Gluconolactone} + \text{GOD/FADH}_2$$
$$\text{GOD/FADH}_2 + 2M \longrightarrow \text{GOD/FAD} + 2M' + 2H^+$$

Electrode

$$2M' \longrightarrow 2M + 2e$$

In this scheme FAD represents a flavin redox centre in glucose oxidase and the mediator, M/M', has been assumed to be a one electron couple. Hill, Higgins, and co-workers (Cass *et al.* 1984*a*, *b*) have shown that various ferrocene ferrocinium couples are efficient mediators; other species such as, $[Fe(CN)_6]^{3-}$ and *N*-methylphenazinium (NMP$^+$) are also mediators.

An even simpler and more direct method is to have no mediator but to find an electrode material on which the reduced enzyme GOD/FADH$_2$ can be directly oxidized:–

180

Glucose + GOD/FAD $\longrightarrow$ Gluconolactone + GOD/FADH$_2$

Electrode

$$GOD/FADH_2 \longrightarrow GOD/FAD + 2H^+ + 2e$$

This reaction scheme is the simplest possible. Examples of this third generation of enzyme electrodes have been recently reported (Albery and Bartlett 1985; Albery *et al.* 1985). Following on from the work of Kulys and co-workers (Kulys *et al.* 1980; Cenas & Kulys 1981), it was found that the oxidation of the enzyme could be achieved using conducting organic salts such as NMP$^+$ TCNQ$^-$ as electrode materials (see also Chapter 15).

NMP$^+$ TCNQ

In developing enzyme electrodes it is important to be able to identify the rate limiting step that determines the overall performance of the device. This step could be transport of the substrate through the membrane, reaction of the substrate with the enzyme, transport of the product back through the membrane, or regeneration of the enzyme. We start therefore by developing a model for the enzyme electrode. Since the third generation electrode has the simplest reaction scheme and we wish to avoid unnecessary algebra, we will develop the model for this type of electrode. We will later extend the treatment to include second generation electrodes. We will present a simple diagnostic plot of experimental data which identifies the rate limiting step.

12.2 The model

Figure 12.1 illustrates the third generation enzyme electrode and the kinetic scheme. As regards the enzyme kinetics we assume the following model for a one substrate one product enzyme, which converts substrate S to product P, and which in the course of this conversion is itself converted from E to E':

$$S + E \underset{k_{-1}}{\overset{k_1}{\rightleftharpoons}} ES \underset{k_{-2}}{\overset{k_2}{\rightleftharpoons}} E'\,P \underset{k_{-3}}{\overset{k_3}{\rightleftharpoons}} E' + P$$

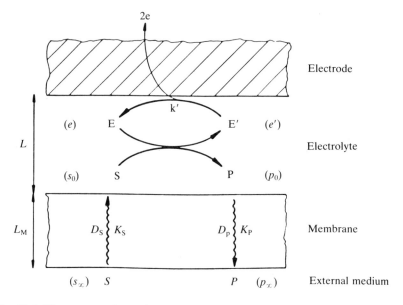

Fig. 12.1 The enzyme electrode.

For each step in the above scheme we write:

$$K_n = k_n/k_{-n}$$

and also

$$K_{TD} = K_1 K_2 K_3$$

where K_{TD} describes the overall equilibrium between S + E and P + E'.

The transport of S and P through the membrane is described by the mass transfer rate constants (Albery 1975) k'_S and k'_P where

$$k'_X = D_X K_X / L_M.$$

X is either S or P, D_X is the diffusion coefficient, K_X the partition coefficient of X in the membrane, and L_M is the thickness of the membrane. The electrode reaction, described by k', is assumed to be irreversible. All the primed rate constants are heterogeneous rate constants, usually measured in cm s^{-1}. Lower case letters are used to denote the concentrations of the different species, and for S and P the subscripts ∞ and 0 refer to the concentrations outside and inside the membrane respectively. We assume that the electrolyte layer behind the membrane is so thin ($\sim$ a few microns) that there is no concentration polarization in this layer. This case occurs most frequently in practice. We have considered elsewhere the effects of concentration polarization (Albery and Bartlett 1985).

12.3 The steady state equation

In the steady state we can write for the flux, j, (usually measured in mol cm^{-2} s^{-1}):

$$j = k'_S(s_\infty - s_0) \tag{12.1}$$
$$= L[k_1 s_0 e - k_{-1} es] \tag{12.2}$$
$$= L[k_2 es - k_{-2} e'p] \tag{12.3}$$
$$= L[k_3 e'p - k_{-3} p_\infty e'] \tag{12.4}$$
$$= k'_P(p_0 - p_\infty) \tag{12.5}$$
$$= k'e'. \tag{12.6}$$

We also have that the total concentration of enzyme, e_Σ, is given by

$$e_\Sigma = e + es + e'p + e'. \tag{12.7}$$

Elimination of the six unknowns, s_0, p_0, and the four enzyme concentrations, between eqns 12.1 to 12.7 gives:

$$\frac{e_\Sigma}{j} = \left\{1 - \frac{j}{k'_S s_\infty}\right\}\left\{\frac{1}{Lk_{cat}} + \frac{1}{k'} + \frac{K_3^{-1}(1 + K_2^{-1})}{k'}\left[p_\infty + \frac{j}{k'_p}\right]\right\}$$
$$+ \frac{1}{s_\infty}\frac{K_M}{Lk_{cat}} + \frac{K_1^{-1}K_2^{-1}K_3^{-1}}{k'}\left[p_\infty + \frac{j}{k'_p}\right]\right\} + \frac{e_\Sigma}{k'_S s_\infty} \tag{12.8}$$

where

$$\frac{1}{k_{cat}} = \frac{1}{k_2} + \frac{1}{K_2 k_3} + \frac{1}{k_3} \tag{12.9}$$

and

$$\frac{K_M}{k_{cat}} = \frac{1}{k_1} + \frac{1}{K_1 k_2} + \frac{1}{K_1 K_2 k_3}. \tag{12.10}$$

These expressions for k_{cat} and K_M/k_{cat} have been discussed by Albery and Knowles (1976). The free energy diagram in Fig. 12.2 shows how each term in eqns 12.8 to 12.10 corresponds to a possible rate limiting free energy difference in the enzyme kinetics. The advantage of the reciprocal expressions in eqns 12.8 to 12.10 is that the different possible rate limiting processes are separated in this way (Albery and Knowles 1976). We now discuss the various terms in eqn 12.8.

First there are two terms which include L. These terms can only be dominant if the enzyme kinetics is rate limiting; the first of these terms with k_{cat} corresponds to the saturated enzyme and the second terms with K_M/k_{cat} to the unsaturated enzyme. If the flux, j, becomes close to the limit imposed by transport through the membrane, $j \approx k'_S s_\infty$, then the concentration polarization means that the enzyme inside the membrane is less saturated than one

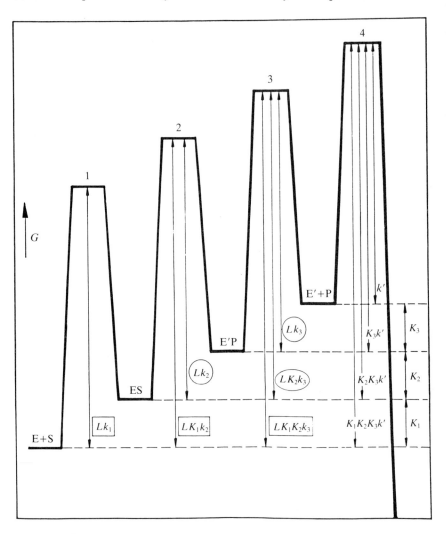

Fig. 12.2 Schematic free energy profile illustrating the free energy differences associated with each of the ten possible rate limiting terms in eqns 12.8–12.10. The three terms that make up k_{cat} in eqn 12.9 are circled and the three terms that make up k_{cat}/K_M in eqn 12.10 are boxed. The four terms in the bottom row where the reactants are E + S make up the s_∞ terms in eqn 12.8. The rest of the terms are found in the first term of eqn 12.8.

would expect from the external concentration s_∞. This effect is described by the first bracket which reduces the significance of the k_{cat} term.

Secondly the simple term k'^{-1} will be dominant if the electrode kinetics are rate limiting and if nearly all the enzyme is converted to E'; these conditions arise when the electrode kinetics are slow and there is no product inhibition. The rate constant k' occurs in the same bracket as Lk_{cat} since in either case the rate limiting step involves turnover of the enzyme. Thirdly the other two terms involving k' are also cases where the electrode kinetics are rate limiting. In the first bracket most of the enzyme is present as either ES or E'P, while in the second bracket most of the enzyme is present as E and therefore requires S to be converted to E'. These terms are larger the larger the concentration of P behind the membrane, whether this is because of the external concentration (p_∞) or because of slow transport of the generated P across the membrane (j/k_P'). This product inhibition arises because in going from E, ES, or E'P to E' and thence to the rate limiting transition state on the electrode, P has to be released. This does not apply if E' is the dominant enzyme species when one obtains the simple k'^{-1} term.

Finally we have the last term on the right of eqn 12.8. This term will dominate if the transport of S through the membrane is rate limiting. Under these condition j does not depend on the enzyme concentration; the kinetics of both the enzyme and the electrode are fast enough to consume S as soon as it passes through the membrane.

12.4 Second generation electrodes

We now extend the treatment to second generation electrodes. For these electrodes the enzyme E' is regenerated by reaction with a mediator M rather than by direct reaction on the electrode. In some cases the mediator is immobilized on the electrode surface. For this case the rate constant k' in the reaction scheme above simply describes the heterogeneous reaction of the enzyme with the immobilized mediator. Hence the same treatment applies.

Another possibility is that the mediator is present throughout the electrolyte layer. Now the k' reaction in the scheme must be replaced by a homogeneous reaction of E' with M:

$$E' + M \xrightarrow{\ k_4\ } E + M'$$

In most cases the concentration of M will be sufficiently large for its concentration to remain uniform. Then we can replace k' throughout eqn 12.8 by the equivalent rate constant describing enzyme regeneration, Lk_4m:

$$\frac{e_\Sigma}{j} = \left\{1 - \frac{j}{k_S' s_\infty}\right\}\left\{\frac{1}{Lk_{cat}} + \frac{1}{Lk_4 m} + \frac{K_3^{-1}(1 + K_2^{-1})}{Lk_4 m}\left[p_\infty + \frac{j}{k_P'}\right]\right\}$$

$$+ \frac{1}{s_\infty}\left\{\frac{K_M}{Lk_{cat}} + \frac{K_1^{-1}K_2^{-1}K_3^{-1}}{Lk_4 m}\left[p_\infty + \frac{j}{k_P'}\right]\right\} + \frac{e_\Sigma}{k_S' s_\infty} \quad (12.11)$$

The discussion of the significance of the different terms is similar to that following eqn 12.8.

In extending the treatment to second generation electrodes, we should perhaps have included the back reaction k_{-4} and the electrochemical regeneration of the mediator:

$$E' + M \underset{k_{-4}}{\overset{k_4}{\rightleftharpoons}} E + M'$$

Electrode

$$M' \xrightarrow{k'} M$$

However considering the fate of M', for the k' transition state to be higher in free energy than transition state 4 we require

$$k' < Lk_{-4}e. \tag{12.12}$$

Since k' describes an electrochemical reaction of a small mediator molecule, the reaction can be driven by the electrode potential, and we can assume that $k' > 0.1$ cm s^{-1}. With typical values for L of 10^{-2} cm and for e of 10^{-4} mol dm^{-3} we find that the inequality in eqn 12.12 can only be satisfied if k_{-4} is greater than 10^5 dm^3 mol^{-1} s^{-1}. Values of k_{-4} are seldom documented but can be calculated from the known values of k_4 and the difference between the standard reduction potentials of the enzyme and mediator respectively. It is found that even if the rate of the forward reaction is diffusion controlled ($\sim 10^9$ dm^3 mol^{-1} s^{-1}) a difference in the E° values of greater than 250 mV will lead to values of k_{-4} of less than 10^5 dm^{-3} mol^{-1} s^{-1}. In practice the values of k_4 are less than this and generally mediators are chosen with sufficient difference in E° so as to allow the reaction to go to completion. Hence we are unlikely to find examples where we have to have the more complicated reaction scheme. This is just as well since the algebra for the more complicated scheme is formidable.

12.5 NADH electrodes

Over 250 enzymes use the ubiquitous cofactor NAD$^+$/NADH. The conducting organic salts are excellent electrodes for the efficient oxidation of NADH (Kulys 1981; Albery and Bartlett 1984). This finding allows us to develop a family of second generation electrodes in which the enzyme turnover is followed by the regenerative oxidation of NADH to NAD$^+$ (Chapter 15). The reaction scheme for a substrate SH$_2$ is:

$$SH_2 + NAD^+ \xrightarrow{Enzyme} S + NADH + H^+$$

$$NADH \xrightarrow[\text{Electrode}]{NMP^+\ TCNQ^-} NAD^+ + H^+ + 2e$$

As regards the detailed enzyme kinetics we assume the following model for a one substrate one product enzyme, which converts substrate S to product P, using the $NAD^+/NADH$ cofactor. We assume that there is sufficient NAD^+ present so that the concentration of free enzyme, E, is much smaller than the concentration of enzyme bound to NAD^+, $ENAD^+$. We also assume that the kinetics of the binding of the enzyme to NAD^+ is sufficiently rapid so that equilibrium is established between E and $ENAD^+$ with a binding constant of K_0:

$$S + E.NAD^+ \underset{k_{-1}}{\overset{k_1}{\rightleftharpoons}} S.E.NAD^+ \underset{k_{-2}}{\overset{k_2}{\rightleftharpoons}} P.E.NADH \underset{k_{-3}}{\overset{k_3}{\rightleftharpoons}} E + NADH + P + H^+$$

$$E + NAD^+ \rightleftharpoons E.NAD^+ \quad K_0$$

Electrode

$$NADH \xrightarrow{k'} NAD^+ + H^+ + 2e$$

For this scheme we have

$$K_{TD} = K_0 K_1 K_2 K_3$$

where K_{TD} describes the overall equilibrium between $S + NAD^+$ and $P + NADH + H^+$.

We then follow a similar argument to that used above, to obtain the following expression for j:

$$\frac{e_\Sigma}{j} = \frac{1}{Lk_{cat}}\left[1 - \frac{j}{k_S' s_\infty}\right] + \frac{K_M}{Lk_{cat} s_\infty} + \frac{je_\Sigma}{k_p' k' K_{TD} s_\infty [NAD^+]} +$$

$$\frac{j^2}{Lk_p' k' K_{TD} s_\infty [NAD^+]}\left[\frac{1}{k_{-1}} + \frac{K_2}{k_{-1}} + \frac{1}{k_{-2}}\right] + \frac{e_\Sigma}{k_S' s_\infty} \quad (12.13)$$

To simplify the expression, we have assumed that the external product concentration, p_∞, is zero. Comparing this expression with eqn 12.8, we find that the enzyme kinetic terms in k_{cat} and K_M/k_{cat} and the substrate transport term in k_S' are the same. This is not surprising since the reaction schemes are identical up to the point where the product is released. For the third generation scheme the k' step on the electrode is one of the sequence of transition states that the enzyme has to cross in each cycle. Hence the k' terms in eqn 12.8 behave like an additional transition state in the saturated and unsaturated parts of the expression. For the NADH electrode, the enzyme E on its release is regenerated by the rapid binding of NAD^+. However the electrochemical turnover of the NADH can be rate limiting. If the third term in eqn 12.13 is dominant then the enzyme concentration, e_Σ, cancels out and the flux, j, does not depend on L the thickness of the electrolyte layer. Remembering that the product concentration, p, is given by j/k_p', we find that the flux is given simply by:

$$j \approx k'[\text{NADH}]_{eq}$$

where $[\text{NADH}]_{eq}$ is the equilibrium concentration of NADH for the particular substrate, product, and NAD^+ conentrations. Under these circumstances the enzyme system is a rapid pre-equilibrium and the rate limiting process is the electrochemical turnover of the NADH.

What about the remaining term, the fourth term in eqn 12.13? At first sight these terms are rather puzzling. They have a mixture of enzyme and electrochemical kinetics and each term seems to depend on a backward going rate constant! In fact these terms really describe the cycling of the enzyme. In the third generation scheme we assumed that the electrochemical k' step was irreversible, so each cycle of the enzyme was cleanly separated by the k' step. In the present scheme the enzyme does not participate in an irreversible step; the NADH is destroyed on the electrode. So now we must not assume that each enzyme cycle starts and ends with E.NAD^+. Like a stage army we must join up the cycles to form a continuous sequence and then look for the biggest barrier. Remembering that, as before, $p = j/k_p'$ and that $[\text{NADH}] = j/k'$, we can interpret the fourth term in eqn 12.13 as shown in the free energy profiles in Fig. 12.3. The backward rate constants arise, because it is more economical to express the free energy difference as the quotient of the full equilibrium constant, K_{TD}, and the backward rate constant rather than the more complicated expression for the forward rate constant. The electrochemical rate constant arises because NADH is released on going to the rate limiting transition state, and the concentration of NADH will depend on the electrode kinetics. It is interesting that eqn 12.13 shows that, depending on which term is dominant, one may find that j varies with $[S]$, $[S]^{1/2}$ or even $[S]^{1/3}$.

In deriving expressions to describe the kinetics of enzyme electrodes, we emphasize the importance first of expressing the result in the reciprocal form, and secondly of interpreting the expression in terms of free energy diagrams. We have used both approaches to good advantage in our work on homogeneous enzyme kinetics (Albery and Knowles 1976; Albery *et al.* 1986).

12.6 No product inhibition

Equations 12.8, 12.11, and 12.13 are complicated equations in j; in our view little insight can be obtained by attempting to solve cubic and quartic equations. It is however unlikely that for any real system all the terms in a particular equation will be significant. The important application of our analysis is the identification of the rate limiting process. When we take the cases where there is no product inhibition, we find that eqns 12.8, 12.11, and

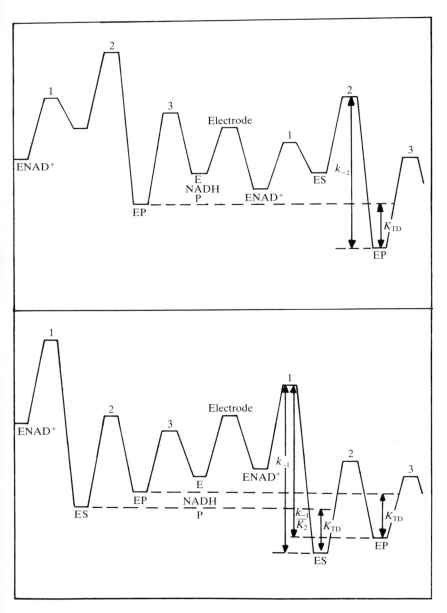

Fig. 12.3 Schematic free energy profile illustrating the fourth term in eqn 12.3. In the top case the k_{-2} term is dominant and the response is controlled by a combination of the equilibrium constant between EP and ES and the rate constant k_2. In the lower case the dominant term is k_{-1}, and the response is controlled by the equilibrium between ES and ENAD$^+$ and the rate constant k_1. In the case where k_1/K_2 is dominant the response is controlled by a combination of the equilibrium between EP and ENAD$^+$ and the rate constant k_1.

12.13 all have the same form, so that our treatment will apply to a wide range of enzyme electrodes.

We will work with eqn 12.8. We start by rearranging it into a form which is similar to a Hanes plot (Hanes 1932) for the analysis of Michaelis–Menten kinetics:

$$\frac{S_\infty}{j} = \frac{1}{k'_{ME}}\left[1 + \frac{S_\infty}{K_{ME}}\left\{1 - \frac{j}{k'_S S_\infty}\right\}\right]. \tag{12.14}$$

In this equation we have introduced the effective electrochemical rate constant for the enzyme electrode at low substrate concentrations, k'_{ME} where

$$1/k'_{ME} = K_M/(e_\Sigma L k_{cat}) + 1/k'_S. \tag{12.15}$$

We have introduced a similar parameter in our treatment of modified electrodes (Albery and Hillman 1981, 1984) and indeed the K_M term corresponds to the layer case of that treatment. Depending on which is the slower, the effective electrochemical rate constant will be determined by either the enzyme kinetics, the K_M/k_{cat} term, or by the transport of the substrate through the membrane, the k'_S term. Again note the reciprocal form.

Secondly we have introduced into eqn 12.14 the equivalent of the Michaelis constant for the enzyme electrode, K_{ME} where

$$K_{ME} = \frac{K_M(Lk_{cat})^{-1} + e_\Sigma(k'_S)^{-1}}{(Lk_{cat})^{-1} + (k')^{-1}}. \tag{12.16}$$

The significance of K_{ME} is similar to that of the Michaelis constant in homogenous enzyme kinetics. For concentrations smaller than K_{ME} the system is unsaturated, the current is proportional to the concentration of substrate and is governed by the rate constant k'_{ME}. For concentrations greater than K_{ME} the system becomes saturated and the flux reaches a maximum value. This flux can be characterized by the equivalent of k_{cat}:

$$(k'_{cat, E})^{-1} = (Lk_{cat})^{-1} + (k')^{-1} = e_\Sigma/j_{max}. \tag{12.17}$$

Because $k'_{cat, E}$ describes a flux per unit area, it has the usual dimensions (cm s^{-1}) of an electrochemical rate constant. Again the reciprocal form shows that depending on which is the smaller the observed $k'_{cat, E}$ will be either determined by the saturated enzyme kinetics, k_{cat}, or by the electrochemical regeneration, k'.

From eqns 12.15 to 12.17 we find,

$$k'_{cat, E}/K_{ME} = k'_{ME}/e_\Sigma. \tag{12.18}$$

For an enzyme electrode under unsaturated conditions, this equation relates the kinetic description used by enzyme kineticists (k_{cat}/K_M) to the electrochemical rate contant (k') used by electrochemists.

The first stage of the analysis is to find k'_{ME} by plotting s_∞/j against s_∞. Equation 12.14 shows that this may be a curve but the limiting value as $s_\infty \to 0$ gives $[s_\infty/j]_0 = (k'_{ME})^{-1}$. Next for values of s_∞/j significantly greater than $[s_\infty/j]_0$ we calculate values of ρ where

$$\rho = [j/s_\infty]/[j/s_\infty]_0 \leqslant 1. \tag{12.19}$$

Substitution in eqn 12.14 gives

$$y = \frac{\rho^{-1} - 1}{s_\infty} = \frac{1}{K_{ME}} \left[1 - \frac{\rho k'_{ME}}{k'_S} \right]. \tag{12.20}$$

Equation 12.20 predicts that plots of y against ρ should be straight lines. From the intercept on the y axis we can find the Michaelis constant for the electrode, K_{ME}. From the intercept ρ_0 on the x axis we can determine the relative importance of enzyme kinetics and transport kinetics in the observed rate constant k'_{ME}. From eqns 12.15 and 12.20 we find that:

$$k'_S = \rho_0 k'_{ME} \tag{12.21}$$

and

$$k_{cat} e_\Sigma L / K_M = \rho_0 k'_{ME}/(\rho_0 - 1). \tag{12.22}$$

If the value of ρ_0, the intercept on the x axis, is unity, then the transport of S across the membrane is cleanly rate limiting. If on the other hand, a horizontal line is found, corresponding to $\rho_0 = \infty$, then the unsaturated enzyme kinetics are rate limiting. Hence the y/ρ plot is a valuable diagnostic plot. Examples of its application are given below.

Figure 12.4 shows typical j versus s_∞ curves, Hanes plots, and plots of eqn 12.20 for different values of k'_{ME}/k'_S. It is interesting that for the case where transport across the membrane is cleanly rate limiting, we obtain a sharp dog leg plot of flux against concentration of substrate. This arises because under these conditions neither of the two rate limiting processes, transport or enzyme turnover under saturated conditions, depends on the internal substrate concentration, s_0; hence the flux is simply limited by the slower of the two processes. In this section we have considered the cases where there is no product inhibition. Elsewhere (Albery and Bartlett 1985) we have considered the effects of product inhibition and have discussed the different types of diagnostic plot that one obtains for these cases.

12.7 Sensitivity versus concentration range

When the kinetic parameters have been determined, and the rate limiting step identified then one is in a much better position to optimize the design of an enzyme electrode. In particular an important design feature is the permeability or otherwise of the membrane to the substrate. There are two

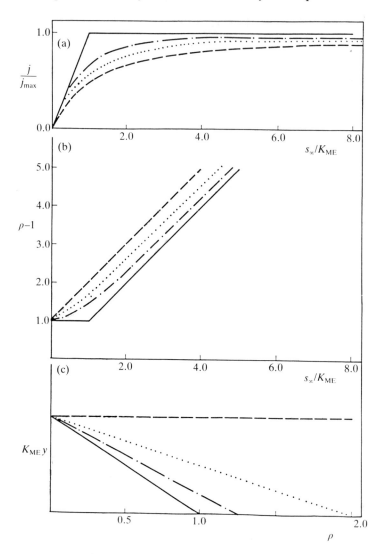

Fig. 12.4 (a) Shows typical plots of flux against substrate concentration for different values of k'_{ME}/k'_{SS} for the case where there is no product inhibition. For these curves, (b) and (c) show the corresponding Hanes plots and plots of eqn 12.20 respectively. The values of k'_{ME}/k'_{S} are as follows:——1.00; — •—0.80; ....0.5; ———— 0.00.

advantages to making the transport of the substrate through the membrane rate limiting. First the response of the electrode then depends on the transport characteristics of the substrate in the membrane. The response does not depend on the enzyme kinetics nor on the electrochemical kinetics. Since both

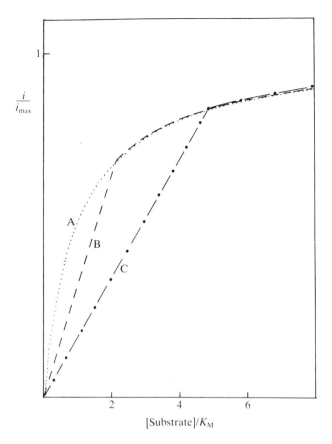

Fig. 12.5 The effect that varying the permeability of the membrane has on the theoretical current response of an enzyme electrode to increasing concentration of substrate. In A the enzyme kinetics are rate limiting, while B and C show the effect of using less and less permeable membranes.

can be unreliable, this is good. Secondly the range of concentration over which the enzyme responds is extended. If enzyme kinetics are rate limiting then the enzyme saturates when the concentration of the substrate is somewhat larger than K_M. However if transport kinetics are rate limiting, a linear response of current to concentration may be obtained for substrate concentration levels that are much in excess of K_M.

This point is illustrated in Fig. 12.5. The different schematic curves show the effect of putting on less and less permeable membranes. In A the membrane is very permeable and enzyme kinetics are rate limiting. In B and C the transport kinetics have become successively slower and at low concentrations the transport kinetics are rate limiting. The dog leg response curves give successively higher values of the electrode Michaelis constant K_{ME}. Of course the thicker membranes mean that there is less current at low concentrations. So if sensitivity is all important then it is best to use as permeable a membrane as possible. But if one has plenty of current then it is sensible to use a membrane that makes the transport of the substrate rate limiting. So far in all of our work we have used membranes prepared from dialysis tubing. Optimization through the proper design of the membrane will become increasingly important.

12.8 Conducting organic salt electrodes

We have investigated a number of different conducting organic salts for use as enzyme electrodes (Albery *et al.* 1985). The donors and acceptors are given in Table 12.1. Many of these materials were first prepared by Melby and co-workers (Melby 1965; Melby *et al.* 1962) and their electrochemistry has been investigated by Jaeger and Bard (1979, 1980). Nearly all the salts we have made show electrochemical activity with glucose oxidase. This finding some-

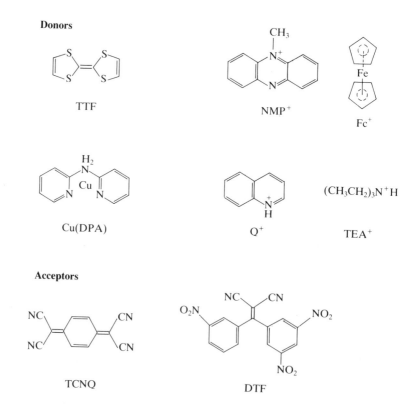

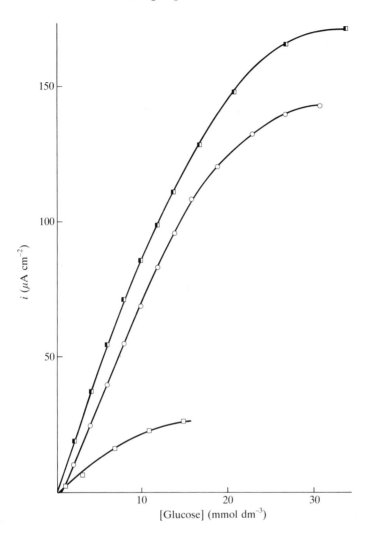

Fig. 12.6 Typical results for currents from membrane electrodes with increasing glucose concentration. The three electrode materials were TTF^+ $TCNQ^-$ (■), NMP^+ $TCNQ^-$ (○), Q^+ $(TCNQ)_2^-$ (□).

what surprised us, since we had thought that there would have to be rather specific interactions between the surface and the enzyme to obtain efficient electron transfer. In fact it turns out that these materials are good electrocatalysts for a number of different flavoproteins. The reason for the ubiquity of this behaviour will be discussed below.

Our preliminary work showed that the three most suitable materials with respect to background currents, and voltage range were the TCNQ salts of

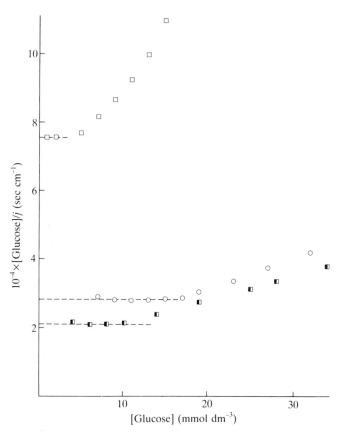

Fig. 12.7 Hanes plots of the data in Fig. 12.6. The three electrode materials were TTF$^+$ TCNQ$^-$ (■), NMP$^+$ TCNQ$^-$ (○), Q$^+$ (TCNQ)$_2^-$ (□).

TTF$^+$, NMP$^+$, and Q$^+$. Membrane electrodes were therefore made of these three materials. The current from these electrodes was measured as the glucose concentration in the external solution was increased. Typical results are shown in Fig. 12.6. The data in this figure are analysed by the procedure presented above.

The first stage of the analysis is to make a Hanes plot [see eqn 12.14] of nFA[Glucose]/i against [Glucose]. To compensate for the different areas of the electrode, we carry out the analysis in terms of the current densities (i/A). These plots are shown in Fig. 12.7. The intercepts at zero concentration is the reciprocal of the electrochemical rate constant, k'_{ME}, defined in eqn 12.15. Values of k'_{ME} are collected in Table 12.2.

Next the parameter ρ (eqn 12.19) is calculated where

$$\rho = i/nFAk'_{ME}[\text{Glucose}]$$

Table 12.2 Results for membrane electrodes

Electrode material	$k'_{ME}{}^{a}$ (cm s^{-1})	$K_{ME}{}^{b}$ (mmol dm^{-3})	$k'_{cat, E}{}^{c}$ (cm s^{-1})
TTF$^+$ TCNQ$^-$	4.7×10^{-5}	20	9×10^{-2}
NMP$^+$ TCNQ$^-$	3.0×10^{-5}	22	8×10^{-2}
Q$^+$ TCNQ$^-$	1.3×10^{-5}	11	1.4×10^{-2}

[a] Calculated from eqn 12.14.
[b] Calculated from eqn 12.20.
[c] Calculated from eqn 12.18.

and from eqn 12.20 y is plotted against ρ. Plots for the three electrodes are shown in Fig. 12.8. In each case good straight lines are obtained, showing the success of the analysis. The fact that in each case ρ_0, the intercept on the x axis, is equal to unity shows, as discussed above (eqns 12.21 and 12.22), that at low substrate concentrations the rate limiting step is the diffusion of glucose through the membrane. The subsequent enzyme and electrode steps are so fast that they are not rate limiting. This is the most desirable condition for a reliable sensor, since the enzyme and electrochemical kinetics do not affect the response of the sensor. As long as this condition is maintained any decay in the enzyme or electrode activity has no effect.

The results in Fig. 12.6 show that glucose concentrations can be determined in the range 50 μmol dm^{-3} to 10 mmol dm^{-3}. The fact that the transport of the glucose through the membrane is rate limiting explains why the values of k'_{ME} in Table 12.2 are all so similar and do not depend on the electrode material. The value of L_M, the thickness of the membrane, is 0.3 mm. Substitution in eqn 12.10 gives values for $K_S D_S$ of the order of 10^{-6} cm^2 s^{-1}. These values are in good agreement with that found by Gough and Leypoldt (1980), who used a rotating disc electrode method to measure the transport properties of a similar membrane.

Returning to Fig. 12.8, from the intercepts and eqn 12.20 we can calculate values of k_{ME}. Results from all our experiments are collected in Table 12.2. We can now explore the rate limiting process when the enzyme electrode is saturated, and its behaviour is determined by $k'_{cat, E}$ defined in eqn 12.17. Values of $k'_{cat, E}$ are collected in Table 12.2.

The two terms of eqn 12.17 describe saturated enzyme and electrochemical kinetics. The ratio of these two terms can be found from a knowledge of K_{ME}, K_M, and the ratio k'_S/k'_{ME} which is determined from plots of eqn 12.20. From eqns 12.15 and 12.16 we obtain:

$$\frac{k_{cat} L}{k'} = \frac{K_M}{K_{ME}(1 - k'_{ME}/k'_S)} - 1 \tag{12.23}$$

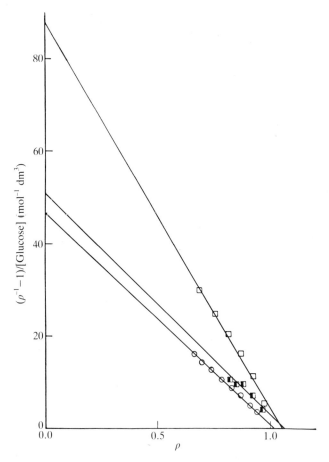

Fig. 12.8 Plots of eqn 12.20 from the data in Fig. 12.7. The three electrode materails were TTF$^+$ TCNQ$^-$ (■), NMP$^+$ TCNQ$^-$ (○), Q$^+$ (TCNQ)$_2^-$ (□).

The literature value for K_M is 7 mmol dm^{-3} (Cardosi 1984). The values of K_{ME} in Table 12.2 are about 5 mmol dm^{-3}. Within experimental error we have found that for all three materials k'_{ME} is equal to k'_S. We can conclude therefore that the bracket in the denominator of eqn 12.15 is smaller than 0.1. We then find that

$$k_{cat}L/k' > 10. \tag{12.24}$$

Hence we can conclude that the rate limiting process in the saturated region is the electrode kinetics and not the enzyme kinetics. The electrochemical rate constants, k', for the three materials are given by the values of $k'_{cat, E}$ in Table 12.2. With a value for k_{cat} of 800 s^{-1} (Wiebel and Bright 1971) and with a value for L of several tens of microns, we find that, in accord with our analysis, the inequality in eqn 12.16 is indeed satisfied. It is very satisfactory that the three materials in Table 12.2 are indeed excellent electrocatalysts for the direct oxidation of glucose oxidase with electrochemical rate constants, k', which are all greater than 10^{-2} cm s^{-1}.

12.9 Electrochemical mechanism

It should be admitted that there has been some controversy as to whether the enzyme is oxidized by direct electron transfer on the electrode surface or whether there is a mediated electron transfer; in the latter case dissolved TTF$^+$ and or TCNQ$^-$ reacts with the enzyme in the electrolyte and then these species are reoxidized on the electrode. Cenas and Kulys (1980) have claimed that the reaction of glucose oxidase on NMP$^+$ TCNQ$^-$ takes place by the mediated mechanism. However, as argued elsewhere in greater detail (Albery *et al.* 1985), we do not find their arguments convincing. Using a ring-disc electrode we have tried to measure the amount of dissolved NMP$^+$ or TCNQ$^-$ in the vicinity of the electrode. Thanks be to God we failed. The concentrations must be significantly less than 1 μmol dm^{-3}. Coupling these concentrations with the homogeneous second order rate constants of the order of 10^4 dm^3 mol^{-1} s^{-1}, measured by Cenas and Kulys, we find that in no way could the homogeneous mediated mechanism give the large values of $k'_{cat, E}$ reported in Table 12.2. The salts are just too insoluble and the homogeneous kinetics too sluggish for the mediated transfer to be an efficient mechanism.

It is interesting to speculate as to why the conducting organic salts are such good electrocatalysts for flavoproteins. We have found that many of these enzymes are strongly adsorbed onto the electrode surface. So much so that one can make a sensor without a membrane. All one has to do is to dip the electrode into a solution of the enzyme, wash off the excess, and the electrode is ready. The adsorbed layer is so strongly held that it is not lost from the surface, even when there is no enzyme in the adjacent solution. The reason for this strong attraction may arise from the fact that the conducting salt consists of alternate stacks of positive and negative ions. A patchwork of positive and negative charges on the surface could be expected to interact strongly with a corresponding patchwork on the enzyme surface. Others prefer to invoke the hydrophobic interaction between the enzyme and the aromatic surface of the electrode. We have shown (Albery *et al.* 1981) the importance of attractive interactions for the catalysis of biological electron transfer. We certainly have such interactions between the flavoprotein enzymes and the conducting salts.

12.10 Electrode stability

Furthermore the stability of these electrode is excellent. A membrane electrode was run continuously for 28 days. The results are shown in

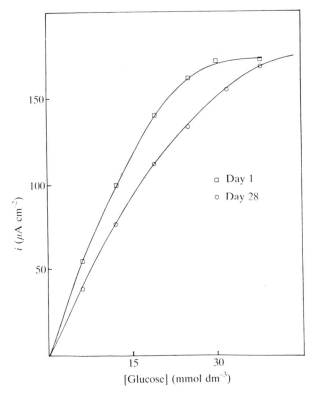

Fig. 12.9 Current response of a glucose enzyme electrode on the day of its fabrication, and the same electrode after 28 days of continuous use.

Fig. 12.9. At the end of the month the sensor had lost only 20% of its original activity. Kinetic analysis, like that presented above, showed that transport of the substrate through the membrane was still the rate limiting step, so that the slight loss of activity must be caused by deterioration of the membrane. Again the importance of knowing that in this case the response is membrane limited is stressed.

12.11 Other enzymes

So far we have concentrated on the glucose oxidase system, but other enzymes will react on these electrodes. Of the different materials we have investigated (Albery *et al.* 1985), the salt $TTF^+ TCNQ^-$, had the lowest background current and is therefore our material of choice. We can now report results for the use of this electrode material with four other enzyme systems containing the flavin prosthetic group, FAD. In each case the reduced enzyme can be directly oxidized on the electrode. Details of the enzymes and

Table 12.3 Enzyme substrate systems

Enzyme	Xanthine oxidase (EC 1.2.3.2)	D-Amino acid oxidase (EC 1.4.3.3)	L-Amino acid oxidase (EC 1.4.3.2)	Choline oxidase (EC 1.1.3.17)
Activity (μ/mg)	1.25	14	0.44	50
Substrate	Xanthine	D-Alanine	Phenylalanine	Betaine aldehyde
pH	7.4	8.0	6.5	7.4
Buffer (0.1 M)	Phosphate	Tris	Phosphate	Phosphate

substrates are given in Table 12.3. For each enzyme a membrane electrode responded to increasing concentration of its substrate. Figure 12.10 shows typical results for all four systems. These curves are analysed according to the treatment presented above. Figures 12.11–12.13 show the y/ρ plots of eqn 12.20 for xanthine oxidase and D and L amino acid oxidase respectively. In all three cases straight lines are obtained which pass through $+1$ on the x axis. This behaviour shows that transport of the substrate across the membrane is rate limiting. Hence we can conclude that, like glucose oxidase, these three enzyme/TTF^+ $TCNQ^-$ electrode combinations have sufficiently fast kinetics to handle all of each of their substrates which diffuses through the membrane.

Values of k_S' are reported in Table 12.4. It can be seen that for these three enzymes the values are very similar and close to that observed for glucose oxidase. This is not surprising. For dialysis membrane we expect K_S to be

Table 12.4

	$[k_S']$/cm s^{-1}	$[K_{ME}]$/mmol dm^{-3}	$[k]$ (cm s^{-1})
Xanthine oxidase	1.1×10^{-4}	0.2	3.7×10^{-4}
D-Amino acid oxidase	2.6×10^{-5}	1.1	2.4×10^{-4}
L-Amino acid oxidase	2.8×10^{-5}	2.6	4.6×10^{-2}
Choline oxidase	2.8×10^{-4}	1.8	3.0×10^{-3}

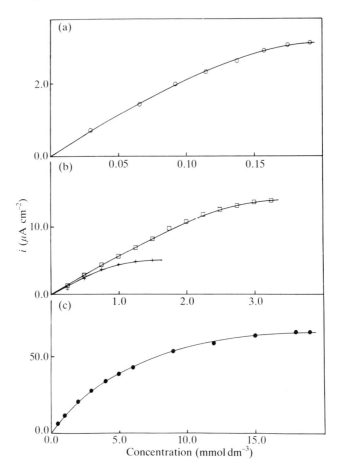

Fig. 12.10 Typical results for current with increasing substrate concentration using (a) xanthine oxidase [○], (b) D-amino acid oxidase (+), L-amino acid oxidase (□), and (c) choline oxidase [●] enzyme electrodes. The electrode material in each case was $TTF^+ TCNQ^-$.

close to unity and hence the different values of k_S' for the different substrates reflect the differences in the diffusion coefficients. For similarly sized substrates these are unlikely to be large.

From the intercepts on the y axis of the y against ρ plots in Figs 12.11–12.13, we can use eqn 12.20 to find K_{ME}. As in our previous work on glucose oxidase, we interpret these results as being caused by the interplay of substrate transport and the electrode kinetics of the enzyme, where

$$K_{ME} = k'e_\Sigma/k'_{ME} \tag{12.25}$$

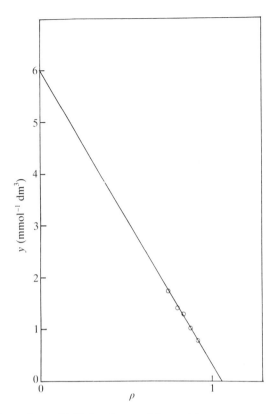

Fig. 12.11 Plots of eqn 12.20 for the xanthine oxidase enzyme electrode using the data in Fig. 12.10.

and k' describes the electrode kinetics of the enzyme. Values of the electrochemical rate constant k' are reported in Table 12.4. It can be seen that these electrochemical rate constants are all greater than 10^{-4} cm s^{-1}. These large values show once again the advantage of using organic conductors as electrode materials for enzymes.

Turning to choline oxidase, the system is somewhat complicated because the product of the enzymatic oxidation of choline is betained aldehyde, which is itself a substrate for the enzyme. In order to simplify the analysis, we have used betaine aldehyde as the substrate for the enzyme electrode. The y/ρ plot is shown in Fig. 12.14. It can be seen in this case that the straight line passes through approximately $+2$ on the x axis as opposed to $+1$ in the previous cases. A value of $+2$ for ρ_0 in eqns 12.20 and 12.21 shows that in this case there is an equal contribution from the enzyme and transport terms to the observed rate constant k'_{ME}. Again the value of k'_S, calculated from eqn 12.21 and reported in Table 12.4, is similar to the values for the other

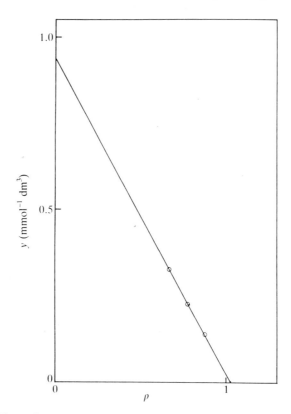

Fig. 12.12 Plots of eqn 12.20 for the D-amino acid oxidase enzyme electrode using the data in Fig. 12.10.

substrates. A value of the electrochemical rate constant, k', can be found by the same procedure as discussed above and is reported in Table 12.4. Again it is satisfactory that the value is as large as 10^{-3} cm s^{-1}.

12.12 NADH electrodes

We now turn to a different strategy in which we use the same type of electrode material together with enzymes that use the ubiquitous cofactor NAD$^+$/NADH. We have found that the electrochemical rate constant for the oxidation of NADH at an electrode made of the conducting organic salt NMP$^+$ TCNQ$^-$ was as large as 10^{-2} cm s^{-1} (Albery and Bartlett 1984). Using this material we have developed an enzyme electrode, which uses yeast ethanol dehydrogenase (EC 1.1.1.1.) to oxidize a number of different alcohols such as ethanol, butan-1-ol, and propan-2-ol. The reaction scheme has been discussed above.

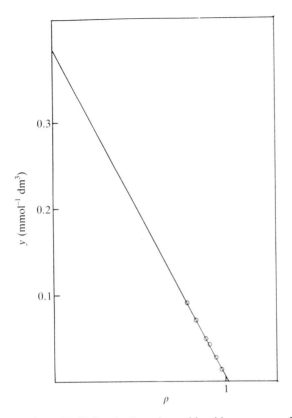

Fig. 12.13 Plots of eqn 12.20 for the L-amino acid oxidase enzyme electrode using the data in Fig. 12.10.

Typical results for the increase in current with increasing ethanol concentration are shown in Fig. 12.15. Application of the usual analysis gives the y/ρ plot shown in Fig. 12.16. In this case a horizontal straight line is obtained. This corresponds to ρ_0 equal to infinity and from eqns 12.21 and 12.22 we find in this case that the enzyme kinetics are rate limiting. The fact that a straight line is obtained also allows us to conclude that the more complicated j and j^2 terms on the right hand side of eqn 12.13 are not significant; eqn 12.13 has reduced to the simple form. Indeed we find that there is no drop in current when the product acetaldehyde is added to the external solution. This means that the saturated behaviour in this case is not governed by the electrochemical kinetics, but by the saturated enzyme kinetics. In keeping with this conclusion the value of K_{ME} of 7.7 mmol dm^{-3} measured from the intercept on the y axis of the data in Fig. 12.16 is in good agreement with literature values for K_M of 13 mmol dm^{-3} (Barman 1969) and 13.1 mmol dm^{-3} (Mazid and Laidler 1982). When enzyme kinetics determines both the

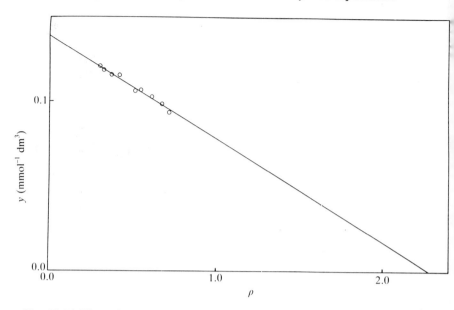

Fig. 12.14 Plots of eqn 12.20 for the choline oxidase enzyme electrode using the data in Fig. 12.10.

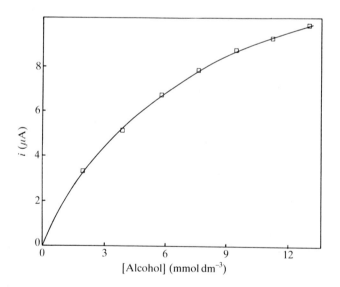

Fig. 12.15 Current response of an alcohol enzyme electrode with increasing concentrations of ethanol.

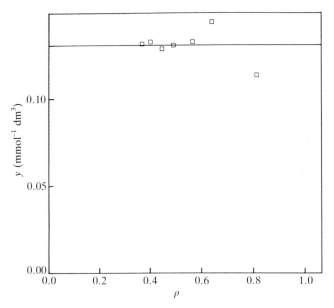

Fig. 12.16 Plots of eqn 12.20 from the data in Fig. 12.15.

unsaturated and saturated behaviour then $K_{ME} = K_M$. Hence the behaviour of this enzyme electrode where enzyme kinetics are always rate limiting may be contrasted with that of the glucose oxidase electrode where enzyme kinetics are never rate limiting.

The advantage of having a good electrode for the oxidation of NADH is that by efficiently scavenging the NADH the electrode reduces its concentration so that one does not get the dreaded back reaction, product inhibition and the j and j^2 terms in eqn 12.13. We estimate that at our current densities the ambient concentration of NADH is as low as 10 μmol dm^{-3}. The electrode helps to drive the reaction forward by destroying the NADH. A large value of k' can compensate for a small value of K_{TD} in the denominators of the product inhibition terms in eqn 12.13.

12.13 Summary

We have seen how different types of behaviour can be elucidated with the y/ρ plot of eqn 12.20. This plot allows us to determine K_{ME} and ρ_0. The determination of these two parameters together with a knowledge of K_M for the enzyme will in many cases be sufficient to determine the rate limiting step of the device. Figure 12.17 shows the behaviour of the transport, enzyme, and electrochemical kinetics as a function of substrate concentration. Inspection of the figure allows us to delineate the different cases summarized in Table

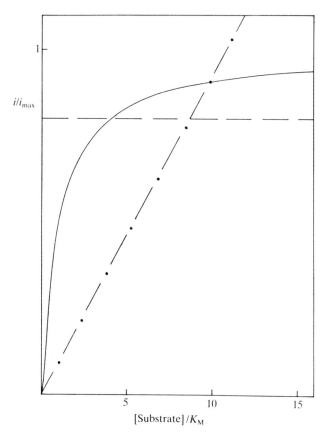

Fig. 12.17 Theoretical plots of current against concentration of substrate when the response of the device is controlled by the rate of substrate diffusion through the membrane (— • — •), the enzyme kinetics (———), and the electrode kinetics (— — —), respectively.

12.5. In developing enzyme electrodes this type of analysis is crucial. For instance there is no point in worrying about the enzyme or the electrode if the problem lies with the membrane.

Acknowledgements

We are most grateful to our colleagues Drs P. N. Bartlett and A. E. G. Cass, M. Bycroft, B. J. Driscoll, and K. W. Sim whose work has been reported in this article. We thank the SERC, BP, the University of London, and Genetics International for financial support. This is a contribution from the Imperial College Sensors Group.

Table 12.5 Summary of mechanistic deductions from K_{ME} and ρ_0

	$K_{ME} < K_M$	$K_{ME} = K_M$	$K_{ME} > K_M$
$\rho_0 = 1$	Transport Electrochemical	Transport Electrochemical	Transport ???
$\rho_0 = \infty$	Enzyme Electrochemical	Enzyme Enzyme	Enzyme Something piscine

References

Albery, W. J. (1975). *Electrode kinetics* p. 58. Oxford University Press, Oxford.
—— and Bartlett, P. N. (1984). An organic conductor electrode for the oxidation of NADH. *J. Chem. Soc., Chem. Commun.* 234-6.
—— (1985). Amperometric enzyme electrodes, Part I. Theory. *J. Electroanal. Chem.* **194**, 211-22.
—— and Hillman, A. R. (1981). Electrode kinetics. *Ann. Rep. Prog. Chem.* Sect C, 377-437.
—— (1984). Transport and kinetics in modified electrodes. *J. Electroanal. Chem.* **170**, 27-49.
—— and Knowles, J. R. (1976). Evolution of enzyme function and the development of catalytic efficiency. *Biochemistry* **15**, 5631-40.
—— Bartlett, P. N. and Craston, D. H. (1985). Amperometric enzyme electrodes, Part II. Conducting organic salts as electrode materials for the oxidation of glucose oxidase. *J. Electroanal. Chem.* **194**, 223-35.
—— Eddowes, M. J., Hill, H. A. O. and Hillman, A. R. (1981). Mechanism of the reduction and oxidation reaction of cytochrome *c* at a modified gold electrode. *J. Am. Chem. Soc.* **103**, 3904-10.
—— Knowles, J. R. (1986). *J. Theoret. Biol.* (in press).
Barman, T. E. (1969). *Enzyme handbook* Vol. 1, p. 23. Springer Verlag, New York.
Cardosi, M. (1984). Ph.D thesis, Department of Biochemistry, Imperial College.
Cass, A. E. G., Davis, G., Francis, G. D., Hill, H. A. O., Aston, W. J., Higgins, I. J., Plotkin, E. V., Scott, L. D. L. and Turner, A. P. F. (1984*a*). Ferrocene-mediated enzyme electrode for amperometric determination of glucose. *Anal. Chem.* **56**, 667-71.
—— Hill, H. A. O., Higgins, I. J., Plotkin, E. V., Turner, A. P. F. and Aston, W. J. (1984*b*). Amperometric enzyme electrode for glucose determination. In *Charge and field effects in biosystems* (ed. M. J. Allen and P. N. R. Underwood) p. 475-82. Abacus Press, Tunbridge.
Cenas, N. K. and Kulys, J. J. (1981). 413-Biocatalytic oxidation of glucose on the conductive charge transfer complexes. *Bioelectrochem. Bioenerg.* **8**, 103-13.
Clark, L. C. and Lyons, C. (1962). Electrode systems for continuous monotoring in cardiovascular surgery. *Ann. N. Y. Acad. Sci.* **102**, 29.
Gough, D. A. and Leypoldt, J. K. (1980). Transient studies of glucose, oxygen, and hydroquinone at a membrane covered rotating disc electrode. *J. Electrochem. Soc.* **127**, 1278-87.

Guilbault, G. G. and Lubrano, G. J. (1973). An enzyme electrode for the amperometric determination of glucose. *Anal. Chim. Acta* **64**, 436.

Hanes, C. S. (1932). CLXVII. Studies on plant amylases. I. The effect of starch concentration upon the velocity of hydrolysis by the amylase of germinated barley. *Biochem. J.* **26**, 1406.

Jaeger, C. D. and Bard, A. J. (1979). Electrochemical behaviour of tetrathiafulvalene-tetracyanoquinodimethane electrodes in aqueous media. *J. Am. Chem. Soc.* **101**, 1690–9.

—— (1980). Electrochemical behavior of donor-tetracyanoquinodimethane electrodes in aqueous media. *J. Am. Chem. Soc.* **102**, 5435–42.

Kulys, J. J. (1981). Development of new analytical systems based on biocatalysers. *Enzyme Microb. Technol.* **3**, 342–352.

—— Samalius, A. S. and Svirmickas, G. J. S. (1980). Electron exchange between the enzyme active centre and organic metal. *FEBS Lett.* **114**, 7–10.

Mazid, M. A. and Laidler, K. J. (1982). pH dependence of free and immobilized yeast alcohol dehydrogenase kinetics. *Can. J. Biochem.* **60**, 100–7.

Melby, L. R. (1965). Substituted quinodimethans. VIII. Salts derived from the 7,7,8,8-tetracyanoquinodimethan anion-radical and benzologues of quaternary pyrazinium cations. *Can. J. Chem.* **43**, 1448–53.

—— Harder, R. J., Hertler, W. R., Mahler, W., Benson, R. E. and Mochel, W. E. (1962). Substituted quinodimethans. II. Anion-radical derivatives and complexes of 7,7,8,8-tetracyanoquinodimethan. *J. Am. Chem. Soc.* **84**, 3374.

Wiebel, M. K. and Bright, H. J. (1971). The glucose oxidase mechanism, interpretation of pH dependence. *J. Biol. Chem.* **246**, 2734–44.

13

The use of electrochemical methods in the study of modified electrodes

P. N. BARTLETT

13.1 Introduction

Over the past twelve years the field of modified electrodes has developed to such an extent that it is now possible, by the application of established synthetic methods, to begin to design the electrode/electrolyte interface. This ability to be able to control the molecular structure of the electrode surface is an important advance for the design of biosensors since it now becomes feasible to tailor the electrode to the requirements of the particular biological redox system. This is a particularly interesting approach to the development of amperometric biosensors since conventional 'clean' metal electrodes are generally very poor voltammetric electrodes for the direct oxidation or reduction of redox enzymes or co-enzymes. In order to proceed down this path it is necessary to know something of the properties of the modified electrode and its interaction with the substrate. In this chapter we will discuss the various techniques available for the study of these processes. Firstly, however, we begin with a brief review of the various strategies for the modification of electrodes and the theoretical models of their properties.

A variety of approaches to the modification of electrodes have been developed and investigated since the early work of Lane and Hubbard (1973 *a, b*) on the adsorption of unsaturated monomers at electrodes. Figure 13.1 summarizes these methods. The various techniques have recently been comprehensively reviewed (Albery and Hillman 1981; Faulkner 1984; Murray 1984) and so we shall restrict ourselves to a short survey of the methods available. The early work of Lane and Hubbard was based upon the adsorption of species at the electrode surface. This type of modification is frequently a reversible process and consequently a suitable concentration of the free species in solution is important in order to maintain the coverage of the electrode surface, furthermore this method usually only yields monolayer or sub-monolayer coverages. Subsequently methods for the direct covalent attachment of redox mediators to the electrode surface were developed by Murray's group (Moses *et al.* 1975), Kuwana's group (Lin *et al.* 1977) and others. These methods rely on a direct chemical linking of the redox group to the electrode surface using silanization of the electrode to produce M-O-Si-

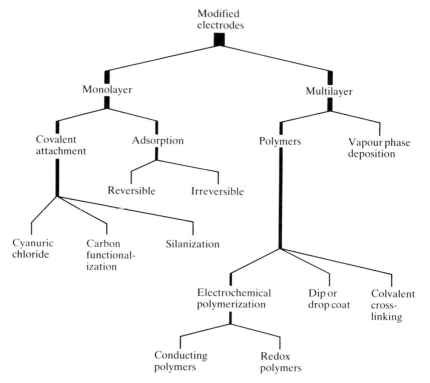

Fig. 13.1 The various types of modified electrode.

linkages, the use of cyanuric chloride to couple the redox group to the electrode, or in the case of carbon electrodes direct reaction with acidic and carbonyl functionalities on the electrode surface. These methods are most frequently employed to produce monolayer coverages, although it is possible by judicious control of the conditions to adapt these approaches to the preparation of multilayer modified electrodes (see for example Bolts and Wrighton 1979).

Multilayer coverage of electrode surfaces is most frequently achieved by the use of polymeric modification of the electrode and this is an area which is rapidly expanding. The available methods include the electrochemical polymerization of suitable monomers to yield adherent redox polymer films, the drop or dip coating of polymers onto electrodes, or the gas phase plasma polymerization of monomers onto the electrode surface. Of these the dip or drop coating method, in which a sample of the polymer is dissolved in a suitable solvent for application to the electrode (somewhat like 'painting' the film on) has the advantage that the bulk physical properties of the polymer may be characterized before it is applied. On the other hand the electrochemical polymerization approach is very attractive because of the ease of formation and control over film thickness provided by the use of the electrochemistry. Further details of the scope of these approaches can be found in the reviews of Albery and Hillman (1981) and Murray (1984).

Given that this variety of methods for the chemical modification of electrodes exists and is continually increasing it is now possible to begin to design suitable electrode surfaces for particular electrochemical reactions. As a example, let us consider the problem of the electrochemical oxidation of β-nicotinamide adenine dinucleotide (NADH) to enzymatically active NAD$^+$. There is considerable interest in this reaction because of the large number (over 250) of dehydrogenase enzymes which use this coenzyme or the closely related β-nicotinamide adenine dinucleotide phosphate (NADP$^+$/NADPH). These dehydrogenases catalyses reactions of the following general type:

$$SH_2 + NAD^+ \longrightarrow S + NADH + H^+$$

where SH$_2$ is the substrate and S is the product.

If the NADH formed in these reactions can be efficiently, electro-chemically reoxidized, then this can form the basis of an amperometric enzyme electrode specific to the particular substrate of the dehydrogenase chosen (Chapter 15). The great attraction of this approach is the diversity of sensors which are possible simply by changing the dehydrogenase used. Unfortunately clean (unmodified) metal or carbon electrodes are unsuitable for the oxidation of NADH. As shown by the work of Elving *et al.* (1976) the oxidation of NADH at clean electrodes only proceeds at high (about 1 volt) overpotentials. Under these conditions the oxidation proceeds through radical intermediates. Clean metal electrodes are thus unsuitable for two reasons. First, the regeneration of NAD$^+$ does not occur cleanly; dimers and other products are also formed. Second, the high overpotential required leads to problems of interferences from other species present in the sample.

In order to overcome these problems a variety of modified electrodes have been investigated. At the modified electrode the reoxidation of NADH occurs through reaction with the immobilized mediator, rather than directly at the electrode surface. Some of the different approaches in the literature are shown in Table 13.1. These include both the use of a monolayer modified electrodes based on the adsorption of orthoquinones (Tse and Kuwana 1978; Jaegfeldt *et al.* 1981), and the use of multilayer modified electrodes based on polymeric orthoquinones (Degrand and Miller 1980). In addition, electro-chemically deposited *N*-methylphenazine has been studied by Torstensson and Gorton (1981). In all these cases some degree of success was achieved in the catalysis of the oxidation of NADH. The overpotential was considerably reduced at the modified electrode, thus alleviating the problem of inter-ference. However, in all cases the modified electrodes proved to be too unstable for prolonged use, either because of side reactions of the mediator, or because of loss of mediator from the electrode surface. For these reasons these systems were not suitable for use in amperometric sensors. More

Table 13.1 Modified electrodes for the oxidation of NADH

Mediator	Reference	Comments
CH$_2$NH$_2$ / OH / OH	Tse and Kuwana 1978	Monolayer. Loss of activity in a few cycles.
CH / CH OH / OH	Jaegfeldt *et al.* 1981	Monolayer. 70% lost in 30 minutes.
[CH$_3$ / C–CH$_2$ / CO / NH$_2$]$_{0.41x}$ [CH$_3$ / C–CH$_2$ / CH$_3$]$_{0.59x}$ CH$_2$–CH$_2$ OH / OH	Degrand and Miller 1980	Polymer. Poor transport through the film. Activity falls on cycling.
CH$_3$	Torstensson and Gorton 1981	Electrochemically deposited. 60% lost in 2 hours.
(CH$_3$)$_2$N O	Gorton *et al.* 1984	Adsorbed layer. Half life of ~ 10 hours at pH 7.

recently Gorton *et al.* (1985) have reported results for the oxidation of NADH at a graphite electrode modified by adsorption of 1,2-benzophenox-azine-7-one. They have carried out a detailed study of the kinetics of the reaction using the rotating disc electrode. They find no significant loss of activity over a period of 7 hours in the pH range 1.1–7.0 and a 17% decrease over the same period at pH 8.0. The problem of stability has been overcome by Albery and Bartlett (1984) who have shown that the one-dimensional conducting salt formed from *N*-methyl phenazine with tetracyanoquinodimethane can be used as an electrode for the reaction (Chapter 12). This material does not suffer from the problems of stability encountered with other approaches.

13.2 The kinetics of modified electrodes

The rational design of a modified electrode for a specific application requires an understanding of three areas. Firstly, it is necessary to know something of the mechanism and kinetics of the corresponding homogeneous redox reaction. Secondly, it is necessary to know something of the electrochemistry of the mediator. Thirdly, it is necessary to have some appreciation of the electrochemical behaviour of modified electrodes in general. It is only in this way that it is possible to predict with any confidence the likely effects of immobilization on the kinetics and thermodynamics of the mediator reactions.

Along with the development of various methods for the modification of electrodes there has been a concomitant interest in various techniques for their characterization. These have included both electrochemical and spectroscopic studies. In this chapter we shall concentrate on the various electrochemical characterization techniques using both steady state and transient measurements at the modified electrode. The various *in situ* spectroscopic techniques for the study of electrode surfaces have recently been reviewed (Robinson 1984). In order to place these measurements in perspective we begin by considering the transport and kinetics in modified electrodes.

Detailed mathematical treatments of reactions at chemically modified electrodes have been published by Andrieux *et al.* (1982) and by Albery and Hillman (1981 and 1984). In these models the authors consider the general case of a multilayer modified electrode and they identify a number of possible rate limiting steps. Monolayer modified electrodes are a special case of this general model. The two treatments are almost identical and their conclusions are in good agreement. For our purposes we will adopt the notation of Albery and Hillman (1984). Figure 13.2 shows the general model for the layer modified electrode. In the model the mediator couple A/B is assumed to be present, immobilized uniformly throughout a layer of thickness L at the electrode surface. The mediator reacts with the substrate Y, present in the bulk solution, to give a product Z. The reaction at the modified electrode is then

$$B + Y \longrightarrow A + Z \tag{13.1}$$

The mediator is then oxidized (or reduced) by the electrode to regenerate B ready to react with another molecule of substrate from the solution. As we shall see a number of kinetic processes can be identified in this general scheme. It is the relative magnitudes of the characteristic rate constants for these processes which determine the behaviour of the modified electrode.

Figure 13.2 shows each of these rate processes. The diffusion of electrons through the layer, assumed to occur by electron hopping between redox centres, is characterized by a diffusion coefficient D_e. (See Daum *et al.* 1980; Oyama and Anson 1980). For reaction to occur within the layer the substrate must penetrate the layer and diffuse within it. The behaviour of the substrate within the layer is characterized by a partition coefficient K and a diffusion coefficient D_y. Albery and Hillman then distinguish three possible types of reaction of the substrate and characterize each with its own rate constant. Firstly, the reaction can occur with the mediator on the outside of the layer with a rate constant k''. Secondly, the reaction can occur, with a rate constant k, with the mediator within the layer. Finally the reaction can occur directly, at the electrode surface with a rate constant k_E'. The distinction between the

ELECTRODE   LAYER   ELECTROLYTE

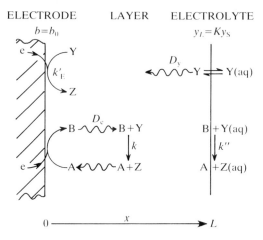

Fig. 13.2 General model for a modified electrode showing the notation. Four processes are shown, electrode surface reaction (k_E'), partition of substrate into the film (K), mediated reaction in the film (k), and surface mediated reaction (k''). (After Albery and Hillman (1984) with permission).

first two cases arises because of the differences in the solvation environment at the surface and within the layer. In these models the electron transfer reaction between the mediator A/B and the electrode is assumed to be fast. The surface concentration of the mediator species B (b_0) is then fixed by the electrode potential. This assumption has been discussed by Anson (1980) in terms of Marcus theory.

Two distinct transport processes within the layer can be identified; electron transport and substrate transport. The electrons enter from the electrode side (on the left in Fig. 13.2), converting A to B, and are transported through the layer by hopping. The substrate, Y, partitions into the layer from the solution (on the right in Fig. 13.2) and diffuses through the layer. The mediated conversion of substrate to product, reaction (13.1), occurs where the two species, diffusing from opposite sides of the layer, meet. The region where this occurs is called the reaction zone. The location of the reaction zone and its thickness are determined by the relative rates of transport of the two species in the layer and the rate of the mediator reaction (13.1). Thus, for example, if the diffusion of electrons in the layer is much faster than the diffusion of substrate, then the reaction is likely to occur close to the solution/layer interface. If, on the other hand, the substrate diffuses much more rapidly through the layer than the electrons, then the reaction is likely to occur close to the electrode/layer interface.

In the full treatment of the problem we can identify a total of ten possible cases associated with six possible locations for the reaction zone. Figure 13.3 shows these six locations for the reaction zone. In the figure the electrode is

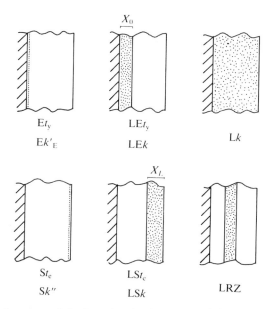

Fig. 13.3 The location of the reaction in the ten possible cases together with the notation used to distinguish them. The electrode is on the left in each case and the location of the reaction is shown by the dotted region.

on the left in each case and the reaction zone is represented by the dotted region. The figure also gives the notation used by Albery and Hillman for each of the ten cases. Their notation uses capital letters to describe the location of the reaction zone followed by a lower case letter to distinguish the various rate limiting processes. Table 13.2 gives the key to this notation. Thus, as an example, LSt_e indicates a layer surface reaction zone determined by transport of electrons through the layer. For further details the reader is referred to the original papers.

Returning to Fig. 13.3 we can see that if we make a modified electrode for which the transport of substrate through the layer far outstrips the transport of electrons, then the reaction occurs close to the electrode (cases Et_y, Ek'_E, LEt_y and LEk). Whether the reaction occurs at the electrode (cases Et_y and Ek'_E) or in a zone of thickness X_0 close to the electrode (cases LEt_y and LEk) depends upon the relative magnitudes of the rate constants k'' and k'_E. On the other hand, if we arrange for the transport of electrons through the layer to be faster than the transport of substrate, then the reaction occurs at the outside of the layer (cases St_e, Sk'', LSt_e and LSk). Whether the reaction only occurs right at the surface (case St_e or Sk'') or occurs in a region of thickness X_L at the surface (case LSt_e or LSk) depends upon the relative values of the rate constants k and k''. Finally, we may find that the two transport terms are in balance. Under these circumstances we find the last two cases, Lk and

Table 13.2 Case notation for modified electrodes

Symbol	Meaning
Location of the reaction zone:	
L	Layer
LS	Layer surface
LE	Layer electrode
S	Surface
E	Electrode
LRZ	Layer reaction zone
Rate limiting kinetics:	
t_y	Transport of substrate
t_e	Transport of electrons
k''	Surface reaction
k	Layer reaction
k_E'	Electrode reaction

LRZ. Now the reaction occurs within the bulk of the layer. If the reaction is slow it will occur throughout the whole layer (case Lk). If the reaction is fast (a large k) the reaction will be confined to a narrow zone were the two reagents meet (case LRZ).

Expressions for the currents appropriate to the various cases can be found in the original papers of Albery and Hillman and of Andrieux *et al.*

These treatments are important for the design of biosensors because they enable us to distinguish a number of distinct strategies for the catalysis of any given reaction. These strategies have been discussed by Albery and Hillman (1984). They conclude that there are two different approaches based upon the two cases Sk'' and LSk. For the interfacial reaction case (Sk''), reasonably efficient catalysis by the modified electrode requires a value of k_2 (the second order homogeneous rate constant for the mediator reaction) of $k_2 > 10^4 \, dm^3 \, mol^{-1} \, s^{-1}$. Under these circumstances the reacton occurs at the layer/solution interface and so the thickness of the layer is unimportant. Indeed the thicker the layer the more likely it is that transport of electrons through the layer will be a problem and so for this case it is logical to use a monolayer electrode. For the layer reaction case (LSk), on the other hand, the thickness of the layer is important. Ideally in this case the layer should be the same thickness as the reaction layer, X_L. For this case we require a value of $k_2 > 10 \, dm^3 \, mol^{-1} \, s^{-1}$. It is not surprising that k_2 is less, under these circumstances, than for the surface case above since now many more catalytic centres throughout the layer are participating in the reaction. However to achieve this advantage it is important to ensure that the diffusion coefficient for the substrate within the layer is large; $D_y \sim 10^{-6} \, cm^2 \, s^{-1}$. This in turn implies a fairly open, porous structure for the layer. For the catalysis of bio-electrochemical redox reactions, particularly those of large molecules such as redox enzymes, this is an important constraint on the layer electrode strategy.

It is interesting to note that in all the studies to date the rate of the homogeneous reaction between mediator and substrate has been a good guide to the rate of the heterogeneous reaction on the electrode or within the layer. This is a significant finding since it means that a logical strategy can be developed for the design of new modified electrodes based on studies of suitable homogeneous mediators. An example of this approach is the work of Kitani *et al.* (1981) on mediators for NADH oxidation.

The mediation of the electrochemistry of solution redox species is not the only application of modified electrodes. There is also interest in their use in the controlled release of drugs, the construction of ion gates, and the design of microelectronic devices (Thackeray *et al.* 1985).

In the applications of modified electrodes to the controlled release of drugs the objective is to make an electrode which has bound to it the drug, or other species, of interest. The method employed to bind the drug should be such that its release can be controlled electrochemically. In practice both electrostatic entrapment and covalent bonding have been used. Such a system, potentially, then has the ability to deliver controlled doses of the drug to localized regions on demand. With such a system the rate of delivery, the intervals between doses, and the amounts delivered are all under electrochemical control. Miller and co-workers have carried out a number of studies on polymer modified electrodes for controlled release (Lau and Miller 1983; Lau *et al.* 1983; Zinger and Miller 1984). In their early work they concentrated on modified electrodes for the release of the neurotransmitter dopamine. To do this they prepared a polymer consisting of a backbone onto which they attached dopamine units using cathodically cleavable covalent bonds. The polymer consisted of a polystyrene backbone with pendant isonicotinate groups. The dopamine was attached to these pendant groups by amide linkages (Lau and Miller 1983). When the polymer was dip coated onto a glassy carbon electrode it proved possible to release dopamine into solution by application of a potential of -1.2 V (*vs.* SCE). Glutamate and γ-aminobutyric acid (GABA) can also be released in this way (Lau *et al.* 1983).

Once again an understanding of the transport and kinetics of modified electrodes is important in their design. In their work Miller *et al.* found that the rate of charge propagation through the films (D_e) was too slow to allow delivery of the neurotransmitters at the rates desired, and that this limited the amount of neurotransmitter that could be released. This problem of slow charge propagation through polymeric layers on electrodes is quite common with non-conducting polymer backbones; especially when two-electron redox mediator groups are used. One way to overcome the problem is to make the polymer backbone conducting. There has been much work on conducting polymers produced by the electropolymerization of heterocyclic aromatic monomers (see, for example, Bidan *et al.* 1984; Bull *et al.* 1983; Diaz and Kanazawa 1979). Although a lot of this work has been carried out in non-aqueous solvents, conducting polymer films can be grown from aqueous solutions. Zinger and Miller (1984) have applied conducting polymers to the problem of controlled release. For this they used a polypyrrole film into which they ion-exchanged glutamate so that it was electrostatically bound in the film. Then by taking the film cathodic, so that they reduced the poly-pyrrole, they were able to expel the glutamate counter ions. Using a con-ducting polymer they avoided the charge transport problem and were thus able to deliver larger amounts of neurotransmitter, and to deliver repetitive pulses.

Conducting polymers have also been used to make electrochemically controlled ion gates (Burgmayer and Murray 1982, 1984). The principle of the ion gate is very similar to that employed in the controlled release of glutamate. In its insulating (reduced) form polypyrrole is uncharged and is impermeable to both anions and cations. Upon oxidation the polymer becomes conducting and in this form is positively charged. The charged polymer is permselective; in other words anions can now penetrate the film much more readily than cations. Burgmayer *et al.* have used this property to make an ion gate for chloride ion. They coated polypyrrole onto a gold gauze electrode to form a coherent, continuous film. In the neutral, insulating form this film was impermeable to ions. On oxidation of the film to the charged form, it becomes permeable to chloride ions. Thus they were able to construct a membrane which could be electrochemically switched between chloride ion permeable and impermeable states.

As we have seen modified electrodes are beginning to find application in a variety of biochemical areas. In order to exploit these applications it is necessary to apply the criteria discussed above to their design. It is also important to be able to characterize the various rate processes and the behaviour of the modified electrode. We now turn to the various electro-chemical techniques available for this characterization.

13.3 Stationary electrode techniques

Stationary electrode techniques have been extensively applied in the study of modified electrodes because of the comparative simplicity of the apparatus required. In particular the techniques of cyclic voltammetry and the more sophisticated pulse and AC modulation voltammetries can be used to provide information on the coverage of the electrode and the kinetics of the electrode reaction. In addition single step potential perturbations have proved use-ful in the study of the kinetics of charge transport processes within the layer.

13.3.1 Cyclic voltammetry

In conventional cyclic voltammetry a triangular potential waveform is applied to the electrode and the corresponding current is recorded. This technique has been widely applied in the studies of the electrochemistry of solution species (see Heinze 1984) and in the study of electrochemical reactions with subsequent chemical reaction steps (see Chapter 14 of this book). The technique has also been widely applied in the study of modified electrodes. Figure 13.4a shows a typical cyclic voltammogram of a ruthenium trisbipyridyl modified electrode as a function of sweep rate. Results of this type are frequently used to estimate the surface coverage of immobilized electroactive species based on the integration of the anodic and cathodic currents observed at the modified electrode in an indifferent electrolyte, where the only Faradaic reaction is the oxidation or reduction of the immobilized redox group. In order to do this it is necessary to estimate the contribution from the double layer charging current, and this is generally carried out 'by eye' since it is not possible to measure this independently. The observed double layer charging current at the clean electrode under the same

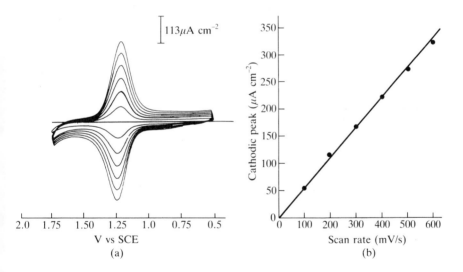

Fig. 13.4 (a) Cyclic voltammograms of a platinum electrode silanized with Ru(bipy)$_3^{2+}$ (electroactive coverage ~ 21 monolayers) in 0.1 mol dm^{-3} TBAP in acetonitrile.

(b) The variation of peak height with sweep rate.

(Ghosh and Spiro 1981, reprinted by permission of the publisher, The Electrochemical Society, Inc.).

conditions can sometimes be used as a guide but this approach should be treated with caution due to the changes in the structure of the double layer likely to be produced by the modification procedure. The integrated charge under the cyclic voltammetric peak will only give an accurate estimate of the total coverage if the whole coat, as opposed to just a few inner layers, undergoes reaction on the timescale of the measurement. Fortunately it is relatively simple to check this since if the process is kinetically controlled, with only part of the coat undergoing the redox reaction, the total charge measured is a function of the sweep rate; the slower the sweep rate the longer the time for the reaction and hence the greater the proportion of the coat that reacts. This is also reflected in the variation of the peak height with sweep rate. When diffusional transport within the film is rate limiting the peak height varies with the square root of the sweep rate ($v^{\frac{1}{2}}$) and is given by precisely the same expression as that for semi-infinite linear diffusion of homogeneous solution species (Daum *et al.* 1980)

$$i_{\mathrm{p}} = 0.4463\,(nF)^{\frac{3}{2}}\,AD_{\mathrm{e}}^{\frac{1}{2}}v^{\frac{1}{2}}b_0/(RT)^{\frac{1}{2}} \tag{13.2}$$

where i_{p} is the peak height, n the number of electrons transferred, A the area of the electrode, F the Faraday constant, D_{e} the diffusion coefficient for charge transport in the film, and b_0 is the concentration of redox species in the film. When there is no diffusional limitation the peak height varies directly with the sweep rate (see Fig. 13.4b). Thus the variation of peak height with sweep rate is a simple diagnostic for the behaviour of the modified electrode. In certain circumstances a changeover from v to $v^{\frac{1}{2}}$ dependence can be observed with increasing sweep rate (see for example Oyama and Anson 1980*a*). This changeover is determined by the interplay between sweep rate and the kinetics of charge transport through the film. Figure 13.5 summarizes the type of behaviour found and shows schematic concentration profiles for the redox film. In an elegant set of experiments on a polyvinyl ferrocene modified electrode Daum *et al.* (1980) have shown that the changeover can also be brought about by reducing the rate of charge transport by cooling the electrode from 20 to $-70\,^{\circ}\mathrm{C}$.

The peak potentials and peak shapes in cyclic voltammetry also contain information on the kinetics of charge transport. For rapid kinetics, when the whole of the layer remains in equilibrium with the electrode the peak separation, ΔE, is expected to be zero (Bard and Faulkner 1980 p. 521). In practice this is seldom observed even for monolayer modified electrodes. In general, for multilayer electrodes, the peak separation increases with increasing sweep rate whilst the mid-peak potential remains essentially constant. The wave-shapes for multilayer modified electrodes have not yet been fully analysed and exhibit a diversity of forms. This is because the processes are more complex for the multilayer electrodes and such effects as changes in solvent swelling, transport of charge compensating counterions,

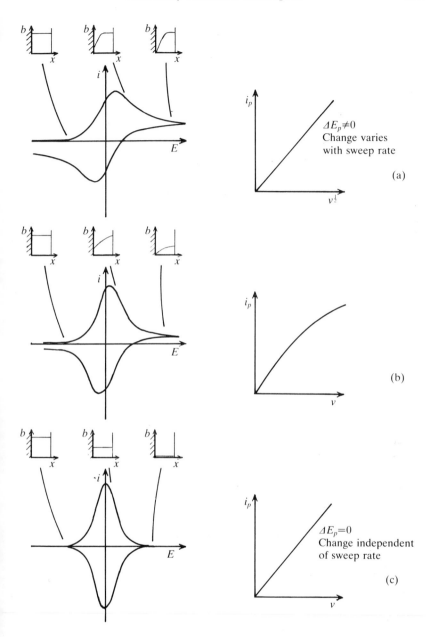

Fig. 13.5 Cyclic voltammetric behaviour of modified electrodes showing the types of behaviour found ranging from semi-infinite linear diffusion (a), through the mixed case (b), to surface reaction (c), and the appropriate dependence of peak height on sweep rate in each case. Schematic concentration profiles are shown for the films.

and interactions between the redox groups themselves all lead to non-idealities in behaviour. Brown and Anson (1977) have proposed a model for these interactions based on activity coefficients. Further details of the mathematical treatment of waveshapes for modified electrodes may be found in the work of Aoki *et al.* (1983) and in a series of papers by Laviron and co-workers (Laviron 1979, 1980, 1981; Laviron and Roullier 1980; Laviron *et al.* 1980).

13.3.2 Pulse polarography

The resolution of cyclic voltammetry as a technique for the study of modified electrodes is essentially limited by the contribution of double layer charging to the observed current. This can be an especially significant problem for the study of low surface coverages encountered when using immobilized enzymes or for sub-monolayer coverage of redox species. One way to overcome this problem is to use a pulse polarographic technique and in particular differential pulse polarography. These techniques have been successfully applied to the determination of metal ions in solution at low concentrations for a number of years (Osteryoung 1981; Bard and Faulkner 1980, p. 190) and in the study of the electrochemistry of bioredox species in solution (see for example Bianco and Haladjian 1982). Pulse polarographic techniques are especially well suited to use with microprocessor controlled electrochemical instrumentation because of the relative ease with which the required waveforms can be generated and the corresponding currents acquired and analysed. For this reason they may be expected to become increasingly popular over the next few years.

Figure 13.6 shows the principle of the technique; a series of potential pulses of amplitude ΔE (usually between 5 and 50 mV) are superimposed on a slow potential sweep (*ca.* 1 mV s^{-1}). The pulse is repeated after a time τ_D and is of duration $\tau_D - \tau$ (τ_D is often referred to as the 'drop time', a reference back to the original implementation of the technique at the dropping mercury electrode). The current is measured over a fixed time interval, δ, just before and again towards the end of the pulse as shown in the figure. The differential pulse polarogram then consists of a plot of the difference in these two current measurements, Δi, as a function of the base potential E_1. It is more convenient in the case of digital instrumentation to use the wave-form shown in Fig. 13.6b, rather than to use a slow potential sweep as the baseline, and indeed this is the wave-form which is most conveniently used in the theoretical treatment (Birke 1978). Brown and Anson (1977) have compared cyclic voltammetry and differential pulse polarography for the study of monolayer modified electrodes. Figure 13.7 shows some of their data for ruthenium pentamine covalently attached to a pyrolytic graphite electrode. It is clear from the figure that the technique is suitable for the study of low surface coverages.

For a monolayer modified electrode the Faradaic reaction of the surface

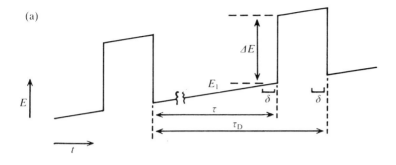

(a)

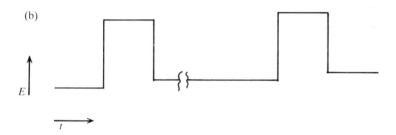

(b)

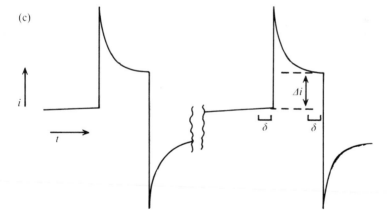

(c)

Fig. 13.6 The principle of differential pulse polarography.
(a) The potential waveform showing the notation.
(b) The corresponding waveform used with digital instrumentation.
(c) The resulting current response.

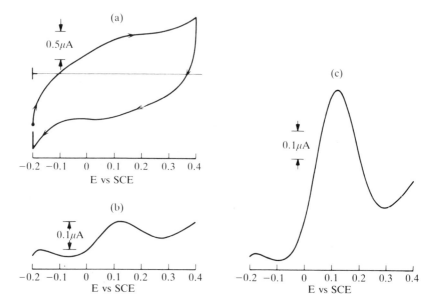

Fig. 13.7 Cyclic and differential pulse voltammograms for an edge-on pyrolytic graphite electrode with approximately 4.2×10^{-11} moles of ruthenium (II) pentamine covalently bound to the surface. Supporting electrolyte 1 mol dm^{-3} CF$_3$COOH.
(a) Cyclic voltammogram at 50 mV s^{-1}.
(b) Differential pulse polarogram with $R_u \sim 100 \ \Omega$.
(c) As in (b) but with $R_u = 1000 \ \Omega$.
(Brown and Anson 1977. Reprinted with permission from *Analytical Chemistry*. Copyright 1977 American Chemical Society).

bound species can be treated as a pseudo-capacitor in parallel with the double layer capacitance and Brown and Anson (1977) have presented a theoretical treatment based on this model and assuming that the surface bound redox couple exhibits a Nernstian response. In other words they assume that the kinetics of electron transfer are rapid and that the concentrations of oxidized and reduced species bound at the electrode surface are therefore related to the electrode potential by the Nernst equation. Care should be exercised in applying this model to other modified electrodes, and in particular multilayer modified electrodes, where this assumption may be invalid due to diffusional limitations within the coating. In their model the charging of the double layer and the surface bound redox species occurs through the uncompensated solution resistance as shown in Fig. 13.8. The current flowing in the circuit after each pulse is then given by:

$$i = \frac{\Delta E}{R_u} \exp - \left[\frac{t}{R_u(C_{dl} + C_F)} \right] \tag{13.3}$$

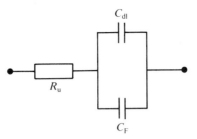

Fig. 13.8 The simple equivalent circuit for irreversibly attached reactant used by Brown and Anson (1977).

where R_u is the uncompensated solution resistance, C_{dl} the double layer capacitance, C_F the Faradaic pseudo capacitance, and t the time from the start of the pulse. By the clever trick of adding an additional uncompensated resistance in the measuring circuit Brown and Anson were able to enhance the sensitivity of the technique by increasing the RC time of the circuit and slowing down the charging of the capacitance.

A full description of the wave-shape of the differential pulse polarogram calls for explicit knowledge of the double layer capacitance and its variation with potential. This is an inaccurate and problematical process because of the uncertain origin of the background currents and the possible changes brought about by the surface modification process itself. The technique is, however, appealing for the detection of low coverages and the peak potentials can provide information on the standard potential of the attached redox couple. Care should be exercised in the choice of experimental parameters such as scan rate since erroneous peak potentials can result. It is therefore prudent to check the constancy of peak potentials with variations in the experimental parameters before concluding that these are in fact the same as the standard potentials for the attached redox species.

Differential pulse polarography has been used to look at enzymes immobilized at electrode surfaces where, again as a result of low coverages, cyclic voltammetry is poorly suited. Ianniello *et al.* (1982*a*, *b*) have used the technique to study the electrochemistry of flavoproteins covalently attached by the cyanuric chloride method to graphite electrodes. Using this method they have observed shifts in the peak potentials for the oxidation/reduction of the flavin prosthetic group on attachment of glucose oxidase, xanthine oxidase, and D- and L- amino acid oxidase to electrodes and the effects of removal and subsequent replacement of the flavin moiety.

The related technique of normal pulse polarography has been used to study polymer modified electrodes (Oyama *et al.* 1983, 1984). In this technique a series of pulses is applied to the electrode each of increasing amplitude but always from the same base voltage at which negligible reaction occurs (Bard and Faulkner 1980, p. 186). The wave-form used is shown in Fig. 13.9. The

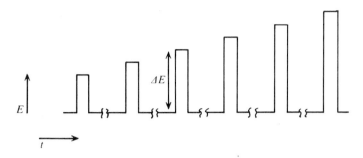

Fig. 13.9 The potential wave-form used in normal pulse polarography.

normal pulse polarogram then consists of a plot of the current measured towards the end of the pulse as a function of the pulse voltage.

13.3.3 AC voltammetry

As a technique for the study of modified electrodes at low coverages AC voltammetry offers similar advantages over conventional cyclic voltammetry as the differential pulse technique. In AC voltammetry a small amplitude sinusoidal modulation is imposed on top of the slow potential scan applied to the electrode. Using a lock-in amplifier the resulting AC modulated component of the current is measured and plotted as a function of the applied mean potential. The technique has been applied by Senda and co-workers to the study of the electrochemistry of redox proteins adsorbed at the surface of mercury electrodes (Ikeda *et al.* 1979, 1981; Kakutani, *et al.* 1980, 1981). The theory for the AC voltammetric response appropriate to this type of modified electrode has been presented by Kakutani and Senda (1979).

13.3.4 Potential step chrono-amperometry

All of the stationary electrode techniques described above have relied upon the use of repetitive potential wave-forms of some type. Single potential step experiments at modified electrodes are also frequently used to probe the kinetics of charge transport through polymeric layers of bound redox species. In this type of experiment a single potential step from an initial potential, E_i, to a final potential, E_f, is applied to a stationary electrode in background electrolyte and the associated current response is recorded as a function of time. Figure 13.10 shows a typical transient for a thionine coated electrode in 0.05 mol dm^{-3} sulphuric acid. The effect of the potential step is to change the redox state of the coat so that the current is made up of a capacitative contribution at short times and the Faradaic reaction of the coat at longer time. The response is then a bounded diffusion problem and is essentially identical to the thin layer cell case. Using Laplace transforms to solve Fick's second law of diffusion as applied to a bounded film of

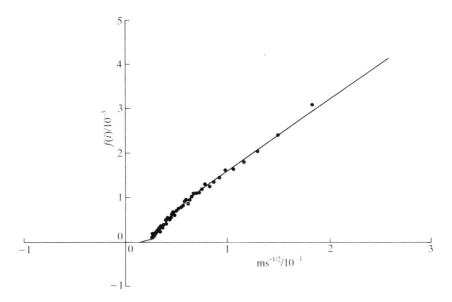

Fig. 13.10. Typical transient for a potential step at a thionine coated electrode in 0.05 mol dm^{-3} H$_2$SO$_4$ recorded using a microprocessor controlled potentiostat. The potential step is from -211 to -191 mV *vs.* SCE and is averaged over eight repeat transients.

thickness L gives the following expression for the transient current (Oglesby *et al.* 1965).

$$i(t) = \left(\frac{D_e}{\pi t}\right)^{\frac{1}{2}} \frac{\Delta Q}{L} \left\{ 1 + 2 \sum_{m=1}^{\infty} (-1)^m \exp\left(\frac{-m^2 L^2}{D_e t}\right) \right\} \quad (13.4)$$

where ΔQ is the change in charge in the coat, L is the thickness of the coat, and D_e the diffusion coefficient for charge within the coat. Equation 13.4 is a modified form of the Cottrell equation (Bard and Faulkner 1980, p. 143). The current transient is most readily analysed by plotting i against $t^{-\frac{1}{2}}$ as shown in Fig. 13.11. At short times ($t \ll D/L^2$), when the concentration polarization within the coating has not reached the outside of the coat, eqn 13.4 reduces to the corresponding Cottrell equation for the unbounded (semi-infinite linear diffusion) case

$$i(t) = \left(\frac{D_e}{\pi t}\right)^{\frac{1}{2}} \frac{\Delta Q}{L}. \quad (13.5)$$

At longer times when $t \sim D/L^2$ the concentration polarization in the coat reaches the surface and the diffusion limited current falls below that given by eqn 13.5. This can be seen in the plot of i against $t^{-\frac{1}{2}}$ by the deviation from the

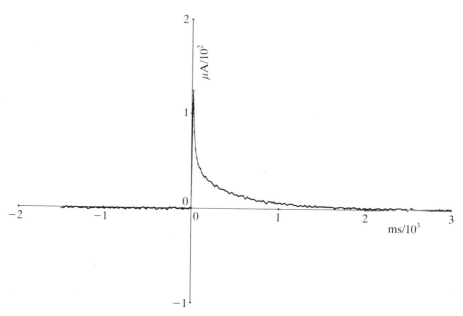

Fig. 13.11 Analysis of the thionine potential step transient according to the Cottrell equation. The line is calculated from eqn 13.4 with $D/L^2 = 0.813\ \text{s}^{-1}$ and $\Delta Q = 2.63 \times 10^{-5}\ \text{C}$. $f(i) = i/\Delta Q$.

straight line through the origin as the exponential terms in eqn 13.4 become significant. The slope of the line through the origin and the short time data gives a value of D_e for the reaction from eqn 13.5 corresponding to the effective diffusion coefficient for charge through the coat providing ΔQ and L are known. ΔQ is usually obtained by integration of the whole transient whilst L can be estimated from the coverage measured by cyclic voltammetry or some other means.

Deviations from the straight line behaviour predicted by eqn 13.5 at very short times are sometimes observed due to the double layer charging current (Peerce and Bard 1980). A number of workers (see for example Murray 1984) advocate the use of large (>500 mV) steps right through the redox peak in the cyclic voltammogram for the coating. This practice should be approached with caution due to the gross changes in morphology and solvation that may be induced by such large changes in the redox state of the coat and also due to the problems of double layer charging this introduces. In the experience of the present author it is much better to use a number of much smaller (10–20 mV) steps backwards and forwards about the region of redox activity of the coating and to compare these for consistency in the values of D_e obtained. The most significant source of error in the evaluation of D_e by this method is frequently to be found in the value of ΔQ used in eqn 13.4. For this reason it is always wise to fit the full equation to the experimental data rather than simply to rely on the initial slopes.

A number of groups have investigated the mechanism of charge transport through polymer films and the nature of the rate limiting process. In certain cases D_e has been found to be dependent upon the nature of the counter ion. Thus varying the size of the counter ion has been shown to have a marked effect on the values of D_e obtained for the thionine coated electrode (Albery *et al.* 1982) with values ranging from 9.1×10^{-13} cm^2 s^{-1} for sulphate ion to 0.9×10^{-13} cm^2 s^{-1} for tosylate ion. The relationship between the observed diffusion coefficient and the various rate limiting processes has been discussed by Murray (1984).

The potential step technique measures the transient response of the electrode to a potential perturbation. A variety of other methods have been used in combination with the potential step to study charge transport and kinetic processes in modified electrodes. Most notable amongst these is the use of spectrascopic detection to monitor the time course of the change in the redox state of the coat. This approach has the advantage of avoiding the problems of the background contributions encountered with current measurements. The most commonly used method is to observe the change in the visible region of the spectrum using an optically transparent tin oxide electrode as the substrate onto which to coat the modified electrode. The spectrascopic measurement follows the integrated change in the redox state of the coating, and so the integrated form of the modified Cottrell equation is appropriate (Albery *et al.* 1982)

$$
\begin{aligned}
\theta &= \frac{(\text{OD})_t - (\text{OD})_0}{(\text{OD})_\infty - (\text{OD})_0} \\[2mm]
&= 2\left(\frac{D_e t}{L^2 \pi}\right)^{\frac{1}{2}} + 2 \sum_{m=1}^{\infty} (-1)^m \left[2\left(\frac{D_e t}{L^2 \pi}\right)^{\frac{1}{2}} \exp\left(\frac{-m^2 L^2}{D_e t}\right) \right. \\[2mm]
&\quad \left. - 2m \operatorname{erfc}\left(\frac{m L}{D_e^{\frac{1}{2}} t^{\frac{1}{2}}}\right) \right]
\end{aligned}
\tag{13.6}
$$

where (OD) is the optical density and the subscripts 0, t, and ∞ denote the initial value, the value at time t, and the final infinity value respectively. L is the film thickness, and D_e the effective diffusion coefficient.

Figure 13.12 shows a typical plot of experimental data for the optical transient at a thionine coated electrode. *In situ* electron spin resonance has also been used to study the changes in polymeric coatings in response to a potential step (Albery *et al.* 1984). In this experiment the authors were able to follow the concentration of bound radicals in a polynitrostyrene coated electrode as a function of time and to analyse the results using eqn 13.6.

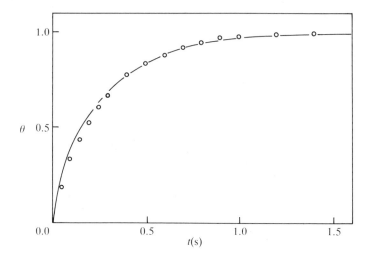

Fig. 13.12 Optical transient at a thionine coated electrode. The solid line was calculated from eqn 13.6. (From Albery *et al.* 1982 with permission).

13.4 Forced convection techniques

The methods described above have all concentrated on the properties of the modified electrode itself and the kinetic processes occurring within the coat. In order to probe the equally important and interesting question of the kinetics and mechanism of the mediated reaction between the bound redox species and the substrate present in solution it is necessary to be able to calculate the surface concentration of substrate. Forced convection electrodes, and in particular the rotating disc and ring-disc electrode geometries, are ideally suited to this type of study. This is because the controlled hydrodynamics of the rotating electrode provides reproducible, calculable, and readily experimentally controlled transport of substrate to, and product from, the electrode surface.

13.4.1 The rotating disc electrode

The hydrodynamics of the rotating disc were first solved by von Karman (1921) and Cochran (1934). The rotating electrode acts as a pump drawing fresh solution up from the bulk of the solution towards the electrode surface, then spinning it around and flinging it out sideways. This flow pattern is shown in Fig. 13.13. The action of the electrode establishes a stationary boundary layer, called the diffusion layer, at the electrode surface which rotates with the electrode. Outside this stationary layer the solution is well stirred. The thickness of the diffusion layer is given by

$$X_D = 0.643\, D^{\frac{1}{3}} \nu^{\frac{1}{6}} W^{-\frac{1}{2}} \tag{13.7}$$

(a)

(b)

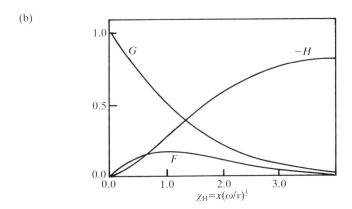

Fig. 13.13 Fluid flow at a rotating disc electrode.
(a) Schematic representation of the streamlines.
(b) The three velocity components of the flow as a function of distance from the electrode surface: $v_\phi = r\omega G(\chi_H)$; $v_r = r\omega F(\chi_H)$; $v_x = (\omega/v)^{\frac{1}{2}}H(\chi_H)$ (where ω is the rotation speed in rad s^{-1}).

where D is the diffusion coefficient, v is the kinematic viscosity (the viscosity divided by the density), and W is the rotation speed of the electrode in Hz. Equation 13.7 has two important features. Firstly the thickness of the diffusion layer is dependent on the rotation speed and so can be varied experimentally. Secondly the thickness is independent of the radial coordinate so that the stationary layer is uniform in thickness over the whole surface of the electrode; the electrode is said to be uniformly accessible and the current density will thus be uniform over the surface of the disc.

Figure 13.14 shows the concentration profiles for species Y reacting at a rotating disc electrode to produce a product Z. At distances greater than X_D the solution is well stirred and there is no concentration polarization of Y or Z. Transport in this region is predominantly by convection. At distances closer to the electrode than X_D the solution is stationary and transport is

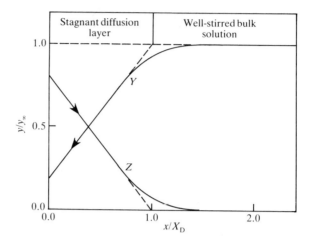

Fig. 13.14 Variation of concentration with distance at a rotating disc electrode.

purely by diffusion. The flux of species reacting at the electrode surface, j, is simply given by Fick's first law

$$j = \frac{D}{X_D}(y_\infty - y_0) = \frac{i}{nAF} \tag{13.8}$$

where y_∞ is the bulk concentration, y_0 the concentration at the electrode surface, n is the number of electrons transferred, A the electrode area and F is the Faraday (96480 C mol^{-1}). Since X_D is readily calculable from eqn 13.7 and the current and bulk concentration are generally known, eqn 13.8 can be used to find the surface concentration of reacting species. This is a significant point for the study of modified electrodes since it is precisely this concentration which is important in the investigation of the kinetics of mediated reactions.

When the electrode potential is poised so that the surface concentration of substrate is reduced to zero ($y_0 = 0$) the current becomes limited by mass transport and we obtain, from eqn 13.7 and 13.8, the Levich equation for the limiting current,

$$i_L = 1.554\, nAFD^{\frac{2}{3}}\, \nu^{-\frac{1}{6}}\, y_\infty W^{\frac{1}{2}}. \tag{13.9}$$

Under these conditions the current is directly proportional to the square root of the rotation speed; the faster the electrode is rotated the thinner the stagnant layer and thus the more efficient the transport of substrate to the electrode surface. It is worth considering the possible effects of surface roughness on the hydrodynamics of the rotating disc electrode since the polymeric coatings applied to the electrode seldom exhibit perfectly smooth surfaces. Bruckenstein, *et al.* (1985) have investigated the effects of surface roughness, produced by polishing electrodes with abrasives of different sizes, on the current response of a rotating disc electrode. They find that there is no effect on polishing with abrasives of 14 μm or less. Bearing in mind that for typical values in aqueous solution the stagnant layer, X_D, is of the order of 10^{-3} cm thick this is not surprising. As a rule of thumb surface roughness is not likely to be important provided it is less than $\sim X_D$.

Simple rotating disc measurements are ideally suited to the investigation of mediated reactions at modified electrodes because of the calculable rate of mass transport of the substrate, and a number of authors have made use of this technique (Anson *et al.* 1983*a*, *b*; Albery *et al.* 1980; Oyama and Anson 1980*b*; Rocklin and Murray 1981; Haas and Zumbrunnen 1981). The Levich limiting current given by eqn 13.9 is seldom observed for modified electrodes since there is often another rate limiting step other than transport of substrate to the electrode surface. Under these circumstances it is most convenient to extrapolate out the mass transport contribution and thus to obtain a value for k'_{ME} the effective heterogenous rate constant for reaction at the electrode. The value of k'_{ME} can then be analysed in terms of the theoretical model for the reactions at modified electrode put forward by Albery and Hillman (1981 and 1984) and by Andrieux *et al.* (1982) and discussed earlier in this chapter.

In order to treat the reaction at a modified electrode we can regard the supply of substrate, Y, from the bulk of solution as introducing an additional step in the reaction mechanism, characterized by a mass transport rate constant k'_D, where

$$k'_D = D/X_D = 1.554 D^{\frac{2}{3}} \, \nu^{-\frac{1}{6}} \, W^{\frac{1}{2}} \tag{13.10}$$

We can then write the scheme for the reaction as

$$Y_\infty \underset{k'_D}{\overset{k'_D}{\rightleftharpoons}} Y_0 \xrightarrow{k'_{ME}} Z \tag{13.11}$$

where Y_∞ is the substrate in the bulk of solution and Y_0 is the substrate at the electrode surface. In doing this we are following an analysis of the type first proposed by Koutecky and Levich (1956) for reactions at rotating disc electrodes. Analysis of the scheme gives the following expression for the flux, j,

$$\frac{1}{j} = \frac{1}{k'_D y_\infty} + \frac{1}{k'_{ME} y_\infty} \tag{13.12}$$

where y_∞ is the bulk concentration of substrate. Substituting in eqn 12 for k'_D and using the fact that $j = i/nAF$ we obtain the Koutecky Levich equation

$$\frac{1}{i} = \frac{1}{1.554 nFA D^{\frac{2}{3}} \, \nu^{-\frac{1}{6}} \, W^{\frac{1}{2}} \, y_\infty} + \frac{1}{nFA k'_{ME} \, y_\infty}. \tag{13.13}$$

Thus a plot of i^{-1} against $W^{-\frac{1}{2}}$ should yield a straight line whose slope is the reciprocal of the Levich slope (eqn 13.9), and whose intercept gives the value of k'_{ME}. This procedure allows the mass transport component to be extrapolated out of the data by going to infinite rotation speed, where the surface concentration equals the bulk concentration. Albery and Hillman (1981) have published a flowchart, based on this type of analysis, for the diagnosis of the mechanism for a reaction at a modified electrode. They also discuss those cases in which the Koutecky Levich plot is non-linear because k'_{ME} itself depends upon y_0. This analysis has been applied to the thionine coated electrode (Albery *et al.* 1985*b*).

The Koutecky Levich analysis is appropriate in most cases in which there is some rate limiting process in addition to mass transport at the rotating disc electrode. As an example of the use of this type of analysis, let us consider the oxidation of NADH at a rotating disc electrode made from *N*-methylphenazinium tetracyanoquinodimethanide (NMP.TCNQ). Figure 13.15 shows the currents obtained plotted against the square root of the rotation speed (Levich plots) for four different concentrations. As can be seen, with increasing rotation speed the current eventually reaches a plateau, the value

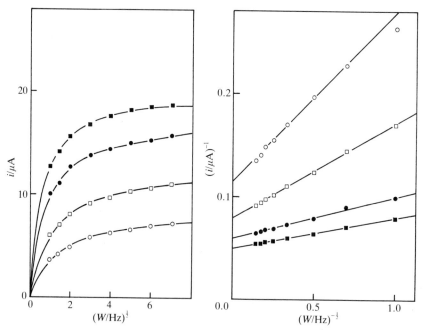

Fig. 13.15 Levich and Koutecky Levich plots for the reaction of NADH at an NMP.TCNQ rotating disc electrode for various concentrations of NADH: 0, 0.38 mmol dm^{-3}; $\square$, 0.25 mmol dm^{-3}; $\bullet$, 0.43 mmol dm^{-3}; $\blacksquare$, 0.063 mmol dm^{-3}. The electrolyte was 0.5 mol dm^{-3} KCl, 0.1 mol dm^{-3} Tris pH 7.0.

of which depends on the concentration. This behaviour is indicative of some additional rate limiting step at the electrode. Figure 13.15 also shows the corresponding Koutecky Levich plots. Now the slopes and intercepts of the straight lines obtained vary with the concentration of NADH. As expected the slopes are in agreement with the predicted slopes from the Levich equation (eqn 13.9). From the intercepts of the Koutecky Levich plots we can determine how the rate of the surface reaction varies with the concentration of NADH *at the electrode surface*. Using this technique Albery and Bartlett (1984) have shown that the oxidation of NADH at the NMP.TCNQ electrode proceeds through the initial adsorption of NADH at the electrode followed by oxidation to NAD^+. A similar study has recently been published by Gorton *et al.* (1985) for the oxidation of NADH at a modified electrode.

The rotating disc electrode has been used by Albery *et al.* (1981) to study the mechanism of the oxidation/reduction of horse heart cytochrome *c* at a gold electrode modified by adsorption of 4-4'-bipyridyl. This reaction is similar to the NADH case described above in that electron transfer occurs to and from the adsorbed cytochrome *c*. (Chapter 15) The overall reaction involves a number of steps. These are mass transport of the protein to the electrode surface, adsorption at a suitable vacant site, electron transfer, desorption of the product, and finally mass transport of the product into the bulk of the solution. The rotating disc electrode is well suited to the study of reactions of this type because it allows the mass transport steps to be readily controlled. Albery *et al.* have presented a full analysis of the rotation speed dependence for this mechanism. They find that for the cytochrome *c* case the rate constants for the adsorption and desorption steps are identical within experimental error. Under these circumstances their full expression simplifies to a form of the Koutecky Levich equation. From an analysis of the rotation speed variation of the current they obtain values for the rate constants for the adsorption and desorption steps at the modified electrode.

Rotating disc electrodes have also been used to study the transport of species through membranes (Gough and Leypoldt 1979, 1980a, b; Freese and Smart 1982). In these studies the membrane is attached to the front face of the rotating disc electrode so that the species must diffuse through the membrane before reacting at the electrode surface. This situation is identical to the electrode reaction cases for polymer modified electrodes discussed above (cases Et_y and Ek'_E of Fig. 13.3). Gough and Leypoldt (1979) have presented an analysis of the mass transport at such a membrane covered electrode. Their resulting expression is identical to the Koutecky Levich equation. This is not surprising since the membrane simply acts as an additional, rotation speed independent, barrier to transport to the electrode (under these conditions $k'_{ME} = KD_y/L$). This technique has been used to measure the diffusion coefficients of oxygen and hydroquinone in membranes (Gough and Leypoldt 1980b). Obviously it is restricted to electroactive species.

13.4.2 *The rotating ring-disc electrode*

The addition of a concentric ring electrode to the rotating disc considerably extends the scope of the technique. The ring electrode is situated downstream from the disc and can thus be used to detect and quantify the products of the disc reaction. The ratio of the current on the ring electrode, i_R, to the current on the disc electrode, i_D, for the detection of a stable product of the disc reaction is known as the collection efficiency, N_0. Thus if the reactions at the two electrodes are:

at the disc: $A + ne \longrightarrow B$
at the ring: $B \longrightarrow A + ne$
then $N_0 = -i_R/i_D$ (13.14)

where (Albery and Hitchman 1971)

$$N_0 = 1 - F(\alpha/\beta) + \beta^{\frac{2}{3}}\{1 - F(\alpha)\} - (1 + \alpha + \beta)^{\frac{2}{3}}$$
$$[1 - F\{(\alpha/\beta)(1 + \alpha + \beta)\}], \tag{13.15}$$

$$F(\theta) = \frac{3^{\frac{1}{2}}}{4\pi} \ln \left\{ \frac{(1 + \theta^{\frac{1}{3}})^3}{1 + \theta} \right\} + \frac{3}{2\pi} \cdot \arctan\left(\frac{2\theta^{\frac{1}{3}} - 1}{3^{\frac{1}{2}}} \right) + \frac{1}{4}, \tag{13.16}$$

$$\alpha = (r_2/r_1)^3 - 1, \tag{13.17}$$

$$\beta = (r_3/r_1)^3 - (r_2/r_1)^3, \tag{13.18}$$

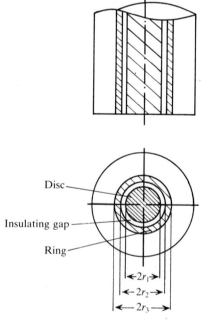

Disc
Insulating gap
Ring
$\leftarrow 2r_1 \rightarrow$
$\leftarrow 2r_2 \rightarrow$
$\leftarrow 2r_3 \rightarrow$

Fig. 13.16 A ring-disc electrode showing the three radii.

and the radii r_1, r_2, and r_3 are shown in Fig. 13.16. It is significant that the collection efficiency, N_0, depends only upon the three radii and is independent of the rotation speed. Values of N_0 for common values of the radius ratios have been tabulated by Albery and Hitchman (1971).

The ring may also be used in the shielding mode. In this case the two electrode reactions are

at both ring and disc: $A + ne \longrightarrow B$

Under these circumstances the ring current is reduced from its limiting value when $i_D = 0$ by a calculable fraction of the disc current (Albery and Hitchman 1971).

$$i_{R,L} = i^0_{R,L} - N_0 i_D \qquad (13.19)$$

where $i_{R,L}$ is the observed limiting ring current and $i^0_{R,L}$ is the value when $i_D = 0$. These relations are easier to understand when the full polarograms are considered, Fig. 13.17. The effect of switching on the disc current from zero to i_D is to shift the ring polarogram (which is assumed to be for a reversible case in the figure) by an amount $N_0 i_D$.

The great advantage of the rotating ring-disc electrode is that the ring electrode can be used to work back from the observed ring current, through the known collection efficiency, to the flux on the disc electrode. This has been used to particular advantage in the study of the electrochemical polymerization of thionine (Albery *et al.* 1980) where only a fraction of the total disc current goes into the polymerization reaction. In this experiment the ring electrode was used to detect the amount of thionine consumed at the disc

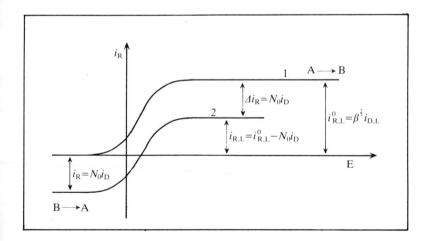

Fig. 13.17 Ring polarograms for a ring-disc electrode. Curve 1 shows the polarogram for $i_D = 0$. Curve 2 shows the case for $i_D \neq 0$ when the reaction at the disc is $A + ne \rightarrow B$.

during polymerization. The measurements using the ring-disc electrode were shown to be in good agreement with the coverage calculated from cyclic voltammetry. Behret *et al.* (1981) have applied the technique to the study of oxygen reduction at electrodes modified by polymeric phthalocyanine coatings. In their experiments the ring electrode is used to determine the proportion of H_2O_2 produced in the oxygen reduction.

The technique has also been successfully applied to the study of immobilized enzyme systems. Kamin and Wilson (1980) have used a rotating ring-disc electrode consisting of a platinum ring electrode and a platinum, graphitic oxide or carbon paste disc onto which glucose oxidase had been immobilized. With this type of electrode they were able to use the ring electrode to measure the fluxes of H_2O_2 produced at the disc by the reaction of glucose and oxygen with the immobilized enzyme. The system has the added advantage that the mass transport of reactants to the disc surface is also controlled and reproducible. In this way Kamin and Wilson were able to investigate the effect of immobilization on the enzyme kinetics.

In addition to its use in the steady state the ring-disc electrode can also be used in combination with transient or sinusoidal perturbation techniques for the study of modified electrodes. In the transient experiments the ring electrode is used to detect the transient in the flux of a product of the disc reaction produced by an imposed change in the disc current or potential. Albery *et al.* (1982) have presented a general method for working back from the observed transient ring response to the generating disc flux. This enables the components of the observed disc transient to be distinguished in those cases in which two or more processes contribute to the observed disc transient. This deconvolution procedure is trivial when the timescale of the observed ring transient is long compared to the time taken for species to cross the gap from the disc to the ring; this time is of the order of X_D^2/D. Under these conditions the steady state relationship is a good approximation and

$$i_D(t) \simeq -i_R(t)N_0^{-1}. \tag{13.20}$$

When however the timescale of the transient is comparable with the characteristic time for crossing the gap it is necessary to use a more complex deconvolution procedure based on a set of trial functions and requiring computer fitting.

The use of sinusoidal modulation at the rotating disc electrode can be used to study adsorption processes. In this method a low amplitude sinusoidal modulated is superimposed on the galvanostatted disc current and the corresponding in and out of phase components of the resulting modulated ring current are recorded as a function of frequency. The complex collection efficiency, N_ω, is then given by

$$N_\omega = -\tilde{i}_R/\tilde{i}_D = X + iY \tag{13.21}$$

where $\tilde{i}_R$ is the modulated component of the ring current and $\tilde{i}_D$ is the modulated component of the disc current. N_ω is made up of three contributions, a transport term N_{tr}, a capacitive collection term N_C, and the Faradaic term N_F. Thus

$$N_\omega = (N_{tr} N_F) + N_C. \tag{13.22}$$

In order to extract the Faradaic term it is necessary to correct the data for the effects of N_C and N_{tr}. This is readily achieved since N_{tr} can be calculated; the theory for N_{tr} has been verified using the ferri/ferrocyanide system at platinum/platinum ring-disc electrode (Albery *et al.* 1971, 1978). N_C can be estimated by extrapolation of data obtained at high frequency where this term dominates. The Faradaic complex collection efficiency, N_F, can thus be extracted and compared with model predictions. One of the advantages of this technique is that the potential of the ring electrode can be chosen to monitor either the reactant or the product. This means that in adsorption studies the two can be measured independently. This approach has been applied to the study of thionine adsorption on platinum (Albery and Hillman 1974), the adsorption of methyl viologen on platinum (Albery *et al.* 1985a), and the study of the reaction of cytochrome *c* at a modified gold electrode (Albery *et al.* 1981). The reaction of cytochrome *c* is greatly facilitated at a gold electrode modified by the adsorption of 4,4'-bipyridyl over that at the clean electrode. Using the AC ring-disc technique in combination with rotating disc studies the authors were able to study the adsorption of the cytochrome *c* to the modified electrode and to calculate the overall free energy profile for the reaction.

13.5 Conclusions

In this chapter we have examined some of the potential applications of modified electrodes in the field of biosensors and in the wider biochemical and biomedical field. This is an area which shows tremendous promise and one that can be expected to grow as people explore the interactions between biological systems and electrodes. In order to make progress in the design and control of these interactions we must be able to design the surfaces of our electrodes. In turn this requires us to model the behaviour of our modified electrodes and to characterized their electrochemistry. I hope this chapter has shown some of the ways which we have available to do this and I hope it will encourage others to try their hand in this interesting area of chemistry.

References

Albery, W. J. and Bartlett, P. N. (1984). An organic conductor electrode for the oxidation of NADH. *J. Chem. Soc., Chem. Commun.* 234-6.
—— and Hillman, A. R. (1979). Ring-disc electrodes. Part 19. Adsorption studies at

low frequency A.C. *J. Chem. Soc., Faraday Trans. 1*, **75**, 1623–34.

—— (1981). Modified electrodes. *Ann. Rep. Prog. Chem., Sect. C*, 377–437.

—— (1984). Transport and kinetics in modified electrodes. *J. Electroanal. Chem.* **170**, 27–49.

—— and Hitchman, M. L. (1971). *Ring-disc electrodes*, Clarendon Press, Oxford.

—— Bartlett, P. N. and McMahon, A. J. (1985*a*). Transport and kinetics at micro-heterogeneous electrodes. Part 5, the methyl viologen platinum system. *J. Electroanal. Chem.* **182**, 7–23.

—— Boutelle, M. G. and Hillman, A. R. (1985*b*). The mechanism of Faradaic reactions at the thionine coated electrode. *J. Electroanal. Chem.* **182**, 99–111.

—— Compton, R. G. and Hillman, A. R. (1978). Ring-disc electrodes. Part 18. Collection efficiency at high frequency A.C. *J. Chem. Soc., Faraday Trans. 1*, **74**, 1007–19.

—— and Jones, C. C. (1984). A novel electrode for electrochemical ESR and its application to modified electrodes. *J. Amer. Chem. Soc.* **106**, 469–73.

—— Drury, J. S. and Hutchinson, A. P. (1971). Ring disc electrodes. Part 15. Alternating current measurements. *Trans. Faraday Soc.* **67**, 2414–18.

—— Boutelle, M. G., Colby, P. J. and Hillman, A. R. (1982). The kinetics of electron transfer in the thionine coated electrode. *J. Electroanal. Chem.* **133**, 135–45.

—— Eddowes, M. J., Hill, H. A. O. and Hillman, A. R. (1981). Mechanism of the reduction and oxidation reaction of cytochrome *c* at a modified gold electrode. *J. Amer. Chem. Soc.* **103**, 3904–10.

—— Foulds. A. W., Hall, K. J. and Hillman, A. R. (1980). Thionine coated electrode for photogalvanic cells. *J. Electrochem. Soc.* **127**, 654–61.

Andrieux, C. P., Dumas-Bouchiat, J. M. and Saveant, J. M. (1982). Catalysis of electrochemical reactions at redox polymer electrodes. Kinetic model for stationary voltammetric techniques. *J. Electroanal. Chem.* **131**, 1–35.

Anson, F. C. (1980). Kinetic behaviour expected from outer sphere redox catalysts confined within polymeric films on electrode surfaces. *J. Phys. Chem.* **84**, 3336–8.

—— Oshaka, T. and Saveant, J.-M. (1983*a*). Diffusional pathways for multiply-charged ions incorporated in polyelectrolyte coatings on graphite electrodes. Cobalt oxalate in coatings of protonated polylysine. *J. Phys. Chem.* **87**, 640–647.

—— (1983*b*). Kinetics of electron transfer cross-reactions within redox polymers. Coatings of a protonated polylysine copolymer with incorporated electroactive anions. *J. Amer. Chem. Soc.* **105**, 4883–90.

Aoki, K., Tokuda, K. and Matsuda, H. (1983). Theory of linear sweep voltammetry with finite diffusion space. *J. Electroanal. Chem.* **146**, 417–29.

Bard, A. J. and Faulkner, L. R. (1980). *Electrochemical Methods*. Wiley, New York.

Behret, H., Binder, H., Sandstede, G. and Scherer, G. G. (1981). On the mechanism of electrocatalytic oxygen reduction at metal chelates. Part III: metal phthalo-cyanines. *J. Electroanal. Chem.* **117**, 29–42.

Bidan, G., Deronzier, A. and Moutet, J.-C. (1984). Electrochemical coating of an electrode by a poly(pyrrole) film containing viologen. *J. C. S. Chem. Commun.* 1185–6.

Birke, R. L. (1978). Current-potential-time relationships in differential pulse polaro-graphy: theory of reversible, quasi-reversible, and irreversible electrode processes. *Anal. Chem.* **50**, 1489–96.

Bolts, J. M. and Wrighton, M. S. (1979). Chemically derivatised *n*-type semi-conducting gallium arsenide photoelectrodes. Thermodynamically uphill oxidation of surface-attached ferrocene centres. *J. Amer. Chem. Soc.* **101**, 6179–84.

Brown, A. P. and Anson, F. C. (1977). Cyclic and differential pulse voltammetric behaviour of reactants confined to the electrode surface. *Anal. Chem.* **49**, 1589–95.

Bruckenstein, S., Sharkey, J. W. and Yip, J. Y. (1985). Effect of polishing with different size abrasives on the current response at a rotating disc electrode. *Anal. Chem.* **51**, 368–71.

Bull, R. A., Fan, F.-R. and Bard, A. J. (1983). Polymer films on electrodes. 13. Incorporation of catalysts into electrochemically conductive polymers — iron phthalocyanine in polypyrrole. *J. Electrochem. Soc.* **130**, 1636–8.

Burgmayer, P. and Murray, R. W. (1982). An ion gate membrane: electrochemical control of ion permeability through a membrane with an embedded electrode. *J. Amer. Chem. Soc.* **104**, 6139–40.

—— (1984). Ion gate electrodes. Polypyrrole as a switchable ion conductor membrane. *J. Phys. Chem.* **88**, 2515–21.

Cochran, W. G. (1934). The flow due to a rotating disc. *Proc. Camb. Phil. Soc. Math. Phys. Sci.* **30**, 365–75.

Daum, P., Lehnard, J. R., Rolison, D. R. and Murray, R. W. (1980). Diffusion charge transport through ultrathin films of radiofrequency plasma polymerised vinylferrocene at low temperature. *J. Amer. Chem. Soc.* **102**, 4649–53.

Degrand, C. and Miller, L. L. (1980). An electrode modified with polymer-bound dopamine which catalyses NADH oxidation. *J. Amer. Chem. Soc.* **102**, 5728–32.

Diaz, A. F. and Kanazawa, K. K. (1979). Electrochemical polymerisation of pyrrole. *J. C. S. Chem. Commun.* 635–6.

Elving, P. J., Schmakel, C. O. and Santhanam, K. S. V. (1976). Nicotinamide-NAD sequence: redox processes and related behaviour: behaviour and properties of intermediates and final products. *CRC Crit. Rev. Anal. Chem.* **6**, 1–67.

Faulkner, L. R. (1984). Chemical microstructures on electrodes. *Chem. and Eng. News*, Feb. 27th, 28–45.

Freese, J. W. and Smart, R. B. (1982). Rotating voltammetric membrane electrode. *Anal. Chem.* **54**, 836–7.

Ghosh, P. K. and Spiro, T. G. (1981). Electroactive coatings of tris(bipy)- and tris(*o*-phen) ruthenium (II) attached to electrodes via hydrosilylation and electro-polymerisation of vinyl derivatives. *J. Electrochem. Soc.* **128**, 1281–7.

Gorton, L., Torstensson, A. Jaegfeldt, H. and Johansson, G. (1984). Electrocatalytic oxidation of reduced nicotinamide coenzymes by graphite electrodes modified with an adsorbed phenoxazinium salt, Meldola blue. *J. Electroanal. Chem.* **161**, 103–20.

—— Johansson, G. and Totstensson, A. (1985). *J. Electroanal. Chem.* **196**, 81–92.

Gough, D. A. and Leypoldt, J. K. (1979). Membrane covered rotated disc electrode. *Anal. Chem.* **51**, 439–44.

—— (1980*a*). Transient studies of glucose oxygen and hydroquinone at a membrane covered rotated disc electrode. *J. Electrochem. Soc.* **127**, 1278–86.

—— (1980*b*). Rotated membrane-coated oxygen electrode. *Anal. Chem.* **52**, 1126–30.

Haas, O. and Zumbrunnen, H.-R. (1981). Electrochemical properties of hydroxy-phenazine coated electrodes. *Helv, Chim. Acta* **64**, 854–63.

Heinze, J. (1984). Cyclic voltammetry — electrochemical spectroscopy. *Angew. Chem., Int. Edn. Engl.* **23**, 831–918.

Ianniello, R. M., Lindsay, T. J. and Yacynych, A. M. (1982*a*). Direct electron transfer in immobilised flavoenzyme chemically modified graphite electrodes. *Anal. Chim. Acta* **141**, 23–32.

—— (1982*b*). Differential pulse voltammetric study of direct electron transfer in glucose oxidase chemically modified graphite electrodes. *Anal. Chem.* **54**, 1098–101.

Ikeda, T., Ando, S. and Senda, M. (1981). Electrochemical oxidation-reduction properties of covalently bound FAD of cholesterol oxidase adsorbed on a mercury electrode surface. *Bull. Chem. Soc. Jpn.* **54**, 2189–93.

—— Toriyama, K. and Senda, M. (1979). Electrochemical behaviour of ferredoxins adsorbed on mercury electrode surface. Cyclic D.C. and A.C voltammetric studies with HMDE. *Bull. Chem. Soc. Jpn.* **52**, 1937–43.

Jaegfeldt, H., Torstensson, A., Gorton, L. and Johansson, G. (1981). Catalytic oxidation of reduced nicotinamide adenine dinucleotide by graphite electrodes modified with adsorbed aromatics containing catechol functionalities. *Anal. Chem.* **53**. 1979–82.

Kakutani, T. and Senda, M. (1979). Theory of A.C. polarisation and A.C. polarography and voltammetry of surface redox reaction. *Bull. Chem. Soc. Jpn.* **52**, 3236–41.

—— Kano, K., Ando, S. and Senda, M. (1981). Electrochemical oxidation and reduction of FMN adsorbed on a mercury electrode surface. *Bull. Chem. Soc. Jpn.* 884–90.

Kakutani, T., Toriyama, K., Ikeda, T. and Senda, M. (1980). Electrochemical oxidation and reduction of ferredoxin adsorbed on a mercury electrode surface. Phase-selective A.C. polarography at DME. *Bull. Chem. Coc. Jpn.* **53**, 947–50.

Kamin, R. A. and Wilson, G. S. (1980). Rotating ring-disc enzyme electrode for biocatalysis kinetic studies and characterisation of the immobilised enzyme layer. *Anal. Chem.* **52**, 1198–205.

Kitani, A., So, Y.-H. and Miller, L. L. (1981). An electrochemical study of the kinetics of NADH being oxidised by diimines derived from diaminobenzenes and diaminopyrimidines. *J. Amer. Chem. Soc.* **103**, 7636–41.

Koutecky, J. and Levich, V. G. (1958). The use of the rotating disc electrode in the study of electrochemical kinetics and electrolytic processes. *Zh. Fiz. Khim.* **32**, 1565–75.

Lane, R. F. and Hubbard, A. T. (1973*a*). Electrochemistry of chemisorbed molecules. I. Reactants connected to electrodes through olefinic substituents. *J. Phys. Chem.* **77**, 1401–10.

—— (1973*b*). Electrochemistry of chemisorbed molecules. II. The influence of charged chemisorbed molecules on the electrode reactions of platinum complexes. *J. Phys. Chem.* **77**, 1411–21.

Lau, A. N. and Miller, L. L. (1983). Electrochemical behaviour of a dopamine polymer. Dopamine release as a primary analog of a synapse. *J. Amer. Chem. Soc.* **105**, 5271–7.

—— and Zinger, B. (1983). Release of neurotransmitters glutamate and γ-aminobutyric acid from an electrode. Catalysis of slow redox propagation through a polymer film. *J. Amer. Chem. Soc.* **105**, 5278–84.

Laviron, E. (1979). Use of linear potential sweep voltammetery and of A.C. voltammetery for the study of the surface electrochemical reaction of strongly adsorbed systems and of redox modified electrodes. *J. Electroanal. Chem.* **100**, 263–70.

—— (1980). A multilayer model for the study of space distributed redox modified electrodes. Part 1. Description and discussion of the model. *J. Electroanal. Chem.* **112**, 1–9.

—— (1981). A multilayer model for the study of space distributed redox modified electrodes. Part III: influence of interactions between the electroactive centres in the first layer on the linear potential sweep voltammograms. *J. Electroanal. Chem.* **122**, 37–44.

—— and Roullier, L. (1980). General expression of the linear potential sweep voltammogram for a surface redox reaction with interactions between adsorbed molecules — applications to modified electrodes. *J. Electroanal. Chem.* **115**, 65–74.

—— and Degrand, C. (1980). A multilayer model for the study of space distributed redox modified electrodes. Part II. Theory and application of linear potential sweep voltammetry for a simple reaction. *J. Electroanal. Chem.* **112**, 11–23.

Lin, A. W. C., Yeh, P., Yacynych, A. M. and Kuwana, T. (1977). Cyanuric chloride as a general linking agent for attachment of redox groups to pyrolytic graphite and metal oxide electrodes. *J. Electroanal. Chem.* **84**, 411–19.

Moses, P. R., Weir, L. and Murray, R. W. (1975). Chemically modified tin oxide electrodes. *Anal. Chem.* **47**, 1882–6.

Murray, R. W. (1984). Chemically modified electrodes. In *Electroanalytical chemistry* (ed. A. J. Bard) Vol. 13, pp. 191–38. Marcel Dekker, New York.

Oglesby, D. M., Omang, S. H. and Reilley, C. N. (1965). Thin layer electrochemical studies using controlled potential or controlled current. *Anal. Chem.* **37**, 1312–6.

Osteryoung, J. (1981). Pulse polarography. In *Water quality measurement*, (eds. H. B. Mark and J. S. Mattson) pp. 85–190, Marcel Dekker, New York.

Oyama, N. and Anson, F. C. (1980*a*). Factors affecting the electrochemical response of metal complexes at pyrolytic graphite electrodes coated with films of poly(4-vinylpyridine). *J. Electrochem. Soc.* **127**, 640–7.

—— (1980*b*). Catalysis of electrode processes by multiply-charged metal complexes electrostatically bound to polyelectrolyte coatings on graphite electrodes, and the use of polymer coated rotating disc electrodes in diagnosing kinetic and conduction mechanisms. *Anal. Chem.* **52**, 1192–8.

—— Oshaka, T. and Ushirogouchi, T. (1984). Charge-transfer reactions of metal complexes at electrode/film interfaces and in films. *J. Phys. Chem.* **88**, 5274–80.

—— Kaneko, M., Sato, K. and Matsuda, H. (1983). Electrode kinetics of $Fe(CN)_6^{3-/4-}$ and $Fe(CN)_5^{2-/3-}$ complexes confined to polymer films on graphite surfaces. *J. Amer. Chem. Soc.* **105**, 6003–8.

Peerce, P. J. and Bard, A. J. (1980). Polymer films on electrodes. Part II: film structure and mechanism of electron transfer with electrodeposited poly(vinylferrocene). *J. Electroanal. Chem.* **112**, 97–115.

Robinson, J. (1984). Spectroelectrochemistry. In *Specialist periodical reports, electrochemistry*, Vol. 9, pp. 101–61. Royal Society of Chemistry, London.

Rocklin, R. D. and Murray, R. W. (1981), Kinetics of electrocatalysis of dibromoalkyl reductions using electrodes with covalently immobilised metallo-tetraphenylporphyrins. *J. Phys. Chem.* **85**, 2104–12.

Thackeray, J.W., White, H.S. and Wrighton, M.S. (1985). Poly(3-methyl-thiophene)-coated electrodes: optical and electrical properties as a function of redox potential and amplification of electrical and chemical signals using poly(3-methylthiophene)-based microelectronic transistors. *J. Phys. Chem.* **89**, 5133–49.

Torstensson, A. and Gorton, L. (1981). Catalytic oxidation of NADH by surface-modified graphite electrodes. *J. Electroanal. Chem.* **130**, 199–207.

Tse, D.C.S. and Kuwana, T. (1978). Electrocatalysis of dihydronicotinamide adenosine diphosphate with quinones and modified quinone electrodes. *Anal. Chem.* **50**, 1315–18.

von Karman, T. (1921). Über laminare und turbulente Reibung. *Z. Angew. Math. Mech.* **1**, 233–52.

Zinger, B. and Miller, L.L. (1984). Timed release of chemicals from polypyrrole films. *J. Amer. Chem. Soc.* **106**, 6861–3.

14

Cyclic voltammetry studies of enzymatic reactions for developing mediated Biosensors

GRAHAM DAVIS

14.1 Introduction

Many amperometric biosensors use an oxidase to catalyse a substrate oxidation reaction (Carr and Bowers 1980). To date, little progress has been made towards inducing the resulting reduced enzyme-cofactor complex to undergo rapid direct electrochemical re-oxidation, consequently electron acceptors have been used to shuttle electrons from the catalytic site to the electrode. Conventionally, oxygen has been chosen since it is the natural electron acceptor for many of these enzymes and is usually available in the analyte (Chapters 1 and 18).

More recent research has attempted to replace oxygen by using non-physiological electron acceptors (or mediators) immobilized on the electrode surface or within the enzyme layer (Chapters 15 and 16). This approach has been encouraged by studies on coating electrodes with redox species using methods including adsorption, polymer coating, and covalent attachment (Bard 1983; Murray 1980; Bartlett, this volume). Adaptation to amperometric biosensor construction may offer some advantages; for example, by using a mediator with a low redox potential a lower operating potential than that required for hydrogen peroxide detection is possible (Cass *et al.* 1984). This can reduce interference from electro-active species generally encountered in biological samples. Increased operational stability may also be achieved by having a fixed concentration of electron acceptor retained within the enzyme layer, thus obviating a problem of oxygen-dependent biosensors where variation in the oxygen tension can alter the response characteristics. Amperometric biosensors incorporating immobilized mediators therefore provide an interesting alternative to peroxide detecting systems (Romette and Boitieux 1984; Shichiri *et al.* 1982, 1984).

To help select a suitable mediator for an amperometric biosensor the electrochemical technique of direct current cyclic voltammetry is useful and enables many important properties of the mediator to be determined. Generally, it is desirable to use a low-potential mediator with a high electrochemical rate constant, the latter is important to ensure that the response of the biosensor is not limited by electrode kinetics. Both parameters can be determined by single-scan cyclic voltammetry. Stability of a mediator as a function of pH, temperature, oxygen tension, enzyme inhibitors, and interferents can also be assessed from changes in the shape of voltammograms with time. Most importantly, the technique can provide qualitative and quantitative information about electrochemically coupled enzymatic reactions, upon which mediated amperometric biosensors are based.

14.2 Direct current cyclic voltammetry

Direct current cyclic voltammetry is based upon the maintenance of the potential of a working electrode with respect to a reference electrode by making a current pass between the working and counter electrode (Bard and Faulkner 1980). This requires a potentiostat with a triangular waveform generator and an $X–Y$ recorder on which the current-potential curves are recorded. Experiments are usually performed with a cell containing a 2–4 mm diameter working electrode (made of gold, platinum, or carbon), a platinum gauze counter electrode, and a saturated calomel electrode (SCE) as reference (Davis *et al.* 1983). As the rate of enzymatic reactions are temperature dependent, experiments are best performed under thermostatic control.

Cyclic voltammetry consists of sweeping the potential of a stationary working electrode at a constant rate in an unstirred solution, between two set limits, with the current being recorded as a function of potential, Fig. 14.1. A single scan can be performed or the electrode can be cycled continuously.

The measured current has two components, a non-Faradaic component resulting from redistribution of charged and polar species at the electrode surface and a Faradaic component resulting from exchange of electrons between the electrode and species in solution. When the rate of electron transfer (at sufficiently oxidizing or reducing potentials) is fast, the Faradaic current is controlled by the rate of diffusion to the electrode. Hence, for the reversible reduction of the redox species O,

$$O + ne^- \rightleftharpoons R \tag{14.1}$$

the surface concentration of the two redox forms will change in accordance with the Nernst equation,

$$[O]/[R] = \exp[nF/RT(E - E^0)] \tag{14.2}$$

and the Faradaic current will depend on the concentration gradient of O at the electrode surface.

$$i_f = nFAD_0(d[O]/dx)_{x=0}. \tag{14.3}$$

A cyclic voltammogram is recorded by holding the working electrode at a positive potential and then sweeping towards and beyond the E^0 of a redox

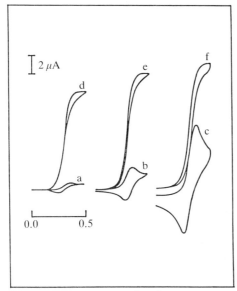

Fig. 14.1 (a–c) DC Cyclic voltammograms at a 4 mm-diameter gold working electrode of ferrocene monocarboxylic acid (200 μM) in 50 mM phosphateperchlorate electrolyte pH 7.0, versus SCE at sweep rates of 1, 10, and 100 mV s^{-1}, respectively. (d–f) With the addition of 11 μM glucose oxidase and 50 mM glucose.

species. As reduction occurs, the concentration of O is depleted in the electrolyte close to the electrode, consequently the current is not maintained but peaks and then decays. When the direction of the potential scan is reversed, a peak resulting from the re-oxidation of R is observed. A redox couple that follows eqn. 14.2, (termed Nernstian or reversible) is illustrated in Fig. 14.1 (a–c). This shows a series of voltammograms of the ferrocene-ferricinium ion redox couple of ferrocene monocarboxylic acid, eqn. 14.4, recorded at different potential sweep rates, v.

[14.4]

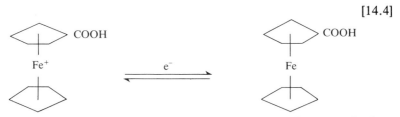

For a reversible reaction of this type, the maximum cathodic current is given by

$$i_p = 0.4463nFA(D_0 nFv/RT)^{1/2}C_0 \qquad [14.5]$$

and occurs at a potential $28.5/n$ mV cathodic of E^0 at 298 K, independent of the potential scan rate.

Experimentally, E^0 can be estimated from the mid-point potential, $E_{1/2}$, of the maximum anodic and cathodic currents. If the mediator is chemically unstable and is converted to a form with different redox properties, the magnitude of the current in the initial voltammogram will decrease with time.

14.3 Electrochemically coupled enzymatic reactions

For a rapid reaction between the reduced enzyme-cofactor complex, Z, of an oxidoreductase and an electron acceptor both the stoichiometry and the relative redox potentials must be favourable to electron transfer (Kuwana *et al.* 1977). In addition, the active site of the enzyme must be 'accessible' to the acceptor molecule.

The reaction can be simplified to the following form

$$Z + O \xrightarrow{k} R; \quad R - ne^- \rightleftharpoons O \qquad [14.6]$$

in which component Z, serves to convert O back to R at potentials where O is generated at the electrode. Qualitatively, the effect on voltammograms is to increase the anodic current and decrease the cathodic current. The theory developed by Nicholson and Shain (1964), shows that two limiting cases are possible. When the pseudo-first order rate constant k_f is small, voltammograms will approximate those of a simple reversible electron transfer reaction, whereas if k_f is large the current will be directly proportional to $k_f^{1/2}$ and independent of the potential scan rate:

$$i = nFA(D_0 k_f)^{1/2} C_0 / 1 + \exp[nF/RT(E - E_{1/2})]. \qquad [14.7]$$

In the latter case a limiting current rather than a peak is observed. An intermediate example is illustrated by Fig. 14.1 (d–f), which shows voltammograms of a redox mediator in the presence of the enzyme glucose oxidase and its substrate. To confirm that a catalytically coupled reaction of the type shown in eqn. 14.6, is occurring, it is useful to plot the current function, eqn. 14.5, versus the potential sweep rate. This allows the effect of sweep rate on the diffusional process to be separated from its effect on the kinetics. Fig. 14.2, curve A shows that a reversible reaction gives a horizontal straight line, as $i_p/v^{1/2}$ is constant. However, for a catalytic reaction the current function only approaches curve A when the potential scan rate is so fast that the reaction does not proceed significantly before the experiment is complete, curve B. In practice, this correlation can be obtained simply by plotting $i_p/v^{1/2}$, which approximates the current function, versus log v. This qualitative aspect of the technique is the most important for a biosensor application,

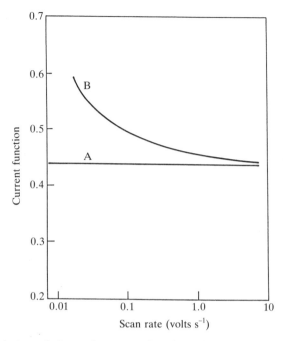

Fig. 14.2 Variation of the peak current function with voltage sweep rate: for a diffusion controlled electrochemical reaction (curve A) and for a catalytically coupled reaction of the type shown in eqn 14.6 (curve B).

as it is usually sufficient to indicate the possibility of detecting an analyte based upon the catalytic reaction under investigation.

To derive kinetic information for the reaction, the mediator must have reversible electrochemistry and the enzyme must be saturated with substrate, $[S] \gg K_M$ (Davis *et al.* 1983). One of the methods is to use a working curve, Fig. 14.3, in which the ratio of the kinetic to diffusion controlled current, i_k/i_d, measured from voltammograms like those shown in Fig. 14.1, is plotted as a function of the kinetic parameter $(k_f/a)^{1/2}$, where $a = nFv/RT$ (Nicholson and Shain 1964). By measuring i_k/i_d at different sweep-rates, a set of values of k_f/a can be obtained at a fixed concentration of the enzyme. The effect of sweep-rate can then be eliminate by plotting k_f/a versus $1/v$. Under pseudo-first order conditions, this bisects the origin with a gradient $k_f RT/nF$, from which the scan-rate independent pseudo-first order rate constant is calculated. The second order rate constant, $k_s = k_f/[Z]$, for the homogeneous reaction between the oxidized mediator and the reduced cofactor-enzyme complex, eqn. 14.6, is estimated by repeating the experiment at different enzyme concentrations.

It is important to note that this analysis assumes the diffusion coefficients of O and Z are equal. This is clearly not true for reactions involving small

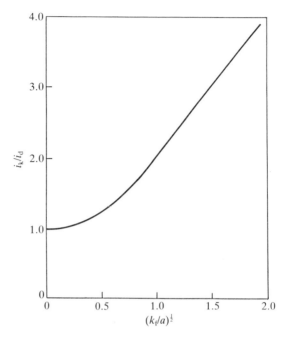

Fig. 14.3 Theoretical plot of the ratio of the kinetic to diffusion controlled peak current, i_k/i_d, versus the kinetic parameter $(k_f/a)^{1/2}$.

molecule mediators and proteins. Ryan and Wilson (1975) have shown that under these conditions, if the reaction is very fast $> 10^6$ l mol^{-1} s^{-1}, this can lead to an underestimation of the rate constant. Nevertheless, the method remains a useful alternative to stopped-flow kinetic techniques for studying these reaction (Weibel *et al.* 1969; Morton *et al.* 1970).

A wide range of oxidoreductases have been studied using cyclic voltammetry with the ferricinium ion of ferrocene monocarboxylic acid, eqn. 14.4, as the mediator, Table 14.1. Apart from the oxygen-specific enzymes cholesterol oxidase, oxalate oxidase, and choline oxidase for which no catalytic reaction was observed (Davis 1984), a rate constant for the other oxidoreductases was estimated (Aston *et al.* 1984b; Cass *et al.* 1984, 1985a, b; Dicks *et al.* 1986; D'Costa *et al.* 1986).

The rates obtained for non-oxygen specific flavoenzymes reacting with ferrocene cover the same range $10^4 - 10^6$ l mol^{-1} s^{-1}, as those for oxygen (Bright and Porter 1975; Gibson and Hastings 1962). The first authors concluded that catalytic activity of these enzymes is associated with substrate oxidation rather than subsequent re-oxidation of the flavin moiety. Comparing these data, it appears that there is no inherent disadvantage in using a non-physiological acceptor with non-oxygen specific flavoenzymes. However, for a

Table 14.1   Electrochemically determined rate constants for the reaction of the reduced form of various enzymes with the ferricinium ion of ferrocene monocarboxylic acid at pH 7.0 and 298 K

Enzyme	Substrate	$k_s \times 10^{-5}$ l mol^{-1} s^{-1}
Glucose dehydrogenase	Glucose	93.0
Flavocytochrome b_2	Lactate	67.0
Galactose oxidase	Galactose	8.5[a]
Xanthine oxidase	Xanthine	4.0
CO oxidoreductase	Carbon monoxide	4.0
Glutathione reductase	NADPH	2.0
Glucose oxidase	Glucose	2.0
Glycollate oxidase	Glycollate	1.2[b]
Alcohol dehydrogenase	Methanol	0.6[c]
L-Amino acid oxidase	Leucine	0.4[d]
Pyruvate oxidase	Pyruvate	0.2
Lipoamide dehydrogenase	NADH	0.2
Sarcosine oxidase	Sarcosine	0.1
Cholesterol oxidase	Cholesterol	—
Oxalate oxidase	Oxalate	—[e]
Choline oxidase	Choline	—

[a] pH 9.0; [b] pH 8.3; [c] pH 10.5; [d] pH 7.8 and 310 K; [e] pH 3.0

practical biosensor based on this type of reaction, it would be important to minimize cross reactivity with oxygen.

To date, the best studied enzyme is glucose oxidase for which rate constants were determined as a function of temperature and pH (Cass *et al.* 1984) with a range of ferrocene derivatives, Table 14.2. Whilst the reaction is thermodynamically favourable for all derivatives it is interesting to note that

Table 14.2   Electrochemically determined rate constants for the reaction of reduced glucose oxidase with the ferricinium ion of a range of ferrocene derivatives at pH 7.0 and 298 K

Ferrocene derivative	$E_{1/2}$ mV *vs.* SCE	$k_s \times 10^{-5}$ l mol^{-1} s^{-1}
1,1'-Dimethyl	100	0.8
Ferrocene	165	0.3
Vinyl	250	0.3
Monocarboxylic acid	275	2.0
1,1'-Dicarboxylic acid	285	0.3
Methyl trimethylamino	400	5.3
Polyvinyl	450	—

a polyvinylferrocene coated electrode, prepared according to the method of Merz and Bard (1978), did not give an observable catalytic reaction with glucose oxidase (Davis 1984). This may result from an inability of polymer-bound ferrocene, unlike the monomer, to approach the active site of the enzyme and facilitate rapid electron transfer.

In addition to studying reactions between oxidoreductases and non-physiologically related redox species, cyclic voltammetry has been used to investigate protein–protein redox reactions *in vitro*. The reversible electro-chemistry of the redox protein horse heart cytochrome *c* at a bipyridyl-modified gold electrode (Eddowes *et al.* 1981) enabled Hill and Walton (1982) to show that cytochrome oxidase can be supplied with electrons for the reduction of oxygen to water. The rate of reaction is enhanced by the presence of a second mediating redox protein, either azurin or cytochrome c_{551}, Table 14.3. Here, data are in good agreement with stopped-flow analysis (Morton *et al.* 1970). The reaction of cytochrome *c* with carbon monoxide oxidoreductase (Aston *et al.* 1984*b*) and the lactate dehydrogenase flavocytochrome b_2 (Cass *et al.* 1985*a*) has also been studied, Table 14.3.

Cyclic voltammetry has been applied qualitatively to the study of coupled reactions involving more than one enzyme. For example, oxidation of lactate by the NAD-linked lactate dehydrogenase can be coupled electrochemically via the lipoamide dehydrogenase-ferrocene system, Table 14.1, and isocitrate can be detected via the NADP-linked isocitrate dehydrogenase coupled to the glutathione reductase-ferrocene system, Table 14.1 (Cass *et al.* 1985*b*).

14.4 Amperometric biosensors

All of the electrochemically coupled enzymatic reactions discussed previously form the basis for the development of mediated amperometric biosensors. In addition, work on the electron transfer protein, cyto-chrome *c*, demonstrates that mediators need not be limited to synthetic redox compounds.

In practical terms, Cass *et al.* (1984) have demonstrated the value of direct current cyclic voltammetry in choosing a suitable mediator for incorporation

Table 14.3 Electrochemically determined rate constants for the reaction with horse heart cytochrome *c* at pH 7.0 and 293 K

Biological redox species	$k_s \times 10^{-5} \, \mathrm{l\,mol^{-1}\,s^{-1}}$
Azurin	0.1
Cytochrome c_{551}	0.2
CO oxidoreductase	0.3
Flavocytochrome b_2	50.0

into an amperometric biosensor. From the data presented in Table 14.2, 1,1′-dimethylferrocene was selected for a glucose sensor operating in whole-blood. In this configuration, a sufficient excess of ferrocene was incorporated to minimize cross reactivity of glucose oxidase with oxygen. For this application it was important that the mediator had a low solubility in aqueous solution thus confining it to the porous carbon base sensor and a low redox potential to facilitate an operating potential at which uric acid and other electroactive components of whole-blood do not cause interference. Ferrocenes are particularly adaptable in this respect as their solubility and redox potential can be controlled by attaching different substituent groups to the cyclopentadienyl rings (Kuwana *et al.* 1977; Deeming 1982).

In addition to assaying blood samples from diabetic subjects, the glucose biosensor could be used to measure the rate of a solution reaction, for example a coupled assay for creatine kinase activity was demonstrated (Green *et al.* 1984). Other mediated amperometric biosensors which use ferrocene have been developed for alcohols (Aston *et al.* 1984*a*), carbon monoxide (Aston *et al.* 1984*b*) glycollate, L-amino acids, and galactose (Dicks *et al.* 1986) based upon the reactions shown in Table 14.1.

References

Aston, W. J., Ashby, R. E., Scott, L. D. L. and Turner, A. P. F. (1984*a*). Enzyme based methanol sensor. In *Change and field effects in biosystems* (eds. M. J. Allen and P. N. R. Usherwood) pp. 491–8, Abacus Press, Tunbridge.

—— Bell, J., Colby, J., Davis, G., Higgins, I. J., Hill, H. A. O. and Turner, A. P. F. (1984*b*). CO: Acceptor oxidoreductase from *Pseudomonas thermocarboxydovorans* strain C2 and its use in a carbon monoxide sensor. *Anal. Chim. Acta* **163**, 161–74.

Bard, A. J. (1983). Chemical modification of electrodes. *J. Chem. Ed.* **60**, 302–4.

—— and Faulkner, L. R. (1980). *Electrochemical methods: fundamentals and applications*. John Wiley, New York.

Bright, W. H. and Porter, D. J. T. (1975). Flavoprotein oxidases. In *The enzymes* (ed. P. D. Boyer) Vol. 12B, pp. 421–505. Academic Press, New York.

Carr, P. W. and Bowers, L. D. (1980). *Immobilized enzymes in analytical and clinical chemistry*. John Wiley, New York.

Cass, A. E. G., Davis, G., Green, M. J. and Hill, H. A. O. (1985*b*) Ferrocene monocarboxylic acid as an electron acceptor for oxidoreductases. *J. Electroanal. Chem.* **190**, 117–27.

—— Hill, H. A. O. and Nancarrow, D. J. (1985*a*). Reaction of flavocytochrome b_2 with cytochrome c and ferrocene monocarboxylic acid: Comparative kinetics by cyclic voltammetry and chronoamperometry. *Biochim. Biophys. Acta* **828**, 51–7.

—— Francis, G., Hill, H. A. O., Higgins, I. J., Aston, W. J., Plotkin, E. V., Scott, L. D. L. and Turner, A. P. F. (1984). Ferrocene mediated enzyme electrode for amperometric determination of glucose. *Anal. Chem.* **56**, 667–71.

Davis, G. (1984). *Studies in applied bioelectrochemistry*. D. Phil Thesis, University of Oxford.

——, Aston, W. J., Higgins, I. J., Hill, H. A. O. and Turner, A. P. F. (1983). Bioelectrochemical fuel cell and sensor based on a quinoprotein, alcohol dehydrogenase. *Enzyme Microb. Tech.* **5**, 383–8.

D'Costa, E. J., Higgins, I. J. and Turner, A. P. F. (1986). Quinoprotein glucose dehydrogenase and its application in an amperometric glucose sensor. *Biosensors* **2**, 71–87.

Deeming, A. J. (1982). Mononuclear iron compounds with hydrocarbon ligands. In *Comprehensive organometallic chemistry* (eds. G. Wilkinson, F. G. A. Stone and E. W. Abel) Vol. 4, pp. 377–512. Pergamon, Oxford.

Dicks, J., Aston, W. J., Davis, G. and Turner, A. P. F. (1986) Mediated amperometric biosensors for D-galactose, glycolate, and L-amino acids based on a ferrocene-modified carbon electrode. *Anal. Chim. Acta* **182**, 103–12.

Eddowes, M. J., Albery, W. J., Hill, H. A. O. and Hillman, A. R. (1981). Mechanism of the reduction and oxidation reaction of cytochromes at a modified gold electrode. *J. Am. Chem. Soc.* **103**, 3904–10.

Gibson, Q. H. and Hastings, J. W. (1962). The oxidation of reduced flavin mononucleotide by molecular oxygen. *Biochem. J.* **83**, 368–77.

Green, M. J., Davis, G. and Hill, H. A. O. (1984). Creatine kinase assay using an enzyme electrode. *J. Biomed. Eng.* **6**, 176–7.

Hill, H. A. O. and Walton, N. J. (1982). Investigation of some intermolecular electron transfer reactions of cytochrome c by electrochemical methods. *J. Am. Chem. Soc.* **104**, 6515–19.

Kuwana, T., Szentrimay, R. and Yeh, R. (1977). Evaluation of mediator titrants for indirect coulometric titrations of biocomponents. *Am. Chem. Soc. Symp. Ser.* **38**, 143–58.

Merz, A. and Bard, A. J. (1978). A stable surface modified platinum electrode prepared by coating with electroactive polymer. *J. Am. Chem. Soc.* **100**, 3222–3.

Morton, R. A., Overnell, J. and Harbury, H. A. (1970). Electron transfer between cytochromes c from horse and pseudomonas. *J. Biol. Chem.* **245**, 4653–7.

Murray, R. W. (1980). Chemically modified electrodes. *Acc. Chem. Res.* **13**, 135–41.

Nicholson, R. S. and Shain, I. (1964). Theory of stationary electrode polarography. *Anal. Chem.* **36**, 706–23.

Romette, J. L. and Boitieux, J. L. (1984). Computerised enzyme electrodes. *J. Biomed. Eng.* **6**, 171–4.

Ryan, M. D. and Wilson, G. S. (1975). Some considerations in spectroelectrochemical evaluation of homogeneous electron transfer involving biological molecules. *Anal. Chem.* **47**, 885–90.

Shichiri, M., Kawamori, R., Hakia, N., Yamasaki, Y. and Abe, H. (1982). Wearable-type artificial endocrine pancreas with needle-type glucose sensor. *Lancet* **2**, 1129–31.

—— (1984). Closed loop glycemic control with a wearable artificial endocrine pancreas. *Diabetes* **33**, 1200–2.

Weibel, M. K., Duke, R. F., Page, D. S., Bulgrin, V. G. and Luthy, J. (1969). The glucose oxidase mechanism: enzyme activation by substrate. *J. Am. Chem. Soc.* **91**, 3904–9.

15

The realization of electron transfer from biological molecules to electrodes

M. F. CARDOSI and A. P. F. TURNER

15.1 Introduction

Over the past decade there has been tremendous interest in the development of cheap reliable biosensors for both clinical and industrial applications. One way of achieving this goal is to combine a biological catalyst with an electrochemical sensor, yielding a device which is both specific and easy to use. Furthermore, sensors based around electrochemical probes offer the most direct route for converting a chemical concentration into an electrical signal and can be readily interfaced to monitoring and control circuitry (Turner, 1985).

In its simplest form an enzyme electrode consists of a thin layer of enzyme(s) held in close proximity to the active surface of a transducer, a suitable reference electrode and a circuit for measuring either the potential difference generated between the two electrodes (potentiometric) or the current that flows between them (amperometric)*. Usually the electrode is covered by a membrane which serves to protect against fouling and/or introduce some desirable partitioning at the interface. To carry out a measurement the enzyme electrode is simply immersed into a solution containing the analyte of interest and the steady state current or potential is read. The relationship is linear for an amperometric electrode and logarithmic for a potentiometric one.

In the potentiometric enzyme electrode the sensing head acts like a battery generating a potential difference which is measured relative to the reference under conditions of zero current flow. This has the advantage that there is no net consumption of material and hence mass transport is unimportant. Such sensors, however, suffer from two major disadvantages. Accurate information about the concentration of analyte in the solution will only be obtained if there is a local thermodynamic equilibrium at the electrode interface. This requires the electrode kinetics to be rapid with a standard electrochemical rate constant greater than 10^{-2} cm s^{-1}. (Albery et al. 1985). This seriously

---

*The effect of the enzyme catalysed reaction may be to generate an electro-active product, which can be detected amperometrically, or to alter the concentration of a particular ionic species, e.g. H$^+$, whereby potentiometry becomes the basis for detection.

257

limits the number of systems that can be used as indicator electrodes. The second disadvantage arises from the exponential dependence of the analyte concentration (c) on the electrode potential (E), i.e.

$$\ln(c) = \text{constant} + nEF/RT$$

where n is the valency of the ion, F the faraday unit, R the gas constant, and T the absolute temperature. Small errors in E can give quite substantial errors in c. For example for $n = 1$ an error in E of 10 mV leads to a 19% error in the value of c (Albery *et al.* 1985). Because of these disadvantages, biosensors based on amperometric indicator electrodes are considered to be more practical although in most cases care must be taken to control the hydrodynamics at the electrode surface.

Enzymes involved in the oxidation and reduction of biological molecules (oxidoreductases) either contain a redox centre such as iron, copper, flavin, quinone at their active site or perform their biological role in conjunction with a redox active cofactor such as $NAD(P)^+$. The difficulty in obtaining direct electrochemistry between an enzyme's redox centre and a naked electrode, together with the absence of an effective electrocatalytic surface for the efficient recycling of reduced cofactor, led to the first enzyme electrodes indirectly exploiting electrochemistry to monitor enzyme activity. The classic example is the glucose sensor proposed by Clark and Lyons (1962) and described by Updike and Hicks (1967) based on the enzyme glucose oxidase and a polarographic oxygen electrode (Chapter 1). Glucose oxidase is an FAD containing enzyme (Fig. 15.1) which catalyses the oxidation of glucose to gluconic acid:

$$\text{Glucose} + O_2 + H_2O = \text{Gluconic acid} + H_2O_2$$

During the catalytic cycle the flavin prosthetic group is first reduced by glucose and then reoxidized by molecular oxygen. The amount of glucose present in the solution is determined by following either the rate of oxygen consumption or the rate at which hydrogen peroxide is produced. Although functional, there are a number of disadvantages to such a system. The current will depend not only upon the glucose concentration but also on the partial oxygen tension (pO_2) of the solution. Secondly, the potentials required to reduce oxygen or oxidize hydrogen peroxide are sufficiently extreme so as to introduce the possibility of interference. Finally, the oxidation of hydrogen peroxide to oxygen is proton dependent, i.e.,

$$H_2O_2 = 2H^+ + O_2 + 2e^-$$

The current would thus vary quite considerably with the pH of the solution. Clearly, reliable application of this probe is only possible if both the pH and pO_2 of the solution can be carefully controlled, a situation not often encountered even in the laboratory. If these problems could be avoided then

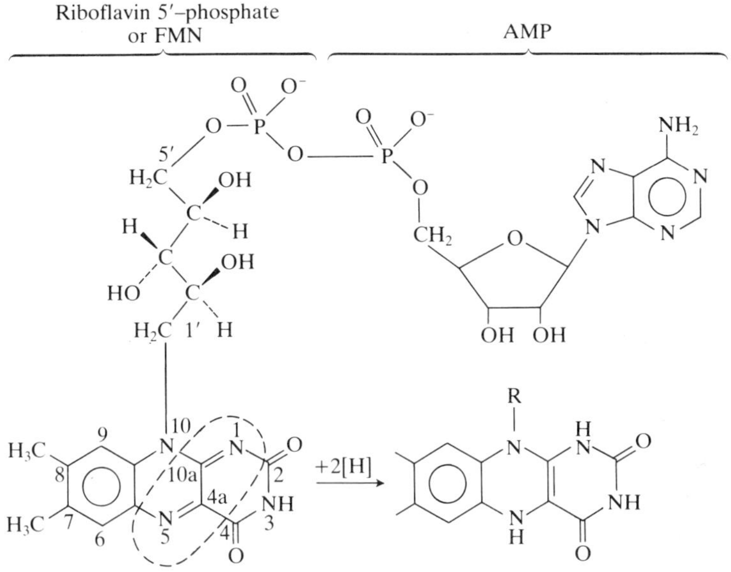

Fig. 15.1 The flavin co-enzyme. Dotted lines indicate the region that is altered following reduction.

it would be possible to develop enzyme electrodes which would gain wider acceptance. It is the development of such electrodes which forms the subject of this chapter.

15.2 Mediators and chemically modified electrodes

Although dioxygen is the physiological electron acceptor for oxidases such as glucose oxidase it can be replaced in the majority of cases by an electron transfer mediator. In this context, a mediator is a low molecular weight redox couple which shuttles electrons from the redox centre of the enzyme to the surface of the indicator electrode. During the catalytic cycle the mediator first reacts with the reduced enzyme and then diffuses to the electrode surface where it undergoes rapid charge transfer. This can be illustrated with reference to glucose oxidase:

in the solution:

$$\text{Glucose} + \text{FAD} + \text{H}_2\text{O} = \text{Gluconic acid} + \text{FADH}_2$$
$$\text{FADH}_2 + \text{M}_{ox} = \text{FAD} + \text{M}_{red} + 2\text{H}^+$$

at the electrode:

$$\text{M}_{red} = \text{M}_{ox}$$

The rate at which the reduced mediator (M_{red}) is produced is measured amperometrically by oxidation at the electrode.

The use of a mediator introduces a number of distinct advantages. Provided the reduced mediator is unreactive with oxygen, it makes the measurement virtually independent of pO_2. Secondly, the working potential of the enzyme electrode is now determined by the formal potential (E^0) of the mediator couple. This can be particularly advantageous if the mediator has a low E^0 since it lessens the chance of interference. Finally, if the oxidation of reduced mediator does not involve protons it can make the enzyme electrode relatively pH insensitive (obviously the device cannot be used at extremes of pH where denaturation of the enzyme takes place).

The use of mediators in conjunction with oxidoreductases is by no means a recent innovation. Molecules such as quinones, organic ions, and inorganic ions such as ferricyanide and redox dyes have all been used with some degree of success (Bright and Porter 1975). A practical mediator, however, should fulfil the following criteria:

i) It should react rapidly with the reduced enzyme.
ii) It should exhibit reversible heterogeneous kinetics.
iii) The overpotential for the regeneration of the oxidized mediator should be low and pH independent.
iv) It should be stable in both oxidized and reduced forms.
v) The reduced mediator should not react with O_2.
vi) For many applications it should be non-toxic.

Although the use of mediators does offer distinct advantages one is faced with the unnecessary complication of having to add it to the sample. A more practical configuration would be to have the mediator firmly anchored to the surface of the electrode in such a way that it was still electrochemically active and able to react with the reduced enzyme. To date, one of the most successful classes of mediator compounds that has been used in this way has been that based on ferrocene (η^5-bis-cyclopentadienyl iron)

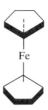

and its derivatives. Ferrocene is a transition metal π-arene complex which consists of an iron atom sandwiched between two cyclopentadienyl rings. It has a well behaved electrochemical redox couple (E^0/(mV) versus SCE = 165) with variation in physical and chemical properties available through substitution in either of the two rings systems (Pickett 1984). The first successful enzyme electrode based on ferrocene contained an insoluble derivative of the mediator and glucose oxidase (Cass *et al*. 1984). In simple terms 1,1′-dimethyl ferrocene was incorporated into a graphite electrode upon which the enzyme glucose oxidase was chemically immobilized (Aston, Chapter 16). In this configuration, electrochemically generated ferricinium ions act as oxidants for reduced glucose oxidase. Once the ferricinium ion has been reduced it is reoxidized at the electrode surface by polarizing the electrode and allowing current to flow. The sequence of reactions occurring at this electrode can be summarized as:

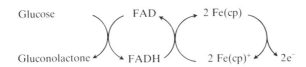

The advantages of this biosensor configuration are as follows:

i) The low formal potential needed to generate the ferricinium species (220 mV versus Ag/AgCl) tends to minimize interference.

ii) Reduced ferrocene does not react with oxygen making the sensor oxygen insensitive.

iii) The electron transfer reaction between the ferricinium ion and the reduced enzyme is fast resulting in rapid response times.

iv) Because of the low solubility of the ferrocene derivative the mediator is essentially confined at the electrode surface thus allowing the probe to be used without prior addition of mediator to the sample.

v) Because the enzyme is itself immobilized to the surface of the transducer the sensor can be used more than once.

The glucose electrode described by Cass *et al*. (1984) exhibited an excellent linear response for glucose (up to 30 mM) beyond the physiologically relevant range whilst retaining rapid response times (60–90 s to 95% steady state current). These response characteristics were achieved by the use of a 'spongy' carbon foil electrode which produced a reasonably defined hydrodynamic restriction to the diffusion of substrate without the need to resort to additional membranes. The electrodes showed essentially no difference in response when the analysis was performed under aerobic or anaerobic conditions and provided an anion exclusion membrane was placed over the electrode they were relatively free from interference from metabolites, such as ascorbate, commonly found in blood plasma.

Since the original communication a varitey of oxidoreductases have been used in conjunction with the ferrocene modified electrode (Table 15.1) and

Erratum Table 15.1 should read:

Table 15.1 Enzymes which have been coupled to ferrocene modified carbon in enzyme electrodes

Substrate	Enzyme
L-Amino acids	L-Amino acid oxidase
Carbon monoxide	Carbon monoxide oxidoreductase
Glucose	Glucose oxidase or PQQ GDH
Glycolic acid	Glycolate oxidase
Lactate	Lactate oxidase or LDH
NADH	Glutathione reductase or Diaphorase
Pyruvate	Pyruvate oxidase

See also Table 14.1

this method of constructing enzyme electrodes is likely to be generally applicable (Turner 1986). NAD(P)$^+$-independent dehydrogenases such as the quinoproteins offer particular advantages in this configuration (Turner *et al.*, 1986). Whilst fericinium ions act as highly efficient electron transfer agents between reduced oxidases and electrodes under anaerobic conditions, oxidases retain a natural affinity for oxygen. The degree of oxygen interference is largely determined by the relative concentrations of oxygen and ferricinium ions at the enzyme's electron transfer site, since the rate of reaction with both reagents is similar (Davis 1985). Consequently, if the assay solutions are saturated with pure oxygen the amperometric response from typical oxidase electrodes decreases by about 30% (Cass *et al.* 1984; Dicks *et al.* 1986). Ferrocene-modified electrodes incorporating NAD(P)$^+$-independent dehydrogenases circumvent this problem completely and show no detectable decrease in current even in oxygen saturated solutions (Aston *et al.* 1984; Turner *et al.* 1984; D'Costa *et al.* 1986). Although it is preferable to avoid the introduction of unstable, expensive, and soluble components such as NAD(P)$^+$ (Turner 1985), cofactor-dependent dehydrogenases (see below) may also be coupled to ferrocene-modified electrodes by the inclusion of a second enzyme. Both lipoamide dehydrogenase (diaphorase) and glutathione reductase may be catalytically coupled to an electrode using ferricinium ions (Cass *et al.* 1985) facilitating the following detection scheme:

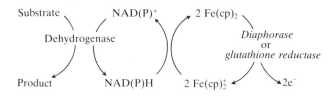

An interesting extension of the glucose oxidase/ferrocene electrode has been to couple it to other analytes using enzymes that compete with glucose oxidase for its substrate. In the presence of ATP and hexokinase, for example, glucose is diverted to glucose-6-phosphate (G-6-P). The glucose electrode, therefore, can be used to detect ATP (Davis *et al* 1984):

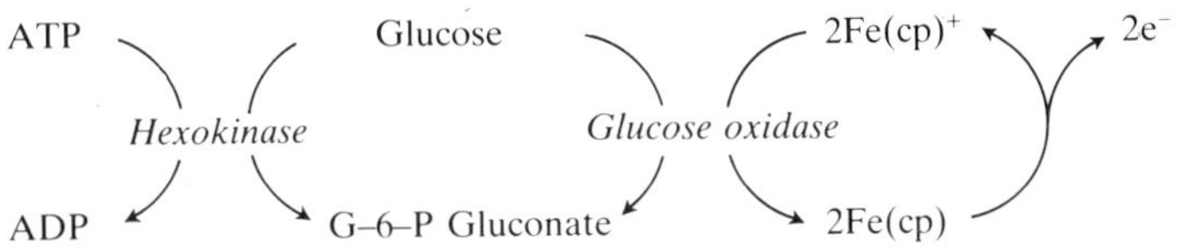

Through the detection of ATP, NAD$^+$, and NADP$^+$ a greater range of analytes become accessible including clinically relevant enzymes. Addition of creatine phosphate to the ATP assay above, for example, allows the detection of the enzyme creatine kinase, which is an important marker in the diagnosis of myocardial infarction.

These examples have concentrated on the ferrocene-based glucose sensor, but a range of other configurations employing enzyme modulation are possible providing novel enzyme electrodes (Scheller *et al.* 1985) and immunosensors (Green, Chapter 4).

Modified electrodes for the regeneration of oxidized enzyme have also been based on redox polymers containing *p*- and *o*- quinone groups adsorbed onto the surface of electrodes Fig. 15.2 (Cenas *et al.* 1983, 1984). These electrodes have been shown to be efficient oxidants for reduced glucose oxidase, L-lactate oxidase, and xanthine oxidase. Cenas *et al.* (1983, 1984)

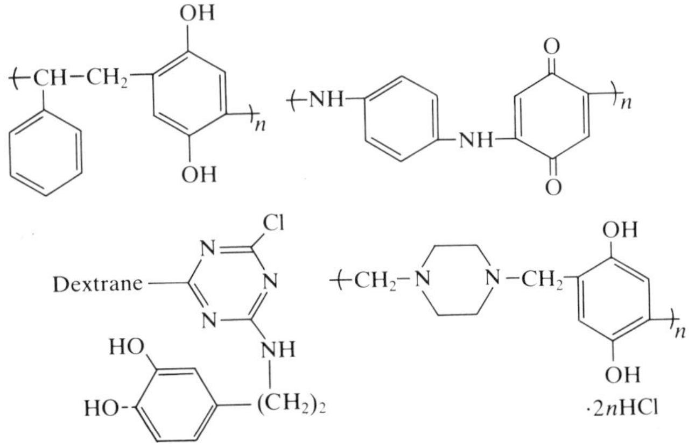

Fig. 15.2 Types of polymers based on *o* and *p*-quinones which have been used to modify carbon and platinum electrodes.

found that these enzymes could be reoxidised in the range 0.05 to 0.5 V (versus Ag/AgCl) at pH7. The oxidation of these enzymes was found to occur at the oxidation potential of the polymer modifier suggesting that these acted in a mediatory way. A major drawback of these redox polymer electrodes, however, was that they lost their electrocatalytic activity after a relatively short period of time, typically 5 days (Cenas *et al.* 1984). More recently, Jonsson and Gorton (1985) have described an amperometric glucose sensor based on glucose oxidase immobilized onto graphite which had been previously treated with *N*-methyl-phenazinium (NMP). The authors found that the response of the electrode to glucose was strictly linear over the range 0.5 to 150μM and the sensor was usable up to about 2 mM. The immobilized glucose oxidase was found to be stable for several months but the mediator had to be renewed on a daily basis.

15.3 Enzyme electrodes based on cofactor regeneration

Another group of enzymes which can be used in biosensor design are the nicotinamide adenine dinucleotide (NAD$^+$ and NADP$^+$) dependent dehydrogenases. These enzymes differ from the aforementioned oxidases in that they do not contain an active site redox centre *per se* but rather carry out

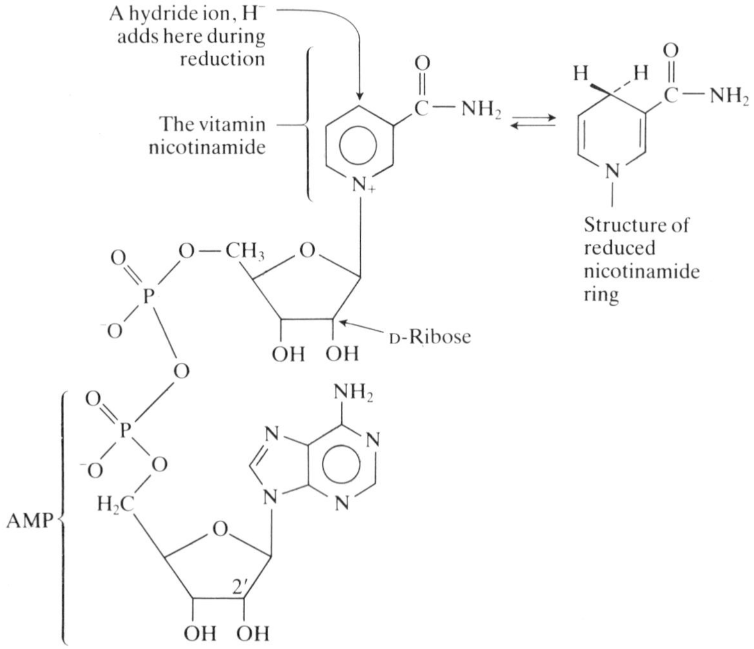

Fig. 15.3 The hydrogen carrying co-enzyme NAD.

their catalytic function with the help of a nicotinamide dinucleotide cofactor, Fig. 15.3

The types of reaction normally associated with the nicotinamide dinucleotide cofactors and hydrogen transfer reactions of the type:

$$NAD^+ + R - \underset{\underset{OH}{|}}{\overset{\overset{H}{|}}{C}} - R' = NADH + R - \underset{\overset{\parallel}{O}}{C} - R' + H^+$$

In this reaction one hydrogen atom of the substrate is directly transferred to NAD^+ and the other appears in the solvent. Both electrons lost by the substrate are transferred to the nicotinamide ring. In an amperometric enzyme electrode based on this type of dehydrogenase the enzymatic activity is measured by recycling reduced $NAD(P)^+$ at a suitable electrode:

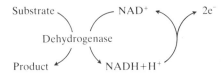

The essential element in making a successful biosensor of this type is to provide a suitable electrocatalytic surface which can reoxidize reduced co-enzyme both efficiently and in the correct biological form, i.e., in a form that will be recognized by the enzyme. Although it is possible to regenerate NAD^+ from NADH at naked electrodes under ideal conditions (0.1 M NADH, pH 7) this approach does have its disadvantages. A large overvoltage is needed, i.e., 1.1 V (versus SCE) for the regeneration of NAD^+ at platinum and prolonged usage results in fouling of the electrode surface due to the accumulation of high molecular weight oxidation products. The need to overcome these difficulties has lead to the development of suitable modified surfaces based on species such as catechols (Jaegfeldt *et al.* 1981), hydro-quinones (Tse and Kuwana 1977), and redox dyes (Huck *et al.* 1984; Gorton *et al.* 1984). The rationale behind the preparation of a chemically modified electrode for NADH oxidation is that if a redox couple in solution can oxidize NADH and can in some way be retained at the surface of the electrode, then the resulting modified electrode should be able to carry out the electro-catalytic regeneration of NAD^+. Preparation of suitable modified electrodes may simply be achieved by passive adsorption of the redox couple to the surface of the electrode, or can involve a synthetic route where the redox couple is covalently bound to the electrode via a bifunctional reagent such as a substituted silane or cyanuric chloride. An excellent review on the topic of chemically modified electrodes is presented by Murray (1984) and the kinetics of such electrodes is discussed in detail by Bartlett (Chapter 13). The oxidation of NADH at a modified electrode procedes by a mediatory route catalysed by the immobilized redox (O/R) couple:

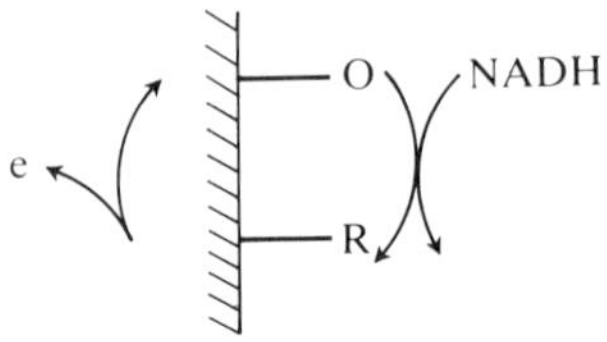

where O and R are the oxidized and reduced forms of the surface mediator. If the rate of the mediation reaction is fast and the rate of reduction or oxidation of the immobilized couple faster, the substrate (NADH) becomes oxidized at a potential near that of the O/R formal potential E^0. This has the effect of greatly lowering the overpotential of the electrochemical reaction, thus reducing interference. Furthermore, the oxidation of NADH is carried out with higher efficiency (in terms of recycling biologically useful NAD^+) and without deleterious effects on the electrode.

Although offering a significant advantage, modified electrodes do suffer from a lack of long term operational stability. Instability usually manifests itself as the desorption of mediator from the electrode surface resulting in decreased electrocatalytic activity. This is particularly the case where the mediator is adsorbed to the electrode surface. Although mediators which are covalently attached to electrode surfaces do exhibit better stability this must be offset by the complicated and often time consuming chemistry involved.

More recently, a novel electrode based on highly conducting organic metals has proved a most useful system for the regeneration of NAD^+ from NADH (Kulys 1981; Albery and Bartlett 1984; Chapter 12). These electrodes are based on stable charge transfer complexes formed by the partial transfer of an electron from a donor such as 7,7,8,8,-tetracyano-*p*-quinodimethane (TCNQ) to an acceptor such as tetrathia-fulvalene (TTF) or *N*-methylphenazinium (NMP):

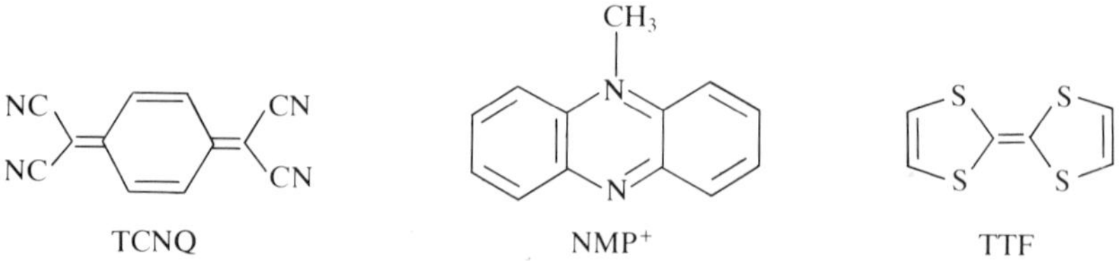

| TCNQ | NMP$^+$ | TTF |

These donor acceptor complexes are metallic at room temperature with a conductivity of 500 (ohms cm)$^{-1}$ for the TTF^+TCNQ^- complex and 200 (ohms cm)$^{-1}$ for the NMP$^+$TCNQ$^-$ complex (Bryce and Murphy 1984). The chemistry and physics of organic metals has been well documented (Engler 1976) as have their electrochemical properties (Jaeger and Bard 1980). Kulys (1981) observed the oxidation of NADH at NMP$^+$TCNQ$^-$ electrodes at -0.2 V (versus Ag/AgCl). When the electrode was used in conjunction with alcohol dehydrogenase the current was found to increase in the presence of ethanol (Kulys and Razumas 1983). The following experimental parameters were observed: $k_{M(app)}$, 15.4 mM; i_{max}, 1.3 μA cm^{-2}. The same electrode could be used to detect acetaldehyde in the presence of NADH with a $k_{M(app)}$ of 54 μM. The oxidation of NADH at the NMP$^+$TCNQ$^-$ electrode is thought to take place via a mediatory route (Kulys 1981). The reaction is believed to involve electrogenerated NMP$^+$ ions since the NMA$^+$TCNQ$^-$ complex does not exhibit any electrocatalytic oxidation of NADH.

A problem that still has to be solved before a dehydrogenase can be incorporated into a practical device is the need to add exogenous cofactor to the solution. This requirement clearly limits any direct or on-line application these sensors may have. A possible way of overcoming this limitation may be the use of perm selective membranes to localize the NAD(P)$^+$ at the electrode surface. Retention could also be achieved by chemical immobilization or by an exclusion principle in which the effective weight of the cofactor is increased by covalent attachment to a high molecular weight species such as dextran (Davies and Mosbach, 1974; Chapter 6).

15.4 Amperometric sensors based on redox proteins

The essence of this type of coupled amperometric enzyme electrode is that the reduced oxidoreductase does not participate in a redox reaction directly at an electrode surface but rather charge transfer occurs via an attendant redox protein such as cytochrome c. In effect, this configuration is analogous to the mediated system described above except that in this example the mediator is not a simple ion but a complex protein molecule. In the coupled electrode the oxidoreductase provides the specificity for the sensor and the redox protein the means of shuttling electrons from the active site of the enzyme to the surface of the electrode. Cytochrome c has proved a useful model in this type of sensor design because not only does it have well defined electrochemistry, but it is also found in nature as the natural electron acceptor in many enzyme complexes. (For a review on the structure and function of cytochrome c the reader is referred to Salemme 1977).

Studies on the electrochemistry of cytochrome c were initiated in the early 1970s by Betso and coworkers (Betso *et al.*, 1972) who were able to show that the iron centre of the protein was reducible at both mercury and platinum electrodes, albeit at a slow rate. Although charge transfer had been observed, the slow kinetics made this an impractical approach for biosensor design. The first major breakthrough in obtaining an analytical device based on cytochrome *c* electrochemistry came when Eddowes and Hill (1977) described a simple treatment of gold which allowed quasi reversible (i.e. fast) charge transfer kinetics. They observed that the addition of 4,4'-bipyridyl (bipy),

to a buffered electrolyte solution enhanced the rate of electron transfer between the heme site of cytochrome *c* and the gold surface. It is important to appreciate that although 4,4'-bipyridyl greatly enhanced charge transfer from the heme centre to the gold electrode it is itself electroinactive in the potential region of interest and thus does not merely act as a charge transfer mediator. The mechanism for the enhanced heterogeneous charge transfer is believed to depend upon the adsorption of bypyridyl to the electrode surface and the rapid on-off binding of the cytochrome at the modified electrode solution interface. This ensures that the protein is held sufficiently close to the electrode surface and in the correct orientation to allow the electron transfer step to take place efficiently (Albery *et al.* 1981; Bartlett, Chapter 13). Fast adsorption/desorption kinetics are considered important otherwise blocking of the modified interface would occur.

The interaction of cytochrome *c* with the gold/bipyridyl electrode has been suggested to occur through specific lysine residues on the surface of the protein hydrogen bonding to one of the nitrogen atoms of the promoter. The reasoning for this suggestion comes from the similarity between the electrochemical system and the protein–protein electron exchange properties of cytochrome *c*. Poly-lysine, for example, has long been known to inhibit the reaction between cytochrome *c* and its biological redox partner cytochrome *c* oxidase. When poly-lysine is added to an electrochemical cell containing cytochrome *c* and the bipyridyl modified gold electrode the heterogeneous charge transfer is similarly inhibited. In an analogous fashion modification of the surface side chains in cytochrome *c* is equally effective in inhibiting both the electrochemical charge transfer step and the reaction with cytochrome *c* oxidase (Cass *et al.* 1984; Pickett 1984; Higgins and Hill, 1985).

Other activating molecules besides 4,4'-bipyridyl have been examined and shown to promote electron transfer from the heme centre of cytochrome *c* to the gold electrode (Eddowes and Hill 1982). The pyridines (III) and (IV), for example, allow a well developed cyclic voltammetric response of the protein to be observed at a gold electrode (Taniguchi *et al*. 1982). Walton and co-workers (Allen *et al*. 1984) have surveyed some fifty five bifunctional organic molecules as possible promoters and concluded that bifunctional molecules containing both a surface active group (a Lewis base with -acceptor properties using N, S, or P) and a weakly basic or anionic functional group appropriately orientated with respect to one another were suitable as promoters. More recently, gold electrodes modified by the chemisorption of pyridine aldehyde thiosemicarbozones (V) have extended this work to promote electrode reactions not only with cytochrome *c* but also with proteins such as plastocyanin, which have a negatively charged binding domain. (Hill *et al*. 1981).

The cytochrome *c* gold/bipyridyl system has been incorporated in enzyme-based sensors for L-lactate (Cass *et al*. 1985), carbon monoxide (Turner *et al*. 1984), and hydrogen peroxide (Higgins and Hill 1985). Horse heart cytochrome *c* is reduced by enzyme catalysed reaction:

(i)

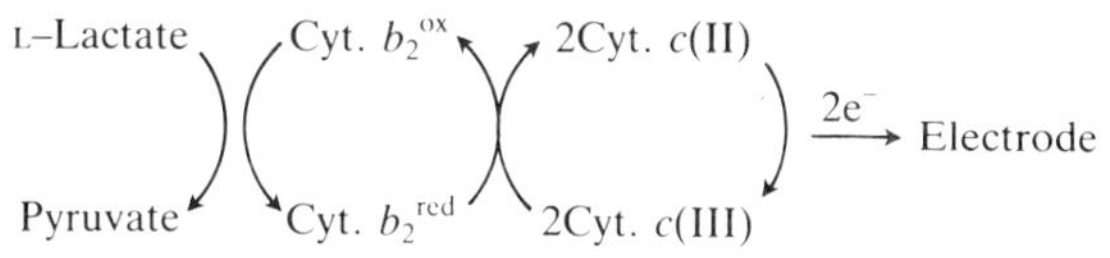

$$\text{L--Lactate} \quad \text{Cyt. } b_2^{ox} \quad 2\text{Cyt. } c(\text{II})$$
$$\xrightarrow{2e^-} \text{Electrode}$$
$$\text{Pyruvate} \quad \text{Cyt. } b_2^{red} \quad 2\text{Cyt. } c(\text{III})$$

(ii)

$$2e \quad 2 \text{ Cyt } c^{3+} \quad \begin{array}{c}\text{CO}\\ \text{Oxidoreductase}\\ \text{(red)}\end{array} \quad \begin{array}{c}\text{CO}_2\\ +\\ 2\text{H}^+\end{array}$$
$$2 \text{ Cyt } c^{2+} \quad \begin{array}{c}\text{CO}\\ \text{Oxidoreductase}\\ \text{(ox)}\end{array} \quad \begin{array}{c}\text{CO}\\ +\\ \text{H}_2\text{O}\end{array}$$

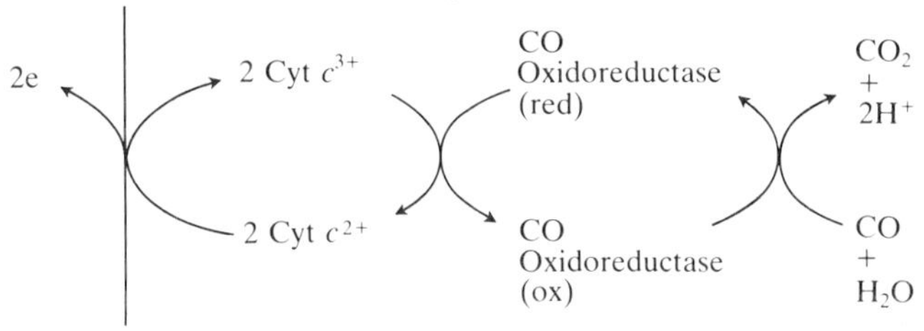

Reaction (i) is catalysed by yeast flavo cytochrome *c* and reaction (ii) by a bacterial carbon monoxide oxidoreductase (Turner *et al*. 1984). The reaction of cytochrome *c* at the 4,4'-bipyridyl electrode has also been coupled via a terminal oxidase to the reduction of dioxygen to water, thus providing the basis for an oxygen sensor, Fig. 15.4 (Hill *et al*. 1981).

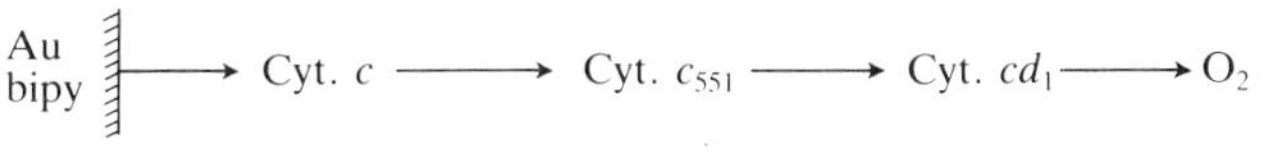

$$\begin{array}{c}\text{Au}\\ \text{bipy}\end{array} \longrightarrow \text{Cyt. } c \longrightarrow \text{Cyt. } c_{551} \longrightarrow \text{Cyt. } cd_1 \longrightarrow \text{O}_2$$

Fig. 15.4 Reaction scheme for a biosensor based on cytochrome *c* for the detection of dioxygen.

Cytochrome c_{551}, the 'blue' copper protein Azurin, was necessary because the rate of electron transfer between horse heart cytochrome c and *Pseudomonas aeruginosa* nitrate reductase cytochrome cd_1 was found to be slow.

The cytochrome c/gold/bipyridyl electrode has been used to facilitate charge transfer to and from intact systems as well as isolated enzymes. For example, when rat liver mitochondria and protoplasts prepared from *Paracoccus denitrificans* were used with the above electrode, electrons could be fed into these systems from the gold electrode. In addition, electrons could be extracted from added reducing agents such as NADH via cytochrome c (Higgins and Hill 1985). Although no practical biosensor has been developed using a coupled intact biological system in this way, a variety of possibilities exist (Hammond *et al.* 1981; Higgins and Hill 1981; Turner *et al.* 1983). Clearly, any system capable of either oxidizing or reducing cytochrome c may be coupled to an electrode in this way providing a route to monitoring chemicals, enzymes, cell components, or intact micro-organisms.

15.5 Conducting organic metal electrodes coupled to oxidases

Another interesting application of the charge transfer type electrodes mentioned above has been to couple them directly to oxidases. Kulys and coworkers, for example, have reported efficient coupling of the redox centres of cytochrome b_2 (L-lactate ferricytochrome c oxidoreductase) (Kulys and Svirmickas, 1979), glucose oxidase (Kulys *et al.* 1980), horse radish peroxidase (Kulys *et al.* 1980) and xanthine peroxidase (Kulys and Razumas 1983) to NMP^+TCNQ^+ or NMA^+ (methyl acridinium) $TCNQ^+$ electrodes. The construction of these electrodes was relatively simple; either powdered enzyme was mixed with a finely divided preparation of the charge transfer complex and pressed into a disc (10^5 pounds in^{-2}) or an aliquot of enzyme solution was entrapped at the electrode surface behind a membrane. Enzyme electrodes containing cytochrome b_2 adsorbed on NMP^+TCNQ^+ electrodes oxidized L-lactate in the region of -0.2 to 0.5 V (versus SCE). The $k_{M(app)}$ of the electrode was approximately 2 mM with an i_{max} of 25–37 μA cm^{-2}. The electrode response was the same in the presence and absence of oxygen. The maximum current was reached at pH 6.6 whereas the native enzyme exhibits maximum activity at pH 7.2. The electrodes were found to retain 45–50% of their initial sensitivity after three to nine days at room temperature.

Electrodes based on glucose oxidase adsorbed on NMA^+TCNQ^- or NMP^+TCNQ^- electrodes responded to glucose only at potentials higher than 0.1 V relative to Ag/AgCl; i.e. the peak oxidation potential of NMP^+ and NMA^+. The electrodes showed a good linear range and remarkable stability retaining their activity for more than 100 days (Kulys *et al.* 1980).

Electroreduction of hydrogen peroxide on NMA^+TCNQ^+ electrodes containing adsorbed peroxidase starts at 0.3 to 0.35 V. Studies using rotating disc techniques have shown that the process is limited by the catalytic activity of the enzyme. The $k_{M(app)}$ of the system is 80 μM and $i_{max} = 0.27$ mA cm^{-2}. The heterogeneous rate constant has been calculated to be 8.5×10^{-4} cm s^{-1}. These electrodes have also been used in conjunction with glucose oxidase to construct bienzyme glucose sensitive electrodes (Kulys *et al.*, 1981). This configuration exploited the bioelectrocatalytic reduction of hydrogen peroxide produced by the action of glucose oxidase.

More recently, Albery and co-workers (1985) have also investigated the use of organic metal electrodes as suitable charge transfer surfaces for redox enzymes (Chapter 12). They have extended this work by looking at the charge transfer properties of glucose oxidase at a variety of different conducting organic electrodes. A common feature they found with all the electrodes was low background currents in the absence of glucose. All materials gave increased currents on the addition of glucose however the best materials were found to be the TCNQ$^-$ salts of NMP$^+$, (TTF$^+$), and quinolinium (Q$^+$)

Q^+

in terms of giving the lowest background currents and widest ranges of operating voltages. Albery *et al.* (1985) have also reported the system to be stable. After a period of 28 days continuous operation, the response of the glucose electrode was found to have decreased by only 20%.

An important point which still has to be resolved is the exact nature of the electrode mechanism, i.e., whether or not the enzyme is oxidized by direct electron transfer to the electrode or whether it is a mediated process. In the latter case TTF$^+$, NMP$^+$, and/or TCNQ$^-$ react with the enzyme and are then oxidized at the electrode. Kulys and his school (Kulys and Svirmickas 1980) claim that in the case of cytochrome *c* and peroxidase containing electrodes the exchange of electrons between the redox centre and the electrode is direct. They cite as their evidence the lack of current dependence of these electrodes on the potential and data from kinetic studies using rotating disc (Kulys and Samalius, 1982). In the case of the flavin containing oxidases, glucose oxidase, and xanthine oxidase, Kulys claims a mechanism mediated by NMP$^+$. This conclusion is supported by the fact that substrate oxidation only proceeds at potentials corresponding to the mediator redox conversion potentials. They suggest that mediators are formed in the layer near the electrode surface during the slight dissolution of the organic metal. In this context it is interesting to note that Kulys and Cenas (1983) have shown that, in solution, TCNQ$^\circ$ is an extremely efficient oxidant of reduced glucose oxidase ($5_{ox} \times 10^{-4}$ (M^{-1} s^{-1}) = 150). We have since shown that graphite electrodes modified with TCNQ act as efficient electrocatalytic surfaces for the oxidation of reduced glucose oxidase and can operate at very modest potentials (O mV vs Ag/AgCl). We have also shown that TTF$^+$ is an efficient mediator for reduced glucose oxidase, both in homogenous solution and when adsorbed on to an electrode surface (Hendry *et al.* 1986). Albery *et al.* (1985) disagree with this final postulate and argue that charge transfer occurs via the direct route for glucose oxidase. They cite rotating ring disc data as their main evidence in that they have not been able to detect the products of electrode dissolution on the down stream ring electrode. (Chapter 12).

15.6 Conclusion

The search for new electron transfer agents and explanations of their mechanism of action will doubtless continue apace, driven by the commercial significance of this type of biosensor configuration.* New products based on this general technology are imminent and it seems probable that the area will be advanced rapidly. The key to success lies in finding simple and stable configurations capable of mass production at low cost. The hope is that this will be achieved without sacrificing the accuracy and sensitivity associated with conventional laboratory analyses.

Acknowledgement

A. P. F. Turner is a Senior Fellow of the British Diabetic Association.

References

Albery, W. J. and Bartlett, P. N. (1984). An organic conductor electrode for the oxidation of NADH. *J. Chem. Soc. Chem. Commun.* 234-6.

—— Craston, D. H. and Hagett, B. G. D. (1985). The development of novel biosensors. In *The World Biotech Report 1985*, Vol. 1, 359-82. Online Publications, Pinner, U.K.

—— Eddowes, M. J., Hill, H. A. O. and Hillman, A. R. (1981) Mechanism of the reduction and oxidation of cytochrome *c* at a modified gold electrode. *J. Amer. Chem. Soc.* **103**, 3904-10.

Allen, P. M., Hill, H. A. O. and Walton, N. J. (1984). Surface modifiers for the promotion for the promotion of direct electrochemistry of cytochrome *c*. *J. Electroanal. Chem.* **178**, 69-86.

Aston, W. J., Ashby, R. E., Higgins, I. J., Scott, L. D. L. and Turner, A. P. F. (1984). Enzyme based methanol sensor. In *Charge and field effects in bio-*

---

*Whilst glucose sensors have been used as the ubiquitous example, the importance of finding a scheme which is applicable to a wide range of enzymatic reactions must be stressed, since this will facilitate the development of multianalyte sensors.

systems (eds. M. J. Allen and P. N. R. Usherwood) 491–8. Abacus Press, Turnbridge Wells.

Betso, S. R., Klepper, M. H. and Anderson, L. B. (1972). The electrochemical behaviour of cytochrome *c*. *J. Amer. Chem. Soc.* **94**, 8197–204.

Bright, H. J. and Porter, D. J. T. (1975). In *The enzymes* (ed. H. Boyer) Vol. **12**, 421–86.

Bryce, M. R. and Murphy, L. C. (1984). Organic metals. *Nature* **309**, 119–26.

Cass, A. E. G. (1984). Protein electrochemistry. *Life. Chem. Reports.* **2**, 321–362.

—— Davis, G., Hill, H. A. O. and Nancarrow, D. J. (1985). The reaction of flavocytochrone b_2 with cytochrome *c* and ferricinium carboxylate. Comparative kinetics by cyclic voltammetry and chronoamperometry. *Biochim. Biophys. Acta.* **828**, 51–7.

—— Francis, D. G., Hill, H. A. O., Aston, W. J., Higgins, I. J., Plotkin, E. V., Scott, L. D. L. and Turner, A. P. F. (1984). Ferrocene-mediated enzyme electrode for amperometric determination of glucose. *Anal. Chem.* **56**, 667–71.

Cenas, N. K., Kanapieniene, J. J. and Kulys, J. J. (1984). NADH oxidation by quinone electron acceptors. *Biochem. Biophys. Acta.* **767**, 108–12.

—— Pocius, A. K. and Kulys. J. J. (1983). Electron exchange between flavin and heme containing enzymes and electrodes modified by redox polymers. *Bioelectrochem. Bioenerg.* **11**, 61–73.

—— and Kulys, J. J. (1984). Bioelectrocatalytic conversion of substances on polymer modified electrodes. *Bioelectrochem. Bioenerg.* **12**, 583–91.

Clark, L. C. and Lyons, C. (1962). Electrode system for continuous monitoring in cardiovascular surgery. *Ann. N. Y. Acad. Sci.* **102**, 29–33.

Davies, P. and Mosbach, K. (1974). The application of immobilized NAD$^+$ in an enzyme electrode and in model enzyme reactors. *Biochim. Biophys. Acta.* **370**, 329–338.

Davis, G. (1985). Electrochemical techniques for the development of amperometric biosensors. *Biosensors.* **1**, 161–78.

—— Green, M. J. and Hill, H. A O. (1984). Electrochemical assay for adenosine-5′-triphosphate and creatine kinase.

D'Costa, E. J., Higgins, I. J. and Turner, A. P. F. (1986). Quinoprotein glucose dehydrogenase and its application in an amperometric glucose sensor. *Biosensors* **2**, 71–89.

Dicks, J. M., Aston, W. J., Davis, G. and Turner, A. P. F. (1986). Mediated amperometric biosensors for D-galactose, glycolate and L-amino acids based on a ferrocene-modified carbon paste electrode. *Anal. Chim. Acta.* **182**, 103–112.

Eddowes, M. J. and Hill, H. A. O. (1977). A novel method for the investigation of the electrochemistry of metalloproteins: cytochrome *c*. *J. Chem. Soc. Chem. Commun.* 71.

—— (1982). Binding as a prerequisite for rapid electron transfer reactions of metalloproteins. *Am. Chem. Soc. Adv. Chem. Ser.* **201**, 173–8.

Engler, E. M. (1976). Organic metals. *Chemtech.* **4**, 274–9.

Gorton, L., Torstensson, A., Jaegfeldt, H. and Johansson, G. (1984). Electrcatalytic oxidation of reduced nicotinamide coenzymes by graphite electrodes modified with an adsorbed phenoxazinium salt, Meldola Blue. *J. Electroanal. Chem.* **161**, 103–20.

Hendry, S. P., Cardosi, M. F. and Turner, A. P. F. (1986). An amperometric enzyme electrode for glucose based on a tetrathiafulvalene-modified carbon electrode. *Biosensors* (submitted).

Higgins, I. J. and Hill, H. A. O. (1979). Microbial energy sources. In *Microbial technology. Current state, furture prospects.* Society of General Microbiology Symposium No 29, pp. 359–62.

—— (1985). Bioelectrochemistry. *Essays in Biochemistry* **21**, 119–45.

Hill, H. A. O., Walton, N. J. and Higgins, I. J. (1981). Electrochemical reduction of dioxygen using a terminal oxidase. *FEBS Lett.* **126**, 282–4.

Huck, H., Schelter-Graf, A., Danzer, J., Kirch, P. and Schmidt, H. (1984). Bio-electrochemical detection systems for substrates of dehydrogenases. *Analyst* **109**, 147.

Jaeger, C. D. and Bard, A. J. (1978). Electrochemical behaviour of tetrathiafulvalene tetracyanoquinodimethane electrodes in aqueous media. *J. Amer. Chem. Soc.* **101**, 1690–99.

—— (1980). Electrochemical behaviour of donor-tetracyanoquinodimethane electrodes in aqueous media. *J. Amer. Chem. Soc.* **102**, 5435–42.

Jaegfeldt. H., Torstensson, A. B. C., Gorton, L. G. O. and Johansson, G. (1981). Catalytic oxidation of reduced nicotinamide adenine dinucleotide by graphite electrodes modified with adsorbed aromatics containing catechol functionalities. *Anal. Chem.* **53**, 1979–82.

Jonsson, G. and Gorton, L. (1985). An amperometric glucose sensor made by modification of a graphite electrode surface with immobilized glucose oxidase and adsorbed mediator. *Biosensors.* **1**, 355–68.

Kulys, J. J. (1981). Development of new analytical systems based on biocatalysers. *Enzyme Microb. Technol.* **3**, 342–52.

—— and Cenas, N. K. (1983). Oxidation of glucose oxidase from *Penicillium vitale* by one- and two- electron acceptors. *Biochim. Biophys. Acta.* **744**, 57–63.

—— and Razamus, V. J. (1983). *Biocatalysis in electrochemistry of organic compounds.* Mokslas, Vilinius. (In Russian.)

—— and Samalius, A. S. (1982). Acceleration of electrode processes by biocatalysts. *Lietuvos. TSR. Mokslu. Akademijas. Darabi. B ser.* **2(129)**, 3–9.

—— and Svirmickas, G. J. S. (1979). Bioelectrocatalysis. Electron transfer from the active centre of cytochrome b_2 to organic metals. *Dokl. Akad. Nauk. SSSR.* **245**, 137–40.

—— (1980). Reagentless lactate sensor based on cytochrome b_2. *Anal. Chim. Acta.* **117**, 115–20.

—— Pesliakiene, M. V. and Samalius, A. S. (1981). The development of bienzyme glucose electrodes. *Bioelectrochem. Bioenerg.* **8**, 81–8.

—— Samalius, A. S. and Svirmickas, G. J. S. (1980). Electron exchange between the enzyme active centre and organic metal. *FEBS Lett.* **114**, 7–15.

Murray, R. W. (1984). Chemically modified electrodes. In *Electroanalytical chemistry*, (ed. A. J. Bard) Vol. 13, pp. 191–387. Marcel Dekker, New York.

Pickett (1984). Electrochemistry of metal complexes. In *Electrochemistry* (ed. D. Pletcher) Vol. 9, pp. 162–221. *Roy. Soc. Chem.* London.

Salemme, R. (1977). Structure and function of cytochrome *c*. *Ann. Rev. Biochem.* **46**, 229–39.

Scheller, F. W., Rennberg, F. S. R., Müller, H., Janchen, M. and Weise, H. (1985). Biosensors: trends and commercialization. *Biosensors.* **1**, 135–61.

Taniguchi, I., Toyosawa, K., Tamaguchi, M. and Yasukouchi, K. (1982). Voltammetric response of horse heart cytochrom *c* at a gold electrode in the presence of sulphur bridged bipyridines. *J. Elecroanal. Chem.* **140**, 187–93.

Tse, D. C. S. and Kuwana, T. (1977). Oxidation of NADH at a modified electrode. *Anal. Chem.* **49**, 1589–95.

Turner, A. P. F. (1985) Biosensors for process monitoring and control. In *The World Biotech Report 1985*, Vol. 1, Online Publications, Pinner, UK, pp. 181–92.

—— (1986). Amperometric biosensors based on mediator-motified electrodes. In *Methods in enzymology: immobilized enzymes and cells* (ed. K. Mosbach.) Academic Press, New York. (In press).

—— D'Costa, E. J. and Higgins, I. J. (1986). The use of glucose dehydrogenase and other quinoproteins in analytical systems. In *Enzyme Engineering*. Plenum, New York. (In press.)

—— Ramsay, G. & Higgins, I. J. (1983). Applications of electron transfer between biological systems and electrodes. In *Industrial and Medical Applications of Bioelectrochemistry*. Biochem. Soc. Trans. **11**, 445–448.

—— Aston, W. J., Davis, G., Higgins, I. J., Hill, H. A. O. and Colby, J. (1984). Enzyme based carbon monoxide sensors. *Microbial Gas Metabolism*. (Eds. R. K. Poole and D. S. Dow). Academic Press, New York, pp. 161–70.

Updike, S. J. and Hicks, G. P. (1967) The enzyme electrode. *Nature* **214**, 986–8.

16

The construction of mediated amperometric biosensors

W. J. ASTON

The ideal method for the determination of substances whether in the field of medical or industrial analysis requires the procedure to be technically simple, rapid, inexpensive, sensitive, precise, and accurate, using stable reagents which are non-hazardous. Biological catalysts such as enzymes possess many of these properties being capable of catalysing specific reactions in mixed samples under mild conditions. It is these properties coupled with their increased availability which has resulted in their incorporation into diagnostic tests replacing many of the earlier non-enzymic assays which involved chemical oxidation-reduction techniques or condensation methods (Dietzler and Smith 1980). These chemical methods were subject to positive error resulting from the reaction with substances that normally occur in the blood and, in the case of the condensation reactions, used hazardous reagents such as hot, highly concentrated sulphuric acid. A frequently assayed metabolite, glucose, may be assayed by a variety of methods (Passey et al. 1977), the National Reference Method for the determination for this substrate for instance is a spectrophotometric assay incorporating two enzymic reactions (Neese et al. 1976). In the presense of glucose the enzymes, hexokinase (EC 2.7.1.1.) and glucose-6-phosphate dehydrogenase (EC 1.1.1.49) result in the production of NADH, the resulting increase in absorbance being measured spectrophotometrically at 340 nm. A commonly encountered technique utilizes the enzyme glucose oxidase, the product of the reaction may be determined spectrophotometrically by incorporation of peroxidase (EC 1.11.1.7) and linking the subsequent oxidation of hydrogen peroxide to a chromogen such as o-dianisidine (Guidotti et al. 1961). The use of chromogens has resulted in new diagnostic products referred to as 'dry chemistry' systems in which all the reagents and auxillary substances necessary for the reaction are embedded in a paper or plastic matrix in their dry state, thus removing the need to prepare reagent solutions (Walter 1983; Sherwood et al. 1983). Although other techniques, such as calorimetric (Mosbach and Danielsson 1981) and opto-electronic methods (Lowe et al. 1983) have been proposed, the most practical alternative is the use of electro-chemical detection systems. It is the construction of these amperometric devices and their possible development which is the subject of this chapter.

The majority of electrochemical devices function by measuring the enzymic consumption or production of a naturally occuring electrochemically active species. Glucose, for instance, may be determined by measuring the production of hydrogen peroxide or consumption of oxygen by the action of glucose oxidase (Chapter 1). Indeed a diverse range of biosensors utilizing electrochemical techniques have been described (Carr and Bowers 1980; Aston and Turner 1984). Few devices, however, have been successfully developed commercially (Thai and Yeo 1983; Chapter 18). An alternative is to link biological redox reactions to an electrode, via a mediator, and measure the flow of electrons amperometrically (Chapter 15). Enzyme electrodes have many advantages as analytical devices enabling particular substrates to be assayed with the minimum of pretreatment. Since these devices are generally non-destructive; multiple determinations of samples may be performed. Although the response may be affected by chemical and physical factors, it is rapid, usually within 30–600 seconds.

16.1 Bio-fuel cells

Biological fuel cells are devices in which the reactions at one or both electrodes are catalysed biologically at ambient temperatures and pressures. The diversity of microbial metabolism allows a large range of fuels to be utilised including many industrial wastes by incorporating either whole organisms (Bennetto 1984; Chapter 17) or enzyme preparations (Plotkin *et al.* 1980, Higgins *et al.* 1984). Bio-fuel cells have generally been classified into one of two types depending on the mode of interaction of the biological catalyst with the electrode (Shaw 1963): in type A cells the fuel, such as hydrogen, is generated biologically in a separate chamber to that in which its subsequent electrochemical oxidation occurs. Type B bio-fuel cells require the direct interaction of the biological catalyst with the electrode to provide a continuous source of electrons, a process often facilitated by the use of a mediator. The mediator should be capable of rapid reversible electron transfer and have a redox potential close to that of the biological catalyst which it is transfering electrons from to the electrode. The mediator should be non-toxic, not a substrate for the catalyst, and must be stable for prolonged periods of time during both storage and operation. It is this latter type of cell, utilizing a mediator, which will be described in this section.

Bio-fuel cells usually consist of two inert electrodes, such as gold, platinum, or carbon, maintained in a buffered solution. Prior to use the electrodes are cleaned by sonication in buffer or by cyclic voltammetry in sulphuric acid (500 mM) in the potential range -0.26 V to $+1.3$ V (versus the standard calomel reference electrode, SCE) until distinct hydrogen/oxygen, oxidation reduction peaks are observed (Sawyer and Roberts 1974). The electrodes are separated by an ion exchange membrane

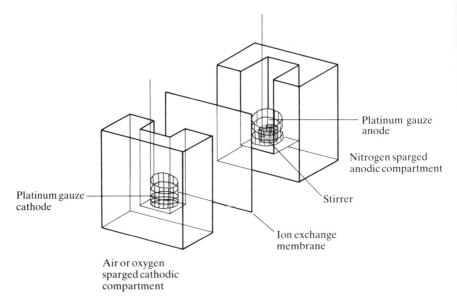

Fig. 16.1 Exploded view of bio-fuel cell. The perspex cell consisted of an anode and cathode ($35 \times 16 \times 15$ mm and $35 \times 15 \times 11$ mm) separated by an ion exchange membrane. Set up as described in the text (see Table 16.1).

and sparged with air/oxygen (cathode) and nitrogen (anode) (Fig. 16.1). The membrane separates the reactions occuring in the two compartments whilst allowing the exchange of protons. A range suitable membranes are available commercially (BDH Ltd., Poole, Dorset, UK; Nafion, DuPont (UK) Ltd., Hemel Hempstead, Herts, UK). Higher charge transfer efficiencies are attained if the nitrogen gas is passed through a gas purification unit (Nilox,

Table 16.1   Components of a glucose oxidase based bio-fuel cell mediated by TMPD

Anodic compartment	Cathodic compartment
Acetate buffer (50 mM, pH 4.5)	Acetate buffer (50 mM, pH 4.5)
Sodium Chloride (150 mM)	Sodium Chloride (150 mM)
Mediator (TMPD) (8.0 mM)	
Glucose oxidase (8.0 mg)	
Total volume 4.2 ml	Total volume 3.5 ml
Pt electrode 50 mesh	Pt electrode 50 mesh
1.6 × 4.8 cm	1.6 × 4.8 cm
Sparged with oxygen free nitrogen and magnetically stirred	Sparged with air

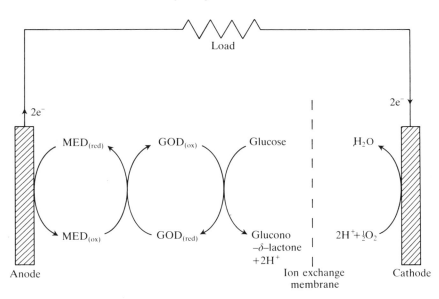

Fig. 16.2 Schematic diagram of a glucose oxidase based bio-fuel cell where $MED_{(ox/red)}$ are the oxidized and reduced forms of the mediator. $GOD_{(ox/red)}$ are the oxidized and reduced forms of the prosthetic group of the enzyme.

Jencons Scientific Ltd, Leighton Buzzard, Bedfordshire, UK) and water prior to use, thereby reducing oxygen interference and loss of solution by evaporation respectively. The addition of glucose to a bio-fuel cell containing glucose oxidase and a soluble mediator, e.g. N,N,N',N'-tetramethyl- p -phenylenediamine (TMPD) (Table 16.1.) maintained at 20°C results in the flow of electrons from the enzyme to the anode, via the mediator. The electrons flow around the external circuit to the cathode, where under ideal conditions in the presence of protons and oxygen, water is produced (Fig. 16.2). The resulting current, measured as a voltage across a known resistance, is proportional to the addition of a limiting component until saturation is achieved. Glucose at concentrations as low as 0.1 mM may be determined rapidly (within five seconds) by measuring steady state currents (Fig. 16.3). Lower concentrations may be determined by measuring the charge passed, determined by integration of the areas under the current/time profiles.

As a sensor the biofuel cell described above suffers limitations due to the presence of an autoxidizable mediator although this may be reduced by the incorporation of an insoluble mediator (Higgins *et al.* 1984), the requirement for an oxygen cathode, and primarily to the need for a membrane. Whilst the diffusion properties of ion-exchange membranes are affected by the pH of

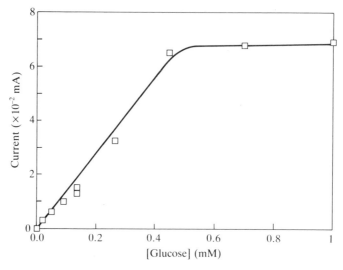

Fig. 16.3 Steady state current response of a glucose oxidase based bio-fuel cell, measured as a voltage across a resistance.

the buffer, the majority retain enzymes whilst allowing the passage of low molecular weight components such as gases, mediators and substrates (Turner *et al.* 1980). The cell is affected by changes in the rate of agitation of the anodic compartment, stirring being required to enhance the rate of electron transfer from the enzyme/mediator to the electrode. The diffusion of components across the membrane results in a reduction in electron transfer efficiency due to competitive side reactions occuring. Due to these limitations the device is unsuitable as a sensor in the majority of situations where the quantitative determinations of a substrate is required.

16.2 Poised potential configurations

The requirement for an air cathode and semi-permeable membrane may be eliminated by the use of a conventional or computer controlled potentiostat. These devices maintain the potential of the working electrode in a cell with respect to a reference electrode, such as a calomel.

Oxygen interference may be reduced by the use of an oxygen independent enzyme such as methanol dehydrogenase. The enzyme is capable of oxidizing a range of primary alcohols to the corresponding aldehydes and acids. Incorporation of methanol dehydrogenase into a fixed potential cell in the presence of a soluble mediator, phenazine ethosulphate, enables methanol to be determined in solution at much lower concentrations than is possible using conventional gas liquid chromatography (Aston *et al.* 1984). The device

(Fig. 16.4) consisted of a jacketed reaction vessel (5.0 ml) (Quickfit, Gallenkamp and Co. Ltd., London, UK) maintained at 30°C, containing borate buffer (3.0 ml, 250 mM, pH 9.0), ammonium chloride (50 mM), phenazine ethosulphate (1.0 mM) and crude extract of *Methylosinus trichosporium* OB3b (3.0 mg protein) prepared from organisms grown on methane as the sole source of carbon and energy (Scott *et al.* 1981). The mixture was continuously stirred using a magnetic stirrer and purged with nitrogen as described above. The platinum working electrode was cleaned by

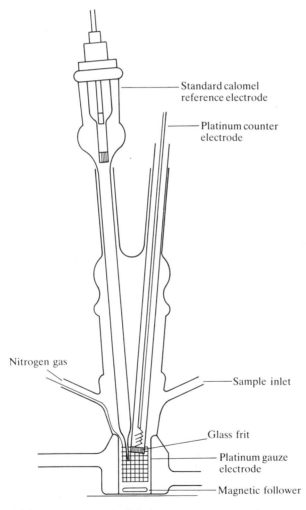

Standard calomel
reference electrode

Platinum counter
electrode

Nitrogen gas

Sample inlet

Glass frit

Platinum gauze
electrode

Magnetic follower

Fig. 16.4 Schematic diagram of a fixed potential enzyme based sensor (containing soluble components). (See text for details).

cyclic voltammetry, immersed in the reaction mixture, and maintained at + 100 mV (versus SCE) using a potentiostat (H. B. Thompson and Associates, Newcastle Upon Tyne, UK). A platinum counter electrode was used; isolated from the reaction mixture by means of a glass frit. It was possible to determine formaldehyde and methanol at concentrations as low as 0.02 μM by measuring the charge passed upon the addition of aliquots of sample using a CDP4 computing intergrator (Pye Unicam Ltd., Cambridge, UK).

This configuration has many advantages over the previously described bio-fuel cell as an electrochemical sensor. The primary advantage being that it does not utilize a membrane or require sparging with oxygen. However, as in the case of the bio-fuel cell, it is dependent upon the rate of stirring and requires to be maintained anaerobic in the presence of an autoxidizable mediator. An alternative is to use a non-autoxidisable mediator such as ferrocene, capable of eliciting a high charge transfer efficiency irrespective of the oxygen tension. Ferrocene and its derivatives are a group of organo-metallic compounds capable of single electron transfer between a range of oxido-reductase enzymes such as glucose oxidase, pyruvate oxidase, xanthane oxidase, oxalate oxidase, sarcosine oxidase, lipoamide dehydro-genase, glutathione reductase (Cass *et al.* 1985), and quinoproteins (Duine and Frank 1981) such as methanol dehydrogenase (Aston *et al* 1984) glucose dehydrogenase (D'Costa *et al.* 1984) and lactate dehydrogenase (Preneta *et al.* 1984). The incorporation of dimethyl-trimethylferrocene methiodate (1.0 mM), a soluble derivative of ferrocene, in the methanol sensor described above enabled methanol (3.0 μM) to be determined irrespective of varying oxygen tension. This was demonstrated by sparging the cell with either oxygen or nitrogen and measuring the resulting peak current and charge passed. Whilst the device did not require highly trained personal or expensive equipment it did require stirring, and was volume and temperature dependent.

16.3 Probe configurations

The incorporation of insoluble mediators into carbon pastes has enabled probe devices to be constructed. The paste, comprising graphite (2.5 g), liquid parafin (1.5 ml) and the mediator (250 mg) is thoroughly mixed and placed in a recess in the electrode (Fig. 16.5). The electrode consists of a disc of platinum set into the end (2.0 mm) of a length of glass tubing (0.6 cm diameter) using a non-conductive epoxy resin (Ciba-Geigy Ltd., Cambridge, UK). Contact to the external circiut is made via a single stranded wire bonded to the disc using a silver loaded epoxy resin (Adams 1969). Prior to use, the platinum disc is cleaned using an aluminium oxide slurry (0.2 μm). The enzyme is retained at the surface of the paste electrode using a membrane held

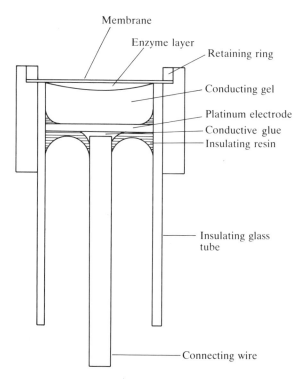

Fig. 16.5 A membrane retained graphite paste enzyme based sensor. The electrode consisted of a platinum disc (6.0 mm diameter) set into a pasteur pipette using conductive and non-conductive resins as described in the text.

in position by an 'O' ring. Whilst this method of retension is suitable for flexible membranes, inflexible membranes such as ion exchange require mounting in a holder (Fig. 16.5). The choice of membrane, of which a variety are available commercially (e.g. dialysis, Nuclepore), affects the response time, interference characteristics, and the linear range of the biosensor. Using dialysis membrane a glucose electrode exhibits a linear response up to 15 mM (Fig. 16.6). As in the case of the previously described configurations the response is rapid with the steady state response being attained within a minute. Generally, the thinner the layer of paste, the more reproducible the electrode response. Poised at $+150$ mV (versus SCE) a glucose oxidase/$1,1'$-dimethylferrocene electrode with a paste 1.0 mm thick measured over ten replicates produced a background current of 1.2 mA $\pm$ 0.5% in the absense of glucose, whilst an electrode with a paste 3.0 mm thick produced a current of 1.4 mA $\pm$ 2.0%. In the presence of glucose (5.0 mM) the current responses with pastes of 1.0 and 3.0 mm thick were 1.4 mA $\pm$ 0.64% and 1.6 mA $\pm$ 2.5%, respectively. A more reproducible surface is achieved by

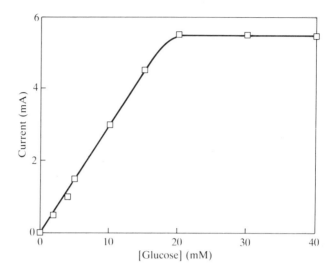

Fig. 16.6 Calibration curve for a membrane retained glucose oxidase based biosensor.

using a glass sphere to form a recess in the carbon paste into which the components may be placed (Fig. 16.5). By incorporating carbon monoxide oxidoreductase in the probe and placing a silver/silver chloride reference around the membrane holder in the presence of buffer has enabled carbon monoxide gas to be detemined (Turner *et al.* 1984).

The covalent immobilization of glucose oxidase in the presence of 1,1′-dimethylferrocene has enabled convenient glucose analyses to be performed (Cass *et al.* 1984). A graphite foil (Union Carbide, Ohio, USA) was adopted as the supporting electrode since it possesses a high surface area for immobilization of the components. Discs of carbon (6.0 mm diameter) are connected to lengths of wire using a silver loaded epoxy resin (Johnson Matthey Chemicals, Royston, UK) and allowed to dry. The electrodes are mounted onto the end of a length of glass tubing (6.0 mm diameter) using a non-conducting epoxy resin (Ciba–Geigy Ltd, Cambridge, UK); care being taken to ensure that the resin does not seal the edges of the carbon, through which the enzyme gains access. Sealing these edges causes up to 75% of the current to be lost due to enzyme immobilization predominantly occuring on the electrode surface. Once dry, the electrode is inverted and insulated using a mixture of epoxy resin (1.8 g, grade 814) and catalyst, triethylenetetramine (0.23 g) (Polysciences Ltd., Moulton Park, Northampton, UK). Drying may be performed overnight at room temperture or more rapidly by heating in an air oven at 60°C for 1.5 hours. Once fabricated, the resistance between the connecting wire and the electrode surface is measured and any electrodes exhibiting resistances greater than 3.0 ohms are discarded. Electrodes with high or variable resistances do not elicit linear responses and are not reproducible. The electrodes are doped with the mediator, 1,1'-dimethyl-ferrocene (25 μl, 100 mM) (Strem Chemicals, Newburyport, USA) dissolved in a suitable solvent, such as toluene, and allowed to air dry, Immobilization of the enzyme is done initially by placing the graphite electrode in acetate buffer (100 mM, pH 4.5) containing 1-cyclohexyl-3(2-morpholinoethyl)-carbodiimide metho-*p*-toluenesulformate (100 mM) for 80 minutes at room temperature. The electrodes are subsequently washed with distilled water and placed in glucose oxidase (50 mg ml^{-1} protein) in acetate buffer (100 mM, pH 4.5) overnight or for an hour using carbonate buffer (100 mM, pH 9.5). After immobilization the electrodes are washed and stored frozen at $-20°$C in phosphate buffer (100 mM, pH 7.4).

Poised at $+150$ mV (versus SCE) and maintained at 30°C, the electrodes exhibited linear responses up to 30 mM glucose within 30 s (Cass *et al.*, 1984). At low glucose concentrations (8.0 mM) they were unaffected by changes in the pH range 7.0–9.0 although an effect was observed at higher concentrations and the response increased with increasing temperature at a rate of 4.0% °C^{-1} up to 45°C, above which inactivation occured. The presence of oxygen caused a reduction in the currents produced since it was the natural electron acceptor for the enzyme. The apparent K_M for glucose by glucose oxidase immobilized by this method was 24 mM. This was unaffected by placing a polycarbonate membrane over the probe although dialysis membrane altered the apparent K_M to 74 mM changing the electrode response from a kinetically controlled configuration to diffusion controlled system a mechanism which can be used to tailor the range over which linearity is desired.

The electrode has advantages over the previously described systems in that it enables rapid, multiple determinations to be performed on samples. It is simple, easily calibrated and when operated at glucose concentrations normally encountered in the body does not demonstrate the pH dependence characteristic of the soluble enzyme. It therefore exhibits many of the properties suitable for clinical analysis and is readily applied to *in vitro* analysis. The application of micromanipulation techniques to minaturized electrodes (Silver 1976; Chapter 21) should facilitate the evolution of *in vivo* devices.

16.4 Strip devices

The low currents produced by these configurations enabled the electronics to be simplified by coupling the reference and auxiliary electrodes, i.e. using a single counter electrode such as the silver/silver chloride reference electrode.

The adoption of the two electrode configuration allows both the working and counter electrodes to be mounted in close proximity on a suitable base material thereby reducing the volume of sample required (Fig. 16.7). The silver/silver chloride reference electrodes made from silver foil (BDH Chemical Ltd., Poole, Dorset, UK) were polished using an aluminium oxide slurry (0.2 μm) (BDH Chemicals Ltd., Poole, Dorset, UK). When used in association with the previously described poised potential devices the foil (40 $\times$ 5.0 $\times$ 0.13 mm) is connected to the external circuit by means of a soldered wire insulated using a non-conductive epoxy resin (Giba–Geigy, Duxford, Cambridge, UK). The electrode is immersed in a solution of hydrochloric acid (1.0 M) at a potential of + 400 mV (versus SCE) for 30 s and rinsed in distilled water prior to use. When incorporated onto a strip device one surface is polished with an aluminium oxide slurry, cut into squares (3.0 $\times$ 3.0 mm), and bonded to the base using a conductive silver resin (Johnson Matthey Chemicals Ltd. UK).

Squares of papyex (3.0 $\times$ 3.0 mm) were bonded onto the base electrode using colloidal graphite, after firmly pressing into position, any excess carbon was removed. Prior to immobilization of the enzyme, as described previously, it is necessary to insulate the reference electrode using a layer of silicone rubber to eliminate inactivation of the enzyme by silver ions. In the

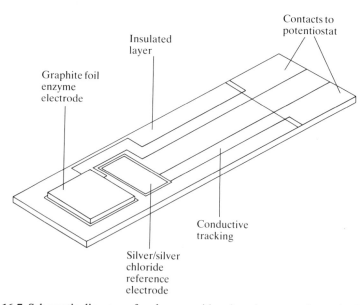

Fig. 16.7 Schematic diagram of a glucose oxidase based enzyme electrode. Both the working and silver/silver chloride electrodes were mounted horizontally on a ceramic base. (See text for details).

case of glucose oxidase, immobilization is performed as described previously with the silicone rubber protector being removed prior to use.

16.5 Manufacturing considerations

Amperometric enzyme electrodes have been shown to operate under laboratory conditions, although they may be considered to be in their infancy and problems may arise when applied to practical situations. These stem from the requirement to control the chemical and physical conditions which influence the catalytic reactions occuring within the electrode. The use of a non-autoxidizable mediator reduces the effect of oxygen interference with a further reduction achieved by the use of an oxygen independent enzyme, e.g. quinoproteins. Temperature and pH dependence may be reduced by the incorporation of an excess of enzyme.

This configuration although overcoming many of the problems encountered with those described previously, is not amenable to mass production. In order to produce enzyme electrodes economically and satisfy commercial requirements several criteria must be fulfilled with the components being available in sufficient quantity and quality and fabricated under stringent manufacturing protocols (Sharp 1983).

If the strip device is developed it is necessary to be able to mount both electrodes in close proximity on the same base and connect these to the external circuit. A variety of possible base materials are available ranging from ceramics to plastics and even cardboard. Once a suitable base material is obtained it is necessary to deposit a low resistance conducting bridge between the edge connector and electrodes. A variety of techniques are available depending on the temperature the base material is capable of withstanding (Bunshah *et al.* 1982). Whilst ceramics are capable of withstanding temperatures in the region of 150°C, plastics deform at these elevated temperatures. Two methods which allow contacts to be deposited at low temperatures include electroless goldplating (Feldstein 1974) and vacuum deposition techniques (Smith 1976). By exposing areas of the base, the desired electrode and connector may be deposited with the connecting tracking subsequenty insulated. Porous carbon electrodes may be manufactued by a continuous technique involving sequential exposure of the material to reagents contained in tanks. Costs may be reduced if immobilization of the enzyme is not incorporated in the procedure and adsorption is sufficient. In the case of the immobilization of glucose oxidase to porous carbon, ommiting 1-cyclohexyl-3(2-morpholinoethyl)-carbodiimide metho-*p*-toluenesulformate from the immobilization procedure causes only a 25% reduction of the initial current indicating that adsorption of the enzyme may be sufficient for these electrodes to function.

Reference electrodes may be preformed as described previously, cut, and bonded to the base. The working electrodes may be coated with a membrane thereby changing the response time and the linearity of the electrode. Whilst commercial membranes are available which may be bonded to the base it is possible to spray coat membranes, such as cellulose acetate; the properties of the membrane being dependent on the particular solvent, or solvents, used. The effect of membranes and electrode configurations on the electrode linearity can be seen from the results presented. In the case of the fuel cell and the first poised potential device described in which a membrane is not used, the response is linear up to 0.45 mM (Fig. 16.3). By variation in the configuration or the use of a membrane, the linearity can be extended to cover the range up to 20 mM (Fig. 16.6).

Once completed, enzyme electrodes must be stable during storage prior to use. The majority of enzymes may be stored frozen in buffer, as above, or refrigerated at 4°C (Yellow Springs Instruments, Ohio, USA; Thai and Yeo 1983). A more practical approach is to store the electrodes dry. This may be achieved by air drying or freeze drying and storing the electrodes desiccated in the manner adopted by manufacturers of diagnostic strip devices (Ames Company Ltd., Bucks, UK).

16.6 Conclusion

Our knowledge of electrochemical biosensors has advanced rapidly over the last few years. This has been due to the interaction of biochemical, electrochemical, and electronic disciplines coupled with corresponding financial stimulation. The commercial development of enzyme electrodes in diagnostic analyses has already been demonstrated enabling metabolites such as glucose concentrations to be routinely determined in clinical laboratories. Self monitoring usually involves patients performing a visual comparison with a colour chart or more accurately using a reflectance meter (Chiasson *et al.* 1984). The amperometric systems described in this chapter have particular advantages over presently available methods including the ability to quantitatively determine the concentration of a specific metabolite, irrespective of the oxygen tension, without pretreating the sample or washing prior to the determination. Electrodes ideally should exhibit stability both during storage and during operation, with their reproducibility of response falling within predetermined constraints. In addition, they must not be subject to interferences from other metabolites. The ability of these electrodes to perform well in turbid solutions such as blood may result in their application in other areas such as environmental and industrial analysis.

Acknowledgements

The author would like to thank his colleagues at Genetics International Inc in particular Dr. D. Scott.

References

Adams, R. M. (1969). *Electrochemistry at solid electrodes* (ed. A. J. Bard) Marcel Dekker, New York.

Aston, W. J. and Turner, A. P. F. (1984). Biosensors and biofuel cells. In *Biotechnology and genetic engineering reviews*, Vol. 1 (ed. G. E. Russel), pp. 89–120. Intercept, Newcastle upon Tyne.

—— Ashby, R. E. A., Scott, L. D., Higgins, I. J. and Turner, A. P. F. (1984). Enzyme based methanol sensor. In *Change and field effects in biosystems*, (eds. M. J. Allen and P. N. R. Usherwood) pp. 491–8. Abacuse Press, Tunbridge Wells.

Bennetto, H. P. (1984). Microbial fuel cells. *Life Chemistry Reports* **2**, 363–453.

Birch, K., Hilderbrandt, P., Marshall, M. O. and Sestoff, L. (1981). Self monitoring of blood glucose without a meter. *Diabetes Care* **4**, 414–16.

Bunshah, R. F., Blocher, J. M., Bomfield, T. D., Fish, J. C., Ghate, P. B., Jacobson, B. E., Mattox, D. M., McGurie, G. E., Schwartz, M., Thornson, J. A. and Tucker, R. C. (1982). In *Deposition technologies for films and coatings, development and applications*, 585pp. Nayes Publications, New Jersey.

Carr, P. W. and Bowers, L. D. (1980). Immobilised enzymes. In *Analytical clinical chemistry*, 460pp. John Wiley, New York.

Cass, A. E. G., Davis, G., Green, M. J. and Hill, H. A. O. (1985). Ferricinium as an electron acceptor for oxido-reductases. *Journal of Electroanalytical Chemistry* (In press).

—— Francis, G. D., Hill, H. A. O., Aston, W. J., Higgins, I. J., Plotkin, E. V., Scott, L. D. L. and Turner, A. P. F. (1984). Ferrocene-mediated enzyme electrode for the amperometric determination of glucose. *Analytical Chemistry* **56**, 667–71.

Chiasson, J. L., Morrisaet, R. and Hamet, P. (1984). Precision and costs of techniques for self-monitoring of serum glucose levels. *Canadian Medical Research Association Journal* **130**, 38–43.

Davis, G., Hill, H. A. O., Aston, W. J., Turner, A. P. F. and Higgins, I. J. (1983). Bioelectrochemical fuel cell and sensor based on a quinoprotein. *Enzyme and Microbial Technology* **5**, 383–8.

D'Costa, E. J., Duine, J. A., Dokter, P., Turner, A. P. F. and Higgins, I. J. (1984). Kinetics of a microbial quinoprotein glucose dehydrogenase. *Society for General Microbiology Quarterly* **11**, M11.

Dietzler, D. N. and Smith, C. H. (1980). Carbohydrates. In *Gradwolls clinical laboratory methods and diagnosis*. (eds. A. C. Sonnenwirth and L. Jareft). Vol. 1, pp. 210–49. C. D. Mosby, St. Louis.

Duine, J. A. and Frank, J. (1981). Quinoproteins: a novel class of dehydrogenases. *Trends in Biological Science* **6**, 278–80.

Feldstein, N. (1984). Electroless plating in the electronics industry. *Plating* 141–53.

Guidotti, G., Colombo, J. P. and Foa, P. P. (1961). Enzymic determination of glucose. *Analytical Chemistry* **33**, 151–2.

Higgins, I. J., Aston, W. J., Best, D. J., Turner, A. P. F., Jezequel, S. G. and Hill, H. A. O. (1984). Applied aspects of methylotrophy: Biochemical applications, purification of methanol dehydrogenase, mechanism of methane monooxygenase. In. *Microbial growth on C1 compounds* (eds. R. L. Crawford and R. S. Hanson). American Society for Microbiology, Washington.

Lowe, C., Goldfinch, M. J. and Lias, R. T. (1983). Some novel biomedical biosensors. In *Biotech 83*, p. 665–78. Proceedings of the International Conference on the Commercial Applications and Implications of Biotechnolog, Online Publications, Northwood, London.

Mosbach, K. and Danielson, B. (1981). Enzyme thermister devices. *Analytical Chemistry* **53**, 83–94.

Neese, J. W., Duncan, P., Bayse, D., Robinson, M., Cooper, T. and Stewart, C. (1976). Development and evaluation of a Hexakinase/glucose-6-phosphate dehydrogenase procedure for use as a National Reference Method. U.S. Department of Health, Education and Welfare. US. Public Health Service Center for Disease control, Atlanta, GA. HEW Publication Number (CDC) 77–8330, 147pp.

Passey, R. B., Gillum, R. L., Fuller, J. B., Urry, F. M. and Giles, M. L. (1977). Evaluation and comparison of 10 glucose methods and the reference method recommonded in the proposed product class standard (1974). *Clinical Chemistry* **23**, 131–9.

Plotkin, E. V., Higgins, I. J. and Hill, H. A. O. (1981). Methanol dehydrogenase bioelectrochemical cell and alcohol detector. *Biotechnology Letters* **3**, 187–92.

Preneta, A. P., Turner, A. P. F. and Higgins, I. J. (1984). Enzyme-based lactate sensor. *Society for General Microbiology Quarterly* **11**, M11.

Sawyer, D. and Roberts, J. (1974). *Experimental electrochemistry for chemists*, p. 67–79. Wiley, New York.

Scott, D. Brannan, J. and Higgins, I. J. (1981). The effect of growth conditions on Intracytoplasmic membranes and methane mono-oxygenase activities in Methylosinus trichosporium OB3b. *Journal of General Microbiology* **125**, 63–72.

Sharp, J. R. (1983). *Guide to good pharmaceutical manufacturing practice*. HMSO publications. Grovenor Press, Portsmouth.

Sherwood, M. J., Warchal, M. E. and Chen, S.-T. (1983). A new reagent strip (Visidex) for determination of glucose in whole blood. *Clinical Chemistry* **29**, 438–46.

Silver, I. A. (1976). An ultramicro glucose electrode. In *Ion and electrode in biology and medicine*. (eds. M. Kessler, L. C. Clark, D. Lubbers, I. A. Silver and W. Simon) pp. 189–92. Urban and Schwarzenberg, Munich, Berlin.

Smith, H. R. (1976). Vacuum deposition techniques, methods of aluminium evaporation. *Metal Finishing* Sept., 42–47.

Thai, A. C. and Yeo, P. P. B. (1983). Stable blood glucose test strips and reflectance meters. *Singapore Medical Journal* **24**, 45–7.

Turner, A. P. F., Aston, W. J., Higgins, I. J., Davis, G. and Hill, H. A. O. (1980). Applied aspects of bioelectrochemistry: Fuel cells, sensors and bioorganic synthesis. *Biotechnology bioengineering Symposium* **12**, 401–12.

—— Bell, J. M., Colby, J., Davis, G. and Hill, H. A. O. (1984). Carbon monoxide: Acceptor oxidoreductase from *Psuedomonas thermocarboxydvorans* strain C2 and its use in a carbon monoxide sensor. *Analytica Chimica Acta* **163**, 161–74.

Walter, B. (1983). Dry reagent chemistry in clinical chemistry. *Analytical Chemistry* **55**, 499a–514a.

17

Redox-mediated electrochemistry of whole micro-organisms: from fuel cells to biosensors

H. PETER BENNETTO, JONATHAN BOX, GERARD M. DELANEY, JEREMY R. MASON, SIBEL D. ROLLER, JOHN L. STIRLING, and CHRISTOPHER F. THURSTON.

17.1 Introduction

17.1.1 'Direct' and 'indirect' whole-cell sensors

Until recently the use of intact microbes in biosensors has been restricted to an 'indirect' mode wherein the biocatalyst functions in conjunction with attractively simple, familiar sensing elements such as the pH electrode (substrate-induced generation of acidic or basic products) or the conventional oxygen electrode (substrate-dependent respiration). The general utility of these devices may be judged from the account given by Karube in chapter 2 of this volume and from recent reviews (Aston and Turner 1984; Guilbault 1984; Mărgineanu *et al.* 1985). In particular, attention has been drawn to their potential for use in clinical analysis of biological fluids, for monitoring fermentation systems, in toxological studies, and for estimation of antibiotics (Kobos 1983; Simpson and Kobos 1984; Corcoran and Rechnitz 1985; Findl *et al.* 1985).

In the present article we discuss a different approach, based largely on recent studies of microbial fuel cells, in which micro-organisms give a 'direct' electrical signal. The biochemical fuel cell containing cells or cell components has long attracted attention as a source of 'alternative energy' from biological fuels (Aston and Turner 1984; Bennetto 1984), and lately as a possible route to synthesis of compounds of potential commercial interest (van Dijk *et al.* 1985). Various types of bio-fuel cell were intensively studied in the 1960s and 1970s, with motivation from NASA-funded research programmes aimed at the development of ancillary power sources. However, most of these devices relied on the principle of electrochemical oxidation of a secondary metabolic product such as formate or hydrogen for production of power, and were relatively inefficient. Nevertheless the production of hydrogen by *Clostridium butyricum* was ingeniously used in the first fuel cell-type microbial sensors for measurement of BOD (biological oxygen demand) in wastewaters (Karube *et al.* 1977) and for the estimation of formic acid (Matsunaga *et al.* 1980).

Recently a renewed interest in microbial fuel cells and sensors has resulted from the discovery that 'redox' coupling reagents can be used to link microbial respiratory processes to an electrode directly and effectively. The source of power in a 'direct' microbial fuel cell is the well-known reducing power of the micro-organisms stemming from 'redox'-active substances produced in the initial or intermediate stages of catabolism. Thus electrons from intracellular electron-rich substances can be diverted from the normal respiratory-chain pathways by appropriate coupling reactions, and thence delivered via the anode to an external circuit (Bennetto *et al.* 1980, 1983). With some design modification it is possible to adapt the fuel cell for sensor use, since the electron-flow resulting from the electrochemical oxidative process is readily available for measurement by amperometric or other methods, and under suitable conditions the signal becomes substrate-dependent (Turner *et al.* 1982). The essential difference between the 'direct' and 'indirect' modes of operation is that in the indirect method signals are generated by the Nernstian response of an electrode to concentrations of stable metabolic products, or by means of the polarographic response to oxygen, whereas in the direct method a true bioelectrochemical connection is established between substrate and electrode via the electroactive products of biocatalysis.

In the following account we outline the bioelectrochemical background, and attempt to draw up guidelines for the construction of mediated whole-cell sensors. Illustrative preliminary results on glucose and alcohol sensors are also presented.

17.1.2 Electron transduction from enzymes and whole cells

There are intrinsic differences between the mechanism of signal-generation from whole cells and that of mediated enzyme electrodes, which is discussed elsewhere in this volume by Cardosi and Turner (Chapter 15) and by Albery and Craston (Chapter 12). In the latter case electrons are taken from reduced enzymes at a donor site (or a limited number of sites) provided that there is relatively free access for the mediator. Access of a mediator to sources of reducing power within an organism is restricted, however, by the cell walls and membrane, and these same sources may be varied in number and location (enzymes, pyridine nucleotides, quinone intermediates, cytochromes). In principle it is possible for a mediator to interact with a particular intracellular electron donor, but since complex interactive redox states are present it is useful for many purposes to view the electrons as residing in a 'reducing pool' within the cytoplasm. Some of the factors to be considered in these systems also relate to sensor applications of protein electrochemistry and electron transduction to and from cytochrome centres, which have been recently reviewed (Turner *et al.* 1982; Cass 1984).

17.2 Whole cells as catalysts in biosensors

Since most of the enzymes employed for use in sensors have been isolated from micro-organisms, it is logical that the organisms themselves should be regarded as potential biocatalysts, even if their manipulation appears to present more complex problems (Aston and Turner 1984). Microbes can be judiciously selected for particular sensor applications from an enormous range at our disposal (aerobes, anaerobes, chemolithotrophs, photosynthetic organisms, etc.), bearing in mind their widely differing respiratory physiology and biochemistry. There are no well-defined guidelines for selection, apart from what is known about the utility of the enzymes and with due regard to the lessons from many previous studies of indirect microbial sensors. The directions of future work with micro-organisms may be influenced, however, by a number of distinct advantages and disadvantages which they offer:

(a) The versatility of micro-organisms makes them potentially suitable as catalysts for a very wide range of substrates, and thus potential analytes, that can be utilized. In principle this covers almost every type of naturally-occuring carbon compound (Gunsalus and Schuster 1961).

(b) The cost of production is very moderate for many organisms, whereas the isolation of an enzyme from its source can be expensive.

(c) Where oxidation in the cells involves several degradative stages to provide reducing intermediates, whole cells might provide a bigger electro-chemical signal than a single enzyme. For example, in one type of glucose sensor the oxidation of glucose to gluconolactone using glucose oxidase yields two electrons per molecule of substrate (e.g. see Cass *et al.* 1984):

$$C_6H_{12}O_6 = \text{Gluconolactone} + 2H^+ + 2e^-$$

In contrast, the complete oxidation of glucose in a whole-cell may be represented by the equation

$$C_6H_{12}O_6 + 6H_2O = 6CO_2 + 24H^+ + 24e^-$$

A substantial proportion of this large electron yield may be realized in practice (Delaney *et al.* 1984). It should be noted, however, that microbial catalysts are bulkier than enzymes, and estimates of the relative activity of whole cells and enzymes in bio-fuel cells suggest that a given weight of whole cells is about as effective as the weight of the relevant enzyme(s) it contains.

(d) Some potentially useful enzymes are unstable, or may need a hydro-phobic environment or sophisticated methods of immobilization in order to function. In whole micro-organisms, stability and activity is conferred by the natural medium of the cell in a way that is difficult to mimic, and the cells themselves can be immobilized by simpler procedures (Guilbault 1984; Karube and Suzuki 1983).

(e) Enzymes might be better shielded within micro-organisms from interfering (signal-generating) substances and inhibitory solutes such as heavy-metal compounds, which would be present in many test samples.

(f) The use of enzymes in bioelectrochemical electron transfer frequently demands the presence of a co-enzyme. Addition of exogenous cofactors is unnecessary, however, in the case of whole organisms, because these substances are regenerated within the cells.

(g) A number of micro-organisms are genetically well characterized, and methods of strain-selection for increasing particular enzyme proteins are well developed. The judicious use of mutants could provide an additional range of activity, selectivity, and specificity.

(h) Both the direct and indirect modes of signal-transduction from whole cells offer scope for *non*-genetic biotechnological manipulations. In particular, the direct method promises a versatility for transduction of electrons from various intermediate stages of the oxidative pathway, possibly with some selectivity provided by differences in the response to different mediators (see section 17.3). In the indirect method, production of a response-producing active product by a multi-step oxidation process is more likely to be subject to kinetic inhibition, whereas in the direct method, electron transduction usually by-passes much of the respiratory chain.

The advantages of using micro-organisms for sensor applications must, however, be balanced against the known disadvantages, and the following points are particularly relevant:

(a) The great flexibility and versatility of micro-organisms might also limit the selectivity and sensitivity of microbial sensors. The organisms may oxidize substrates other than the ones(s) we wish to sense, which could be a particular problem in biological fluids containing high concentrations of active substances such as glucose. Also cells deprived of one substrate may 'switch' to an alternative metabolic path.

(b) There may be problems of biological stability attached to the storage and retention of activity of organisms over long periods. Surprisingly little is known of the long-term stabilities of either enzymes or whole cells.

(c) In reductive reactions of organisms, the 'tapping' of respiratory activity with the aid of mediators may be subject to interference from atmospheric oxygen.

(d) Difficulties are associated with the need to prevent loss of soluble mediators by immobilization or other methods of retention.

Work in progress suggests the feasibility of constructing sensors containing both gram-positive and negative organisms, as well as strict aerobes and facultative anaerobes (see Table 17.1). Several of the advantages and disadvantages outlined above are borne out by our recent experimental findings,

Table 17.1 Whole-organism sensors based on the bio-fuel cell principle: organisms used or under investigation

Organism	Substrate	Reference[a]
Clostridium butyricum	BOD[b,c]	Karube *et al.* 1977
Clostridium butyricum	Formic acid[c]	Matsunaga *et al.* 1980
E. coli	Glucose	Hanazato and Shiono 1983
E. coli ML308	Lactose	Roller *et al.* 1983
Proteus vulgaris	Glucose, sucrose	
Anabaena variabilis	CO_2, hν	Bennetto *et al.* 1984
Methylomonas methylovora	Ethanol, methanol	Box and Mason 1986
Alcaligenes eutrophus	Succinate, pyruvate	
Pseudomonas putida	Succinate	
Erwinia carotovora	Sucrose	
Nocardia salmonicolor	Acetate	
Hansenula anomala	D, L-Lactate	Scheller *et al.* 1985
Lactobacillus fermenti	Vitamin B$_1$	Scheller *et al.* 1985

[a]This work, and unpublished results, unless otherwise stated.
[b]BOD = biological oxygen demand.
[c]'Indirect' fuel-cell sensor depending on microbial production of hydrogen (no mediator).

some of which are detailed in Section 17.4, while possible methods of improvement are discussed in Section 17.5.

17.3 Generation of electricity by micro-organisms

17.3.1 Microbial fuel cell studies

Studies of biochemical fuel cells have demonstrated that electron-transduction from micro-organisms is remarkably efficient if a suitable 'redox' mediator is included in the anolyte (Bennetto *et al.* 1980, 1983). Progress in the development of direct bio-fuel cells has been reviewed elsewhere (Wingard *et al.* 1982; Aston and Turner 1984; Bennetto 1984). The aim of many of these studies has been to identify factors which generally govern the generation of electricity from microbes, in particular the crucial rôle of redox mediators in promoting transfer of electrons across the cell wall and membrane (Roller *et al.* 1984; Delaney *et al.* 1984), but the potential for bio-anode sensor applications was also established (Turner *et al.* 1982). We also note that the rate of decolourization of redox dyes such as resazurin has long been used to measure bacterial activity in foods and milk (e.g. Proctor and Greenlie 1939); it is but a short step to couple this type of reaction to an electrode or an optical sensor.

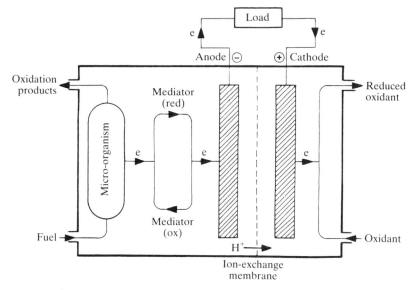

Fig. 17.1 Microbial fuel cell; schematic representation. See Delaney *et al.* (1984) and Bennetto (1984) for details.

The mode of operation of the microbial fuel cell is shown in Fig. 17.1 (Roller *et al.* 1984). The typical discharge behaviour observed, and the effect produced by further addition of substrate, is shown in Fig. 17.2 for the thionine-mediated glucose/*P. vulgaris* cell. The amount of electricity drawn from the cell, given by the area under the graph, is proportional to the quantity of substrate added. A recent detailed analysis of this system has established the fate of glucose in the anode compartment, and confirms that the coulombic yield from oxidation of glucose is about 50% (Thurston *et al.* 1985). These results were obtained with 30 mg freely suspended bacteria, which easily generate a signal of milliamp or hundreds of mV proportions. Figure 17.2 also illustrates the rapid regeneration of power on a subsequent addition of substrate. For sensing purposes, however, such a device is rather bulky (15 cm³ anode compartment) and the response rather slow (several minutes), so that substantial changes of size and configuration are required to convert it to a convenient sensor format. These developments are considered in Section 17.5.

17.3.2 Mediator–organism interactions

Fuel cell studies have revealed much information which has a direct bearing on the development of whole-cell sensors. Mediator reduction rates affect

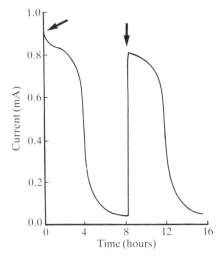

Fig. 17.2 Electricity generation from a glucose/*P. vulgaris* microbial fuel cell. The anolyte contained 0.1 M phosphate buffer, pH 7.0; 1 mM thionine; 30 mg (dry wt.) organism; (30°C). Discharge of the cell was through 560 ohm load. Arrows mark additions of 10 μmol glucose.

the efficiency of signal-transduction, and the considerable variation for particular organisms and mediators is illustrated by a selection of data in Table 17.2 taken from recent work (Stirling *et al.* 1983; Roller *et al.* 1984). Such differences in reactivity, whatever the cause, might be used to differentiate between types of organism, and could be applied to differential sensing and cell-counting. The rates of reduction generally show a dependence on concentrations of organisms, mediator (up to certain limits), and substrate (depending on load conditions). For a given organism and mediator they are

Table 17.2 Rates of reduction of mediators by micro-organisms, μmol g^{-1} s^{-1} (substrate, glucose; 30°C)

Organism	Q_{O_2}	TH	MB	BCB	BV
E. coli B/r	1.76	3.65	4.16	0.99	2.23
P. vulgaris	0.69	7.10	1.70	1.03	6.11
P. aeruginosa	1.03	1.54	—	0.63	0.31

TH, thionine; MB, methylene blue; BCB, brilliant cresyl blue; BV, benzyl viologen; Q_{O_2} is the respiratory quotient, or rate of reduction of dioxygen. (It should be noted that the reductions involve 4, 2, 2, 2, and 1 electrons for O_2, TH, MB, BCB, and BV respectively).

quite reproducible and show only small variations (up to 20%) depending on growth rates.

The question of what type of mediator molecule or molecular property gives fast electron transfer in whole-cell systems is one which cannot be easily answered. There is no simple dependence on mediator charge, but lipophilicity may play an important rôle in aiding penetration of lipid membranes (Bennetto *et al.* 1981). The various factors involved have been extensively reviewed elsewhere (Bennetto 1984). The redox levels which are accessible appear to vary for different organisms and mediators, but it is not easy to identify specific reducing centres. Attempts at pinpointing the reducing source may not be meaningful, since the species immediately interacting with the mediator might not be the key source of electrons, and the concentrations and redox states of both the cellular intermediates and the mediator will be interdependent. Some insights into the mechanistic aspects might be gained, however, from kinetic differences in the reduction of mediators. An example is provided by thionine and 2-hydroxy-1,4-naphthoquinone (HNQ), which can both be used to good effect as mediators with whole cells (Bennetto *et al.* 1985). Thionine reacts particularly rapidly with free NADH in buffer solution (and orders of magnitude faster than many of its derivatives); in contrast, HNQ is not reduced at all by free NADH. This suggests that NADH alone cannot reduce HNQ in the cell, and that electrons must therefore come from a different intermediate. Interestingly, HNQ is reduced by NADH in the presence of membrane particles (Box and Mason 1986).

A drawback of many mediator substances for sensor use is their poor long-term stability, usually more serious for reduced forms. It should also be noted that many of the requirements of mediators for use in bio-fuel cells differ from those for use in sensors, where some compromises are necessary. Soluble mediators present a problem of mediator loss, whereas insoluble ones may give rise to diffusion-limited currents. The effects of solubilizing groups are complex: positively charged groups will encourage migration of reduced mediator to the anode but tend to promote undesirable absorption there (as in the case of thionine), while negative charges inhibit penetration of negatively charged cell walls and charge transfer to a negative electrode, though this is not evident in the case of the HNQ anion. Attention has been focused recently on the use of ferrocene and its derivatives as mediators, mainly because the solubility and electrochemical properties of these compounds can be varied by substituents as required. Insoluble ferrocenes have been exploited in the construction of a glucose enzyme sensor (Cass *et al.* 1984), but some uncertainty remains relating to the mechanism of mediation. Thus importance is attached to the diffusion of oxidized ferrocene cation away from the electrode, but it is not clear how the very insoluble neutral forms move electrons to the electrode following reduction of the cation by the enzyme.

17.3.3 Electrochemical considerations

17.3.3.1 Mode of operation of microbial sensors   Direct sensors will probably be operated to greater advantage in the amperometric, rather than the potentiometric mode, and will depend on the rapid establishment of poised steady-state electrode potentials and currents through the action of a mediator. Following the addition of substrate, generation of electrons by the organism leads to an increase in the concentration of reduced mediator (and hence the redox ratio), which in turn gives a potential shift and drives a current through an external load. With an appropriate choice of load resistance and component concentrations, the amperometric response is measured under steady-state conditions, and the depolarizing action of the organism becomes substrate-dependent. The limits of sensitivity, the accuracy, and the response time of the sensor will depend upon the amount of current obtainable from a given amount of organism and substrate. Apart from the biological considerations, this current will depend on the efficiency of electron transfer reactions at each end of the electron-transduction process: (a) electron transfer from the electron source in the micro-organism to a mediator, and (b) transfer of electrons from the mediator to the base electrode. Both of these are affected by electrochemical activation or mass transport limitations, and could lead to high polarization effects and poor performance.

17.3.3.2 Polarization effects   In considering first the reducing action [process (a)], an essential requirement for the potential to be established rapidly is fast penetration of the mediator both into and out of the cell surface, as in the case of the microbial fuel cell. If rapid penetration is not achieved, either of these steps may become rate-determining, and the sensor will respond only sluggishly. (In unfavourable cases, where the cell exterior is less permeable, some improvement might result from the use of more sophisticated mediating systems, as discussed in Section 17.5). Since the permeation rates are concentration-dependent, there are advantages in poising the potential of the system artificially by potentiostatic means (as illustrated in the example below), so that the concentrations of either the reduced or oxidized mediator do not become too small, and the redox ratio does not approach extreme values. Also, when current is drawn, it should not be so great as to remove excessive amounts of mediator from the reaction area, which would amount to an undesirable effect of concentration polarization. Let us suppose, by way of illustration, that a sensor is designed which uses 1 mg (dry wt.) organism, and the equivalent of 0.1 ml of 1.0 mM mediator solution (a one-electron redox reagent). It therefore contains 10^{-7} mol mediator, and, using the Faraday constant $F = 10^5 C \, mol^{-1}$, would require 10^{-2} coulombs of electricity for complete reduction of the mediator. Experiment shows that many active organisms are capable of sustaining mediator-coupled currents of up to 100 μA mg^{-1}, equivalent to 10^{-4} C s^{-1}, and would thus produce a relatively small perturbation in mediator concentration. Such a system would (for glucose) remove substrate from the test solution at rates of the order of 10 nmol s^{-1}, so that the test would be virtually non-destructive over an experimental period of, say, 0.5–5.0 min.

Considerations of permeability into the lipid membranes of cells indicate that the ingress or escape of a mediator should equally not be limiting at mediator concentrations of around millimolar (Bennetto 1984). In practice, rapid reduction of the mediator lends itself to a fast-responding sensing device in favourable cases. Thus, response times of 0.5–5 min have been observed in fuel cells, and these can be much reduced in designs having a mediator which is localized at or near the electrode surface. The rate determining step for the response of such electrodes may then be the uptake of substrate by the micro-organisms, which is often a very rapid process and should not present serious problems. It is interesting to note that uptake of glucose by *P. vulgaris* in a fuel cell is more rapid when the cell is under load. (Thurston *et al.* 1985).

To assess the importance of the electron transfer step [process (b), above] it is instructive to use the previous example and express the current in terms of the electrochemical rate equation

$$i = FkcA$$

where c is the concentration of reduced mediator delivering charge to the electrode, A is the area of the working electrode (conveniently taken as 1 cm^2), and k is the specific electrochemical rate constant. Cyclic voltammetry measurements show that several effective mediators have k values of around $10^{-2} - 10^{-3}$ cm s^{-1}. Using these figures, the equation above predicts that they would be capable of supporting 0.1–1.0 mA at 1.0 mM concentration, and polarization of the electrode should therefore be negligible.

By comparison, many indirect sensors depending on oxygen tension or product concentration are poorly poised and provide sluggish electrode kinetics. This, in part, arises from diffusional limitations; the dependence on oxygen consumption is a particular weakness of many systems containing dense populations of aerobic organisms, in which oxygen tension may become vanishingly small and oxygen transfer may be very slow (Clarke *et al.* 1985). A distinction should therefore be made between whole-cell sensing methods employing the oxygen electrode, which is essentially a polarographic device, and redox-mediated amperometry, which is not.

17.3.3.3 Electrode potentials of mediators For microbial fuel cells, mediators of low redox potential have been favoured in order to maximize the obtainable voltage, but this is not essential for sensors, provided that an adequate signal is produced. Likely mediators are those of higher E^0 which are generally more stable and less prone to re-oxidation by molecular oxygen. Interference from oxygen might be less serious, however, where the kinetics of mediator–organism and mediator–electrode interactions are favourable for rapid electron transduction.

17.3.3.4 Electrode materials Presently available information favours the use of carbon electrodes for satisfactory interfacing of the biocatalyst. These have a range of useful properties (Wang 1981; Besenhard and Fritz 1983) and surface modification by controlled oxidation can provide groups which are ideal for constructing binding links to whole organisms (see section 17.5)

17.4 Experimental whole-cell biosensors

The use of electrical outputs from 'direct' bio-fuel cells operated in a sensor mode is illustrated below with results for glucose and ethanol. The two substrate-dependent parameters considered were

   (i) total coulombic output of cells under constant load,
   (ii) rate of current (or potential) rise.

Peak current, potentiometric, potentiostatic, impedance, and capacitative responses are all also worthy of investigation. Figure 17.3 shows the

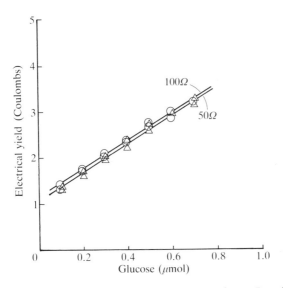

Fig. 17.3 Correlation of electrical output with glucose for a *P. vulgaris* fuel-cell sensor. 60 mg (dry wt.) organism. Resistive loads were 100 ohm, ○; and 50 ohm, △ (30°C).

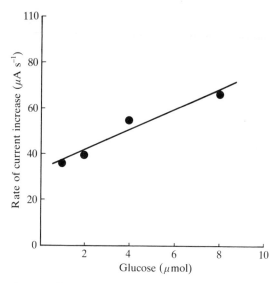

Fig. 17.4 Rate of current increase *vs.* glucose for a *P. vulgaris* sensor fuel cell. 8 mM 2-hydroxyl-1, 4-naphthoquinone; 50 mg (dry wt.) organism, (30°C). Resistive load was varied authomatically to maintain constant 0.53 volts.

correlation of coulombic output with glucose concentration for *P. vulgaris* sensor cells similar to those described above (Fig. 17.2). Figure 17.4 shows the concentration dependence of current-time response for a similar cell using HNQ as mediator, and a constant anode potential maintained with an active load device.

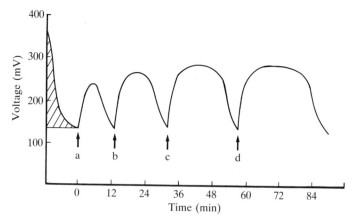

Fig. 17.5 Current-time behaviour of *Methylomonas methylovora* fuel cell. 1 mM thionine; 60 mg (dry wt.) organism; 560 ohm. Additions of 0.5, 1.0, 1.5, 2.0 μmol ethanol were made at a, b, c, d.

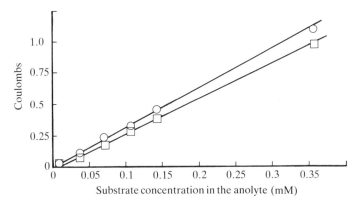

Fig. 17.6 Coulombic output of ethanol/methanol fuel-cell sensor as a function of substrate concentration in anolyte. Conditions as for Fig. 17.5. □, ethanol; ○, methanol.

The current–time plots for a *Methylomonas methylovora* fuel cell from successive additions of ethanol are shown in Fig. 17.5. In this experiment the endogenous capacity of the system was first exhausted (shaded portion). The system responds equally well to ethanol or methanol, the carbon source on which the organisms were grown. The correlation of coulombic output with quantity of ethanol or methanol added is illustrated in Fig. 17.6. The increase of cell voltage (decrease in bio-anode potential) following additions of ethanol was also followed as a function of time over a 30 s period, and Fig. 17.7 shows the relationship between these rates and the substrate concentration. This system clearly obeys Michaelis–Menten kinetics over the ethanol range 0.05–1.5 mmol (anolyte concentration 3.5–105 μM), and thus functions as a very sensitive and reasonably fast sensor. It is interesting that the active enzyme in this methylotroph is an NAD-linked dehydrogenase (*cf.* Section 17.2.1 (f)) and can be used selectively, since it will not oxidize carbohydrates (*cf.* section 17.2.2 (a)). On the debit side, however, it is rather unstable (*cf.* 17.2.2 (b)).

17.5 Future developments

17.5.1 General considerations for design of microbial sensors

Modifications are under way in many laboratories which will transform the 'fuel cell' sensor into the form of a probe. Reduction in the volume of a fuel cell-type sensor from 15 cm^3 to 0.5 cm^3 reduces the 'dead' time (for mixing and equilibration at porous electrodes) from several minutes to less than 30 s, and the logical development is to localize organisms within a small volume adjacent to the electrode.

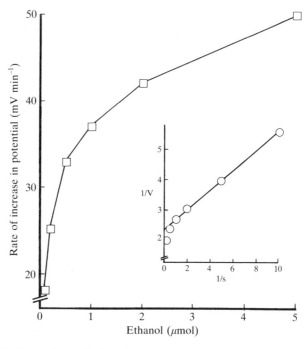

Fig. 17.7 Kinetic response of ethanol sensor. Rates were measured over a 30 s period after addition of substrate to the cell. Inset shows the data as a Lineweaver–Burk plot; S is ethanol concentration (μmol); V is rate of potential increase $\times$ 100; $K_S = 18$ μM.

A schematic representation of a multi-layer sensor in the form of a conventional electrode-probe is shown in Fig. 17.8. As with other sensors, a choice of design may be made between the durable and 'throwaway' types in which the working part of the probe is a disposable electrode disc or something similar. The latter possibility is attractive in view of the simplicity of construction and inexpensive bulk manufacture promised by electrodes formed with a carbon film coating on a paper or plastic base (popularly known as 'credit card' technology). A miniaturized version used in conjunction with a retractable probe would have advantages for clinical use; it is possible to extract samples (e.g. blood) and carry out an *ex vivo* test, so eliminating any possibility of contamination by sensor components (the main toxicity risks being presented by the organism and mediator). A needle-type glucose probe is described by Shichiri *et al.* in Chapter 23 of this volume.

17.5.2 Design and construction of bio-active layers

The simple representation given in Fig. 17.8 is clearly only a rough guide to the possibilities for sensor design. Various configurations for enzyme sensors

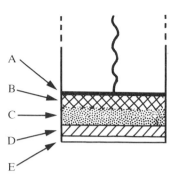

Fig. 17.8 Proposed construction of microbial sensor. A, carbon backing plate; B, porous carbon matrix; C, bio-active layer; D, filtering layer; E, protective membrane.

have been outlined previously, notably be Scheller and co-workers (Scheller *et al* 1984), who focus attention on the characteristics of the bio-active layer which forms the essential working part of the biosensor. One of the main goals in the development of prototype microbial sensors is to understand what happens in such an active layer containing biocatalyst, mediator(s), and other essential components; its composition and structure can then be modified in the light of test experiments. Various strategies for constructing the active layer are discussed below.

17.5.3 Immobilization of micro-organisms

Many techniques for immobilization of organisms have been developed (Chibata and Wingard 1983). Of these, the following are best suited to retain organisms on or adjacent to the electrodes:

17.5.3.1 Adsorption   In the absence of a binding agent, micro-organisms bind strongly to absorbent surfaces, including carbons, but to a widely varying degree (Ward and Berkeley 1980). This simple approach suffers from the disadvantages that the biomass loading is difficult to control, and desorption effects may result from changes in pH, ionic strength, etc.

17.5.3.2 Physical entrapment   Physical entrapment of organisms within a porous electrode may be achieved using a gel matrix such as alginate, polyacrylamide, carrageenan, or a photo-cross-linked polymer which can be specifically tailored to modify its hydrophobicity (Fukui and Tanaka 1982). Mild preparation conditions allow the biomass loading to be carefully controlled. Although penetration times for a test solution containing substrate should be of the order of a few seconds, mass-transfer limitations may arise. These same properties could be used to advantage, however, since judicious selection of physical characteristics might facilitate the specific exclusion of contaminating substances in the anolyte, or the regulation of mediator mobility and redox properties.

17.5.3.3 Covalent attachment   Covalent attachment methods used for enzymes can be adapted for whole cells (Wiseman 1985). A high density of cells may be conveniently and firmly held at the surface, while diffusion problems are avoided. The more successful methods employ a two-stage process in which surface groups such as carboxylate are activated, e.g. using a carbodiimide coupling reagent, and the resulting surface polymer is reacted with the organisms. High biomass loading may be achieved, and biological stability can be enhanced considerably. Recent results show that satisfactory sensor signals (microamps) can be obtained using a monolayer bound to the electrode having 1 mg (dry wt.) of micro-organism per 100 cm^2 (real area) attached by this method.

17.5.4 Redox mediating systems

Previous work with mediated fuel cells (outlined above) and enzyme electrodes has provided insight on the various questions relating to redox mediators. There is a particular need to identify or synthesize suitable mediators for incorporation into systems which can couple the biocatalyst to the electrode while not allowing the active redox component to be leached out during measurement, though loss of mediators and other components may be tolerable in 'throwaway' designs. In durable probes, where the signal may be dependent on mediator concentration and loss of mediator could lead to poor reproducibility, the concentration could be maintained by a controlled delivery from a reservoir of micro-encapsulated reagent (Williams 1984; Kost and Langer 1984). Alternatively, mediators or derivatized mediators could be found which would be too large to escape from the network of a substrate-permeable gel or some other structure which itself could be part of the immobilizing support for the micro-organisms. Ionic mediators might also be held by an oppositely charged polymer or co-polymer component, appropriately located or distributed. Several other possible approaches currently being explored are considered below.

17.5.4.1 'Anchored' mediators   In recent years there have been significant advances in synthesis of 'speciality' polymers (Ise and Tabushi 1983) and there are numerous ways in which organic or inorganic mediators could be 'anchored' on polymer supports (Sheats *et al.* 1984), or attached to the cell wall. For example, an arrangement such as that illustrated in Fig. 17.9 can be envisaged in which a redox-active pendant mediator is suspended by a flexible molecular chain from an anchoring site (P) on a linear chain polymer of open structure. In this 'swinging arm' arrangement the oxidized moiety (M_{ox}) gains access to the intracellular source of electrons by penetrating the outer cell wall

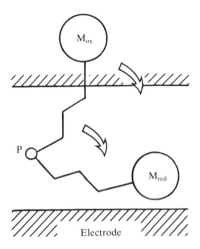

Fig. 17.9 Design of biocatalyst layers containing micro-organisms: the polymer-anchored pendant mediator.

(upper part of figure) and on reduction the reduced form (M_{red}) diffuses to the electrode and is re-oxidized.

The outer cell walls of micro-organisms are extremely varied in structure and composition, and the feasibility of the mechanism proposed above will therefore depend on the type of organism under study; generally 'gram negative' organisms are more complex than 'gram positive'. Access to reducing areas will be easy where the organism has exoenzymes but progressively more difficult for periplasmic enzymes, cytoplasmic enzymes, and mitochondria in eukaryotic cells. But many bacteria, for example, have walls of 5–20 nm thickness consisting principally of peptidoglycan, a chain-like disaccharide heteropolymer glycan with peptide substituents (Ward and Berkeley 1980; Inoue 1980). A pendant chain of 10–15 $-CH_2-$ groups would in principle enable electrons to be ferried across a 5–10 nm gap by this mechanism, sufficient to mediate charge transfer from many organisms even with a 'thinly spread' mediator. (A single mediator moiety in every 20 nm², or 1 per 100 nm³ for a 5 nm gap, gives a mediator density of 0.01 molecules nm⁻³, i.e. a local concentration = 0.01 mol dm⁻³).

17.5.4.2 'Functionalized' organisms Much is known about the electron transfer which constitutes the 'internal circuitry' of biochemical pathways (Losada *et al*. 1983; Dreyer 1984), but various ways of making connections to external circuits by manipulation and 'functionalization' of organisms await exploration. Mechanisms for mediation other than via mobile mediators can be envisaged, such as depicted in Fig. 17.10, which involves direct

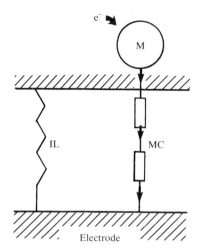

Fig. 17.10 Transduction from micro-organism via molecular conductor. M, receptor-mediator; IL, immobilizing link; MC, molecular conductor.

transduction through a molecular conductor. Here a mediator centre accepts electrons from the reducing pool inside the organism and channels them to the electrode along a conducting organic pathway (Aviram 1983; Munn 1984; Bryce and Murphy 1984). The molecular conductor (MC) should of course be 'bio-compatible' with the outer cell structure. There could be advantages in the development of an immobilizing/conducting matrix made of conducting polymers such as doped poly(*N*-vinylcarbazole) which have been proposed for battery construction (Kakuta *et al.* 1985).

   In more complex organisms the interfacing process presents many difficulties, particularly where the reducing centres are located in mitochondria, but 'functionalization' of the micro-organism by implanting appropriately modified redox reagents could allow electrons to 'hop' to accessible outer parts. Such electron-bridging systems are a real possibility in view of recent evidence on the long-distance tunneling of electrons in functionalized proteins (Williams and Concar 1986). Properties required for the acceptor centre might be achieved by the tailoring of a functionalizing reagent such as a transition metal complex to a desired redox potential whilst matching it to the intracellular enzyme and its predominantly hydrophobic environment, and then partitioning it into the organism. Organic solvent components, mild detergents, and other reagents designed for facilitated transport of solutes across membranes might be employed for introducing and positioning 'foreign' components within organisms, which can tolerate such treatments for limited periods (Felix 1982; Leive 1968).

17.5.4.3 Electrodes and electrochemical considerations   The incorporation of a mediator in either the biocatalyst layer or an adjacent layer introduces diffusion requirements which might affect electrochemical behaviour. Transfer of oxidized and reduced forms of mediators (free or bound) should not be so slow as to affect seriously the response time or the steady-state amperometric currents through concentration polarization. The limiting current density, i_d, for a mobile species of diffusion constant, D, at a concentration, c, in a diffusion layer of thickness, δ, is approximated by the expression

$$i_d = \frac{DFc}{\delta} \cdot$$

The value of i_d for the pendant mediator scheme described above (calculated using a conservatively estimated value of D of 10^{-7} cm^2 s^{-1}, and with $c = 0.01$ mol dm^{-3}, $\delta = 5$ nm), is 0.2 A cm^{-2}, which suggests that mediator diffusion need not present a serious limitation on sensor signals. Experimental checks on such restrictions imposed by the matrix can be assessed by comparisons of electrochemical responses (cyclic voltammetry) of immobilized forms with those from freely suspended components (organisms and mediators). Appropriate interfacing of the active layers through modified electrodes (Murray 1980, 1984; Albery and Hillman 1981) may be achieved using carbon electrodes, making use of surface carboxylate, quinone, and sulphur-containing groups.

17.5.5 Selectivity, specificity, and interference

Many ways of tailoring the sensor to avoid interferences and improve selectivity present themselves, and we here outline just some of the areas for investigation:

17.5.5.1 Manipulation of organisms

By comparison with a single enzyme, a micro-organism is a multi-function biocatalyst which imposes multi-parameter restrictions, but affords a wide range of opportunities for manipulation. Although use of an organism which utilizes both ascorbate and glucose as substrates, say, may give rise to signal interference when assaying one in the presence of the other, the uptake or catabolism of the interferent could be repressed in a number of ways. For example, the K values afford differing selectivity over different concentration ranges, and could be modified according to the design of the bioactive layer or by biological manipulation. Another approach to increased specificity lies in the use of mutants: strains which do not metabolize glucose, for instance, could be used to detect a second substrate in a glucose-rich medium.

The use of micro-organisms in a secondary capacity as filters for substances, e.g. glucose and oxygen, which affect the primary electrochemical or bio-electrochemical sensing reactions, can in principle extend the range of usefulness of biosensors and other sensors. Such a 'scavenging layer' might be usefully placed between the active layer and the test solution (see Fig. 17.8).

17.5.5.2 Differential measurements   In common with general analytical practice, interference problems for measurements in biological and industrial fluids can be minimized by judicious use of 'blanks'. For example, measurements could be carried out in a differential cell in which two cells are placed 'back to back'. The sensing part consists of two thin bio-anodes placed on one probe module, an arrangement which has advantages for calibration using a null method and gives additional compensation for temperature, pH, and ionic strength variations. Compensation for the effect of interfering substrates can also be devised by a 'blank' sensor having no analyte biocatalyst but which contains a biocatalyst for the interferant, matched appropriately to blank out its amperometric effect in the sensor proper.

17.5.5.3 Other modifications of the bioactive layer   For a probe which depends on reductive biological action for its signal, the sensitivity and time of response may be affected by the oxygen tension. Although some sensors might function even in the presence of competitive oxidation reactions, particularly with very active organisms which rapidly establish their own anaerobic environment, it may be convenient to use oxygen-insensitive mediators, such as ferrocenes (Cass *et al.* 1984). These problems might also avoided by the use of a scavenging layer rendered inactive or partly inactive to the analyte, or by the use of 'electrochemical modulation' (Scheller *et al.* 1985). In this approach the oxygen tension can be controlled by use of an internal electrode grid. Such methods have also been used to increase the selectivity of a glucose enzyme electrode by decreasing the flux of ascorbate to the biocatalytic area.

   In the preliminary work described in section 17.4, the substrate was diluted in the measuring cell from a small aliquot of added test solution. The dilution step could be avoided by use of a microbial probe, but the micro-organisms may become substrate-saturated in concentrated solutions, which might confer a long-lasting reducing activity and so limit the substrate-sensitivity. This problem (which would be less serious for a single measurement) might be solved by limiting the amount of substrate penetrating through to the active layer. Use could be made of a scavenging layer or diffusion-limiting gel/polymer membrane between the solution and the biocatalyst (*cf.* section 17.5.3.1). The extent of substrate utilization would also be dependent on the particular mediator used, as well as its concentration and location, and could accordingly be de-sensitised by tailored design.

17.6 Future prospects

In this article we have attempted to describe an emerging biosensor technology which promises faster response times and sensitivity as a result of the mechanism of signal transduction, i.e. electrical 'connection' to the early stages of microbial catabolism. This avoids the requirement of the indirect method for the organism to reach a steady state of product generation in response to the analyte concentration. It is clear, however, that 'direct' microbial biosensors share many of the advantages and disadvantages already revealed for those of the 'indirect' type: many of the applications will be the same (*cf.* section 17.2), and much work remains to be done in further exploration of both methods.

At the time of writing there are reservations about the acceptibility of whole-cell sensors for many applications, for example clinical use, fermentation control, and the food industries. Though such reservations do not affect the impetus of research work in some countries, notably Japan, it is worth examining the possible reasons for this scepticism. If we accept that the biosensors could be made economically, perhaps along the lines suggested here and elsewhere in this volume, the two main requirements are that they should work, and that they should be safe. At present it may be unrealistic to expect the implementation of test procedures which would, for example, satisfy the (rather demanding) standards of the best industrial analytical chemistry laboratories, but results in the literature and work carried out in industrial laboratories suggest that some whole-cell sensors do not behave very reproducibly, and have not been adequately or objectively tested. Improvements can be expected to follow, however, from a closer examination of the fundamental mechanistic aspects, together with the use of new materials and designs. The risk of contamination of test materials by whole-cell biocatalysts, and the fears it engenders, present a serious problem which will only be overcome after rigorous demonstrations of safe application, which will be all the more convincing if the performance of biosensors can generally be improved. Biotechnological innovations are becoming rapidly assimilated and accepted, however, and some of the prejudice directed against the use of 'bugs' will perhaps soon be swallowed and digested, together with helpings of mycelial protein now available in supermarket pies!

Acknowledgements

We thank Johnson Matthey for the loan of electrode materials and (in part) Cambridge Life Sciences plc. for support (for SDR).

References

Albery, W. J. and Hillman, R. A. (1981). Modified electrodes. *Ann. Rep. Prog. Chem., C,* **78**, 377–437.

Aston, W. J. and Turner, A. P. F. (1984). Biosensors and biofuel cells. In *Biotech. Genet. Eng. Rev.* (ed. G. Russell) Vol. 1, pp. 89–120. Intercept, Newcastle-upon-Tyne.

Aviram, A. (1983). Molecular components for electronic device function — an overview. *Proc. First World Conf. Commercial Applications and Implications of Biotechnology* (Biotech '83), pp. 695–704. Online Publications, London.

Bennetto, H. P. (1984). Microbial fuel cells. In *Life chemistry reports* (eds. A. M. Michelson and J. V. Bannister) Vol. 2, no. 4, pp. 363–453. Harwood Academic, London.

—— Stirling, J. L. and Tanaka, K. (1985). Reduction of 'redox' mediators by NADH and electron transduction in bioelectrochemical systems. *Chem. and Ind. (Lond.),* 695–7.

—— Tanaka, K. and Matsuda, K. (1984). Bio-fuel cell containing algae. In *Charge and field effects in biosystems* (eds. M. J. Allen and P. N. R. Usherwood) pp. 515–522. Abacus Press, Tunbridge Wells.

—— Dew, M. E., Stirling, J. L. and Tanaka, K. (1981). Rates of reduction of phenothiazine 'redox' dyes by *E. coli. Chem. and Ind. (Lond.)* 776–8.

—— Stirling, J. L., Tanaka, K. and Vega, C. A. (1980). Microbial fuel cells. *Soc. Gen. Microbiol. Quarterly*, **8**, 37.

—— (1983). Anodic reactions in microbial fuel cells. *Biotechnol. Bioeng.* **25**, 559–68.

Besenhard, J. O. and Fritz, H. P. (1983). The electrochemistry of carbon blacks. *Angew. Chemie* **22**, 950–975.

Box, J. and Mason, J. R. (1986). An alcohol fuel cell sensor based on whole *Methylomonas methylovora*. In preparation.

Bryce, M. R. and Murphy, L. C. (1984). Organic Metals. *Nature* **309**, 119–126.

Cass, A. E. G. (1984). Protein electrochemistry: current studies and potential applications. In *Life Chemistry Reports* (eds. A. M. Michelson and J. V. Bannister) Vol. 2, no. 4, pp. 321–362. Harwood Academic, London.

Cass, A. E. G., Davis, G., Francis, G. D., Hill, H. A. O., Aston, W. J., Higgins, I. J., Plotkin, E. V., Scott, L. D. L. and Turner, A. P. F. (1984). Ferrocene-mediated enzyme electrode for amperometric determination of glucose. *Anal. Chem.* **56**, 667–71.

Chibata, I. and Wingard, L. B. Jr. (1983). *Applied biochemistry and bioengineering; Vol. 4: Immobilized cells*. Academic Press, London.

Clarke, D. J., Calder, M. R., Carr, R. J. G., Blake-Coleman, B. C., Moody, S. C. and Collinge, T. A. (1985). The development and application of biosensing devices for bioreactor monitoring and control. *Biosensors* **1**, 213–320.

Corcoran, C. A. and Rechnitz, G. A. (1985). Cell-based biosensors. *Trends in Biotechnol.* **3**, 92–6.

Delaney, G. M., Bennetto, H. P., Mason, J. R., Roller, S. D., Stirling, J. L. and Thurston, C. F. (1984). Electron transfer coupling in microbial fuel cells. 2. Performance of fuel cells containing selected micro-organism–mediator–substrate combinations. *J. Chem. Tech. Biotechnol.* **34B**, 13–27.

Dreyer, J. L. (1984). Electron transfer in biological systems: an overview. *Experientia* **40**, 653–776.

Felix, H. (1982). Permeabilized cells. *Anal. Biochem.* **120**, 211–234.

Findl, E., Strope, E. R. and Conti, J. C. (1985). Electrochemical techniques in the biological sciences. In *Comprehensive treatise of electrochemistry, Vol. 10, Bio-electrochemistry*, (eds. S. Srinivasan, Y. A. Chizmadzhev, J. O.'M. Bockris, B. E. Conway and E. Yeager) pp. 491–529. Plenum Press, New York.

Fukui, S. and Tanaka, A. (1982). Immobilized microbial cells. *Ann. Rev. Microbiol.* **36**, 145–72.

Guilbault, G. G. (1984). *Analytical uses of immobilized enzymes* Chapter 3v, pp. 211–26. Marcel Dekker, New York.

Gunsalus, I. G. and Schuster, C. W. (1961). Metabolism. In *The bacteria* (eds. I. Gunsalus and R. Y. Stanier) Vol. 2. Academic Press, New York.

Hanazato, Y. and Shiono, S. (1983). Bioelectrode using two hydrogen ion sensitive field effect transistors and a platinum wire pseudo reference electrode. In *Chemical sensors* (eds. T. Seiyama, K. Fueki, J. Shiokawa and S. Suzuki) Analytical Chem. Symp. Series, Vol. 17, pp. 513–8. Kodansha/Elsevier, Tokyo.

Inoue, M. (1980). *Bacterial outer membranes: Biogenesis and functions*, Academic Press, London.

Ise, N. and Tabushi, I. (1983). *Introduction to speciality polymers*, Cambridge University Press, London.

Kakuta, T., Shirota, Y. and Mikawa, H. (1985). A rechargeable battery using electro-chemically doped poly(*N*–vinylcarbazole). *J. Chem. Soc. Chem. Commun.* 553–5.

Karube, I. and Suzuki, S. (1983). Application of biosensor to fermentation processes. *Ann. Rep. Ferment. Processes* 6, 203–236.

—— (1984). Amperometric and potentiometric determinations with immobilised enzymes and micro-organisms. *Ion-selective Elec. Rev.* **6**, 15–58.

—— Matsunaga, T. and Suzuki, S. (1977). A new microbial electrode for BOD estima-tion. *J. Solid Phase Biochem.* **2**, 97–104.

Kobos, R. K. (1983). Microbe-based electrochemical sensing systems. *Trends in Analyt. Chem.* **2**, 154–7.

Kost, J. and Langer, R. (1984). Controlled release of bioactive agents. *Trends in Biotechnol.* **2**, 47–51.

Leive, L. (1968). Studies on the permeability change produced in coliform bacteria by ethylenediaminetetracetate. *J. Biol. Chem.* **243**, 2373–2380.

Losada, M., Hervas, M., De La Rosa M. A. and De La Rosa, F. F. (1983). Energy transduction in bioelectrochemical systems. *Bioelectrochem. Bioenerg.* **11**, 193–230.

Mărgineanu, D.-G., Vais, H. and Ardelean, I. (1985). Bioselective electrodes with immobilized bacteria. *J. Biotechnol.* **3**, 1–9.

Matsunaga, T., Karube, I. and Suzuki, S. (1980). A specific microbial sensor for formic acid. *European J. Appl. Microbiol. Biotech.* **10**, 235–43.

Munn, R. W. (1984). Molecular electronics. *Chem. in Britain*, **20**, 518–24.

Murray, R. W. (1980). Chemically modified electrodes. *Accounts Chem. Res.* **13**, 135–41.

—— (1984). Chemically modified electrodes. In *Electroanalytical chemistry* (ed. A. J. Bard) Vol. 13. pp. 191–368. Marcel Dekker, New York and Basel.

Proctor, B. E. and Greenlie, D. G. (1939). Reduction-oxidation potential indicators in quality control of foods. 1. Correlation of resazurin reduction rates and bacterial plate counts. *Food Res.* **4**, 41–9.

Roller, S. D., Bennetto, H. P., Delaney, G. M., Mason, J. R., Stirling, J. L. and Thurston, C. F. (1984). Electron transfer coupling in microbial fuel cells. 1. Comparison of redox-mediator reduction rates and respiratory rates of bacteria. *J. Chem. Tech. Biotechnol.* 34B, 3–12.

—— and White Jr., D. R. (1983). A bio-fuel cell for utilisation of lactose wastes. *Proc. First World Conf. Commercial Applications and Implications of Biotechnology* (Biotech '83), pp. 655–663. Online Publications, London.

Scheller, F. W., Strnad, G., Renneberg, R. and Kirstein, D. (1984). Potentialities of protein electrochemistry in analytics. In *Charge and field effects in biosystems* (eds. M. J. Allen and P. N. R. Usherwood) pp. 483–90. Abacus Press, Tunbridge Wells.

—— Schubert, F., Renneberg, R., Muller, H.-G., Janchen, M. and Weise, H. (1985). Biosensors: trends and commercialisation. *Biosensors* 1, 135–160.

Sheats, J. E., Pittman, C. U. Jr. and Carraher, C. E. Jr. (1984). Organometallic polymers. *Chem. in Britain* 20, 709–15.

Simpson, D. L. and Kobos, R. K. (1984). Ammonia gas sensor for microbial assay of tetracycline, gentamycin, streptomycin and neomycin. *Anal. Chim. Acta* 164, 273–7.

Stirling, J. L., Bennetto, H. P., Delaney, G. M., Mason, J. R., Roller, S. D., Tanaka, K. and Thurston, C. F. (1983). Microbial fuel cells. *Biochemical Society Transactions* 11, 451–3.

Thurston, C. F., Bennetto, H. P., Delaney, G. M., Mason, J. R., Roller, S. D. and Stirling, J. L. (1985). Glucose metabolism in a microbial fuel cell. Stoichiometry of product formation in a thionine-mediated *Proteus vulgaris* fuel cell and its relation to coulombic yields. *J. Gen. Microbiol.* 131, 1393–1401.

Turner, A. P. F., Aston, W. J., Higgins, I. J., Davis, G. and Hill, H. A. O. (1982). Applied aspects of bioelectrochemistry; fuel cells, sensors and bioorganic synthesis. *Biotech. Bioeng. Symp. No. 12*, 401–12.

van Dijk, C., Laane, C. and Veeger, C. (1985). Biochemical fuel cells and amperometric sensors. *Recl. Trav. Chim. Pays-Bas* 104, 245–52.

Wang, J. (1981). Reticulated vitreous carbon — a new versatile electrode material. *Electrochim. Acta* 26, 1721–6.

Ward J. B. and Berkeley, R. C. W. (1980). The microbial cell surface and adhesion. In *Microbial adhesion to surfaces*, (eds. R. C. W. Berkeley, J. M. Lynch, J. Melling, P. R. Rutter, and B. Vincent) pp. 47–66, Soc. Chem. Ind./Ellis Horwood, Chichester.

Williams, A. (1984). The controlled release of bioactive agents. *Chem. in Britain* 20, 221–4.

Williams, R. J. P. and Concar, D. (1986). Long-range electron transfer. *Nature* 322, 213–4.

Wingard, L. B., Jr., Shaw, C. H. and Castner, J. F. (1982). Bioelectrochemical fuel cells. *Enzyme Microb. Technol.* 4, 137–142.

Wiseman, A. (1985). *Handbook of Enzyme Biotechnology.* (2nd edn.) Ellis Horwood, Chichester.

18

Application of enzyme-based amperometric biosensors to the analysis of 'real' samples

FRIEDER W. SCHELLER, DOROTHEA PFEIFFER,
FLORIAN SCHUBERT, REINHARD RENNEBERG,
and DIETER KIRSTEIN

18.1 Introduction

Amperometric biosensors represent the highest developed branch of bio-specific electrodes as it is reflected by the number of publications, patents, and commercialized analysers. They combine the advantages of faradaic electrode processes, e.g. high sensitivity, linear concentration dependence, selectivity by changing the electrode potential, and independence of sample buffer capacity with the high substrate specificity of enzymes or higher integrated biocatalytic systems like organelles, micro-organisms, or tissue slices. Based on the principle of detecting a concentration gradient of the electrode-active product, amperometric sensors are only able to detect the formation or consumption of reaction partners, and are not suited to indicate changes of the electron density resulting from the sole complex formation process without chemical conversion. Furthermore, amperometric sensors are generally restricted to two-substrate reactions catalysed by oxidoreductases, since redox reactions are based on the transfer of electrons between two substances. Therefore the concentrations of both the substrate and the cofactor influence the reaction rate. This stimulated the development of principles which eliminate the limitations of the cofactor concentration, e.g., the oxygen regenerating auxiliary electrode, mediator chemically modified indicator electrodes, or the exploitation of the direct electron transfer between the protein prosthetic group and the redox electrode resulting in a reagentless measuring regime. In this way, in addition to the enzyme the cofactor is also eliminated as a reagent in analyses using amperometric biosensors. In addition to the drastic reduction of reagent costs the most important advantage of applying amperometric biosensors is the considerable simplification of the measuring devices: They represent the spatial unity of dialyser, enzyme reactor, and electrochemical detector (Fig. 18.1). This is the predominant feature of analysers based on amperometric biosensors.

Among biosensors, oxidase-catalysed reactions dominate. This fact is related to the simple handling of electrochemical O_2 and H_2O_2 detection.

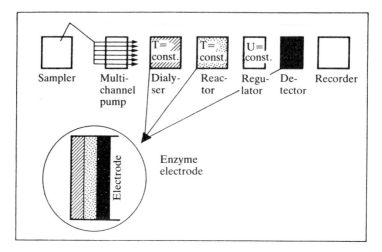

Fig. 18.1 The unit of dialyser, enzyme reactor, and electrochemical sensor in enzyme electrodes.

When no useful product is obtained in the analyte molecule conversion, a readily measurable substance can be formed in a succeeding enzyme reaction. These sequence-type reactions are generally used with esters, oligosaccharides, and amides. Other types of coupled reactions are based on the recycling of the molecule of interest in order to produce a multiple of product, or they result in the elimination of disturbing substances.

In patents and publications, amperometric biosensors have been described for the determination of about 80 different substances including substrates, cofactors, prosthetic groups, enzyme activities, antibodies, inhibitors, and activators. Linear concentration ranges of these sensors usually extend over two to four decades with a limit of detection at 1–100 micromolar concentration. Analysers based on amperometric biosensors for the determination of eleven different substances have been commercialized.

The aim of this contribution is to illustrate the potentials and limitations of the routine application of amperometric biosensors in clinical diagnostics, fermentation control, food production, and pollution control.

18.2 Application of amperometric biosensors

18.2.1 Low-molecular weight soluble substances

The majority of analytically important substances belong to this group. Typical representatives are monosaccharides, oligosaccharides, alcohols, organic acids, and amino acids. Also uric acid and creatinine, being soluble in the micromolar range, shall be discussed in this chapter. The electroenzymatic measurement of these substances is to some extent used in the analytical routine. Furthermore, inorganic ions acting as activators or inhibitors and prosthetic groups, e.g. FAD, have been determined on laboratory scale using amperometric biosensors.

18.2.1.1 Determination of glucose Exact and rapid determination of glucose is essential not only in analytical clinical laboratories but also for on line supervising of diabetic patients. In microbiological and food industries the glucose sensor is important for process control, and application should be expanded to di- and polysaccharides and amylase determinations. In order to meet these requirements, about 50 groups from various countries deal with the development and optimization of glucose sensors and analysers.

18.2.1.2 Blood glucose The determination of blood glucose levels is an indispensable test for the exact diagnosis and therapy of diabetes mellitus as well as for many kinds of disorders. Whereas the normal blood glucose level is about 5 mmol/l, the pathological value may increase up to 50 mmol/l. In the case of urine glucose the normal value is about 1 mmol/l but with most glucose assays the interferences cause serious problems.

Approximately 5 per cent of the adult population of industrialized countries has diabetes. Analytical chemistry has played and is continuing to play a major role in the conquest of diabetes mellitus. Innumerable methods have been developed but the specificity of enzyme reactions and the sensitivity of electrochemical techniques resulted in the popularization of glucose sensors. The scheme of glucose oxidase (GOD, EC 1.1.3.4) catalysed glucose oxidation reveals two main possibilities for glucose measurement.

$$\text{D-Glucose} + O_2 \xrightarrow[\text{oxidase}]{\text{Glucose}} H_2O_2 + \text{D-Gluconolactone} \qquad (18.1)$$

One can registrate either the consumption of oxygen by cathodic reduction or the production of hydrogen peroxide by anodic oxidation.

18.2.1.3 Interferences Various reducing substances present in biological samples, for instance ascorbic acid, uric acid, glutathione, etc., may considerably influence the oxidation of H_2O_2. To eliminate this disadvantage, four fundamental approaches are possible.

i) Lobel and Rishpon (1981) eliminated a part of the interference by using a negatively charged dialysis membrane, which rejected up to 0.0852 mmol/l of ascorbic acid and 0.464 mmol/l of uric acid. Higher concentration of these substances and also glutathione and bilirubin influence the glucose signal.

ii) Thévenot *et al.* (1982 and Chapter 22) included a compensating electrode with a non-enzymatic collagen membrane and registrated the difference between the two sensor currents.

iii)   A H_2O_2-selective asymmetrical cellulose acetate membrane excluding most of the potentially interfering substances in front of the electrode is used by Yellow Springs Instruments Corp., USA (Newman 1976) and by the Japanese company Fuji Electric (Tsuchida and Yoda 1981). But this composed membrane costs more.

iv)   Without a permselective membrane exact and fast glucose measurements are possible by the derivative method in connection with an additional diffusion resistance behind the enzyme layer (Scheller and Pfeiffer 1978).

In the case of blood glucose detection by means of electrochemical oxygen detection deoxyhemoglobin binds oxygen in the measuring solution. Therefore the measured values do not agree with the true ones.

18.2.1.4 Sensitivity   Contrary to H_2O_2-assay which starts from a very low background current and permits a sensitive detector (detection limit of 10^{-6} mol/l glucose), in the case of O_2-reduction a difference from the basic oxygen current is registrated. Therefore the sensitivity is usually lower by two to three orders of magnitude (Thévenot 1982). The linear measuring region of glucose sensors extends over four decades. Obviously it is limited by the oxygen diffusion into the reaction layer. By applying an additional external diffusion barier in front of the glucose oxidase membrane (Scheller and Pfeiffer 1978) the linear measuring range can be shifted to much higher concentrations.

18.2.1.5 Stability   The stability of glucose in blood samples is an important problem in clinical diagnostics. With intact erythrocytes the concentration of blood glucose is decreased up to 20% within two hours, also in the presence of 24 mmol/l NaF, a glycolysis inhibitor. By diluting the blood sample with a hypotonic buffer leading to blood hemolysis, glycolysis is completely eliminated and the glucose concentration is stable over 24 hours (A.B.2 1985).

18.2.1.6 Glucose analysers   The effort of studying the sensor problems resulted in the development of various glucose analysers by relevant companies. A comparison of analytically interesting parameters is represented in Table 18.1. The first amperometric enzyme electrode-based glucose measuring device was developed by Yellow Springs Instruments Corp. in 1979 (YSI-23 A) (see Chapter 1). The correlations between values obtained by the usual hexokinase-glucose 6-phosphate-dehydrogenase method and those by the YSI-23 A are satisfactory for plasma and serum. Results with whole blood are not presented (Chua and Tan 1978). The research kit of the Hungarian company Radelkis (Havas *et al.* 1980) and the Glucoroder-E from

Table 18.1 Glucose analysers based on amperometric enzyme electrodes

Company	Enzyme + added reactant	Measuring range (mmol/l)	Sample (μl)	Measuring frequency (sample/hr)	Serial precision (%)	Stability
Manual analysers						
Yellow Springs Instruments Corp. (USA): Model 23 A	glucose oxidase (GOD)	1.0–45.0	25	40	2.0	300 samples
ZWG, Acad. of Sciences (GDR): Glukometer GKM 01	GOD	0.5–50.0	20–25	60–90	1.5	1000 samples
Radelkis (Hungary): OP-G1-7113-S	GOD	1.7–2.0	100	40	5.0–10.0	250 days
Inst. Biochem. Vilnius (USSR): Enzalyst-G	GOD	0.5–30.0	50	60	5.0	n.c.
Ferment (USSR): Aplama	GOD	2.5–30.0	n.c.	20	3.0	n.c.
Fuji Electric (Japan): Gluco 20 A	GOD	0–27.0	20	80–90	1.7	500 samples
Seres (France): Enzymat	GOD	1.0–22.0	200	60	n.c.	500 samples
Solea-Tacussel (France): Glucose electrode	GOD	0.0001–1.0	n.c.	n.c.	2.0	1000 samples
Hoffmann-La Roche & Co. (Switzerland): Glucose Analyzer 5410	GOD + $[Fe(CN)_6]^{-3}$	2.5–27.5	100	$t_r = 60$ s	1.5	8 weeks
Inst. Techn. Chem., Acad. Sciences GDR	GOD + *p*-quinone	0–55.5	800	15	3.0	8 weeks

Table 18.1 *con't*

Company	Enzyme + added reactant	Measuring range (mmol/l)	Sample (µl)	Measuring frequency (sample/hr)	Serial precision (%)	Stability
Analytical Instruments (Japan): Glucoroder-E	GOD	0–55.5	20–40	120–150	2.0	n.c.
Automatic flow analysers						
Daiichi (Japan): Auto & Stat GA-1110	GOD	1.0–40.0	100–250	n.c.	1.0	n.c.
MLW (GDR): ME Glucose 6	GOD	1.0–44.0	20	80–120	1.2	1000 samples
Charles Univ. Prague (Czechoslovakia) Dept. Biochem.	GOD	0.0006–5.0	n.c.	60	3.5	30 d
On-line devices				*lag time (min)*		
Life Science Instr., Div. Miles Lab. (USA): Biostator GC IIS	GOD	up to 27.5		2	5	50 h
Centr. Inst. Diabetes, Karlsburg (GDR)	GOD	up to 40.0	15–20		n.c.	n.c.
Osaka Univ. Med. School Dept. Med. (Japan)	GOD	2.85–22.0	n.c.		n.c.	3 d

n.c., not communicated
t_r, response time

Analytical Instruments (Japan) are based on the oxygen consumption mode. Therefore these devices are not appropriate for blood glucose measurements.

No data about correlations between usual methods and precision are published by Seres (France), Solea-Tacussel (France), and the Biochemical Institute of Vilnius (USSR). Similarly, only a little information has been published about enzyme electrodes available from Universal Sensors (USA) (Guilbault 1984; Chapter 9).

One of the most significant problems of blood glucose measurement is demonstrated by the Japanese companies Fuji Electric Co. and Daiichi. In the Gluco 20 A (Fuji) the sensor works with 20 μl of undiluted whole blood and good correlation between Gluco 20 A and the hexokinase method for serum is obtained. However, comparative studies show that the glucose values of whole blood are always 13% smaller than those of serum (Niwa *et al.* 1981). Similar results with whole blood are obtained with the Auto and Stat GA-1110 (Daiichi, Japan). The following correlation to an enzymatic method is published: $y = 0.793x + 0.471$ mmol/l. The problem was investigated by the author's group. Using the Glukometer GKM 01 from ZWG Berlin (GDR), undiluted, EDTA-stabilized blood and 1:10-diluted samples in isotonic dextrane phosphate buffer were compared. The correlation curve obtained is shown in Fig. 18.2. At direct injection of undiluted blood the

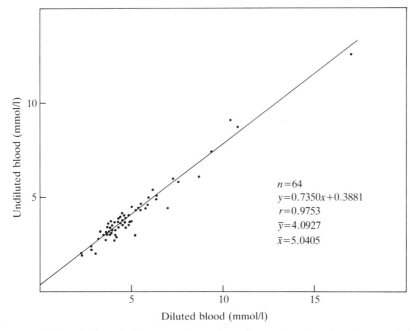

$$n = 64$$
$$y = 0.7350x + 0.3881$$
$$r = 0.9753$$
$$\bar{y} = 4.0927$$
$$\bar{x} = 5.0405$$

Fig. 18.2 Correlation of glucose concentration of 1:10-diluted and undiluted whole blood samples by glucose oxidase electrode.

values are 18.8% lower than those obtained with 1:10-prediluted samples. This difference reflects in the case of direct injection of undiluted whole blood an incomplete indication of the glucose present in erythrocytes. That is why the glucose determined by this mode does not represent the real value. Using 1:10-diluted blood or serum and the derivative hydrogen peroxide method the results obtained with the Glukometer GKM 01 agree well with the glucose oxidase-peroxidase-method. With the same GOD-sensor the values of blood glucose assay carried out by the ME Glucose 6 (Müller *et al.* 1985) excellently agree with the highly specific glucose dehydrogenase method:

$$y = (1.003 \pm 0.006)x - (0.015 \pm 0.045) \text{ mmol/l},$$
$$r = 0.996,$$
$$n = 196.$$

Supervizing of diabetic patients demands a glucose-controlled insulin infusion system. Great efforts are being made to overcome difficulties like stability of enzyme membrane and wide linear concentration range. Fogt *et al.* (1978) published the first feedback control system, the Biostator®. Using diluted blood, the enzyme electrode is stable for up to 50 hours, the linearity extends up to 27.5 mmol/l. Implantable sensors are being developed by Abel *et al.* (1984) and Shichiri *et al.* (1984; Chapter 23) for glucose monitoring using needle-type electrodes. Both make use of the smaller glucose concentrations of the interstitium as compared with venous blood. Shichiri's investigations resulted in a wearable artificial endocrine pancreas (400 g) consisting of the needle-type sensor, minicomputer, and two syringe driving systems.

A ferrocene-modified glucose oxidase sensor was used for the prototype of a personal glucose monitor for diabetes in easily portable form by the Cranfield/Oxford groups (Cass *et al.* 1984). The signal does not depend on oxygen and for undiluted whole blood a good agreement with standard methods for plasma is obtained (see also Chapters 15 and 16).

18.2.1.7 Fermentation control   In fermentation control, monitoring of various substrates and products of biochemical reactions is a key problem (Enfors 1982). The varying concentration of oxygen in fermentation broth and the need for oxygen in the glucose oxidase-catalysed reaction are the main difficulties in this field.

For discrete measurements of fermentation samples, Mor and Guarnaccia (1977) performed a differential measurement between a glucose sensor and an auxiliary electrode using hexacyanoferrate (III) as electron acceptor. The increase of the concentration of the reduced hydrogen acceptor, *p*-quinone, with additional inert gas was used by Asperger and Krabisch (1985).

Romette *et al.* (1979) developed a glucose electrode with an enzyme membrane possessing a high oxygen solubility. The membrane is loaded with air prior to the analysis. This reservoir supplies the GOD reaction with sufficient oxygen but would not be applicable to *in situ* analysis in fermentation processes.

The most interesting development in this field is an oxygen-stabilized glucose electrode based on electrolytic generation of oxygen (Enfors 1982). Thus, variation of sample-dissolved oxygen does not disturb the signal output (see also Chapter 19).

18.2.1.8 Galactose and lactose Galactose provides an alternative carbohydrate source and improves homeostatic regulation of glucose in the premature infant. Because of its potentially toxic effects, sensitive methods for monitoring its concentration are needed. The normal range of serum galactose is below 0.24 mmol/l. The disaccharide lactose is present uniquely in milk. The average concentration in human milk is 0.3–0.6 mol/l and in cows milk 0.25–0.28 mol/l. There has been considerable interest in the development of methods for the determination of lactose, as the lactose content in foodstuffs is indicative of the amount of skimmed milk powder that has been added.

Both galactose and lactose have been determined using galactose oxidase (EC 1.1.3.9) immobilized on a hydrogen peroxide-selective cellulose acetate membrane in front of the electrode (Taylor *et al.* 1977). The linear range of the measurement was at least 0 to 30 mmol/l of galactose or lactose with a membrane working life of typically 10 days. The repeatability was shown to be 2%. The only physiologically important interference found was dihydroxyacetone.

Determination of lactose using an immobilized enzyme electrode is included as a special kit in the YSI Industrial Analyzer Model 27 and the automatic device Enzymat from Seres (France). In addition Yellow Springs describes in the specification sheet the determination of fructose on the basis of immobilized galactose oxidase, a reaction unknown in literature up to now (Johnson *et al.* 1982).

Lactose sensors have been also developed by co-immobilizing β-galactosidase (EC 3.2.1.23) and glucose oxidase (Cordonnier *et al.* 1975; Bertrand *et al.* 1982).

18.2.1.9 Sucrose Sucrose is the most important representative of disaccharides contained in different foods and drinks as a sweetener and as a nutrient in fermentation broths. It is produced from sugar cane or sugar beets having a typical content of sucrose between 15 and 25%. Sucrose determination is required in sugar production processes, quality control of foods, and fermentation control.

Up to now all enzyme electrodes for sucrose are based on invertase (EC

3.2.26) -catalysed sucrose hydrolysis and subsequent glucose oxidation producing the electrode-active species. (Bertrand *et al.* 1981, Kulys *et al.* 1979, Macholán and Konečna 1983). Since GOD converts only the β-conformer of glucose, the co-immobilization of mutarotase (EC 5.1.3.3) which accelerates the conversion of the originally produced α-glucose into the β-form results in an almost tenfold increased sensitivity, however, in parallel the linear measuring range is reduced by the same factor (Scheller and Karsten 1983; Cordonnier *et al.* 1975). This effect is based on the increased rate of mutarotation by the enzyme as compared to the slow spontaneous reaction.

For sucrose determination with the YSI analyser the procedure is the same as that for glucose, except that an invertase-mutarotase-GOD membrane has to be installed. The sucrose reading takes about 60 seconds to reach steady state. Raffinose and melibiose give readings of two per cent and eight per cent, respectively. The linear range extends up to 90 mmol/l, the membrane life time is typically 10 days. Since the final enzyme reaction is the same as that used in glucose determination, sucrose determination is subject to interference by the glucose content of the sample. For such samples YSI suggests determining the sum of glucose and sucrose and additionally the glucose content by using the 'sucrose membrane' and the simple 'glucose membrane', respectively. This procedure appears to be not very convenient, since the membranes have to be exchanged during the measurement. It is more reasonable to carry out the inversion of sucrose outside the measuring cell using soluble invertase and to measure the glucose content before and after splitting of sucrose of soluble invertase.

The problem of glucose interference in sucrose determination can be solved by converting the glucose by GOD and catalase to non-disturbing products. For this purpose the indicating enzyme layer is covered with an anti-interference layer containing GOD and catalase (EC 1.11.1.6). β-D-Glucose permeating into the anti-interference layer is completely eliminated. Using this anti-interference layer, determination of sucrose (Scheller and Renneberg 1983) is unaffected by endogenous glucose if the glucose concentration in the measuring cell does not exceed 2 mmol/l. In this manner sucrose concentrations were determined directly in the juice of sugar beets or in samples of instant cocoa using the Glukometer (Scheller and Renneberg 1983). The same principle was extended to the elimination of other interfering substances, e.g. lactate.

18.2.1.10 Lactate   Many critically sick patients develop acidosis as a result of respiratory, hemodynamic, or metabolic abnormalities. Elevated plasma lactate levels commonly result from metabolic disturbances producing acidosis particularly with associated vascular collapse. Determination of blood L-lactate is important to distinguish lactic acidosis from other causes

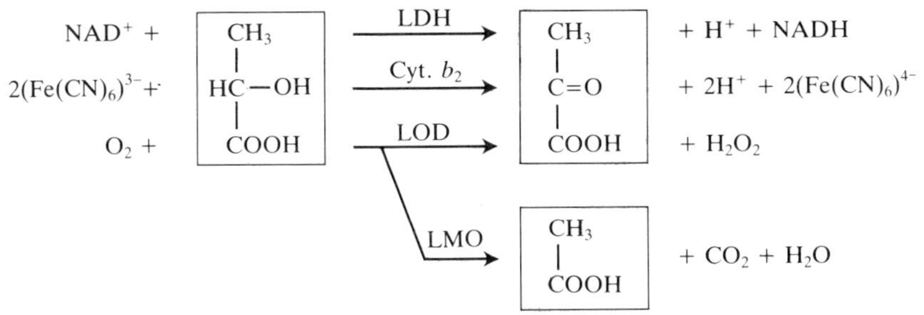

$$NAD^+ + \boxed{\begin{array}{c} CH_3 \\ | \\ HC-OH \\ | \\ COOH \end{array}} \xrightarrow{\text{LDH}} \boxed{\begin{array}{c} CH_3 \\ | \\ C=O \\ | \\ COOH \end{array}} + H^+ + NADH$$

$$2(Fe(CN)_6)^{3-} + \qquad \xrightarrow{\text{Cyt. } b_2} \qquad + 2H^+ + 2(Fe(CN)_6)^{4-}$$

$$O_2 + \qquad \xrightarrow{\text{LOD}} \qquad + H_2O_2$$

$$\xrightarrow{\text{LMO}} \boxed{\begin{array}{c} CH_3 \\ | \\ COOH \end{array}} + CO_2 + H_2O$$

Scheme 18.1 Enzyme reactions for lactate determination.

and in the following treatment. A particular field where rapid and accurate blood lactate determination is desired is exercise control in sports medicine. Furthermore, lactate measurement in cerebrospinal fluid is of help in the differentiation between viral and purulent meningitis and in the detection of cerebral oxygen deficiency. Reference lactate values in blood and liquor are below 2.7 mmol/l and 1.2–2.1 mmol/l, respectively. Lactate measurement in serum does not reflect the true blood concentration, since the increase of lactate strongly depends on the time between blood withdrawal and separation of corpuscular constituents.

Four different enzymes are suited for L-lactate determination with amperometric biosensors: Lactate dehydrogenase (LDH, EC 1.1.1.27), cytochrome b_2 (EC 1.1.2.3), lactate oxidase (LOD, EC 1.1.3.2), and lactate monooxygenase (LMO, EC 1.13.12.4). Their catalytic reactions are shown in Scheme 18.1. The LDH reaction can be coupled to redox electrodes by anodic oxidation of NADH, either directly (Yao and Musha 1979; Blaedel and Engstrom 1980; Laval *et al.* 1984; Čenas *et al.* 1984) or via electron mediators such as phenazine methosulphate (Malinauskas and Kulys 1978) or flavine mononucleotide (Suzuki *et al.* 1975). These sensors provided insight into the problems of electrochemical cofactor regeneration and mediated electron transfer but are not suited for routine application, presumably because of the electrode fouling by NADH or mediator oxidation products.

In biosensors based on LMO, a decarboxylating enzyme which is often designated as 'lactate oxidase', the immobilized enzyme is fixed to Clark-type oxygen electrodes (Schindler and von Gülich 1981; Mascini *et al.* 1984). With such a sensor, Mascini *et al.* (1984) obtained a linear concentration dependence of up to 0.25 mmol/l in the measuring cell and a correlation coefficient of $r = 0.995$ ($y = 1.094x - 0.128$ mmol/l) for measurement in reconstituted human sera. However, as with all O_2-electrode-based sensors, problems may arise from differences in the oxygen content of buffer and sample.

The reaction of the pyridine nucleotide-independent lactate dehydrogenase, cytochrome b_2, is coupled to amperometric electrodes by the enzymes ability to transfer electrons from lactate to several mediators including thionine, dichlorophenol indophenol, and potassium ferricyanide, of which the latter reacts with highest rate (Kulys and Razumas 1983). Also the anodic oxidation of organic metal complexes co-immobilized with the enzyme and functioning as mediators has been employed (Kulys and Švirmickas 1980; Chapter 15). As an approach to *in vivo* lactate determination the natural electron acceptor, cytochrome c, has been co-immobilized with cytochrome b_2 and its reduced form then measured electrochemically (Durliat and Comtat 1980). These studies did not exceed the laboratory scale.

Lactate determination with LOD is appropriately carried out with the immobilized enzyme combined with a hydrogen peroxide probe.

Self-contained enzyme electrode based L-lactate analysers are marketed by La Roche, Switzerland, OMRON Tateisi Electronics Co., Japan, and Yellow Springs Instruments Corp., USA. The Roche Lactate Analyzer 640, which was introduced in 1976, uses a cytochrome b_2 sensor, the enzyme solution being simply entrapped in a reaction chamber in front of a platinum probe polarized to $+ 0.28$ V for ferrocyanide oxidation. The device permits analysis of 20–30 blood samples of 100 μl per hour with lactate concentration between 1 and 12 mmol/l, with a precision of 5%. Results are obtained within 2–3 min after blood withdrawal from the patients. The stability of one sensor preparation containing about 2 U of enzyme is one month. Correlation with an optical LDH-method yields $r = 0.998$ ($y = 1.094x - 0.215$ mmol/l).

LOD electrodes are applied in the OMRON HER 100 and YSI Model 23L lactate analysers, both introduced in 1983. The OMRON instrument allows up to 8.9 mmol/l of blood lactate to be measured with a response time of 80 s and a precision $< 5\%$. The sample amount required is 100 μl. The temperature dependence of the enzyme reaction is compensated by a built-in thermistor in close proximity to the H_2O_2-indicating probe. Stability of the LOD sensor is 13 days and a correlation coefficient of $r = 0.998$ is obtained with control serum (Tsuchida *et al.* 1985). Lactate in cell cultures can also be measured with the device. The YSI Model 23L is applicable to lactate determination in whole blood as well as plasma and liquor cerebrospinalis. The respective correlation coefficients with the photometric Boehringer method are 0.997, 0.997, and 0.9996. Linearity is obtained up to 15 mmol/l and only 25 μl sample are needed. 42 samples per hour can be assayed.

A sensor for determination of the medically unimportant D-isomer of lactate is part of the Enzymat analyser offered by Seres, France. It is based on D-lactate oxidase-containing cell-free extract coupled to a dissolved O_2-probe. The measurable concentration range is 0.5 to 20 mmol/l.

A L-lactate sensor with immobilized LOD was successfully used by Mascini *et al.* (1985) for *in vivo* studies with an endocrine artificial pancreas, the Biostator®. The sensor was inserted downstream from the glucose sensor and permitted to measure the body response of a diabetic patient to exercise, glucose infusion, and insulin infusion. This method should be of help in the design of infusion algorithms for extreme cases such as surgery of diabetics.

An innovative principle for L-lactate measurement is being introduced in the Glukometer analyser. With a lactate pyruvate recycling system consisting of LDH and cytochrome b_2 the sensitivity to lactate is amplified by at least one order of magnitude (Schubert *et al.* 1985*a*). With this sensor lactate can be assayed using as little as 1 μl blood. Use of an anti-interference membrane containing LMO to oxidize endogenous blood lactate to non-disturbing acetate and CO_2 makes the sensor also applicable to fast determination of alanine aminotransferase activity (Schubert *et al.* 1984*b*).

18.2.1.11 Urea The urea concentration in blood, which is usually expressed by blood urea nitrogen (BUN) concentration is an important parameter in clinical chemistry, because it is a good index of the kidney function. The normal value is 3.6–8.9 mmol/l.

Methods of amperometric urea determination have been developed much later than potentiometric and conductometric procedures. The first amperometric urea electrode developed by Suzuki's group in Japan consisted of a combination of a urease membrane with nitrifying bacteria which metabolize the formed ammonia and consume oxygen (Chapter 2). This oxygen consumption was measured with a Clark-type electrode (Okada *et al.* 1982). The described electrode contained five membranes and therefore a relatively high response time of 2 min for rate assays or 7 min for steady state measurements is obtained. The absence of buffer interference, a correlation coefficient with optical methods of 0.97, an operational stability of 10 days, and a linear signal-concentration relationship between 2 and 200 mmol/l are quite sufficient. The large measuring volume of 50 ml at high final concentrations and a serial variation coefficient of 5% at 150 mmol/l characterize this method as applicable for urine analysis only.

Another possibility of amperometric urea determination has been developed on the basis of pH-dependent hydrazine oxidation by Kirstein *et al.* (1985*a*). The advantages of this method are the linear calibration curve contrary to the logarithmic response of potentiometric sensors (Fig. 18.3), the excellent reproducibility (CV = 1%), a sample throughput of 40 per hour using rate assays (Kirstein *et al.* 1985*b*), and a linear signal-concentration curve between 0.025 and 2 mmol/l (1–80 mmol/l sample concentration with 50 μl sample volume). The sensitivity is 75 nA mmol^{-1}l, whereas 4.4 is obtained with the hybrid urea sensor described above. However this pH-sensitive method suffers from interferences of compounds which determine

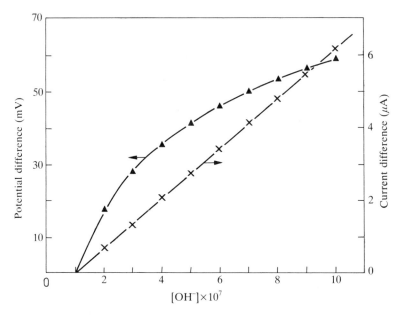

Fig. 18.3 Response characteristics of the amperometric and a potentiometric pH sensor.

pH and buffer capacity of biological fluids, such as proteins or hydrogen carbonate.

18.2.1.12 Creatinine and creatine Determination of creatinine and creatine in biological fluids is of significant value for diagnosis of renal, muscular, and thyroid function. Normal concentrations are at about 100 μmol/l.

Two types of amperometric multi-enzyme sequence electrodes have been developed by Tsuchida and Yoda (1983) for creatinine and creatine determination. Hydrogen peroxide selective asymmetric cellulose acetate membranes bear co-immobilized creatinine amidohydrolase (CA, EC 3.5.2.10), creatine amidinohydrolase (CI, EC 3.5.3.3), and sarcosine oxidase (SO, EC 1.5.3.1), or only CI and SO, respectively. Hydrogen peroxide is the final product determined amperometrically. Both electrodes respond linearly up to 760 μmol/l of the substrates. The response time is 20 s (rate assay) and the detection limit 7.6 μmol/l. The required sample volume is 25 μl, the sensitivity 11 nA mmol^{-1}l. The CV (within-day) is between 1.3 and 11.7% for creatinine and between 4.8 and 7.6% for creatine. The correlations with the optical Jaffé method are $y = 1.078 x - 23.0$ μmol/l; $r = 0.985$ for creatinine and $y = 1.101 x - 19.0$ μmol/l; $r = 0.962$ for creatine in serum. Within 11 days there is less than 20% loss of activity.

18.2.1.13 Uric acid The assay of uric acid for diagnosis and treatment of hematology disorders has been recognized. The normal range is 140–420 μmol/l.

Uric acid is oxidized in presence of uricase (urate oxidase, EC 1.7.3.3) by molecular oxygen according to:

$$\text{Uric acid} + O_2 \longrightarrow \text{Allantoin} + CO_2 + H_2O_2 \qquad (18.2)$$

The first amperometric method for the quantitative determination of uric acid in biological fluids was published by Nanjo and Guilbault (1974). These authors measured the disappearance of dissolved oxygen because they could not separate the signals of H_2O_2 and the unreacted uric acid. In subsequent studies by other authors uric acid electrodes have been developed on the basis of H_2O_2 and/or uric acid electrooxidation. A survey of the results is given in Table 18.2. Different modes of operation (rate or steady state measurements) for oxygen and H_2O_2 sensitive electrodes, respectively, and a direct electrochemical uric acid oxidation were compared by Jänchen *et al* (1983) (Fig. 18.4). The elimination of interferences by other electrode-active constituents of biological samples (e.g. ascorbic acid) was achieved by Kulys *et al.* (1983) when horse radish peroxidase served as catalyst for the reaction between H_2O_2 and hexacyanoferrate (II) followed by reduction of the Fe^{III}-complex at O V *vs.* Ag/AgCl on glassy carbon. Yoshino and Osawa (1980) coupled uricase at a H_2O_2 permselective membrane which is applied in the commercial uric acid analyser UA 300 A (Fuji Electric, Japan). Similar results were obtained with the GKM 02 variant of the Glukometer (Jänchen *et al.* 1983).

18.2.1.14 Ethanol Ethanol is the most common toxic substance involved in legal cases. Drunk driving and acute ethanol intoxication require fast and reliable determination of ethanol in blood. Measurement of the substance is also important in food and beverages and in fermentation processes.

So far, amperometric biosensors employing alcohol dehydrogenase (Malinauskas and Kulys 1978; Blaedel and Engstrom 1980) have not been successfully applied to ethanol analysis in 'real' samples. In contrast, alcohol oxidase (EC 1.1.3.13) from various microbial sources appears well suited for use in alcohol sensors. The enzyme catalyses the oxidation of lower primary alcohols according to

$$R - CH_2OH + O_2 \longrightarrow R - CHO + H_2O_2 \qquad (18.3)$$

Guilbault *et al.* (1983) measured ethanol added to blood samples with an O_2-electrode-based enzyme sensor employing a commercial alcohol oxidase from *Candida boidinii*. Deviation of the results from those obtained by gas chromatography was only 2.5%. An alcohol oxidase sensor was also applied in a flow injection system for ethanol determination in beer (Schelter-Graf

Table 18.2 Uricase electrodes

Measured species	Sample volume (μl)	Linear up to (mmol/l)	Operational stability	Precision (%)	Correlation with optical methods $y = ax + b$; r			References
					a	b(mmol/l)	r	
O_2	500	0.5	100 days, 70% residual activity	9 4	0.96 0.97	0.049 0.357	1.02 1.0	Nanjo and Guilbault (1974)
$[Fe(CN)_6]^{3-}$ (via HRP)	10	0.035	40 days, 50% residual activity	—	—	—	—	Kulys *et al.* (1983)
O_2	100	1.2	7 days	3.2–4.8				Jänchen *et al.* (1983)
H_2O_2	100	1.2		1.8–2.0	0.943	0.0198	0.9948	
H_2O_2	20	0.6	500 samples	0.5–2.7	1.10	2.44×10^{-3}	0.974	Yoshino and Osawa (1980)
H_2O_2	25	3.0	17 days (1000 samples)	0.6–2.2	0.977	3×10^{-3}	0.985	Tsuchida and Yoda (1983)

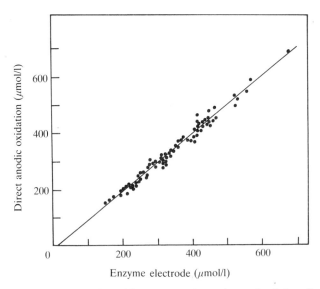

Fig. 18.4 Correlation of uric acid concentrations determined by direct anodic oxidation (ordinate) and by a uricase enzyme electrode (abscissa); $y = 1.018x + 12.5$ μmol/l; $r = 0.9921$.

et al. 1983). Linearity of the method was up to 30 mmol/l, the sensor half life 6.5 days, and the measuring frequency 60 per hour. Accurate measurement of beer ethanol with the system was possible.

Using alcohol oxidase from *Hansenula polymorpha* together with catalase, Verduyn *et al.* (1984) developed a sensor for direct, continuous ethanol measurement in fermentation processes. The dissolved oxygen tension in the fermenter was kept between 95 and 100% by vigorous stirring and aeration. In the fermentation broth the electrode was stable only for 3–5 days as compared with several weeks when used in buffer. Another drawback of the method is the narrow range of substrate concentration for which a linear response is obtained (up to 1 mmol/l). Therefore ethanol production can only be followed for a short period of fermentation time. Nevertheless, the sensor enables a rapid estimation of the fermentative capacity of aerobic yeast cultures to be made.

Alcohol analysis is possible with the YSI Model 27 industrial analyser. In this device the alcohol oxidase membrane is sandwiched between a polycarbonate and a cellulose acetate membrane. It has a lifetime of seven days. The instrument permits ethanol to be determined in beverages (Mason 1983) in concentrations up to 94 mmol/l with good accuracy. Precision is below 2%. The method is subject to severe interference by methanol, but this substance is scarcely present in ethanol samples of interest.

18.2.1.15 Glutamate, lysine A large number of amperometric biosensors for amino acids using either non-specific or highly selective amino acid oxidases have been studied. Of these only the sensors for glutamate and for L-lysine are likely to be applicable for routine analytical purposes. In the lysine electrode highly selective L-lysine α-oxidase (EC 1.4.3.-) from *Trichoderma viride* immobilized in a gelatin matrix and fixed to an O_2-electrode is used (Romette *et al.* 1983). The properties of the carrier minimize the influence of sample oxygen content. The linear measuring range of the sensor is small, but approximation of the calibration curve and use of a microcomputer provide easy access to values between 0.2 and 3 mmol/l. Enzyme inactivation during the course of the reaction is kept minimal by kinetic measurement, so that 3000 assays can be performed with one lysine oxidase membrane. The lysine sensor is employed in a flow system and its application in fermentation control is possible. The sensor is used in the Enzymat analyser offered by Seres, France.

A L-glutamate sensor using L-glutamate oxidase (EC 1.4.3.11), a newly isolated enzyme, was developed by Yamauchi *et al.* (1984) (see also Section 18.2.4.2). Glutamate in soy sauce is determined with good accuracy (correlation with L-glutamate decarboxylase method, $r = 0.978$).

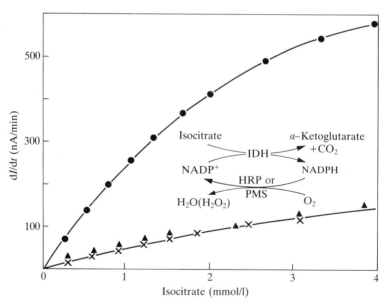

Fig. 18.5 Scheme and calibration curves of amperometric isocitrate determination with isocitrate dehydrogenase (IDH)-membrane electrodes. Cofactor recycling by: ×, soluble PMS;   ▲, co-immobilized PMS; ●, co-immobilized HRP (and soluble co-catalysts).

18.2.1.16 Isocitrate Isocitrate is a byproduct of microbial citric acid production. High contents in fermentation broths can reduce the yield of crystalline citric acid. Its content depends on the strain of micro-organisms as well as on process conditions and therefore an analytical observation of the production can be advantageous.

Isocitrate is oxidatively decarboxylated by isocitrate dehydrogenase (IDH, EC 1.1.1.42), which is a $NADP^+$-dependent enzyme (Fig. 18.5). It was determined amperometrically with unsatisfactory results by Nakamura *et al.* (1980), who utilized mediators immobilized together with the enzyme on the electrode surface. Better results are obtained when the oxygen consumption during catalytic NADPH reoxidation was measured by a Clark electrode. For this purpose, IDH was co-immobilized with horseradish peroxidase (HRP, EC 1.11.1.17). The bi-enzyme electrode was used for isocitrate determination in pure isocitrate solutions by Schubert *et al* (1985*b*). Application in fermentation solutions suffered from interferences by other constituents of the sample. Therefore HRP was replaced by phenazine methosulphate (PMS) in soluble form by Kirstein *et al.* (1984) or immobilized together with IDH (see Fig. 18.5). In all cases the cofactor was included in the background solution thus permeating the enzyme layer before isocitrate was injected.

18.2.1.17 Phosphate Phosphate determination in blood and urine is important in diagnosis of renal failure, Vitamin D deficiency, and hypervitaminosis, bone diseases, diabetic keto acidosis, and other disturbances. Phosphorous is also of interest in agricultural chemistry and environmental protection, since it occurs in fertilizers and detergents.

Already in 1975, Guilbault and Nanjo proposed to use the combination of the phosphate-inhibitable enzyme, alkaline phosphatase, and GOD in a biosensor for phosphate ion. Using a similar approach, an acid phosphatase (EC 3.1.3.2)- containing potato tissue slice was immobilized on a layer of GOD in front of an oxygen electrode to assemble a phosphate sensor which is readily applicable in the Glukometer instrument (Schubert *et al.* 1984*a*). Glucose 6-phosphate present in the background buffer is hydrolysed by acid phosphatase, the glucose thus formed giving a stable base signal of the sensor. Addition of the phosphatase inhibitor, inorganic phosphate, causes a signal corresponding to the diminished glucose liberation. With this plant tissue hybrid sensor phosphate is measured in concentrations between 1 and 30 mmol/l using a 100 μl sample. The stability is 300 assays or three weeks, precision below 2%, and 15 samples per hour can be analysed. Of 14 substances tested, only tetraborate and molybdate, and to a lower extent borate and nitrate, interfere. Phosphate in urine and fertilizer samples is measured with good accuracy. For determination of blood phosphorous, however, where the normal concentrations are 0.5–1.8 mmol/l, the sensor is not sensitive enough.

18.2.2 *Low molecular weight, highly surface active substances*

Organic substances possessing both a hydrophobic and a hydrophilic part tend to form micelles. This peculiarity is generally found with different lipids and cholesterol esters. In order to overcome this problem, detergents are added to the sample to get a molecular disperse solution. However, the presence of detergents changes the solubility of oxygen thus interfering with the oxygen consumption measurement. These detergents may be accumulated at the membranes of the electrode resulting in alteration of the mass transport rates.

Together with plasma phospholipids and triglycerides, cholesterol is transported through the bloodstream bound to specific proteins. These lipoproteins can be visualized as a sphere with an outer solubilizing coating of protein and phospholipid and an inner hydrophobic, neutral core of triglyceride and cholesterol. Neutral lipids (triglycerides), phospholipids, and cholesterol esters are split by specific hydrolases to form a substrate for the respective oxidase. Owing to the problems described above, the hydrolytic reaction catalysed by soluble enzyme is separated from the concentration measurement which is performed with an amperometric oxidase electrode.

18.2.2.1 *Cholesterol*

Today everyone worries about cholesterol, because a relationship was found between the concentration of cholesterol in plasma and the amount of cardiovascular diseases, i.e., the number of heart attacks increases with the value of cholesterol (Levy 1981). A plasma cholesterol of 3.1–6.7 mmol/l would be the average or 'normal' for a man or woman in middle age where about 70% of the total cholesterol is esterified by fatty acids.

Enzyme electrodes for the determination of free cholesterol have been developed by Satoh *et al.* (1977), Bertrand *et al.* (1979), and Mascini *et al.* (1983) using cholesterol oxidase (COD, EC 1.1.3.6) immobilized at the surface of collagen membranes or at a nylon net. The concentration of free cholesterol was determined with an accuracy of about 5–25%. After incubating the serum in triton X100-or deoxycholate-containing background solutions with cholesterol ester hydrolase (CEH, EC 3.1.1.13), total cholesterol concentration is also susceptible. The same reaction sequence is used in the lipid analyser ICA-LG 400 from Toyo Jozo, Japan. 30 μl of the serum sample are pretreated with 7.5 μl CEH solution for 11 min at 37°C to give the free cholesterol. Its concentration is measured using COD immobilized in front of an oxygen electrode. The fast response of only 15 s is based on the rate method of oxygen consumption and the measuring value is corrected by the signal of an enzyme-free oxygen sensor. Cholesterol concentration of 40 samples per hour is measured together with the simultaneous determination of triglycerides and phospholid concentration (see below). Ascorbic acid and

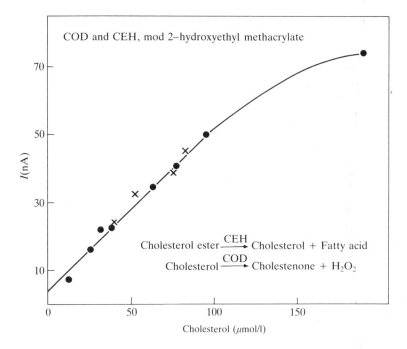

Fig. 18.6 Calibration graph for the determination of total cholesterol in aqueous cholesterol standards (●) and serum solutions (×) obtained with the CEH/COD enzyme sequence electrode.

bilirubin do not interfere. A correlation equation to a non-specified reference method of

$$y = 1.03x - 0.15 \text{ mmol/l}; r = 0.985 \ (n = 50)$$

for total cholesterol is given.

An enzyme electrode with direct spatial contact of COD and CEH immobilized at the surface of spheron particles has been described by Wollenberger *et al.* (1983). Both free cholesterol and cholesterol esters were measured with the same sensitivity (Fig. 18.6) giving evidence for complete ester hydrolysis. Five minutes after addition of 50 μl of serum sample the total cholesterol content is indicated in the H_2O_2 steady-state mode. However the two-enzyme sensor is stable only for one day.

18.2.2.2 Triglycerides Serum triglyceride analysis is a crucial test in the diagnosis and classification of hyperlipidaemia. Hyperlipidaemia, primarily known as a coronary risk factor, is also associated with many other disorders. The normal concentration of serum triglycerides is 0.35–1.7 mmol/l.

In triglyceride determination the first step of the reaction sequence is catalysed by microbial lipoprotein lipase (EC 3.1.1.3) where glycerol and fatty acids are formed. The following reactions couple the glycerol conversion to the formation of an easily measurable substance. Soluble or immobilized glycerol dehydrogenase (EC 1.1.1.6) coupled with the diaphorase-catalysed conversion of NADH has been used in the amperometric determination of triglycerides (Kelly and Christian 1984; Winartarsaputra *et al.* 1982). On the other hand, glycerol kinase (EC 2.7.1.30) and glycerophosphate oxidase (EC 1.1.3.-) are used in the lipid analyser ICA-LG 400 (Toyo Jozo, Japan) where the rate of oxygen consumption is evaluated in the same manner as described for cholesterol. Forty serum samples per hour can be analysed. A possible application of glycerol oxidase should result in a considerable simplification of the reaction system.

18.2.2.3 Phospholipids   The normal concentration range of phospholipids in plasma extends from 2.5 to 3.0 mmol/l. The main constituent is phosphatidyl choline. Enzymatic determination of phospholipids involves the combination of phospholipase D (EC 3.1.4.4) and choline oxidase (EC 1.1.99.1). Preincubation of the serum sample with soluble phospholipase D is combined with measurement of the free choline by an amperometric oxidase electrode in the ICA-LGA 400 of Toyo Jozo.

The hydrogen peroxide formed in an enzyme reactor has been measured electrochemically using the enzymes immobilized together on a hydrophobic agarose gel (Karube *et al.* 1979). The response time of the enzyme reactor flow device is 2 min and the linear range between 0 and 4 mmol/l.

18.2.3 High molecular weight soluble substances

There are two ways to determine enzymatically inactive, water-soluble high-molecular substances with amperometric biosensors:

(i) They have to be split into units small enough to penetrate the membranes covering the immobilized enzyme layer where they are converted to electrode-active products.

(ii) They can be detected by immunological reactions if the respective antibodies or antigens are available.

Potentiometric biosensors have been proposed which are based on indication of the changes of charge density resulting from the specific complex formation of a bioaffin and the high-molecular analyte.

18.2.3.1 Polysaccharides   The most abundant carbohydrate is cellulose, a polymer of glucose connected by 1,4-β-glycosidic bonds. Its worldwide use is estimated at 800 million tons per year. Another homopolymer made up of glucose is starch where glucose units are connected in the main chain by 1,4-α-glycosidic bonds. The new biotechnological product pullulan is a linear polysaccharide containing maltotriose units connected by 1,6-α-glycosidic bonds.

Prior to analysis, polysaccharides are acid-hydrolysed to glucose or they are split by specific enzymes, e.g. cellulases, amylases, or pullulanases.

18.2.3.2 Starch The YSI Industrial Analyzer Model 27 equipped with a glucose oxidase membrane is adaptable by pretreatment procedures to starch determination. It uses two approaches to starch measurement:

(i) For internal starch hydrolysis a constant amount of glucoamylase is injected into the measuring solution and after equilibration the starch sample is added. Sixty seconds later, a reading of the glucose produced by the starch hydrolysis is displayed.

(ii) In external hydrolysis procedures for starch hydrolysis glucoamylase alone or together with α-amylase (EC 3.2.1.1) is used, and the glucose content in the hydrolysed starch sample is determined.

Corn, rice, wheat, and potato starch, but also starch in cornmeal, breakfast cereals, and pancake mixes have been determined. The glucose measured ranges from 0 to 25 mmol/l with a reproducibility of $\pm 2\%$.

A more elegant and economical approach is to co-immobilize glucose oxidase with glucoamylase for measurement of saccharides able to penetrate the protective dialysis membrane in front of the two-enzyme layer. Using the Glukometer GKM 01 with a glucoamylase-glucose oxidase enzyme electrode (Renneberg *et al.* 1983*b*) starch is directly determined within 0.5–1 min with a linear range of up to 0.3% (final concentration) if a constant amount of α-amylase (1 U) is added to the measuring solution (Fig. 18.7). The problem of interference by endogenous glucose was solved by covering the glucoamylase-glucose oxidase electrode with an anti-interference enzyme later containing glucose oxidase and catalase (Fig. 18.7) (see also Section 18.2.1.9).

Pullulan concentrations can be measured using the Glukometer GKM 01 equipped with a glucoamylase-glucose oxidase membrane on a modified oxygen electrode (Renneberg *et al.* 1985). After addition of a constant amount of soluble pullulanase (2 U/ml) to the measuring solution, pullulan was determined up to 0.1% (final concentration). The Glukometer was also used to determine soluble cellulose by adding a constant amount of cellulase (EC 3.2.1.4) into the measuring solution and following the glucose produced hydrolytically (Pfeiffer *et al.* 1980).

18.2.3.3 Antigens and antibodies Up to now no commercial biosensor system has been described for antigens and antibodies. The recently developed enzyme immunosensors measure the activity of marker-enzymes bound to a defined amount of antigen. The enzyme-marked antigen and the

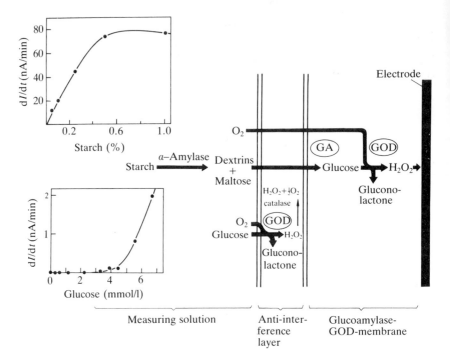

Fig. 18.7 Principle of starch determination using a glucose eliminating multi-layer sensor.

unlabelled antigen to be determined compete for the binding sites of antibodies on the membrane covering the electrode. The unknown concentration of unlabelled antigens is inversely related to the activity of the marker-enzymes measured by the electrode. However, at present the sensitivity is low as compared with established enzyme immunoassays; fast measurements are impossible because the measuring cell is occupied for the whole incubation time (up to several hours) to permit formation of the antigen–antibody complex.

At present, the development of both potentiometric and amperometric electrode-based enzyme immunoassays seems to be the only practical way to avoid these disadvantages. The antigen–antibody complex formation is carried out independently of the sensor system. When the incubation period is finished, the substrate of the marker enzyme is added and the rate of substrate conversion is followed by the sensor. With the Glukometer, 1.6 to 16 ng of factor VIII related antigen could be measured with a glucose sensor in human plasma using alkaline phosphatase as marker-enzyme and glucose 6-phosphate as substrate (Renneberg *et al.* 1983*a*).

Amperometric detection of superoxide anion formed on interaction of neutrophils with IgG adsorbed at the electrode surface seems to open up new possibilities to more direct immunoelectrodes (Green *et al.* 1984; Chapter 4).

18.2.4 Enzyme activities

In clinical diagnostics the determination of enzyme activities in body fluids is a rapidly developing field. Elevated enzyme activities found in blood, serum, plasma, or urine are due to leakage from damaged tissues and cells. For fermentation control the measurement of the activity of industrial enzymes, e.g. proteases or amylases, is of great importance. Sensors for enzyme activity determination are mainly based on the measurement of the initial rate of substrate conversion by the enzyme of interest, which is added to the measuring solution containing a saturating concentration of the substrate. The high concentration of substrate is required to obtain zero order reaction kinetics, where the substrate conversion rate depends only on the enzyme activity. To date commercial self-contained enzyme sensors are available only for α-amylase (Fuji Electric, Japan).

18.2.4.1 Lactate dehydrogenase Lactate dehydrogenase (LDH) is a tetramer allowing the formation of five isoenzymes of LDH differing in subunit structure and electrophoretic mobility. In mammalian cells LDH is only located in the cytoplasm. Thus, after cellular damage (liver and heart diseases), LDH is readily released from the cytoplasm. Total LDH activity in serum is of clinical importance in differentiating disorders, such as acute myocardial infarction, congestive heart disease, pernicious anemia, and hepatitis. The normal ranges for serum of adult males and females are 63–155 and 62–131 U/l.

With a pyruvate oxidase (EC 1.2.3.3) based sensor the LDH activity of human sera was determined in the range 25–135 U/l (Minoura *et al.* 1982) using the maximum current decrease. The sensor of Mizutani *et al.* (1983) using immobilized lactate oxidase permits the sequential determination of both L-lactate and LDH. The minimum activity of LDH which could be determined was 1 U/l. The relative standard deviation is 2.6% in ten successive measurements. The total measuring time for LDH activity is 5 min. The sensor is stable for two weeks with ten measurements per day. Serum samples with LDH activities ranging from 138 to 414 U/l can be determined with a correlation coefficient of 0.995 between the sensor and a conventional method.

No self-contained LDH-analysers have been described up to now. However, the L-lactate analysers of La Roche, OMRON, Yellow Springs Instruments Corp., and the Glukometer could well be adapted to LDH activity measurements (see also Section 18.2.1.10). Problems could arise from the relatively small amounts of lactate formed in the LDH reaction demanding a pre-incubation step, and from the lactate present in serum.

18.2.4.2 Amylases Amylases catalyse the hydrolysis of oligosaccharides and polysaccharides (starch and glycogen). α-Amylase yields primarily maltose and some other oligosaccharides (4–12 glucose units). Determination of α-amylase in blood and urine is of decisive importance in the diagnosis of acute pancreatitis. The normal activity of α-amylase in serum extends from 60 to 150 U/l.

The activity of α-amylase in serum has been determined by different biosensor systems. The commercial analyser of Fuji Electric (Osawa *et al.* 1981) uses a GOD sensor measuring first the endogenous glucose concentration of the sample and, after addition of maltopentaose and a constant amount of α-glucosidase (maltase, EC 3.2.1.20), the α-amylase activity of the sample. However, this method is expensive due to high consumption of the soluble enzyme and the special substrate and gives wrong results if the endogenous glucose concentration is high. A more efficient approach seems to be the use of bi-enzyme sensors with co-immobilized GOD and glucoamylase (Pfeiffer *et al.* 1980) or α-glucosidase (Yoda and Tsuchida 1983). In both cases maltose and oligosaccharides formed in the α-amylase-catalysed starch hydrolysis diffuse into the bi-enzyme membrane where they are converted by glucoamylase or α-glucosidase to glucose which is indicated by the GOD reaction. α-Amylase activity in human serum is determinable with the α-glucosidase-GOD membrane mounted on an electrode of the Yellow Springs Instruments Glucose Analyzer 23 A. Thirty seconds after injection of 25 μl of human serum into a phosphate buffer containing 0.1% soluble starch, the current increase is recorded for 30 s. Total assay time is 100 s. Within-day precision with three different sera (*n* = 20) is between 4.4 and 7.3%. Repeated assays of control human sera over 17 days showed a between-day coefficient of variation of 5%. After 1000 assays in over 17 days 70% of the initial activity was still present.

α-amylase activities of bacterial origin have been measured with the Glukometer GKM 01 and the bi-enzyme sensor (glucoamylase and GOD). The calibration curve is linear up to 4.0 U α-amylase in the measuring solution (Renneberg *et al.* 1983*b*). With the same bi-enzyme sensor pullulanase activity was also determined (Renneberg *et al.* 1985). A linear range of the maximal slope of the current-time curve is obtained with a constant amount of 0.1% pullulan up to a pullulanase activity of 0.7 U/ml. The limit of detection is 0.05 U/ml.

18.2.4.3 Transaminases The importance of determination of alanine and aspartate aminotransferase (ALT, EC 2.6.1.2 and AST, EC 2.6.1.1, formerly: GPT and GOT) activities ranges not far below that of glucose measurement. Increased serum activities of these enzymes indicate myocardial, hepatic, and jaundice diseases, all of which are increasingly common in industrialized countries. Normal activities are 5–24 U/l for ALT and 5–20 U/l for AST. They can increase 100–1000 fold, especially in acute hepatitis and alcoholism. Therefore a large detection range is desirable for biosensors measuring these activities.

According to the reactions catalysed by ALT (eqn. 18.4) and AST (eqn. 18.5)

L-alanine + α-Ketoglutarate $\rightarrow$ L-Glutamate + Pyruvate (18.4)

L-Aspartate + α-Ketoglutarate $\rightarrow$ L-Glutamate + Oxaloacetate (18.5)

biosensing of the products, glutamate, pyruvate, or oxaloacetate, is possible. Kihara *et al.* (1984) applied a bi-enzyme electrode comprising poly (vinyl chloride)-adsorbed oxaloacetate decarboxylase (EC 4.1.1.3) and pyruvate oxidase (EC 1.2.3.3) for the sequential measurement of both transaminases. The base sensor was a hydrogen peroxide electrode. First, AST activity is determined by adding the sample to aspartate- and α-ketoglutarate-containing measuring solution. The slope of the current-time curve reflects AST activity. Then a substrate solution containing alanine is added and a further increase of the slope observed. The difference between the two slopes is linearly related to ALT activity. The measuring range is up to 1500 U/l with either enzyme. Assay of both activities is completed within less than 4 min. The correlation coefficients between the sensor procedure and spectrophotometric methods as calculated for 25 serum samples are 0.99 for ALT as well as AST determination.

Another, equally promising approach is to use L-glutamate oxidase. This newly isolated flavoprotein selectively catalyses the oxidative deamination of the amino acid, yielding NH_3, α-ketoglutarate, and H_2O_2. Coupling of immobilized glutamate oxidase to an O_2 or H_2O_2 probe results in a glutamate sensor also useful for ALT and AST measurement (Yamauchi *et al.* 1984). However, the method requires pre-incubation of the sample with the respective substrate mixtures for 30 min. Linearity between anodic H_2O_2 oxidation current and ALT and AST activity, respectively, is at least up to 200 U/l.

Fast ALT measurement is possible with the cytochrome b_2/LDH sensor described in the Section 18.2.1.10 (Schubert *et al.* 1984*b*).

18.3 Conclusions

Amperometric biosensors for substrate determination are a reliable and highly specific tool. Highest economical benefit is effected if they are applied in automatic flow devices like the ADM 300 of VEB MLW, the Enzymat of Seres, and the announced flow injection analyser of Control Equipment Co., Princeton. Whilst in commercial analysers the highest sample throughput is

120 per hour, in a flow injection analysis apparatus 300 glucose samples per hour can be measured (Olsson *et al.* 1986). Substrate recycling results in a considerable increase in sensitivity allowing high sample dilution or reduction of sample volume to the order of less than 1 μl. This principle opens up a new avenue to measurements in the picomolar range — the range of hormones and antigens. Further progress will be achieved by combining biocatalysts with microelectronic elements which transduce and amplify signals.

References

Abel, P., Müller, A. and Fischer, U. (1984). Experience with an implantable glucose sensor as a prerequisite of an artificial beta cell. *Biomed. Biochim. Acta* 43, 577–84.

A. B.2 — GDR (1985). *Arzneimittelbuch der DDR*. Akademie-Verlag, Berlin.

Asperger, L. and Krabisch, Ch. (1986). Überprüfung amperometrischer Meßprinzipien zur Glucosebestimmung mit Enzymelektroden. *Acta Biotechnol.* In press.

Bertrand, C., Coulet, P. R. and Gautheron, D. C. (1979). Enzyme electrode with collagen-immobilized cholesterol oxidase for the microdetermination of free cholesterol. *Anal. Lett.* 12, 1477–88.

—— (1981). Multipurpose electrode with different enzyme systems bound to collagen films. *Anal. Chim. Acta* 126, 23–34.

Blaedel, W. J. and Engstrom, R. C. (1980). Reagentless enzyme electrodes for ethanol, lactate, and malate. *Anal. Chem.* 52, 1691–7.

Cass, A. E. G., Davis, G., Francis, G. D., Hill, H. A. O., Aston, W. J., Higgins, I. J., Plotkin, E. V., Scott, L. D. L. and Turner, A. P. F. (1984). Ferrocene-mediated enzyme electrode for amperometric determination of glucose. *Anal. Chem.* 56, 667–71.

Čenas, N., Rozgaite, J. and Kulys, J. (1984). Lactate, pyruvate, ethanol, and glucose-6-phosphate determination by enzyme electrode. *Biotechnol. Bioengn.* 26, 551–3.

Chua, K. S. and Tan, I. K. (1978). Plasma glucose measurement with the Yellow Springs Glucose Analyzer. *Clin. Chem.* 24/1, 150–2.

Cordonnier, M., Lawny, F., Chapot, D. and Thomas, D. (1975). Magnetic enzyme membranes as active elements of electrochemical sensors. Lactose, saccharose, maltose bienzyme electrodes. *FEBS Lett.* 59/2, 263–7.

Durliat, H. and Comtat, M. (1980). Reagentless amperometric lactate electrode. *Anal. Chem.* 52, 2109–12.

Enfors, S.-O. (1982). A glucose electrode for fermentation control. *Appl. Biochem. Biotechnol.* 7, 113–9.

Fogt, E. J., Dodd, L. M., Jenning, E. M. and Clemens, A. H. (1978). Development and evaluation of a glucose analyzer for a glucose controlled insulin infusion system (Biostator®). *Clin. Chem.* 24, 1366–76.

Green, M. J., Hill, H. A. O., Tew, D. G. and Wolton, N. J. (1984). An opsonised electrode. *FEBS Lett.* 170, 69–72.

Guilbault, G. G. (1984). *Analytical uses of immobilized enzymes*, p. 350. Marcel Dekker, New York.

—— and Nanjo, M. (1975). A phosphate-selective electrode based on immobilized alkaline phosphatase and glucose oxidase. *Anal. Chim. Acta* **78**, 69–80.

—— Danielsson, B., Mandenius, C. F. and Mosbach, K. (1983). Enzyme electrode and thermistor probes for determination of alcohols with alcohol oxidase. *Anal. Chem.* **55**, 1582–5.

Havas, J., Porjesz, E., Nagy, G. and Pungor, M. (1980). Glucose selective sensor. Determination of glucose content of blood and urine. *Hung. Sci. Instruments* **49**, 53–9.

Jänchen, M., Walzel, G., Neef, B., Wolf, B., Scheller, F., Kühn, M., Pfeiffer, D., Sojka, W. and Jaross, W. (1983). Harnsäurebestimmung in verdünntem Serum mit enzymelektrochemischem und enzymlosem Sensor. *Biomed. Biochim. Acta* **9**, 1055–65.

Johnson, J. M., Halsall, H. B. and Heineman, W. R. (1982). Galactose oxidase enzyme electrode with internal solution potential control. *Anal. Chem.* **54**, 1394–9.

Karube, I., Hara, K., Satoh, I. and Suzuki, S. (1979). Amperometric determination of phosphatidyl choline in serum with use of immobilized phospholipase D and choline oxidase. *Anal. Chim. Acta* **106**, 243–50.

Kelly, T. A. and Christian, G. D. (1984). Amperometric determination of glycerol and triglycerides using an oxygen electrode. *Analyst* **109**, 453–6.

Kihara, K., Yasukawa, E. and Hirose, S. (1984). Sequential determination of glutamate-oxalacetate transaminase and glutamate-pyruvate transaminase activities in serum using an immobilized bienzyme-poly (vinyl chloride) membrane electrode. *Anal. Chem.* **56**, 1876–80.

Kirstein, D., Schubert, F., Scheller, F., Abraham, M. and Boross, L. (1984). Amperometrische Isocitrat-bestimmung in Fermentationslösungen der mikrobiologischen Citronensäureproduktion. Abstracts of the 16th Annual Meeting of the Biochemical Society of the GDR, p. 37.

Kirstein, D., Kirstein, L. and Scheller, F. (1985*a*). Enzyme electrode for urea with amperometric indication: part I — basic principle. *Biosensors* **1**, 117–30.

—— Scheller, F., Olsson, B. and Johansson, G. (1985*b*). Enzyme electrode for urea with amperometric indication: part II — electrode with diffusional limitation. *Anal. Chim. Acta* **171**, 345–50.

Kulys, J. J., Ralys, E. V. and Penkova, R. S. (1979). Automatic analyzer of sucrose using immobilized enzymes. *Prikl. Biokhim. Mikrobiol.* **15/2**, 282–90.

—— and Razumas, V. J. (1983). *Biocatalysis in electrochemistry of organic compounds* (Russian). p. 61, Mokslas, Vilnius.

—— and Švirmickas, G.-J. S. (1980). Reagentless lactate sensor based on cytochrome b_2. *Anal. Chim. Acta* **117**, 115–20.

—— Laurinavičius, V. S. A., Pesliakiene, M. V. and Gurevičiene, V. V. (1983). The determination of glucose, hypoxanthine and uric acid with use of bi-enzyme amperometric electrodes. *Anal. Chim. Acta* **148**, 13–18.

Laval, J.-M., Bourdillon, Ch. and Moiroux, J. (1984). Enzymatic electroanalysis: electrochemical regeneration of NAD^+ with immobilized lactate dehydrogenase modified electrodes. *J. Am. Chem. Soc.* **106**, 4701–06.

Levy, R. (1981). Cholesterol, lipoproteins, apoproteins, and heart disease: Present status and future prospects. *Clin. Chem.* **27**, 653–62.

Lobel, E. and Rishpon, J. (1981). Enzyme electrode for determination of glucose. *Anal. Chem.* **53**, 51–3.

Macholán, L. and Konečna, H. (1983). A biospecific membrane sensor for the determination of sucrose. *Coll. Czech. Chem. Commun.* **48**, 798–804.

Malinauskas, A. and Kulys, J. (1978). Alcohol and glutamate sensors based on oxidoreductases with regeneration of nicotinamide adenine dinucleotide. *Anal. Chim. Acta* **98**, 31–7.

Mascini, M., Moscone, D. and Palleschi, G. (1984). A lactate electrode with lactate oxidase immobilized on nylon net for blood serum samples in flow systems. *Anal. Chim. Acta* **157**, 45–51.

Mascini, M., Tomassetti, T. and Iannello, M. (1983). Determination of free and total cholesterol in human bile samples using an enzyme electrode. *Clin. Chim. Acta* **132**, 7–15.

Mascini, M., Fortunati, S., Moscone, D., Palleschi, G., Massi-Renedetti, M. and Fabietti, P. (1985). A L-lactate sensor with immobilized enzyme for use in *in-vivo* studies with an endocrine artificial pancreas. *Clin. Chem.* **31**, 451–3.

Mason, M. (1983). Determination of glucose, sucrose, lactose and ethanol in foods and beverages, using immobilized enzyme electrodes. *J. Assoc. Off. Anal. Chem.* **66**, 981–4.

Minoura, N., Yamada, S., Karube, I., Kubo, I. and Suzuki, S. (1982). Determination of lactate dehydrogenase in serum by using a pyruvate sensor. *Anal. Chim. Acta* **135**, 355–7.

Mizutani, F., Sasaki, K. and Shimura, Y. (1983). Sequential determination of L-lactate and lactate dehydrogenase with immobilized enzyme electrode. *Anal. Chem.* **55**, 35–8.

Mor, J.-R. and Guarnaccia, R. (1977). Assay of glucose using an electrochemical enzymatic sensor. *Anal. Biochem.* **79**, 319–28.

Müller, E., Kühnel, S., Trommler, Ch. and Günther, R. (1985). Automatisierte elektrochemische Bestimmung mit Durchfluß-meßzellen. *Labortechnik*, **18**, 8–9.

Nakamura, K., Nankai, S. and Iijime, T. (1980). Bioelectrochemical sensor using immobilized enzyme electrodes. *National Tech. Rep.* **26**, 497–506.

Nanjo, M. and Guilbault, G. G. (1974). Enzyme electrode sensing O_2 for uric acid in serum and urine. *Anal. Chem.* **46**, 1769–72.

Newman, D. P. (1976). Membrane for enzyme electrodes. US-Patent 3 979 274, Int.Cl. G 01 N 27/46.

Niwa, H., Itoh, K., Nagata, A. and Osawa, H. (1981). Studies on the rapid determination of glucose level in blood using the enzyme electrode, the 'glucometer'. *Tokaj. J. Exp. Clin. Med.* **6/4**, 403–14.

Okada, T., Karube, I. and Suzuki, S. (1982). Hybrid urea sensor using nitrifying bacteria. *Eur. J. Appl. Microbiol. Biotechnol.* **14**, 149–54.

Olsson, B., Lundbäck, H., Johansson, G., Scheller, F. and Nentwig, J. (1986). Theory and application of diffusion-limited amperometric enzyme electrode detection in flow injection analysis of glucose. *Anal. Chem.* **58**, 1046–52.

Osawa, H., Akiyama, S. and Hamada, T. (1981). Determination of uric acid, glucose and amylase in whole blood using enzyme electrode. *Proc. 1st Int. Sensor Symp.* 163–8.

Pfeiffer, D., Scheller, F., Jänchen, M. and Bertermann, K. (1980). Glucose oxidase bienzyme electrodes for ATP, NAD$^+$, starch and disaccharides. *Biochimie* **62**, 587–93.

Renneberg, R., Schößler, W. and Scheller, F. (1983*a*). Amperometric enzyme sensor-based immunoassay for factor VIII related antigen. *Anal. Lett.* 16 (B 16), 1279–89.
—— Kaiser, G., Scheller, F. and Tsujisaka, Y. (1985). Enzyme sensor for pullulan and pullulanase activity. *Biotechnol. Lett.* **11**, 809–12.
—— Scheller, F., Riedel, K., Litschko, E. and Richter, M. (1983*b*). Development of anti-interference enzyme layer for α-amylase measurement of glucose containing samples. *Anal. Lett.* 16 (B 12), 877–90.
Romette, J. L., Froment, B. and Thomas, D. (1979). Glucose-oxidase electrode. Measurements of glucose in samples exhibiting high variability in oxygen content. *Clin. Chim. Acta.* **95**, 249–53.
—— Yang, J. S., Kusakabe, H. and Thomas, D. (1983). Enzyme electrode for specific determination of L-lysine. *Biotechnol. Bioengn.* **25**, 2557–66.
Satoh, I., Karube, I. and Suzuki, S. (1977). Enzyme electrode for free cholesterol. *Biotechnol. Bioeng.* **19**, 1095–100.
Scheller, F. and Karsten, Ch. (1983). A combination of invertase reactor and glucose oxidase electrode for the successive determination of glucose and sucrose. *Anal. Chim. Acta* **155**, 29–36.
—— and Pfeiffer, D. (1978). Enzymelektroden. *Z. Chem.* **18**, 50–57.
—— and Renneberg, R. (1983). Glucose-eliminating enzyme electrode for direct sucrose determination in glucose-containing samples. *Anal. Chim. Acta* **152**, 265–9.
Schelter-Graf, A., Huck, H. and Schmidt, H.-L. (1983). Rasche und genaue Bestimmung von Ethanol mittels einer Oxidase-Elektrode in einem Strömungs-in jektionssystem. *Z. Lebensm. Unters. Forsch.* **177**, 356–8.
Schindler, J. G. and von Gülich, M. (1981). L-Lactat-Durchflußelektrode mit immobilisierter Lactat-Oxidase. *Fresenius Z. Anal. Chem.* **308**, 434–6.
Schubert, F., Kirstein, D., Schröder, K. L. and Scheller, F. W. (1985*a*). Enzyme electrodes with substrate and coenzyme amplification. *Anal. Chim. Acta,* **169**, 391–6.
—— Renneberg, R., Scheller, F. W. and Kirstein, L. (1984*a*). Plant tissue hybrid electrode for determination of phosphate and fluoride. *Anal. Chem.* **56**, 1677–82.
—— Kirstein, D., Abraham, M., Scheller, F. and Boross, L. (1985*b*). Horseradish peroxidase based bienzyme electrode for isocitrate. *Acta Biotechnol.* **5**, 275–8.
—— Scheller, F., Kirstein, D., Schröder, K. L. and Chojnacki, A. (1984*b*). Verfahren zur elektrochemischen Bestimmung von Lactat, Pyruvat und der Activität von Alaninaminotransferase. DD-Patent 222 896, Int. Cl. C 12 Q1/26.
Shichiri, M., Kawamori, R., Hakui, N., Asakawa, N., Yamasaki, Y. and Abe, H. (1984). The development of wearable-type artificial endocrine pancreas and its usefulness in glycaemic control of human diabetes mellitus. *Biomed. Biochim. Acta* **43**, 561–8.
Suzuki, S., Takahashi, F., Satoh, I. and Sonobe, N. (1975). Ethanol and lactic acid sensors using electrodes coated with dehydrogenase-collagen membranes. *Bull. Chem. Soc. Japan* **48**, 3246–9.
Taylor, P. J., Kmetec, E. and Johnson, J. M. (1977). Design, construction, and applications of a galactose selective electrode. *Anal. Chem.* **49**, 789–94.
Thévenot, D. R. (1982). Problems in adapting a glucose oxidase electrochemical sensor into an implantable glucose-sensing device. *Diabetes Care* **5/3**, 184–9.

—— Sternberg, R. and Coulet, P. (1982). A glucose electrode using high-stability glucose-oxidase collagen membranes. *Diabetes Care* **5/3**, 203–6.

Tsuchida, T. and Yoda K. (1981). Immobilization of D-glucose oxidase onto a hydrogen peroxide permselective membrane and application for an enzyme electrode. *Enzyme Microb. Technol.* **3** 326–30.

—— (1983). Multi-enzyme membrane electrodes for determination of creatinine and creatine in serum. *Clin. Chem.* **29**, 51–6.

—— Takasugi, H., Yoka, K., Takizawa, K. and Kobayashi, S. (1985). Application of l – (+) – lactate electrode for clinical analysis and monitoring of tissue culture medium. *Biotechnol. Bioengn.* **27**, 837–41.

Verduyn, C., Zomerdijk, T. P. L., van Dijken, J. P. and Scheffers, W. A. (1984). Continuous measurement of ethanol production by aerobic yeast suspensions with an enzyme electrode. *Appl. Microbiol. Biotechnol.* **19**, 181–5.

Winartasaputra, H., Kuan, S. S. and Guilbault, G. G. (1982). Amperometric enzymic determination of triglycerides in serum. *Anal. Chem.* **54**, 1987–90.

Wollenberger, U., Kühn. M., Scheller, F., Deppmeyer, V.and Jänchen, M. (1983). Amperometric enzyme sequence electrodes for cholesterol. *Bioelectrochem. Bioenerg.* **11**, 307–17.

Yamauchi, H., Kusakabe, H., Midorikawa, Y., Fujishima, T. and Kuninaka, A. (1984). Enzyme electrode for determination of L-glutamate. *Abstr. 3rd Eur. Congr. Biotechnol.*, pp. I–705–10, Verlag Chemie, Weinheim.

Yao, T. and Musha, S. (1979). Electrochemical enzymatic determination of ethanol and L-lactic acid with carbon paste electrode modified chemically with NADH. *Anal. Chim. Acta* **110**, 203–9.

Yoda, K. and Tsuchida, T. (1983). Bi-enzyme electrode for determination of α-amylase activity in serum. *Proc. 2nd Int. Sensor Symp. Fukuoka,* 648–53.

Yoshino, F. and Osawa, H. (1980). Rapid measurements of glucose and uric acid in whole blood using the enzyme electrodes. *Clin. Chem.* **26**, 1060.

19

Compensated enzyme-electrodes for *in situ* process control

SVEN-OLOF ENFORS

19.1 Introduction

A great number of the enzyme electrodes described in the literature are based on oxygen utilizing enzymes. These electrodes must be furnished with enough oxygen to permit the reaction to run without oxygen limitation unless other electron carriers are utilized. Enzyme electrodes are mostly designed to operate according to the dynamic mode, which means that the initial rate of signal change after the exposure of the electrode to the sample is used as the measure of concentration of the analyte. In this mode of operation oxygen limitation can be avoided through oxygenation of the sample prior to its injection into the measuring chamber of the electrode. A further improvement which permits injection of samples without oxygen has been presented by Romette *et al.* (1979). They developed an enzyme membrane with high ·oxygen solubility and showed that it is possible to saturate the membrane with oxygen prior to the exposure of the electrode to oxygen-free samples.

However, the dynamic mode of operation complicates the utilization of enzyme electrodes for process control. This mode offers the very important advantage of easy re-calibration during the measurements but an automatic sampling procedure is required if it is to be used for process control.

A possibility to avoid the sampling problem in fermentation control with enzyme electrodes would be to design electrodes for *in situ* operation in the bioreactor. However, this mode of operation introduces several problems that must be solved: (i) sterilizability of the probe, (ii) continuous operation with a steady state signal representing the analyte concentration, (iii) operation without sample treatment like dilution or addition of oxygen or other co-substrates of the reaction, and (iv) re-calibration during the operation.

This chapter describes two principles that contribute to the solution of the problems of continuous operation of glucose electrodes *in situ* in a bioreactor: the oxygen stabilized glucose electrode and the externally buffered glucose electrode. In both systems the micro-environment of the enzyme is controlled by the operator to compensate for unfavourable conditions for the enzyme.

347

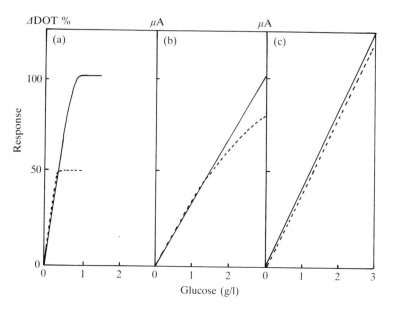

Fig. 19.1 Steady state responses of glucose electrodes to increasing concentrations of glucose in phosphate buffer at pH. (a) An oxygen diffusion dependant electrode. (b) An oxygen stabilized electrode working with an internal oxygen tension corresponding to 50% of the air saturation value. (c) An oxygen stabilizied electrode working at an internal oxygen tension of 100% of the air saturation value. Solid lines: Oxygen tension of sample is 100% of air saturation. Dotted lines: Oxygen tension of sample is 50% of air saturation.

19.2 The oxygen stabilized glucose electrode

The net enzyme reaction of a glucose oxidase based glucose electrode with catalase is:

$$\beta\text{-D-Glucose} + \tfrac{1}{2}O_2 \longrightarrow \text{Gluconate} + H^+$$

The oxygen solubility in water is about 0.25 mM and the K_M value of glucose oxidase with respect to oxygen is unusually high — about 0.5 mM (Linek *et al.* 1980). In order to respond linearly to increasing concentration of glucose the reaction rate of the electrode must be controlled by the rate of diffusion of glucose into the enzyme layer. However, the high K_M value in relation to the low oxygen solubility makes the response non-linear at glucose concentrations above about 1 g/l, (Fig. 19.1a). Furthermore, the oxygen concentration in a fermenter is normally much lower and may approach zero which turns the enzymatic reaction from glucose limitation to oxygen limitation at a point that cannot be controlled. Thus, oxygen diffusion dependent glucose electrodes are not suitable for *in situ* operation in a fermenter.

The principle of oxygen compensation of the enzymatic reaction was developed to solve this problem (Enfors 1981). It is depicted in Fig. 19.2. The enzymes glucose oxidase (EC 1.1.3.4) from *Aspergillus niger*, and catalase (EC 1.11.1.6) from beef liver are immobilized by cross-linking in bovine serum albumine with glutaraldehyde on a platinum screen. This screen is then attached close to the oxygen sensitive tip of an oxygen electrode. If the enzyme is contaminated with micro-organisms during the assembling of the electrode it must be desinfected, e.g. by dipping in a 2.5% glutaraldehyde solution. Finally, the sterile unit is inserted into the autoclaved electrode housing fitted with a cellulose acetate membrane at its end. The enzyme-screen must be tightly pressed against the cellulose acetate membrane to reduce the response time. The platinum electrode is connected as the anode in the electrolysis circuit shown in Fig. 19.2. When glucose diffuses into the enzyme layer the enzymatic reaction consumes oxygen at a rate that is proportional to the rate of glucose transport which, at steady state, is proportional to the sample concentration of glucose.

The signal from the oxygen electrode is compared with a constant reference signal and the enzyme reaction causes oxygen depletion and a deviation between these potentials. The electronic circuit generates a current through the anode on which the enzyme is immobilized and oxygen is formed by electrolysis of water at the platinum surface. The oxygen diffuses into the enzyme layer and supplies the reaction. The electrolysis current is controlled by the difference between the two potentials in such a way that the oxygen

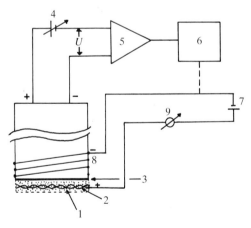

Fig. 19.2 Design principle of the oxygen stabilized glucose electrode. 1, Immobilized enzymes. 2, Platinum net. 3, Teflon membrane of oxygen electrode. 4, Reference voltage. 5, Differential amplifier. 6, PID-controller that controls the current through the electrolysis circuit to keep the differential voltage (U) zero. 7, Voltage source of electrolysis circuit. 8, Platinum coil around the electrode. 9, Microammeter.

Table 19.1 Summary of enzymatic and electrochemical reactions of the oxygen stabilized glucose electrode

$$C_6H_{12}O_6 + O_2 + H_2O \xrightarrow{\text{Glucose oxidase}} C_6H_{12}O_7 + H_2O_2$$

$$H_2O_2 \xrightarrow{\text{Catalase}} 1/2\ O_2 + H_2O$$

Anode: $\quad H_2O \longrightarrow 1/2\ O_2 + 2H^+ + 2e^-$

Cathode: $\quad 2H^+ + 2e^- \longrightarrow H_2$

Net reaction: $C_6H_{12}O_6 + H_2O \longrightarrow C_6H_{12}O_7 + H_2$

Two electrons are transported between anode/cathode per molecule of glucose oxidized.

production rate increases until the deviation is reduced to zero. Thus, the oxygen tension is maintained constant in the enzyme layer independent of the glucose concentration but the higher the reaction rate the higher is the electrolysis current. A platinum wire around the electrode body is connected as cathode of the electrolysis circuit.

The enzymatic and electrochemical reactions in this oxygen stabilized electrode are summarized in Table 19.1; each oxidized molecule of glucose corresponds to two electrons through the electrolysis circuit. Thus, if there is no exchange of oxygen between the enzyme electrode and the sample medium the electrolysis current should be a measure of the glucose concentration. The linear relationship between electrolysis current and glucose concentration is shown in Fig. 19.1b, and c.

One way to minimize the exchange of oxygen would be to use an external oxygen sensor as a reference signal for the electrolysis control. This is possible, but during fermentation process control the external oxygen concentration can be very low and then the response range is considerably reduced because the oxygen tension in the enzyme will be low (compare b and c in Fig. 19.1). By applying high reference voltages the oxygen tension in the electrode can be forced to values exceeding the air saturation value and this is a way to increase the linear response range.

However, when the oxygen tension in the electrode is higher than in the sample an error will occur that is caused by loss of electrolytically produced oxygen through diffusion to the sample medium. A compensation method for this has been developed (Enfors and Cleland 1983) and the correct glucose concentration is given by:

$$S = (I - k_D (DOT_i - DOT_o))/k_G$$

where $S =$ glucose concentration (g/l), $I =$ electrolysis current (μA), $k_D =$ mass transfer coefficient (μA/% air saturation), DOT_i and DOT_o

taneous transluminal coronary angioplasty, with a Grunzig balloon catheter for coronary artery stenosis (a newly developed technique for dilating narrowed blood vessels without recourse to major surgery), a K^+ electrode was placed in the coronary sinus (this receives blood that has circulated through the heart muscle). Three consecutive ballon inflations were performed with a duration of 20 seconds at 80 second intervals. During angioplasty occlusion the patients did not experience any chest pain nor were there any significant changes in the surface electrocardiogram. No change in coronary sinus K^+ was seen during balloon inflation but 4.5 seconds after deflation, there was a transient rise in coronary sinus K^+ of 0.3 mmol/l above a base line level of 4.0 mmol/l. This was intepreted as the washout of K^+ from myocardial cells following a few seconds of ischaemia. If coronary sinus K^+ is an early indicator of myocardial ischaemia, indwelling K^+ electrodes may prove to be a useful adjunct in the management of patients following acute myocardial infarction, or coronary artery surgery.

20.4 Hydrogen ion concentration

Continuous *in vivo* recording of pH has not yet become an established or routine practice but several investigations point to clinically useful applications, especially for intravascular, tissue, and gastric pH measurement.

Catheter-tip pH electrodes for insertion into vessels may be constructed using a variety of ion-selective membranes, such as those incorporating the H^+ ionophore *p*-octadecyloxy *m*-chlorophenylhydrazine-mesoxalonitrite, OCPH (Coon *et al.* 1976; LeBlanc *et al.* 1976; Cobbe and Poole-Wilson 1979). Such electrodes are less fragile than conventional glass pH sensors.

Rithalia *et al.* (1979) have investigated continuous subcutaneous tissue pH monitoring in 22 adults, 14 during and after open heart surgery. They used a miniature glass pH probe, and found a highly significant correlation with arterial blood pH measurements made by intermittent sampling. However, as expected, the relationship was poor in those patients with impaired tissue perfusion.

Twenty-four hour oesophogeal pH monitoring uses an indwelling pH electrode, place in the lower oesophagus, to detect gastro-oesophageal reflux (Johnson and DeMeester, 1974). To avoid the problems of continuous intubation, and restriction of acticity by electrical contacts, portable, radio-telemetry systems have recently been developed and evaluated (Falor *et al.* 1981; Branicki *et al.* 1982).

20.5 Glucose

Diabetic patients have a relative or absolute lack of insluin which causes the blood glucose concentration to exceed the normal narrow limits (about

3.5–5 mmol/l in the fasting state). About 20% of diabetics, who mostly contract the disease under the age of about 30 years, have suffered a complete or near-complete destruction of the insulin-secreting cells (islets of Langerhans) in the pancreas; this type of diabetes is called insulin-dependent or type I diabetes and these patients need insulin replacement to live. Insulin is usually given by subcutaneous injection and although preserving life and largely preventing the symptoms of acute hyperglycaemia, injections cannot maintain non-diabetic blood glucose levels ('control'). The values sometimes slip too low (hypoglycaemia), causing unpleasant symptoms and dangerous impairment of consciousness; and often are too high, causing, it is strongly suspected, serious long-term tissue complications in the eyes, nerves, kidneys and blood vessels.

There has, therefore, been an intense drive in the last few years to improve diabetic control. One important approach has been the controlled infusion of insulin from 'open-loop' portable pumps (Pickup *et al.* 1978; Pickup and Rothwell 1984), a strategy aiming at mimicking non-diabetic insulin secretion profiles. Near-normoglycaemia can be obtained with these devices for periods of at least several years but control can be lost in a variety of circumstances such as after strenuous exercise and during intercurrent illness and menstruation. A logical development of these systems is 'closed-loop' feedback-control of the insulin infusion rate via an implanted glucose sensor. Ultimately, this type of artificial endrocrine pancreas may become totally implantable but progress in this direction is at a very early stage and immense technological, biological, and ethical problems must be met and solved for it to become a reality.

In the interim, implantable glucose sensors which are not connected to pumps would still have the considerable advantages of providing an hypoglycaemia alarm, of warning against impending hyperglycaemia and

---

Table 20.2   Characteristics of the ideal *in vivo* glucose sensor

1. Site: Non-invasive or subcutaneous
2. Size: <25 G needle
3. Biocompatible: Minimal tissue reaction
4. Linearity: 0–20 mM
5. Resolution: <1 mM (for a hypoglycaemia monitor)
6. Specificity: not affected by metabolites
7. Drift: <10% per day
8. *In vitro* response time: 95% < 2–3 minutes
9. Calibration: Factory or easy single point home calibration
10. Storage: In stable and convenient form
11. Construction: Amenable to mass production
12. Cost: Cheap

---

ketoacidosis, and generally supplying continuous information of blood glucose control to enable the patient to correct and adjust insulin therapy himself.

At this point it is appropriate, then, to consider the characteristics (Table 20.2) of an ideal *in vivo* glucose electrode.

20.5.0.1 Site   Although the concentration of glucose in the blood is the parameter of main clinical interest, the risk of serious infection and the formation of thrombi on the sensing element preclude the blood stream as a site for long-term monitoring. A non-invasive technique such as transcutaneous monitoring would be the method of choice. At present there is little information on the permeability of the skin to glucose, but Clark (1979) has shown in the anaesthetized cat that if glucose oxidase is injected under the skin and a transcutaneous PO_2 electrode is placed over the injection site, the PO_2 reading of the electrode changes in response to an intravenous injection of glucose. Furthermore, he suggests that it may be possible to retain the enzyme in a silastic membrane which could be implanted on a long-term basis.

The aqueous humor of the eye has also been proposed as a site for monitoring glucose. Using an optical rotation technique, March *et al.* (1982) reported a good correlation between the glucose concentration of samples of rabbit aqueous humor and blood glucose but problems of bulky, inconvenient instrumentation and interfering substances would seem to limit the method for *in vivo* human use.

From a practical point of view, the subcutaneous tissue seems to be the most suitable site; it has been used as an implantation site for continuous insulin infusion for several years without serious infection or untoward local tissue reaction (Pickup *et al.* 1980). Moreover, it is an injection site that is well tolerated by most diabetic patients. However, there is little independent information at present on the concentration of glucose in subcutaneous tissue and its relationship to blood glucose levels. Wolfson *et al.* (1982) implanted modified Guyton capsules, dialysis sacs, and Milipore membrane devices in the subcutaneous extracellular space, pericardium, pleura, and peritoneum of baboons and/or rabbits for periods of up to six months. The glucose concentration of the fluid in these devices ranged between 50 and 115 mg/dl (2.8–6.4 mmol/l) but this technique did not reveal any information on the dynamics of blood tissue exchange. See below for sensor information on this topic.

20.5.0.2 Size   This is an important consideration from at least three aspects. Firstly, patient acceptability of a large sensor is obviously low. Secondly, large sensors inevitably cause more tissue damage during insertion than smaller sensors and, apart from causing haemorrhage, may alter the tissue/blood glucose relationship through changes in local blood flow and vascular permeability. Thirdly, fine needle-type sensors seem to cause less tissue reaction than larger, flat configurations (Woodward 1982).

20.5.0.3 Biocompatibility   A variety of factors determine the biocompatibility of an implantable device, but the nature of the material is probably most important. Although volumes have been written on the biocompatibility of polymers and plastics, most of it is not relevant to biosensors. Let us consider the materials that would be used in constructing a glucose sensor. In all probability, the sensor will be a needle and will be made of metal; platinum and stainless steel both have good biocompatibility and mechanical properties.

Most glucose sensors are coated with a membrane such as polyurethane or cellulose acetate (e.g. Shichiri *et al.* 1982; Chapter 23; Pickup and Claremont 1985) and it is essentially this which creates the interface between the body and the sensor proper and determines the biocompatibility. Membranes also have the function of trapping at the electrode sensor components such as enzymes, mediators, and cofactors, controlling the access of glucose and potentially interfering substances to the sensor, imposing a diffusional barrier which extends the linear range without sample dilution and determining sensor kinetics in general (Pickup 1985).

20.5.0.4 Linearity   Since diabetics commonly display blood glucose values of 2–30 mmol/l the sensor should be linear or of predictable response within approximately this range.

20.5.0.5 Resolution   The level of resolution should be about 1 mM or less if the device to be effective as an hypoglycaemia indicator but in the higher ranges (about 15 mmol/l, say) an accuracy of $\pm$ 20% may suffice.

20.5.0.6 Specificity   The sensor should be specific for glucose. The output of the instrument should not be affected by drugs or by the many other metabolites which are disordered in diabetes, other than glucose.

20.5.0.7 Drift   The sensor should be stable and not drift by more than about 10% a day.

20.5.0.8 In vitro *response time*   At present, there is little information on the relative timing of changes of blood and tissue glucose concentration. From our studies in pigs (see below), it seems that there is reasonably close temporal relationship between blood glucose and subcutaneous tissue glucose levels. An *in vitro* 95% response time of <2 minutes should be suitable in these circumstances.

20.5.0.9 Calibration Ideally, the sensor should be so stable and reliable that factory calibration would be possible. Failing this, an easy single point home calibration would have to suffice.

20.5.0.10 Construction The design of the electrode should be such that it can be manufactured reproducibly in large numbers, easily sterilized and produced at low cost.

The numerous reports on possible sensing strategies have been reviewed recently (e.g. Pickup 1985; Turner and Pickup 1985) and are discussed elsewhere in this volume. Most glucose sensors consist of amperometric or potentiometric enzyme electrodes, electrocatalytic sensors without enzymes, and optoelectronic systems such as the bioaffinity probe of Mansouri and Schulz (1984), see Chapter 32. Here, we shall confine our review to the reports of *in vivo* testing of some of the glucose sensors in humans and/or animals.

Soeldner *et al.* (1973) were amongst the first to evaluate *in vitro* and *in vivo* an electrocatalytic glucose sensor in a fuel cell configuration. Disc-shaped sensors 2 × 0.2 cm were implanted in the subcutaneous tissue of Rhesus monkeys and rabbits. During acute studies, sensor current followed blood glucose after a meal or administration of intravenous glucose with a latency of about 0–15 min. There was apparently no conversion of the sensor responses to glucose concentrations and although sensors were implanted for several weeks at a time, little information on drift and biocompatibility were reported. Lewandowski *et al.* (1982) used an electrocatalytic glucose sensor in a blood flow-through chamber inserted in an arteriovenous shunt in dogs. A decrease in total anodically directed current in the range − 0.4 to − 0.8 V was closely related to blood glucose concentrations during short-term experiments.

A glucose oxidase enzyme electrode based on the detection of oxygen consumption was constructed and tested in dogs by Bessman *et al.* (1981). The sensor consisted of two oxygen electrodes covered by polypropylene membrane within a circular (15 mm diameter) plastic housing; the enzyme was immobilized over one electrode and current decreases compared with the control electrode. The relationship between the difference current and glucose concentration was non-linear over the range 0–20 mmol/l and responses substantially decreased by a lowered oxygen tension. Electrodes implanted in the subcutaneous tissue of dogs recorded glucose levels which were approximately half those of the blood. An implantable closed-loop system was also constructed consisting of the sensor and a reciprocative insulin pump, but this failed to maintain euglycaemia in the diabetic dogs. The authors considered that this was because the sensor underestimated the true tissue glucose levels because of the lower tissue PO_2, in spite of the differential sensor operating mode.

Kondo *et al.* (1982) also used as differential glucose sensor based on the measurement of oxygen consumption at a Clark-type oxygen electrode. The sensor was tested in dogs where an external arterio-venous shunt was created between the carotid artery and the jugular vein and the electrodes placed in the shunt. Four of eleven experiments failed because of thrombosis or electrical problems, but in other studies there was a good correlation between sensor output and blood glucose concentrations.

An amperometric sensor based on immobilized glucose oxidase and detecting hydrogen peroxide production was tested *in vivo* by Clark and Duggan (1982; Chapter 1). A variety of provisional short-term studies in sub-cutaneous tissue and blood were performed but few results therefrom presented. Shichiri and his colleagues (1982, 1983; chapter 23) have developed a similar needle-type hydrogen peroxide detector and have per-formed extensive testing in animals and man. There was a significant relationship between subcutaneous glucose and blood glucose levels in dogs although after acute intravenous glucose loads the subcutaneous increases were delayed by 5–15 min and were about 65% lower than blood peaks. The sensitivity of the subcutaneously implanted sensor decreased to 94% at 24 h, 90% at 48 h, and 57% at 72 h, compared with the initial output. Current outputs were not significantly affected by a drop in tissue oxygen tension from about 38 to 25 mm Hg. The device was also incorporated in a wearable closed-loop system and tested in three pancreatectomized dogs. Good control was obtained for 7 days by renewing the sensor every fourth day.

Shichiri *et al.* (1984) have also tried their needle-type sensor and wearable 'artificial pancreas' in human diabetics and succeeded in obtaining near-normoglycaemia over several days. The glucose concentrations were reported as being about 25% lower in subcutaneous tissue compared to blood but followed almost immediately an increase in blood glucose (Shichiri and Kawamori 1983).

Another amperomeric glucose oxidase/hydrogen peroxide detector was recently tested in dogs by Abel *et al.* (1984) using either an *ex vivo*, extra-corporeal blood flow-through system or subcutaneous implantation. The tissue glucose concentration was found to be 30–50% of the blood concentration.

We have recently begun (Pickup and Claremont 1985) *in vivo* testing of an amperometric sensor using the ferrocene-mediated electron transfer principle originally decribed by Cass *et al.* (1984) (see also Chapters 15 and 16). We constructed miniaturized sensors based on 1 mm wide strips of graphite foil, impregnated with 1,1'-dimethylferrocene and immobilized glucose oxidase, and covered with a polyurethane membrane. *In vitro*, the sensors were linear to at least 20 mmol/l and were virtually insensitive to the changes in oxygen tension likely to be found *in vivo*. When implanted in the subcutaneous tissue of non-diabetic pigs, sensor glucose concentra-

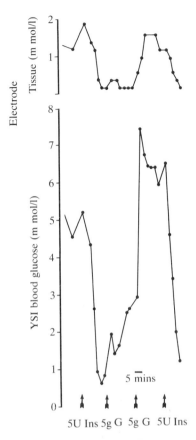

Fig. 20.6 Results from an experiment when a ferrocene mediated amperometric glucose electrode was implanted into the subcutaneous adipose tissue of an anaesthetized pig. Blood glucose concentration was manipulated by intravenous injections of insulin (Ins) or glucose (G).

tions were generally some 20% of those recorded in the blood by intermittent sampling and conventional laboratory assay. However, acute changes in blood glucose concentration caused by intravenous injection of insulin or glucose solution were mirrored by electrode responses, with little detectable latency (Fig. 20.6).

The fibre-optic bioaffinity glucose sensor based on concanavalin A as a binding agent (Mansouri and Schulz 1984; Chapter 32) has been evaluated in dogs in a blood flow-through chamber. Sensor responses corresponded reasonably well to blood glucose levels estimated conventionally but gave lower values after about two hours, the authors attributing this to a fall in blood temperature and pH over this time.

In conclusion, we can say that *in vivo* testing of glucose sensors is still at an early stage. Several sensor configurations perform adequately in the short-term but there is very little study of sensor drift and biocompatibility over periods of weeks. The subcutaneous tissue is a feasible site for sensor implantation; generally, the glucose levels here are lower, but significantly correlated with blood concentrations. Problems such as how to sterilize the sensor, how to calibrate *in vivo*, will the device be patient-acceptable, and can it ever be reliable enough to incorporate into a closed-loop system for routine use, are all largely unaddressed.

20.6 Concluding remarks

In this chapter we have attempted to review what we consider to be the most significant clinical applications of *in vivo* biosensors. The first clinical use of an *in vivo* biosensor was reported by Clark and co-workers some 25 years ago (Clark *et al.* 1959) when they used an intravascular platinum cathode to detect a left-to-right cardiac shunt. Over the last two decades, blood gas monitoring has progressed from relatively crude (bio-incompatible, unreliable) intravascular electrodes to sophisticated, non-invasive devices. Continuous blood gas monitoring has undoubtedly made a significant contribution to the management of patients with severe cardiopulmonary disorders.

Potassium monitoring is still in its infancy, and it will probably only have a limited clinical application.

Although the development of *in vitro* glucose electrodes began at about the same time as blood gas electrodes, progress has been much slower. At present, there are no commercially available *in vivo* glucose sensors. However, recent work will, hopefully, rectify this shortcoming.

One can tentatively speculate that in the future *in vivo* sensors for drugs (e.g. cytotoxics) may be useful in trying to establish the optimal dose (i.e. a concentration which produces the desired therapeutic effect with minimal unwanted side effects) for an individual patient.

Biosensors and biotechnology are currently in vogue and are a source of immense scientific interest. However, when developing *in vivo* biosensors, careful thought should be given to the clinical value of continuously monitoring a particular analyte (see Chapter 36).

References

Abel, P, Miller A, Fischer U. (1984). Experience with an implantable glucose sensor as a prerequisite of an artificial beta cell. *Biomed. Biochim. Acta.* 5, 577–84.

Andstritch, R. F., Muravchick, S., Gold, M. I. (1981). Temperature correction of blood gas parameters. *Anaesthesiology* 55, 311–16.

Armstrong, R. F., Secker-Walker, J., St. Andrew, D., Cobbe, S., Cohen, S. L. and Lincoln, J. C. R. (1981). Continuous monitoring of mixed venous oxygen tension in cardio-respiratory disorders. *Lancet* 1, 632–4.

Baumberger, J. P. and Goodfriend, R. B. (1951). Determination of arterial oxygen tension in man by equilibration through intact skin. *Fed. Proc.* **10**, 10–11.

Bessman, S. P., Thomas, L. J, Kojima, H., Sayler. D. F. and Layne, E. C. (1981). The implantation of a closed-loop artificial beta cell in dogs. *Trans. Am. Soc. Art. Int. Org.* **27**, 7–17.

Branicki F. J., Evans, D. F., Ogline, A. C., Atkinson, M. and Hardcastle J. D. (1982). Ambulatory monitoring of oesophageal pH in reflux oesophagitis using a portable radiotelemetry system. *Gut* **23**, 992–8.

Cass, A. E. G., Davis, G., Francis. G. D., Hill, H. A. O., Aston, W. J., Higgins, I. J., Plotkin, E. V., Scott, L. D. L. and Turner, A. P. F. (1984). Ferrocene-mediated enzyme electrode for amperometric determination of glucose. *Anal. Chem.* **56**, 667–71.

Claremont, D. J. and Pagdin, T. M. (1985). Evaluation of a new re-usable electrode for continuous monitoring of blood PO_2 during open heart surgery. *J. Med. Eng. Tech.* **9**, (4), 174–9.

—— Walton, N. (1984). Continuous monitoring of blood PO_2 in extracorporeal systems. *Anaesthesia* **39** 362–9.

Clark, L. C. Jr (1979). Continuous measurement of circulating glucose using the transcutaneous PO_2 electrode. In: *Continuous transcutaneous blood gas monitoring. Birth Defects.* Original Article Series (eds. A. Huch, R. Huch, and J. F. Lucey) XV, no. 4, pp. 39–42. Alan R Liss Inc., New York.

—— and Bargeron L. M. (1959). Left-to-right shunt detection by an intravascular electrode with hydrogen as an indicator. *Science.* **130**, 709–710.

Clark L. C., Duggan C. A. (1982). Implanted electroenzymatic glucose sensors. *Diabetes Care* **5**. 174–80.

Cobbe S. M. and Poole-Wilson P. A. (1979). Continuous measurement of pH in central arteries and veins. *Lancet* 2, 444–5.

Conway, M., Durbin, G. M., Ingram, D., McIntosh, N., Parker, D., Reynolds, E. R. and Soutter, L. P. (1976). Continuous monitoring of arterial oxygen tension using a catheter-tip polarographic electrode in infants. *Paediatrics* **57**, 244–50.

Coon, R. L., Lai, N. C. J. and Kampine, J. P. (1976). Evaluation of a dual-function pH and PCO_2 *in vivo* sensor. *J. Appl. Physiol.* **40**, 625–9.

Downs, J. B. (1983). Monitoring oxygen delivery in acute respiratory failure. *Respiratory Care* **28** (5), 608–13.

Eberhardt, P., Hammacher, K. and Minat, W. (1973). Methode zur kutanen Messung des asuerstoff-druckes. *Biomed. Techn.* (Stuttg), **6**, 216–21.

Falor, W. H., Change, B., White, H. A., Kraus, J. M., Taylor, B, Hansel, J. R., Kraus, F. C. (1981). Twenty-four hour oesophageal pH monitoring by telemetry. *Am. J. Surg.* **142**, 514–16.

Fatt, I. and Deutsch, T. A. (1983). The relation of conjunctival PO_2 to capillary bcd PO_2. *Critical Care Med.* **11** (6), 445–8.

Huch, R. and Huch, A. (eds) (1983). *Continuous transcutaneous blood gas monitoring. Reproductive medicine.* Vol. 5. Marcel Dekker Inc., New York and Basel.

Huch, A., Huch, R. and Lubbers, D. W. (1969). Quantitative polarographische sauerstoffdruckmessung auf der kopfhaut des neurgebornen, *Arch, Gynaekol.* **207**, 443–52.

—— and Lucey, J. R. (eds) (1979). *Continuous transcutanenous blood gas monitoring. Birth defects.* Original Article Series XV, no. 4, Alan R. Liss, New York.

Hutchison, D. C. S., Rocca. G. and Honeybourne, D. (1981). Estimation of arterial oxygen tension in adult subjects using a transcutaneous electrode. *Thorax* **36**, 473–7.

Isenberg, S. J. and Shoemaker, W. C. (1983). The transconjunctival oxygen monitor. *Am. J. Opthalmol.* **95**, 803–6.

Jamieson, W. R. E., Turnbull, K. W., Larriea, A. J., Dodds, W. A., Allison, J. C. and Tyers, G. F. O. (1982). Continuous monitoring of mixed venous saturation in cardiac surgery. *The Canadian Journal of Surgery* **25 (5)**, 538–43.

Johnson, L. F. and DeMeester, T. R. (1974). Twently-four hour pH monitoring of the distal esophagus. A quantitative measure of gastroesophageal reflux. *Am. J. Gastroenterol.* **62**, 325–32.

Kandel, G. and Aberman, A. (1983). Mixed venous oxygen saturation: its role in the assessment of the critically ill patient. *Arch. Intern. Med.* **143**, 1400–2.

Kelman, G. R., Nunn, J. F. (1966). Nomograms for correction of blood PO_2, PCO_2 pH and base excess for time and temperature. *J. Appl. Physiol.* **21**, 1484–90.

Kondo, T., Ito, K., Ohkura, K., Ito, K. and Ikeda, S. (1982). A miniature glucose sensor, implantable in the blood stream. *Diabetes Care* **5**, 218–21.

LeBlanc, D. H., Brown, J. F., Klebe, J. F., Niedrach, L. W., Shusartzuk G. M. J. and Stoddard, W. H. (1976). Polymer membrane sensors for continuous intravascular monitoring of blood pH. *J. Appl. Physiol.* **40**, 644–7.

Lewandowski, J. J. Szczepanska-Sadowski, E., Krzymien, J. and Nalecz, M. (1982). Amperometric glucose sensor: short-term *in vivo* test. *Diabetes Care* **5**, 238–44.

Mansouri, S. and Schulz, J. S. (1984). A miniature optical glucose sensor based on affinity binding. *Biotechnology* **2**, 885–90.

March, W. F., Rabinovitch, B, Adams R. L., Wise, J. R. and Melton, M. (1982). Ocular glucose sensor. *Trans. Am. Soc. Artif. Intern. Organs* **XXVIII**, 232–5.

McKinley, B. A., Saffle, J., Jordan, W. S., Janata, J., Moss, S. D. and Westernskow, D. R. (1980). *In vivo* continuous monitoring of K$^+$ in animals using ISFET probes. *Medical Instrumentation* **14**, 93–7.

Moxham, J. and Armstrong, R. F. (1981). Continuous monitoring of right atrial oxygen tension in patients with myocardial infarction. *Intensive Care Med.* **7**, 157–64.

Parker, D., Delpy, D. T. and Halsall, D. N. (1983). A new approach to in-line gas monitoring. Development of an oxygen sensor. *Med. Biol. Eng. Comp.* **21**. 134–7.

—— Key, A. and Davies, R. S. (1971). Catheter-tip transducer for continuous *in vivo* measurement of oxygen tension. *Lancet* **1**, 952.

Pickup, J. C. (1984). Clinical applications of infusion systems. *J. Med. Eng. Technol.* **8**, 101–7.

—— (1985). Biosensors: a clinical perspective. *Lancet* **2**, 817–20.

Pickup J. C., Claremont D. J. (1985). A potentially implantable glucose sensor with direct electron transfer. *Diab. Res. Clin, Prac.* Suppl. 1, 447.

—— and Rothwell, D. (1984). Technology and the diabetic patient. *Med. Biol. Eng. Comput.* **22**, 385–400.

—— Keen, H., Parsons, J. A. and Alberti, K. G. M. M. (1978). Continuous subcutaneous insulin infusion: an approach to achieving normoglycaemia. *Brit. Med. J.* **1**, 204–7.

—— Viberti, G. C., White, M. C., Kohner, E. M., Parsons, J. A., Alberti, K. G. M. M. (1980). Continuous subcutaneous insulin infusion in the treatment of diabetes mellitus. *Diabetes Care* **3**, 290–300.

Pollitzer, M., Soutter, L. P., Reynolds, E. R. and Whitehead, M. (1980). Continuous monitoring of arterial oxygen tension in infants: four years of experience with an intravascular oxygen electrode. *Paediatrics* **66 (1)**, 31–6.

Prescott, L. F. and Nimmo, W. S. (eds) (1985). *Rate Control in Drug Therapy.* Churchill Livingstone, Edinburgh.

Rithalaia, S. V. S., Herbert, P. and Tinker, J. (1979). Continuous monitoring of tissue pH, *BMJ* **1**, 1640.

Rooth, G., Sjostedt, S. and Caligora, F. (1957). Bloodless determination of oxygen tension by polarography. *Science Tools* **4**, 37–45.

Severinghaus, J. W. (1966). Blood gas calculation. *J. Appl. Physiol.* **21**. 1108–16.

Shichiri, M. and Kawamori, R. (1983). Feasibility of needle-type glucose sensor and the wearable artificial endocrine pancreas. In *Diabetes treatment with implantable insulin infusion systems.* (eds. K. Irsigler, H. Kritz, and R. Lovett.) pp. 224–30. Urban and Schwarzenberg, Munich.

—— Hakui, N., Yamasaki, Y. and Abe, H. (1984). Closed-loop glycemic control with a wearable artificial endocrine pancreas. *Diabetes* **33**, 1200–2.

—— Yamasaki, Y., Haukui, N. and Abe, H. (1982). Wearable-type artificial pancreas with needle-type glucose sensor. *Lancet* **2**, 1129–31.

—— Goriya, Y., Yamasaki, Y., Abmura, M., Kaui, N. and Abe, H. (1983). Glycaemic control in pancreatectomised dogs with a wearable artificial pancreas. *Diabetologia* **24**, 179–84.

Soeldner, J. S., Change, K. W., Aisenberg, S., Hiebert, J. M. (1973). Progress towards an implantable glucose sensor and an artificial beta cell. In *Temporal aspects of therapeutics* (eds. J. Urquhart and F. E. Yates) pp. 181–207. Plenumn, New York.

Thomas, L. J. (1972). Algorithms for selected blood acid-base blood gas calculations. *J. Appl. Physiol.* **33**, 154–8.

Treasure, T. and Band D. M. (1977). A catheter-tip potassium selective electrode. *J. Med. Eng. Tech.* **1**, 271.

Turner, A. P. F. and Pickup, J. C. (1985). Diabetes mellitus: biosensors for research and management. *Biosensors* **1**, 85–115.

Walpoth, B., Dernierre, D., Eglott, L. and Turina, M. (1981). Continuous oxygen partial pressure monitoring in cardiac surgery. *Proc. Eur. Soc. Art. Org.* **8**, 301–8.

Webb, S. C., Rickards, A. F., Poole-Wilson, P. A. (1983). Coronary artery potassium concentration recorded during coronary angioplasty. *Br. Heart. J.* **50**, 146–8.

Wolfson, S. K., Tokarsky, J. F. and Krupper, M. A. (1982). Glucose concentration at possible sensor sites. *Diabetes Care* **5**, 162–5.

Woodward, S. C. (1982). How fibroblasts and giant cells encapsulate implants: considerations in design of glucose sensors. *Diabetes Care* **5**, 278–81.

Yamanouchi, I., Igarashi, I. and Ouchi, E. (1983). Successful prevention of retinopathy of prematurity via transcutaneous oxygen partial pressure monitoring In *Continuous transcutaneous blood gas monitoring. Reproductive medicine* (eds R. Huch and A. Huch) Vol. 5, pp. 333–40. Marcel Dekker, New York and Basel.

21

Thin-film micro-electrodes for *in vivo* electrochemical analysis

O. PROHASKA*

21.1 Summary

Multiple parameter monitoring is required in order to analyse complex bio-medical processes within living tissue. Most often the probes have to be extremely small and the sensors closely spaced. Methods developed in thin-film physics and solid-state electronics provide the possibility to realize mini-aturized multiple sensor arrays which have been successfully used in brain research. Besides the specific design problems, caused by the fabrication constraints, the miniaturized thin-film metal electrodes display all the dis-advantages of metal wire electrodes. A new chamber-type electrode design will be discussed which seems to be able to overcome most of these problems, enabling, in addition, the construction of miniaturized electrochemical cells.

21.2 Introduction

Investigations of miniaturized chemical sensors are motivated by economic as well as methodological reasons. Improvement in monitoring techniques can be accomplished in part by arranging 'on-chip' sensors close to the inte-grated electronic circuit and by keeping the sensors extremely small in order not to damage or destroy the sample. In brain research, for example, multiple electrode arrangements are required in order to elucidate the spatial neuronal interconnections (Petsche *et al.* 1984; Krueger 1983) and multiple parameter recordings have to be performed in order to explain normal as well as path-ological neuronal activities (Caspers *et al.* 1980; Elger *et al.* 1981). Conventi-onal glue techniques allow the arrangement of only a limited number of glass or metal micro-electrodes in order to form a multiple sensor. Techniques which were developed in modern thin-film physics and solid-state electronics, and which enable the fabrication of precisely defined structures in the micro-meter dimension range, might be very helpful in designing new instruments

*The above described work was performed at the Institut fuer Allgemeine Elektrotechnik und Elektronik at the University of Vienna, Austria together with H. Dragaun, P. Goiser, A. Jachimowicz, F. Kohl, W. Morais, F. Olcaytug, K. Pirker, P. Pfundner, R. Schallauer, and G. Urban.

377

for medical research, surgery, and intensive care patient monitoring.

This Chapter will be concerned with the fabrication and design problems, the limitations, and new aspects of miniaturized electrical and electrochemical thin-film sensors for *in vivo* research studies. The design of mechanically and electrically stable miniaturized Ag/AgCl reference electrodes, as well as the construction of new miniaturized chamber-type sensors, will be described.

21.3 Miniaturized thin-film multiple electrode probes

Thin-film and solid-state techniques (Maissel and Glang 1970), mainly developed in order to improve the quality, density, and mass production of integrated circuits, enable the fabrication of precisely arranged electrode arrays (Prohaska *et al.* 1981). These are placed on small, needle-shaped substrates, which can be inserted in tissue. An example of such a multiple electrode probe is shown in Fig. 21.1. The probe was designed in order to measure the electrical activity of brain tissue, especially within the cortex of rabbits. Eight electrodes with recording site areas of 2500 μm^2 are placed in one row 300 μm apart from one another; a ninth electrode is located 1 mm beneath the eighth in order to simultaneously monitor the hippocampus activities underneath the cortical structure (Petsche *et al.* 1984).

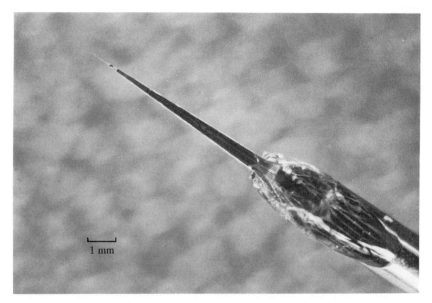

1 mm

Fig. 21.1 Thin-film multiple electrode probe designed in order to register the electrical activities of the brain in animals. It contains nine recording sites, 2500 μm^2 in size, placed in one row on a needle-shaped 0.1 mm-thick glass carrier.

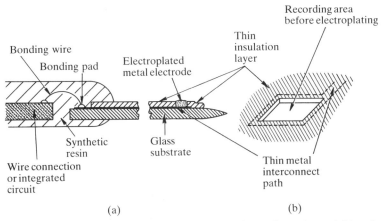

Fig. 21.2 (a) Cross section of a thin-film multiple electrode probe and (b) enlarged view of a thin-film electrode.

21.3.1 Probe fabrication

The schematic drawings in Fig. 21.2 show a cross-section (a) of the probe and a thin-film electrode (b). The photolithographic production steps provide a high degree of flexibility in the electrode and electrode arrangement design and allow a match of an adequate electrode pattern with the anatomical tissue structure:

First, a layout is drawn of the metal and insulator structure and photographically reduced up to several hundred times, defining the desired electrode size and arrangement on a so-called mask. Figure 21.3 shows an example of a metal (a) and an insulation layer mask (b) of a 16-fold electrode probe. The electrodes are arranged in one row 100 μm apart with recording sites of 225 μm^2.

Second, a 0.1 μm thick Cr-Au-Cr triple layer (Cr serves as an adhesion layer) is evaporated onto the surface of a carefully cleaned 100 μm thick glass substrate. The metal layer is then completely covered by a layer of photoresist which changes its solubility in a solvent after having been exposed to ultraviolet light. After the first UV exposure through the metal mask and proper solvent treatment ('development'), the photoresist only covers the parts of the thin metal film which form the electrode areas, the thin metal interconnect paths, and the bonding pads. The uncovered metal film is etched off in selective Cr and Au etchants (Vossen and Kern 1978). Afterwards a 2–3 μm thick Si$_3$N$_4$ insulation layer is produced by plasma enhanced chemical vapour deposition methods (Vossen and Kern 1978), covering the metal structure as well as the glass substrate. After a second photolithographic step using the insulation layer mask, the photoresist covers the insulation layer with the exception of the recording site and bonding pad areas. Plasma etching

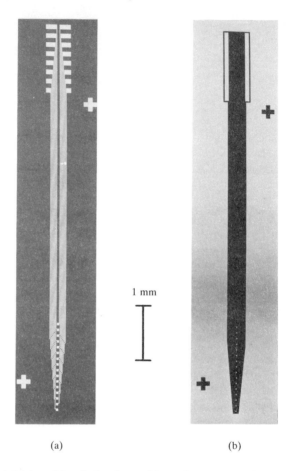

1 mm

(a)   (b)

Fig. 21.3 Metal (a) and insulation layer (b) mask structure of a 16-fold electrode probe; any required two dimensional electrode array can be produced using the described photolithographic fabrication procedures.

techniques allow the fabrication of precisely defined electrode areas, even in the μm size range. Thereafter, the glass substrate is cut in a needle-like shape by a diamond scriber under microscopic control. By means of a modified glass micro-electrode fabrication procedure, a fine probe tip is created which, in turn, allows smooth insertion of the probe into the brain tissue. The thin metal structure can be bonded to insulated copper leads or directly to integrated electronic circuits. The bonding areas have to be electrically as well as mechanically protected and are embedded in synthetic resin and silicone rubber. The upper Cr layer is removed at the recording sites so that the thin Au layer can be covered electrolytically by various metal layers such as gold, platinum, or silver (which can be converted to AgCl to provide a reference electrode in order to create a smooth probe surface as well as to serve various application purposes, which will be discussed below.

Other substrate, insulation, and metal layer materials are also used (Shamma-Donaghue *et al.* 1982; May *et al.* 1979; Wise and Angell 1975; Kuperstein and Whitington 1981; Eddel 1982) for multiple electrode probes and a wide range of applications is opened up by the integration of electronic circuits directly behind the electrode structure. The possibility of adding the integrated circuit directly onto the same silicon substrate is also being investigated (Wise and Najafi 1984; Takahashi and Matsuo 1984).

21.3.2 Electrical probe characteristics

The electrodes form an electrode–electrolyte system with the tissue. The electrical properties of that system determine the signal transfer, the cross talk between two thin metal interconnect paths, and the signal coupling across the insulation layer. In order to assure disturbance-free recordings, the electrical characteristics of that system have to be analysed, since it is dependent on the signal frequency, the electrode size, the electrode material, and the electrolyte.

The electrode–electrolyte interface can be represented by an equivalent electronic circuit, taking into account the charge transfer processes at the electrode–electrolyte double layer as well as the diffusion, crystallization, and reaction processes at the electrode surface (Vetter 1982).

In recording the electrical activity of the brain tissue, the potential changes between the thin-film electrodes and a large reference electrode are measured. The current flow during the measurements has to be minimized in order to avoid tissue irritation. This means that crystallization and reaction processes at the electrode surfaces can be excluded and the equivalent circuit, representing the electrode–electrolyte interface, can be reduced to a

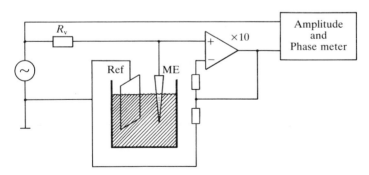

Fig. 21.4 Electrode–electrolyte impedance measurement set-up; amplitude and phase measurements allow the calculation of the capacitive and ohmic part of the impedance.

resistance–capacitance (*R-C*) combination. *R* and *C* can be determined by current–voltage measurements. In order to be able to compare the results with larger sized electrode impedances (Geddes 1972) the *R-C* series equivalent circuit will be used here as well.

Figure 21.4 shows the measurement set-up which was used in order to determined the electrode–electrolyte impedance *Z* and it's ohmic and capacitive components. *R* and *C* were calculated according to the voltage divider rule from the measured relation between the applied voltage and the voltage drop at the electrode impedance as well as their offset in phase. Our experiments showed, in accordance with theory (Vetter 1962) and other recordings (Geddes 1972), that the electrode–electrolyte impedance becomes a function of the current density as soon as a critical current density value is exceeded during the impedance measurements; we therefore kept the current density below 1 μA/mm^2 throughout the electrode–electrolyte interface investigations.

Figure 21.5 shows the strong frequency dependence of *Z*, *R*, and *C* of thin-film gold electrodes with electrode areas of 0.25 mm^2 (subscript 1), 0.01 mm^2 (subscript 2), and 2500 μm^2 (subscript 3). The recordings also show that the electrode impedances are, in accordance with the theory, inversely proportional to the electrode area. The capacitive part of the impedance is almost frequency independent, indicating that the double layer capacitance determines the capacitive part of the metal electrode impedance; the ohmic part,

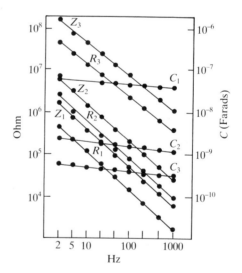

Fig. 21.5 Frequency dependence of *Z*, *R*, and *C* of think-film gold electrodes; subscript 1, electrode area of 0.25 mm^2; subscript 2, electrode area of 0.01 mm^2, subscript 3 electrode area of 2500 μm^2.

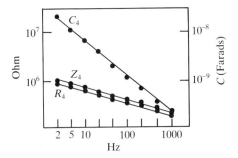

Fig. 21.6 Frequency dependence of Z, R, and C of a mechanically and electrically stable thin-film Ag/AgCl electrode, 2500 μm^2 in geometrical size (the actual electrode surface area is much larger).

however, is strongly frequency dependent and therefore mainly determined by the diffusion resistance.

High quality Ag/AgCl electrodes show a very different behaviour; their fabrication procedure is discussed below. In Fig. 21.6 Z and R of an Ag/AgCl electrode, 2500 μm^2 in geometrical size, are almost frequency independent, whereas the capacitive part of the impedance is negligible. Furthermore, the impedance value of Ag/AgCl electrodes is more than 100 times smaller than that of Au electrodes of the same geometrical size for frequencies below 10 Hz.

The different electrode characteristics make these two types of electrodes preferable for various applications. Single neuronal activities will be better studied with miniaturized gold electrodes, whereas potential changes in the frequency range below 100 Hz will be recordable with less perturbances as long as Ag/AgCl electrodes are used.

The fabrication of mechanically stable Ag/AgCl electrodes is a precondition for their electrical stability. This is particularly important since Ag/AgCl electrodes can also be used as miniaturized reference electrodes. Therefore, appropriate fabrication steps shall be briefly outlined. The thin-film gold electrode areas are first electrolytically covered by a 1 μm thick silver layer which is electrolytically converted to AgCl in a 1% NaCl solution. The amplitude and the frequency dependence of Ag/AgCl electrode impedances depend strongly on the amount of charge which was used for the chloridizing process. Figure 21.7 shows the impedance changes of Ag/AgCl electrodes which were produced, using a current density of 0.03 mA/mm² for 10 s (subscript 5), 50 s (subscript 6), 100 s (subscript 7), and 180 s (subscript 9). These impedance changes support the assumption that the Ag/AgCl growth starts at energetically prefered points on the silver surface (Jaenicke *et al.* 1955); a strong frequency dependence below 100 Hz is caused by the remaining silver surface. With ongoing electrodeposition time a continuous Ag/AgCl

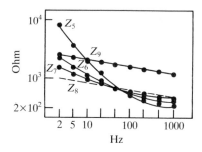

Fig. 21.7 Frequency dependence changes of the electrode–electrolyte impedance of a silver electrode which was chlorided for 10 s (5), 50 s (6), 100 s (7), and 180 s (9) with a current density of 0.03 mA/mm².

layer will be formed with minimum impedance values (Z_8). Further electrolysis results in an increase of the Ag/AgCl layer thickness, increasing the impedance of the Ag/AgCl layer due to the fact that silver chloride has a resistivity of only 10^5 Ohm/cm² (Jaenicke *et al.* 1955).

The formation of mechanically stable Ag/AgCl layers depends on the current density used during the process: SEM photos of Ag/AgCl layers which were produced using current densities of 0.15 mA/mm² for 2 s (Fig. 21.8a), 25 s (Fig. 21.8b) and 35 s (Fig. 21.8c) show the large surface structure difference compared with the mechanically very stable Ag/AgCl layer which was formed with a current density of 0.03 mA/mm² for 200 s (Fig. 21.8d). The latter fabrication procedure was successfully used for the production of all our miniaturized Ag/AgCl electrodes.

21.3.3 Sources of signal disturbances and application limits

An adequate probe design is necessary in order to obtain disturbance-free signals from the thin-film multiple electrodes. Significant signal transfer distortions can be caused by the Johnson noise (Johnson 1928) of the electrode–electrolyte impedance, by the shunt capacitance along the thin-film metal interconnect paths across the insulation layer, and by the cross talk between evaporated conducting paths. The electrode size and material determines the dimensions of the thin metal interconnecting paths and the thickness of the insulation layer (Prohaska *et al.* 1986). It should be emphasized at this point, that the available thin-film and solid-state equipment enables the fabrication in principle of even sub-micrometer structures and may enable a broader field of applications for micro-miniaturized electrodes.

In covering the thin-film electrodes with a reference electrolyte and an ion selective membrane (Burgess *et al.* 1982), thin-film ion selective electrodes can be fabricated. Two and three electrode arrangements might be able to serve as voltammetric recording systems with the advantage of the better

a   b   c   d

2 µm

Fig. 21.8 Changes of the Ag/AgCl surface, depending on the electrolysis time: (a) 2 s; (b) 25 s; (c) 35 s. The current density was 0.15 mA/mm^2 respectively. (d) Ag/AgCl electrode surface after a chloriding procedure with 0.03 mA/mm^2 for 200 s.

recording qualities which are observed with micro working electrodes (Caudill *et al*. 1982).

The main application limitations of thin-film electrodes are set by the quality of the electrode and insulation material and by the way potentiometric and voltammetric chemical sensors have to be designed. One problem is that the Ag/AgCl electrodes are Cl$^-$ ion concentration dependent, a fact which can cause severe signal distortions. Another problem is that the reference electrode for voltammetric recordings in the case of a two electrode system should be larger by far then the working electrode; in the case of a three electrode system, the minimum size of the Ag/AgCl reference electrode is determined by the leakage current of the amplifier system since this current can be large enough to modulate the AgCl deposit on the Ag/AgCl electrode and thereby change the electrode potential. Furthermore, *in vivo* voltammetric studies become impossible as soon as the tissue becomes irritated

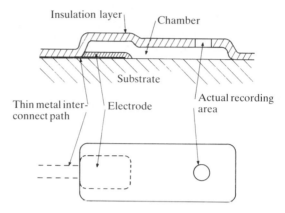

Fig. 21.9 Cross section and top view of a chamber-type electrode.

by the voltammetric current. A first step in order to overcome these problems was made by developing new miniaturized chamber-type electrodes.

21.4 Chamber-type electrodes

Figure 21.9 shows a cross section and a top view of a chamber-type electrode. In contrast to the flat thin insulation layer in Fig. 21.2 which covers the thin metal interconnecting paths of the thin-film electrode arrangement, the insulation layer is now bent upward and forms a chamber which covers the electrode. The contact between the electrode and the sample is effected through a hole in the chamber which defines the actual recording site size. The chamber is filled with an electrolyte. The SEM photo in Fig. 21.10 shows

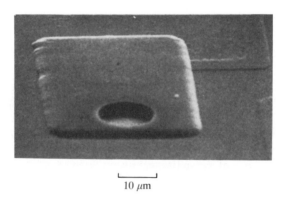

10 µm

Fig. 21.10 SEM photo of a chamber-type electrode.

a chamber-type electrode formed by a 3 μm thick Si_3N_4 insulation layer which is produced by plasma enhanced chemical vapour deposition. (Vossen and Kern 1978; Olcaytug *et al*. 1980). The holes have, in this case, a diameter of 15 μm. The chamber is about 3 μm high, 45 μm wide and 80 μm long. The measured impedance–frequency relationship indicates that the resistance of the electrolyte bridge in that chamber is below the MΩ range. Furthermore, the Ag/AgCl electrodes, covered by these chambers, become insensitive to rapid fluctuations in chloride ion concentration. The response time for Cl^- concentration changes can be increased up to 8 s if the distance between the Ag/AgCl electrode and the hole is 30 μm and up to 150 s if that distance is 80 μm. These results let us hope that a chamber design can be found which drastically improves miniaturized reference electrode qualities.

The main advantages of the chamber construction are:

a) The direct contact between tissue and electrode material can be avoided.

b) The recording area, being independent of the size of the electrodes, is defined by the size of the hole.

c) Since larger electrode areas can be used, signal disturbances can be kept minimal.

d) Miniaturized electrochemical cells can be designed, forming potentiometric and voltammetric sensors.

In filling the chamber with an ion selective membrane, these types of sensors can be used as ion selective electrodes. An enzyme electrode can be designed by supplying the chamber with an enzyme layer. The chamber not only protects the selective membranes and layers from being mechanically affected by the sample or the measuring process, but it also allows only a small portion of the selective membrane to be exposed to the sample, thus increasing the life time of the miniaturized sensor. In the event that the chamber is covering an electrode set, voltammetric recording techniques can be used advantageously to analyse the sample composition; the chamber construction is especially valuable in the case of diffusion controlled processes, as it protects the electrode and provides it with a stable environment.

By using a 25 μm^2 gold electrode placed directly beneath the hole and a 1600 μm^2 Ag/AgCl reference electrode, an oxygen sensor was designed for amperometric measurements in the brain of animals. The response time is in the range of 0.3 s, which agrees well with calculated values. The main advantage of this arrangement is that the current flow takes place only within the chamber and does not affect the sample under test, which is especially important in the case of nerve tissue.

21.5 Concluding remarks

Thin-film and solid-state techniques seem to offer a large variety of possibilities in designing miniaturized electrochemical sensors. Although intensive studies will still be necessary in order to reach the quality and stability of macroscopic sensors, advantageous features of miniaturized thin-film electrodes have already been demonstrated (Davis *et al.* 1986). A major advantage might also be that multiple parameter measurements could be possible; closely spaced chamber-type sensors, forming in themselves closed units, do not interfere with each other and physical parameters may be recordable at the same time using high resolution thin-film temperature sensors (Urban *et al.* 1982) and pressure sensors (Guckel *et al.* 1984; Lee and Wise 1982; Ko *et al.* 1982) integrated onto the same substrate.

Acknowledgement

The research was sponsored by the Austrian Fonds zur Foerderung der wissenschaftlichen Forschung, project no. S22/09 as well as by the Austrian Ludwig Boltzman Society. We want to thank Professors W. Fallmann, F. Paschke, H. Petsche, and R. Vollmer for the stimulating discussions and their support.

References

Burgess, B., Burleigh, P. and Diamond, H. (1982). Thin film solid state electro-chemical sensors. *Proc. Biosensors*, 48–50. Los Angeles, 1982.

Caspers, H., Speckmann, E. J. and Lehmenkuehler, A. (1980). Electrogenesis of cortical DC potentials, In *Motivation, motor and sensory processes of the brain.* (eds. H. H. Kornhuber and L. Duecke) *Progr. Brain Res.* **54**, 3–15.

Caudill, W. L., Howell, J. O. and Wightman, R. M. (1982). Flow rate independent amperometric cell. *Anal. Chem.* **54**, 2532–5.

Davis, G., Prohaska, O. and Olcaytug, F. (1986). Enzyme coupled reactions at micro-voltammetric electrodes, Communication for *Anal. Chem.* In preparation.

Edell, D. J. (1982). A biocompatible, multi-channel neuroelectric interface, *Proc. 35th ACEMB*, p. 6.

Elger, C. E., Speckmann, E. J., Prohaska, O. and Caspers, H. (1981). Pattern of intracortical potential distribution during focal interictal epileptiform discharges (FIED) and its relation to spinal field potentials in the rat. *Electroenceph. Clin. Neurophysiol.* **51**, 393–402.

Geddes, L. A. 1972. *Electrodes and the measurement of bioelectric events*, Wiley-Interscience, New York.

Guckel, H. and Burns, D. W. (1984). Planar processed polysilicon sealed cavities for pressure transducer arrays, *Technical Digest* IEEE IEDM, p. 223.

Jaenicke, W., Tischer, R. P. and Gerischer, H. (1955). Die anodische Bildung von Silberchlorid–Deckschichten und Umlagerungserscheinungen nach ihrer kathodischen Reduktion zu Silber, *Z. Elektrochem. Angew. Physik. Chem.* **59**, 448–55.

Johnson, J. B. (1928). Therminal agitation of electricity in conductors. *Phys. Rev.* **32**, 97–109.

Ko, W. H., Bao, M. and Hong, Y. (1982). A high-sensitivity integrated-circuit capacitive pressure transducer, *IEEE Trans. Electron Devices* **29**, 48–56.

Krueger, J. (1983). Simultaneous individual recordings from many cerebral neurons: techniques and results. *Rev. Physiol. Biochem. Pharmacol.* **98**, 177–233.

Kuperstein, M. and Whitington, D. A. (1981). A practical 24 channel microelectrode for neural recording *in vivo. IEEE Trans. BME* **28**, 288–293.

Lee, Y. S. and Wise, K. D. (1982). A batch-fabricated silicon capacitive pressure transducer with low temperature sensitivity *IEEE Trans. Electron Devices* **29**, 42–48.

Maissel, L. and Glang, R. (1970). *Handbook of thin-film technology*. McGraw–Hill, New York.

May, G. A., Shamma, S. A. and White, R. L. (1979). A tantalum–on–sapphire microelectrode array, *IEEE Trans. Electron Devices* **26**, 1932–39.

Olcaytug, F., Riedling, K. and Fallmann, W. (1980). A low temperature process for the reactive formation of Si_3N_4 layers on InSb. *Thin Solid Films*, **67**, 321–4.

Petsche, H., Pockberger, H. and Rappelsberger, P. (1984). On the search for the sources of the electroencephalogram. *Neuroscience*, **11**, 1–29.

Prohaska, O., Olcaytug, F., Pfundner, P. and Dragaun, H. G. (1986). Thin-film multiple electrode probes: possibilities and limitations. *IEEE Trans. Biomed. Eng.* **33**, 223–9.

—— Womastek, K. and Petsche, H. (1981). A multielectrode for intracortical recordings produced by thin-film technology, *Electroenceph. Clin. Neurophysiol.* **42**, 421–2.

Shamma–Donoghue, S. A., May, G. A., Cotter, N. E. and White, R. L. (1982). Thin-film multiple arrays for a cochlear prostheses, *IEEE Trans. Electron Devices* **29**, 136–144.

Takahashi, K. and Matsuo, T. (1984). Integration of multi-microelectrode and interface circuits by silicon planar and three-dimensional fabrication technology, *Sensors and Actuators* **5**, 89–99.

Urban, G., Kohl, F., Olcaytug, F., Vollmer R. and Prohaska, O. (1982). Duennschichttemperaturfuehler fuer Mehrfachmessungen im Kortex, Wiss. Berichte, Jahrestagung Oesterr. Ges. BMT, 273–6.

Vetter, K. J. (1962). *Electrochemical kinetics*. Academic Press, New York.

Vossen, J. L. and Kern, W. (1978). *Thin-film processes*. Acad. Press, New York.

Wise, K. D. and Najafi, K. (1984). A micromachined integrated sensor with on-chip self-test capabilities, Proc. IEEE Solid-State Sensor Conference, 12–16.

Wise, K. D. and Angell, J. B. (1975). A low-capacitance multielectrode probe for neurophysiology, *IEEE Trans. Biomed. Eng.* **22**, 212–19.

22

The design and development of *in vivo* glucose sensors for an artificial endocrine pancreas

GILBERTO D. VELHO, GERARD REACH, and DANIEL R. THÉVENOT

22.1 Introduction

Insulin, a polypeptide hormone produced by the beta-cells of the pancreas, is essential in many metabolic pathways for carbohydrates, proteins, and fats; in the absence of normal insulin secretion, body fuel homeostasis is deranged. Diabetes mellitus is characterized by a relative or an absolute insulin deficiency manifested by loss of control of the circulating blood glucose levels, and by other metabolic abnormalities.

Diabetes is a common disease in affluent societies, affecting from one to three per cent of the population, and often five to ten per cent of those over 40 years of age (Hamman 1983). Where systematic surveys have been performed in the developing nations, rates of one to two per cent of the total population prevail (Bennett 1983). Thus, diabetes is a major worldwide health problem with a great social and economic impact due largely to its later complications. Albisser and Spencer (1982) referring to the Report of the National Commission on Diabetes to the Congress of the United States (1976) suggest that, in that country, diabetics are 25 times more prone to blindness than non-diabetics, 17 times more prone to kidney disease, 5 times more prone to gangrene, twice as prone to heart disease, and have a life expectancy of approximately one-third less than the general population.

Diabetes mellitus is an heterogeneous disease and only a minority of patients, representing however 3 per 1000 of the general population, are so severely insulinopenic as to require insulin therapy. Since its introduction in the early twenties up to the last years of the seventies, insulin therapy was possible only through discontinuous insulin administration, by one, two, or occasionally, several daily insulin injections.

The search for better methods for treating insulin-dependent diabetes and its complications has led to the development of new devices for insulin therapy in the last decade. Infusion systems for continuous insulin delivery (insulin pump), including a reservoir, a pump, and a power supply packed into a portable single unit, have been made available to clinicians and diabetic patients. Efforts to develop a portable self-regulated system, associating an

390

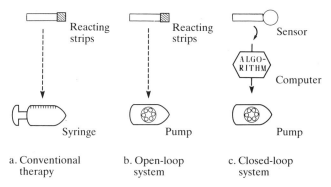

Fig. 22.1 Scheme of three possible methods of insulin therapy.
(a) Intensive conventional therapy: multiple insulin injections dependent on manual glucose measurement with reacting strips.
(b) Open-loop system: continuous preprogrammed insulin infusion dependent on manual glucose measurement with reacting strips.
(c) Closed-loop system: continuous self-regulated insulin infusion. The glucose level, continuously measured by the sensor, is translated by the computer in a variable rate of insulin delivery.

implantable glucose sensor with the insulin delivery device, are in progress in several laboratories. This system is referred to as a closed-loop system, in contrast to the former, non self-regulated system, known as the open-loop system (Fig. 22.1). The control of insulin delivery by open-loop and closed-loop systems, as compared to the physiological regulation of insulin secretion, is shown in Fig. 22.2.

This chapter will review the advantages of the closed-loop system of insulin therapy, the requirements for an implantable glucose sensor, and the state of present development and applications of glucose sensors.

22.2 Are closed-loop insulin infusion systems really necessary?

The evidence of a relationship between the microvascular complications of diabetes mellitus and hyperglycaemia (Tchobroutsky 1978) led to the intensification of insulin therapy, either by multiple daily insulin injections or continuous insulin infusion, in the hope that it would improve metabolic control and therefore prevent the occurrence of these late complications. Rizza *et al.* (1980) comparing the control of blood sugar by an artificial endocrine pancreas (closed-loop system), continuous subcutaneous insulin infusion (open-loop system), and intensified conventional insulin therapy, in insulin-dependent diabetes, found no significant differences among the three regimens and suggested that all three methods have the potential to achieve a similar near-normalization of glycaemia.

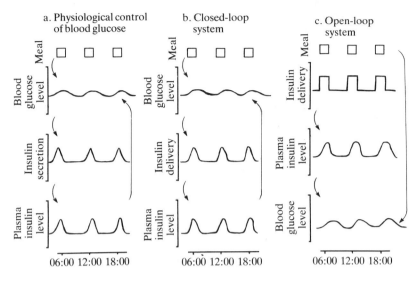

Fig. 22.2 Physiological regulation of blood glucose by the endocrine pancreas (a), control of insulin delivery in closed-loop (b) and open-loop (c) systems. In the open-loop system, insulin delivery is programmed to normalize the blood glucose but it is not regulated by the glucose level.

The main advantages and disadvantages presented by these three methods of insulin therapy are summarized in Table 22.1. Intensive conventional insulin therapy is inexpensive, calls for no special equipment and is immediately available to every patient. However, multiple daily injections of insulin are necessary to achieve a near normal glycaemic control.

Open-loop devices do not have this limitation. Nevertheless, they are expensive, must be carried by the patient, and like any mechanical devices, are subject to malfunction. The problem of insulin aggregation, with loss of biological activity and obstruction of the internal passages of the device has been described (Lougheed *et al*. 1980). Both conventional insulin therapy and open-loop therapy need frequent glucose measurements by the patient to maintain adequate glycaemic control since diet and exercise demand an adaptation of insulin doses. Both therapy methods present, however, further advantages concerning the timing of mealtime insulin bolus and the route of insulin delivery. The mealtime insulin bolus is not controlled by nutrient absorption in the gut, as in normal individuals and in closed-loop therapy (Fig. 22.2), and thus, must be controlled by the patient. As the post-prandial blood glucose and insulin levels are affected by the interval between insulin administration and meal ingestion, this interval, if appropriately chosen, may contribute to the normalization of glycaemia and insulin

Table 22.1 Main advantages and disadvantages of different methods of insulin therapy

	Conventional therapy	Open loop	Closed loop
Disadvantages	Multiple injections	Expensive	Portable device not available
	Frequent glucose measurement	Frequent glucose measurement	Hyperinsulinaemia
		Must be carried by the patient	Venous injection
			Must be carried by the patient
		Subject to malfunction	Subject to malfunction
		Insulin aggregation	Insulin aggregation
Advantages	Immediately available	Immediately available	Independent of external glucose measurements
	Inexpensive: no special equipment	Free of multiple injections	Auto-adaptation to exercise and diet changes
	Subcutaneous injection	Subcutaneous injection	

profile. Dimitriadis and Gerich (1983) compared the effects of 30-min subcutaneous insulin infusions started 60 min, 30 min, and immediately before meal ingestion on postprandial plasma glucose and insulin profiles in subjects with insulin dependent diabetes mellitus. They found that administration of insulin 60 min before meal ingestion provided plasma glucose and insulin profiles closest to normal and permitted less insulin to be used. This anticipation of 60 minutes may be necessary for two complementary reasons: first, part of this time may be required to build up a physiological hepatic insulinization from insulin delivered subcutaneously. Second, insulin secretion in non-diabetic subjects is not controlled only by blood glucose rise: the response of insulin secreting cells is anticipated under the influence of different nerves and of gastroenteric hormones. Thus, if insulin doses and the timing of injection or bolus infusion are carefully chosen, near normal glucose control can be obtained by intensive conventional therapy and open-loop systems through the subcutaneous route of insulin delivery. In that way the complications associated with long-term vascular access for intravenous insulin infusion can be avoided.

The main advantage of a closed-loop insulin delivery device is its independence of external glucose measurements and its ability to cope with the variations of insulin requirement brought about by exercise and diet. Nevertheless, the glycaemic normalization achieved by these devices is frequently associated with peripheral hyperinsulinaemia (Horwitz, Zeidler, *et al.* 1980). Hyperinsulinaemia is a common feature of any insulin administration through a peripheral route, and is mainly due to the absence of the portal-peripheral insulin gradient. Furthermore hyperinsulinaemia might also be the consequence of the time lag in insulin administration in response to the glucose challenge. Thus, this hyperinsulinaemia can be avoided by the combination of the feedback controlled insulin administration with a pre-programmed preprandial insulin infusion (Calabrese, *et al.* 1982). Therefore, the possibility of a 'manual' or 'semi-automatic' mode should be considered in the design of closed-loop systems.

Currently, closed-loop systems present several disadvantages. They are cumbersome bedside devices that need continuous blood withdrawal from the subject in order to ensure the automatic glucose analysis. A small portable device is not yet commercially available. Closed-loop systems, portable or not, need long term venous access for insulin delivery. Insulin absorption by a subcutaneous or peritoneal route is not fast enough to enable an efficient feedback control of the infusion rate. Finally, closed-loop systems, being automatic devices, should be extremely reliable, both mechanically and in the reading of the glucose sensor, otherwise their main advantage, i.e. less demanding glucose control by the patient, would be lost. Pump-induced insulin aggregation seems to be an additional problem to be solved (Brennan *et al.* 1985).

22.3 Why is a portable closed-loop insulin infusion device not yet available?

Such a device consists essentially of a glucose sensor, a pump and a computer that translates the information provided by the sensor into a variable rate of insulin infusion. The pump and the computer components of the device are commercially available. By contrast, implantable glucose sensors that prove to be reliable are still to be developed.

The great majority of the glucose sensors developed so far operate through the oxidation of β-D-glucose by dissolved oxygen in the presence of β-D-glucose oxidase (GOD EC 1.1.3.4.), according to the following reaction:

$$\text{Glucose} + O_2 \xrightarrow{\text{Glucose oxidase}} \text{Gluconic acid} + H_2O_2$$

They consist of electrochemical detectors (electrodes) associated in different ways with the enzyme support. The chemical reaction may be monitored via three of its constituents, i.e., oxygen depletion, gluconic acid, or hydrogen peroxide formation.

Table 22.2 Main requirements for a glucose sensor for an artificial beta-cell

High specificity for glucose
Linearity of response from 1 to 15 mmol/l of glucose
Response time less than 10 minutes
Response independent of hydrodynamics and oxygen variations in tissues
Stability of glucose oxidase membrane at 37 °C in tissues
Biocompatibility
Prolonged lifetime (at least several days)
Miniaturization of the sensor head

The requirements to be fullfilled by a portable or implantable glucose oxidase type of sensor for use in a closed-loop device (Thévenot 1982) are described below and summarized in Table 22.2. General requirements, also valid for other types of glucose sensors, are marked with an asterisk.

1) High specificity for glucose*. In the case of glucose oxidase sensors this includes high enzymatic specificity and high electrochemical specificity of associated detectors. The first condition is always valid since glucose oxidase catalyses the oxidation of only very few species besides glucose, and at a much lower rate (Barman 1969). On the contrary, the second condition is often non-valid and depends mainly upon the type of electro-chemical detector used (see Section 22.4).

2) Linearity of *in vivo* response from 1 to 15 mmol/l (Fig. 22.3b)*; this rather limited linear range is justified by the recent findings of Harrison *et al.* (1985) who described the properties of isolated human islets of Langerhans (Fig. 22.3a). The threshold concentration of glucose required for stimulation of insulin release was between 2 and 4 mmol/l, insulin secretory response to glucose stimulation had half-maximal values at a glucose concentration of approximately 5 mmol/l and a plateau at 10 mmol/l. Under *in vivo* conditions the calibration curve of a glucose oxidase sensor may not always be linear over this range (example: Fig. 22.4, curve A). In fact, the tissue or blood glucose level, especially in diabetics, may be higher than the apparent Michaelis constant (K_M) of glucose oxidase solutions for glucose in air-saturated solutions, i.e. 4 to 10 mmol/l (Apotheker A., Thévenot D. R., Wilson G. S., unpublished data). However, it is possible to get a calibration curve linear over a much higher concentration range, i.e. up to 20–30 mmol/l, if the glucose flux is reduced by membranes of low permeability to glucose. This may be achieved by an external membrane covering the enzymatic membrane (Fig. 22.4, curve C) or by the enzymatic membrane itself (Fig. 22.4 curve B).

3) Response time less than 10 min*; Sorensen, *et al.* (1982) using a theoretical physiological pharmacokinetic model of glucose homeostasis

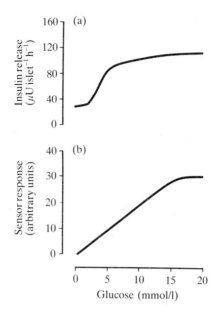

Fig. 22.3 (a) Insulin secretion by isolated islets in respone to glucose (after Harrison *et al.* 1985). Note the sigmoidal relationship and the plateau observed at values higher than 10 mmol/1. (b) Linearity of an implantable glucose sensor for the artificial endocrine pancreas. Due to the response of natural beta cells, the linearity of the sensor response may be limited to 15 mmol/l of glucose.

showed that increases in sensor delay resulted in progressive loss in glucose regulation, exacerbation of hyperinsulinaemia, and increased insulin requirements.

4) Independence of sensor response to fluid hydrodynamics in vessels or tissues*.

5)Independence of sensor response to oxygen level variations in the sensor surroundings and oxygen consumption by the sensor itself. Oxidation of glucose by dissolved oxygen is an irreversible process with a steady state that may be controlled either by the enzymatic oxidation reaction with high temperature dependence (6–10%/°C) or by substrate diffusion with low temperature dependence (2–4%/°C) (Racine and Mindt 1971; Kamin and Wilson 1980). Under such heterogeneous kinetics, the glucose electrode consumes what it is supposed to monitor. This is a characteristic common to Clark's oxygen sensor (see Section 22.4.1.). Whatever the electrochemical detector associated with the glucose oxidase membrane, the stability of its readings is affected by external diffusion (i.e. fluid flow rate near the membrane), internal diffusion (i.e. permeability to substrates), as well as by oxygen concentration level in or near the mem-

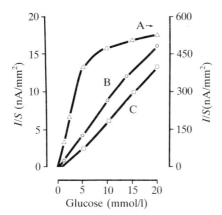

Fig. 22.4 Different types of calibration curves for a glucose sensor using different glucose oxidase membranes (after Sternberg R., Tallagrand T., Thévenot D. R.. Unpublished data): (a) GOD collagen membrane (right-side *Y* axis). (b) GOD cellulose acetate membrane (left-side *Y* axis). (c) GOD collagen membrane covered with a pinholed Teflon membrane (left-side *Y* axis). Note that the use of an additional non-enzymatic membrane or of a cellulose acetate membrane both extends the linear range of the system and impairs its sensitivity.

branes. In an ideal situation these factors should be kept constant. In the case of implantable glucose electrodes these ideal conditions are difficult to obtain. Clark's oxygen detectors that have a cathode diameter approximately equal to the membrane thickness (10–20 microns), are less dependent on hydrodynamics, due to the hemispheric diffusion pattern (in contrast with the linear pattern) obtained under this particular situation (Bard and Faulkner 1980; Wightman 1981). Accessibility of substrates and adequate oxygen level at enzymatic sites can be indirectly controlled by using an additional external membrane more permeable to oxygen than to glucose and/or by using enzymatic layers with a high partition coefficient for oxygen.

6) Long-term mechanical, chemical, and enzymatic stability of glucose oxidase and its support at 37°C, in whole blood, lymph, or tissue.

7) No leaking of glucose oxidase into fluids and tissues surrounding the sensor; being a foreign enzyme, its recognition by the immune system would provoke an immune reaction.

8) Biocompatibility of all implanted parts of the sensor; absence of implant encapsulation by fibroblasts and giant cells*. Woodward (1982) suggested that the optimal configuration for a subcutaneously implantable sensor is in the form of a wire or filament. Such a structure, if measuring less than about 2 mm in diameter, would evoke a minimal tissue response.

9) The scaling down of the sensor should not modify the geometrical, physical, and enzymatic characteristics which control its analytical properties.

10) The system should require minimal calibration and zero adjustment*.

11) Finally, the sensor should have a prolonged lifetime, it should be easily replaceable if necessary and not be expensive if it has to be replaced*. In the case of sensors to be partially inserted in the subcutaneous tissue, in a needle-like fashion, a lifetime of several days, if not weeks, could be accepted. Obviously, a totally implantable device would require a much longer lifetime.

In the remaining sections of this chapter an overview is presented of the significant results obtained in the development of glucose sensors and their application in closed-loop insulin infusion devices.

22.4 Glucose oxidase electrochemical sensors for the artificial endocrine pancreas: types of detectors.

22.4.1 Oxygen detectors

Clark and Lyons (1962) described the first specific glucose electrode (Chapter 1). The enzyme was retained on a polymer membrane and an amperometric oxygen electrode estimated the decrease of oxygen as the reaction proceeded. The Clark-type oxygen electrodes are almost insensitive to all types of interfering substances, but they are obviously very sensitive to variations in partial pressure of oxygen within the fluid in contact with the electrode. Thus, misreadings due to physiological or pathological fluctuations of oxygen partial pressure are to be expected under *in vivo* conditions. This problem may be surmounted by the addition of a second electrode, not associated with a glucose oxidase membrane, forming a differential system (Updike and Hicks 1967).

Improvements in this system by Bessmann and Schultz (1973) led to a prototype implantable sensor using two galvanic oxygen electrodes as detector. Oxygen had access to the electrodes through a polypropylene membrane, the external side of which was fastened to a matrix of nylon cloth. Glucose oxidase was covalently bound to the matrix, in the working electrode, by glutaraldehyde. The whole was contained in a plastic disc of 2 cm diameter by 0.25 cm depth. The sensor had a useful *in vivo* lifetime of four days but a less than optimal sensitivity to glucose, due in part to the low oxygen partial pressure in subcutaneous tissues (Bessman *et al.* 1977).

An additional problem with this type of sensor (Fig. 22.5a) is the competition for oxygen between the glucose oxidase membrane (flux v_2) and the oxygen detector itself (flux v_1); if the cathode is not small enough, the latter flux may interfere with the apparent glucose oxidase activity.

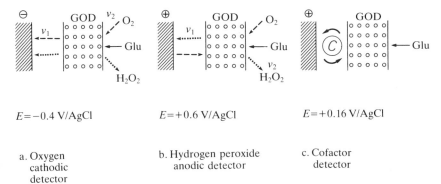

a. Oxygen
cathodic
detector

b. Hydrogen peroxide
anodic detector

c. Cofactor
detector

Fig. 22.5 Types of detectors used in glucose oxidase electrochemical sensors for artificial endocrine pancreas: (a) oxygen cathodic; (b) hydrogen peroxide anodic; and (c) cofactor detector. See text for explanation.

22.4.2 pH detectors

Glucose sensors based on the detection of gluconic acid via a pH electrode have been developed. Nevertheless they present poor sensitivity, selectivity, and linearity of calibration curves (Nilson *et al.* 1973) and thus cannot be implanted in the highly buffered body fluids.

22.4.3 Hydrogen peroxide amperometric detectors

Amperometric detection of enzymatically generated hydrogen peroxide is probably the most developed type of glucose sensor (Guilbaut and Lubrano 1973; Scheller *et al.* 1977; Thévenot *et al.* 1978) (Fig. 22.5b). Clemens *et al.* (1977) adapted one of such sensors for use in a bedside-type artificial pancreas. Similar sensors have been adapted for the same purpose by several groups (see Section 22.7). Over the last ten years, improvements have been made in the sensor design, the binding of the enzyme to its support, and the functional characteristics of the electrodes.

This type of detector is very sensitive to glucose; its lowest detection limit may reach 10 nmol/l (Thévenot *et al.* 1978). Hydrogen peroxide amperometric detection is also very sensitive to naturally occurring electron donors, such as ascorbate, urate, and tyrosine. Methods have been developed to increase the selectivity of the glucose electrode towards such interfering substances. Either the response is compensated by a non-enzymatic detector (Thévenot *et al.* 1978) or the platinum anode is covered by selectively impermeable membranes (cellulose acetate, for instance) with pores that will exclude ascorbate and most other potential interfering substances (Yellow Springs Instrument Co. 1975).

The independence on oxygen concentration of hydrogen peroxide detection is an advantage in sensor design. Nevertheless the local oxygen level necessary for the enzymatic reaction to occur must be taken into account: in that way, membrane partition and diffusion coefficient for oxygen play an important role in glucose response patterns. Oxygen is regenerated during the electrochemical oxidation of hydrogen peroxide on the platinum surface according to the reaction:

$$H_2O_2 \longrightarrow O_2 + 2H^+ + 2e^-$$

Optimization of the collection efficiency of the detector (Fig. 22.5b) i.e., the ratio between the part of the enzymatically generated hydrogen peroxide flux oxidized on the platinum (v_1) and the total flux ($v_1 + v_2$), v_2 being the part of the flux diffusing towards the bulk solution, would result in a greater availability of oxygen in the enzymatic layer and in a greater independence of oxygen diffusion from the bathing fluids, once the reaction had started (Coulet *et al.* 1980).

   Finally, hydrogen peroxide anodic oxidation is not always diffusion controlled and its rate may limit the signal from the sensor. This rate may depend on electrode conditioning (Dubois 1984).

22.4.4 Hydrogen peroxide potentiometric detection

Potentiometric measurement of glucose concentration is the principle of a sensor developed by Schiller, Wingard, and Liu (1982; Chapter 10). Glucose oxidase is immobilized directly on the platinum surface of the working electrode by methods including entrapment in polyacrylamide gel, crosslinking in an albumin matrix with glutaraldehyde, and coupling to platinum through gamma-aminopropyltriethoxy silane (Wingard *et al.* 1979).

   In contrast to amperometric detections in which an external potential is applied between the electrodes, and in which oxygen or hydrogen peroxide local concentrations are directly monitored through the generated current, potentiometric detection measures a pseudo-equilibrium potential inside the system. The electrochemical reaction responsible for this potential appears to result from the interactions between the enzymatically generated hydrogen peroxide and the platinum surface (Wingard *et al.* 1982). The electrode cleaning procedure is always critical to the functioning of the system. Linearity of response, as the logarithm of glucose concentration, was achieved in *in vitro* studies over the range of about 0.6 to 22 mmol/l. Theoretical advantages of this system for *in vivo* utilization, due to the low potential generated, include minimal electrochemical interference and the possibility of micro-miniaturization of the electrode.

22.4.5 Cofactor detectors

The concept of cofactor detectors is based on the ability of cofactors to act as temporary acceptors of the protons and electrons released during the oxidation of substrates by oxidation-reduction enzymes (Chapter 15). The general idea is to have a solid state type electrode in which a naturally-occurring or an artificial cofactor is an integral part of the electron conducting support and the enzyme is immobilized with the cofactor. The electrode, as a whole, behaves as a cofactor, i.e. an electron acceptor or donor for an enzymatic reaction (Fig. 22.5c).

The coupling of riboflavin to solid carbon, forming a solid state pathway for easy electron transfer, has been described (Wingard 1982). Subsequent developments (Wingard 1983a) included the conversion of immobilized riboflavin to FAD and the appearence of enzymatic activity on the addition of the apoenzyme of glucose oxidase. Later, Cass *et al.* (1984) used entrapped ferrocene derivatives, as ferricinium ions, which may be electrochemically oxidized and react with reduced glucose oxidase. If such reagents are present in sufficient excess, then the supply of oxygen to the catalytic layer would have little effect on the enzymatic rate (see Chapters 15 and 16). Recently, Ikeda *et al.* (1985) described a glucose sensor using benzoquinone as a cofactor. Glucose oxidase was immobilized on the surface of a *p*-benzoquinone-carbon paste electrode by coating the enzyme-loaded surface with a nitrocellulose film. Properties of the sensor include the electrocatalytic oxidation of glucose with a linear range up to 15 mmol/l, the response time of about 20 seconds and the insensitivity to variations of oxygen tension in sample solutions.

22.5 Designs of *in vivo* glucose oxidase sensors

The latest developments towards an implantable glucose sensor have favoured three types of sensor design: the plane-geometry type, the vessel-shaped, and the needle type. Plane geometry sensors consist basically of a plane surface support containing the metal working electrode and the reference and counter electrodes coated by various combinations of enzymatic and non-enzymatic, hydrophilic and hydrophobic membranes. The membranes provide a support for the enzyme, an environment for the chemical reaction, and a diffusion barrier assuring the optimal concentrations of glucose and oxygen in this environment. Fischer and Abel (1982) described a plane-geometry sensor mounted into a flow chamber. It consisted of a platinum anode for the measurement of hydrogen peroxide, a silver/silver chloride reference and counter electrode, glucose oxidase immobilized onto sepharose and held by hydrophilic cellulose acetate membranes, and an hydrophobic perforated Teflon membrane in front of the anode. *In vivo* tests using normal and diabetic dogs showed reasonable correlation between the sensor output and the plasma glucose reference values with a response time between 90 and 120 seconds. The linear range for *in vitro* calibration was up to 40 mmol/l of glucose.

An original approach was described by Kondo *et al.* (1981): the sensor is a vessel-shaped device through which the blood flows. Oxygen-type electrodes and membranes are disposed around its wall. The sensor is introduced into the circulatory system in a fashion similar to an external arterio-venous shunt for hemodialysis. The linear range is up to 16 mmol/l of glucose and the response time is about 10 minutes.

The needle-type sensors are usually micro-electrodes having a platinum core (anode) isolated from an external silver/silver chloride cathode reference and counter-electrode. The electrode is coated with glucose oxidase immobilized in a solution of a matrix material (cellulose diacetate, for instance) in a volatile solvent (acetone, for instance). Shichiri, *et al.* (1982; Chapter 23) have described a subcutaneously implantable needle-type sensor having an *in vivo* response time of 2 to 5 min and a linear response of up to 27 mmol/l of glucose (see Section 22.7).

22.6 Glucose sensors: possible alternative approaches

Glucose sensors based on non-enzymatic approaches have been known for many years. Although they purport to avoid the difficulties associated with heterogeneous enzyme kinetics none of these systems is presently sufficiently developed to permit *in vivo* implantation.

The characteristics of direct electrochemical sensors, consisting of platinum electrodes not associated with glucose oxidase have been studied (Soeldner *et al.* 1973; Gebhardt *et al.* 1978; Richter, *et al.* 1982). The signal is generated by direct glucose oxidation at the anodic surface of a platinum electrode, in response to alternate anodic and cathodic potentials. Their specificity to glucose, in biological fluids, is still less than optimal, due to the interference of endogenous oxidizable substances such as amino acids, urea, ascorbic acid, and of exogenous substances such as alcohol and several drugs. The selection of adequate working potentials and the use of an external selective membrane brings real improvement to the system specificity. An additional problem with this type of detector is the poisoning of the platinum surface by adsorption of gluconic acid and amino acids, which leads to the gradual deactivation of the anode catalyst and inhibition of further oxidation. The deactivation can be offset with regeneration of the working electrode by repeated surface oxidation by electrochemical pulsing. Nevertheless, oxidized radicals are generated and desorbed from the electrode surface together with products of electrode degradation. The present status of the electrocatalytic glucose sensor does not favour its use as an implantable device.

The competition of glucose and fluoresceine-labelled polydextran for the binding sites of the protein concanavalin A, immobilized on the inside surface of a hollow dialysis fibre, is the principle of a sensor developed by Schultz, *et al.* (1982; Chapter 32). This affinity sensor is completed by an optical fibre inserted in the lumen of the dialysis fibre that allows the measuring of the unbound labelled dextran. This approach presents an advantage, compared to glucose oxidase sensors: the response is determined by the competitive equilibrium between glucose and the signal producing ligand. Thus, kinetics of enzyme reactions and electrode fouling do not affect the magnitude of the sensor response. Optimal specificity and sensitivity could be obtained by the selection of appropriate binding protein and com-petitive ligand; specific antibodies could be used, for instance. The sensor still suffers from limited stability and relatively long response times when employed as an *in vivo* sensor.

The concept of non-invasive glucose monitoring of the aqueous humor of the eye, by the measurement of the degree of optical rotation produced by the local concentration of glucose, has been advanced by March *et al.* (1979). The requirement of heavy optical equipment is an important drawback in terms of its development into a portable device.

Several endogenous enzymes that use glucose as the primary substrate might be utilized in an enzymatic glucose sensor. They include glucose dehydrogenase, glucokinase, glucose-6-phosphatase and glucose-isomerase (Wingard 1983*b*). In the case of glucose dehydrogenase $NAD^+/NADH$ concentrations could be monitored using a miniature fibre optic spectrometer. At the present time this system is still a theoretical speculation.

The last part of this chapter will deal will the glucose sensor as a part of a closed-loop insulin infusion system. The main characteristics of some implantable sensors are described in Table 22.3.

Table 22.3 Main characteristics of some implantable glucose sensors

	Authors			
	Bessman	Fischer	Kondo	Shichiri
Type of detector	Galvanic cell	Pt anode/ H_2O_2	O_2 (Clark)	Pt anode/H_2O_2
Enzymatic membrane material	Nylon	Sepharose	Nylon	Cellulose acetate
Immobilization procedure	Covalently bound by glutaraldehyde	Covalently bound by cyanogen bromide	Covalently bound by glutaraldehyde	Covalently bound by glutaraldehyde
Non-ezymatic (1) membrane material	Polypropylene	Cellulose acetate	Polypropylene	Polyurethane
Non-enzymatic (2) membrane material		Perforated Teflon	Perforated Teflon	Polyvinyl-alcohol
Sensor geometry	Plane geometry	Plane geometry	Vessel-shaped	Needle-shaped

22.7 The artificial beta cell

The earliest external electromechanical device used as a closed-loop insulin infusion system was described by Kadish (1964). Whenever the blood glucose exceeded 1.5 g/l (8.33 mmol/l) or fell under 0.5 g/l (2.77 mmol/l), insulin or glucagon, respectively, were infused. However this on–off system was not able to normalize the glycaemia. A resurgence of interest in the seventies for this bedside instrument, which became known as artificial beta-cell, led to the refining of the feed-back controlled systems commanding the insulin delivery. Kadish's device was improved by Albisser *et al.* (1974) who subjected the control of insulin delivery to a computer calculated predicted value based on the minute–to–minute variations of blood sugar. Clemens *et al.* (1977) constructed the first of these devices to be commercially available. It was named Biostator Glucose-Controlled Insulin Infusion System (60 kg, $42 \times 46 \times 46$ cm). A number of similar artificial beta cells, using extra-corporeal glucose sensors, have been since then fabricated and evaluated by several groups, including Mirouze *et al.* (1977), Slama *et al.* (1977), Kraegen *et al.* (1979), Goriya, *et al.* (1979) and Fischer, *et al.* (1980).

Bessman *et al.* (1977) reported the implantation into a diabetic dog of a small artificial beta cell consisting of an oxygen-detector glucose sensor, electronics, a micro pump, and a power supply. The sensor was similar to the one previously described in Section 22.4.1. The pump was a piezoelectric device separated from the insulin reservoir by a solenoid valve. Insulin was delivered into the peritoneal cavity when appropriately phased pulses were applied to the pump and valve. However, in this experiment, as well as in the observations on seven additional dogs (Bessman *et al.* 1981), the amount of insulin administered to the dogs was clearly insufficient, due to the inadequate response of the glucose sensor to the glucose levels.

A remarkable achievement in terms of miniaturization was reported by Shichiri *et al.* (1982) who developed a wearable closed-loop device (400 g, $12 \times 15 \times 6$ cm) associated with an implantable needle-type sensor. Short term glycaemic control was achieved in diabetic patients connected to the instrument (Shichiri *et al.* 1984). These results are presented in Chapter 23 of this book.

22.8 Conclusion

Our understanding of the physiological, physicochemical, and electro-chemical mechanisms underlying the basic requirements for an *in vivo* glucose sensor has expanded in recent years. The fruits of this understanding, in terms of technology, are beginning to be available. However, several questions remain unanswered and several answers are still not translated into practice.

Concerning the sensor functioning under conditions of *in vivo* implantation, the optimal arrangement of the glucose oxidase support and the protective membranes has still to be found, allowing long term enzymatic stability and adequate glucose and oxygen local concentrations with minimal tissue reaction. A better understanding of the operational properties of such sensors, both *in vitro* and *in vivo*, would allow their design and performance to be optimized.

Other approaches than the glucose oxidase sensor may prove to be worthwhile. The affinity type of sensor could be a promising alternative. Implantable sensors usually require a membrane barrier between the sensing element and the biological fluid. It is clear that the failure of such membranes to maintain reproducible analyte transport characteristics is a major cause of biosensor malfunction.

Finally, the expectations aroused by the development of a reliable sensor for long term use in a portable closed-loop insulin infusion system justify the efforts being made in ongoing studies. More easily attainable good glycaemic control in diabetic subjects could, hopefully, prove to be a major step in the prevention of the late complications of diabetes.

Acknowledgements

The support of the Caisse Nationale de l'Assurance Maladie des Travailleurs salariés (France Grant CNAMIS-INSERM 85. 3. 54. 8. E, of National Institute of Health (U.S.) Grant AM 30718, and of Association des Jeunes Diabétiques (Paris, France) are gratefully acknowledged. Furthermore, Dr Gilberto Velho was supported by a grant from C.N.Pq.

References

Albisser, A. M. and Spencer, W. J. (1982). Electronics and the diabetic *IEEE Trans Biomed Eng.* **29**, 239–48.

Albisser, A. M., Leibel, B. S., Ewart, G., Davidovac, Z., Botz, C. K. and Zingg, W. (1974). An artificial endocrine pancreas. *Diabetes* **23**, 389–96.

Bard, A. J. and Faulkner, L. R. (1980). Mass transfer by migration and diffusion. In *Electrochemical methods. Fundamentals and applications.* (eds. A. J. Bard and L. R. Faulkner) pp. 119–35. Wiley, New York.

Barman, T. E. (1969). Glucose oxidase. In *Enzyme handbook* (ed. T. E. Barman) Vol. 1, pp. 112–113. Springer–Verlag, Berlin.

Bennett, P. H. (1983). Diabetes in developing countries and unusual populations. In *Diabetes in epidemiological perspective* (eds. J. I. Mann, K. Pyorala and A. Teuscher) pp. 43–57. Churchill Livingstone, Edinburgh.

Bessman, S. P. and Schultz, R. D. (1973). Prototype glucose-oxygen sensor for the artificial pancreas. *Trans. Am. Soc. Artif. Intern. Organs.* **19**, 361–4.

—— Hellyer, J. M., Layne, E. C., Takada, G., Thomas, L. J. Jr. and Sayler, D. (1977). The total implantation of an artificial β-cell in a dog: Progress report. *Diabetes, Excerpta Medica-International Congress Series* **413**, 496–501.

—— Thomas, L. J., Kojima, H., Sayler, D. F. and Layne E. C. (1981). The implantation of a closed loop artificial beta cell in dogs. *Trans. Am. Soc. Artif. Intern. Organs.* **27**, 7–17.

Brennan, J. R., Gebhart, S. S. P. and Blackard, W. G. (1985). Pump-induced insulin aggregation: a problem with the Biostator. *Diabetes* **34**, 353–9.

Calabrese, G., Bueti, A., Zega, G., Giombolini, A., Bellomo, G., Antonella, M. A., Massi–Benedetti, M. and Brunetti, P. (1982). Improvement of artificial endocrine pancreas (Biostator; GCIIS) performance combining feedback controled insulin administration with a pre-programmed insulin infusion. *Horm. Metabol. Res.* **14**, 505–7.

Cass, A. E. G., Davis, G., Francis, G. D., Hill, II. A. O., Aston, W. J., Higgins, I. J., Plotkin, E. V., Scott, L. D. L. and Turner, A. P. F. (1984). Ferrocene-mediated enzyme electrode for amperometric determination of glucose. *Anal. Chem.* **56**, 667–71.

Clark, L. C. Jr. and Lyons, C. (1962). Electrode systems for continuous monitoring in cardiovascular surgery. *Ann. N. Y. Acad. Sci.* **102**, 29–46.

Clemens, A. H., Chang, P. H. and Myers, R. W. (1977). The development of Biostator, a glucose controlled insulin infusion system (GCIIS). *Horm. Metab. Res.* suppl. 7: 23–33.

Coulet, P. R., Sternberg R. and Thévenot, D. R. (1980). Electrochemical study of reactions at interfaces of glucose oxidase collagen membranes. *Biochim. Biophys. Acta* **612**, 317–27.

Dimitriadis, G. D. and Gerich, J. E. (1983). Importance of timing of preprandial subcutaneous insulin administration in the management of diabetes mellitus. *Diabetes Care* **6**, 374–7.

Dubois, C. (1984). Caractérisation électrochimique des membranes utilisées dans les électrodes à enzymes. *D.E.A. de Cinétique Chimique Appliquée.* Université Pierre et Marie Curie, Paris.

Fischer, U. and Abel, P. (1982). A membrane combination for immplantable glucose sensors. Measurements in undiluted biological fluids. *Trans. Am. Soc. Artif. Intern. Organs* **28**, 245–8.

Fischer, U., Jutzi, E., Bombor, H., Freyse, E. J., Salzsieder, E., Albrecht, G., Besch, W. and Bruns, W. (1980). Assessment of an algorithm for the artificial β-cell using the normal insulin–glucose relationship in diabetic dogs and men. *Diabetologia* **18**, 97–107.

Gebhardt, U., Luft, G., Richter, G. J. and Von Sturm F. (1978). Development of an implantable electrocatalytic glucose sensor. *Bioelectrochemistry and Bioenergetics* **5**, 607–24.

Goriya, Y., Kawamori, R., Shichiri, M. and Abe, H. (1979). The development of an artificial beta cell system and its validation in depancreatized dogs: the physiological restoration of blood glucose homeostasis. *Med. Prog. Technol.* **6**, 99–108.

Guilbault, G. G. and Lubrano, G. J. (1973). An enzyme electrode for the amperometric determination of glucose. *Anal. Chim. Acta.* **64**, 439–45.

Hamman, R. F. (1983). Diabetes in affluent societies. In *Diabetes in epidemiological perspective*. (eds. J. I. Mann, K. Pyorala and A. Teuscher) pp. 7–42. Churchill Livingstone, Edinburgh.

Harrison, D. E., Christie, M. R. and Gray, D. W. R. (1985). Properties of isolated human islets of Langerhans: insulin secretion, glucose oxidation and protein phosphorylation. *Diabetologia* **28**, 99–103.

Horwitz, D. L., Zeidler, A., Gonen, B. and Jaspan, J. B. (1980). Hyperinsulinism complicating control of diabetes mellitus by an artificial beta cell. *Diabetes Care* **3**, 274–7.

Ikeda, T., Hamada, H., Miki, K. and Senda, M. (1985). Glucose oxidase immobilized benzoquinone — carbon paste electrode as a glucose sensor. *Agric. Biol. Chem.* **49**, 541–3.

Kadish, A. (1964). Automation control of blood sugar. A servomechanism for glucose monitoring and control. *Am. J. Med. Electron.* **3**, 82–6.

Kamin, R. and Wilson, G. S. (1980). Rotating ring-disk enzyme electrode for bio-catalysis kinetic studies and characterization of the immobilized enzyme layer. *Anal. Chem.* **52**, 1198–205.

Kondo, T., Kojima, H., Ohkura, K., Ikeda, S. and Ito, K. (1981). Trial of new vessel access type glucose sensor for implantable artificial pancreas *in vivo*. *Trans. Am. Soc. Artif. Intern. Organs.* **27**, 250–3.

Kraegen, E. W., Whiteside, R., Bell, D., Chia, Y. O. and Lazarus L. (1979). Development of a closed-loop artificial pancreas. *Horm. Metab. Res.* suppl. 8, 38–42.

Lougheed, W. D., Woulfe-Flanagan, H., Clement, J. R. and Albisser, A. M. (1980). Insulin aggregation in artificial delivery systems. *Diabetologia* **19**, 1–9.

March, W., Engerman, R. and Rabinovitch, B. (1979). Optical monitor of glucose. *Trans. Am. Soc. Artif. Intern. Organs.* **25**, 28–31.

Mirouze J., Selam J. L., Pham, T. C. and Cavadore, D. (1977). Evaluation of exogenous insulin homeostasis by the artificial pancreas in insulin dependent diabetes. *Diabetologia* **13**, 273–8.

Nilson, H., Akerlind, A. C. and Mosbach, K. (1973). Determination of glucose, urea and penicillin using enzyme-pH electrodes *Biochim. Biophys. Acta.* **320**, 529–34.

Racine, P. and Mindt, W. (1971). On the role of substrate diffusion in enzyme electrodes. *Experientia* suppl. 18, 524–34.

Report of the National Commission on Diabetes to the Congress of the United States (1976). U.S. Dep. Health, Educ., Welfare, Public Health Service, Nat. Inst. of Health, *DHEW Publication* No. (NIH) 76, 1021–8.

Richter, G. J., Luft, G. and Gebhardt, U. (1982). Development and present status of an electrocatalytic glucose sensor. *Diabetes Care* **5**, 224–8.

Rizza, R. A., Gerich, J. E., Haymond, M. W., Westland, R. E., Hall. L. D., Clemens, A. H., and Service, F. J. (1980). Control of blood sugar in insulin dependent diabetes: comparison of an artificial endocrine pancreas, continuous subcutaneous insulin infusion, and intensified conventional insulin therapy. *N. Engl. J. Med.* **303**, 1313–8.

Scheller, F., Janchen, M., Pfeiffer, D., Seyer, I. and Muller, K. (1977). Enzymelektrode zum Nachweis von Glucose. *Z. Med. Labor. Diagn.* **18**, 312–16.

Schiller, J. G., Wingard, L. B. Jr. and Liu, C. C. (1982). Potentiometric detection of hydrogen peroxide and apparatus therefore. *U.S. Patent* 4,340,448.

Schultz, J. S., Mansouri, S. and Goldstein, I. J. (1982). Affinity sensors: a new technique for developing implantable sensors for glucose and other metabolites. *Diabetes Care* 5, 245–53.

Shichiri, M., Yamasaki, Y., Kawamori, R., Hakui, N. and Abe, H. (1982). Wearable artificial endocrine pancreas with needle-type glucose sensor. *Lancet* 2, 1129–31.

—— Kawamori, R., Hakui, N., Yamasaki, Y. and Abe, H. (1984). Closed-loop glycaemic control with a wearable artificial endocrine pancreas. Variation in daily insulin requirements to glycaemic responses. *Diabetes* 33, 1200–2.

Slama, G., Klein, J. C., Tardieu, M. C. and Tchobroutsky, G. (1977). Normalisation de la glycémie par pancréas artificial non miniaturisé. Application pendant 24 heures chez 7 diabétiques insulino-dépendants. *Nouv. Presse Med.* 6, 2309–15.

Soeldner, J. S., Chang, K. W., Aisenberg, S. and Hiebert, J. M. (1973). Progress towards an implantable glucose sensor and an artificial beta cell. In *Temporal aspects of therapeutics* (eds. J. Urquhart and F. E. Yates) pp. 181–207. Plenum Press, New York–London.

Sorensen, J. T., Colton, C. K., Hillman, R. S. and Soeldner, J. S. (1982). Use of a physiologic pharmacokinetic model of glucose homeostasis for assessment of performance requirements for improved insulin therapies. *Diabetes Care* 5, 148–57.

Tchobroutsky, G. (1978). Relation of diabetic control to development of microvascular complications. *Diabetologia* 15, 143–52.

Thévenot, D. R. (1982). Problems in adapting a glucose oxidase electrochemical sensor into an implantable glucose-sensing device. *Diabetes Care* 5, 184–9.

—— Coulet, P. R., Sternberg, R. and Gautheron, D. C. (1978). A highly sensitive glucose electrode using glucose oxidase collagen film. *Bioelectrochem. Bioenerg.* 5, 548–53.

Updike, S. J. and Hicks, G. P. (1967). The enzyme electrode. *Nature* 214, 986–8.

Wightman, R. M. (1981). Microvoltametric electrodes. *Anal. Chem.* 53, 1125–34 A.

Wingard, L. B. Jr. (1982). Possibility for an immobilized flavin fuel cell electrode for glucose measurement. *Diabetes Care* 5, 222–3.

—— (1983*a*). Prospects for electrochemical devices and processes based on bio-technology. In *Biotech 83* pp. 613–24. Online Publications Ltd. Northwood, UK.

—— (1983*b*). Immobilized enzyme electrodes for glucose determination for the artificial pancreas. *Federation Proc.* 42, 288–291.

—— Liu, C. C., Wolfson, S. K., Yao, S. J. and Drash, A. L. (1982). Potentiometric measurement of glucose concentration with an immobilized glucose oxidase/catalase electrode. *Diabetes Care* 5, 199–202.

—— Schiller, J. G., Wolfson, S. K., Liu, C. C., Drash, A. L. and Yao, S. J. (1979). Immobilized enzyme electrodes for the potentiometric measurement of glucose concentration: immobilization techniques and materials. *J. Biomed. Mater. Res.* 13, 921–35.

Woodward, S. C. (1982). How fibroblasts and giant cells encapsulate implants: considerations in design of glucose sensors. *Diabetes Care* 5, 278–81.

Yellow Spring Instruments Co. (1975). *Instruction manual Y.S.I. model 23 A.*

23

Needle-type glucose sensor and its clinical applications

MOTOAKI SHICHIRI, RYUZO KAWAMORI, and YOSHIMITSU YAMASAKI

23.1 Introduction

Several types of glucose sensors have been proposed, however, only a few have been applied to *in vivo* clinical use. Chang *et al.* (1972) proposed a disc-shaped electrochemical (non-enzymatic) glucose sensor. They reported that on the 117th day of implantation in the subcutaneous tissue of a Rhesus monkey the glucose electrode produced a signal which correlated significantly with corresponding blood sugar levels following intravenous glucose administration (Soeldner *et al.* 1976). However, since some other electrochemically active species influence the sensor output, this sensor has not yet applied to *in vivo* monitoring of human subjects (Gough *et al.* 1978).

In contrast, glucose sensors using glucose oxidase (Updike and Hicks 1967; Guilbault and Lubrano 1973) have been used for *in vitro* and *in vivo* monitoring because of their specificity to glucose and precision in glucose determination. Bessman *et al.* firstly reported an implantable glucose sensor consisting of two galvanic oxygen electrodes, which was incorporated into an implantable closed-loop artificial beta cell (Bessman *et al.* 1981). They reported that all of these units had functioned fairly well but none had brought the animal under complete control, partially because the glucose sensors were insensitive to the tissue glucose concentration, giving about half of the expected level. There have been no reports on human monitoring by this type of glucose sensor.

The authors have developed a needle-type glucose sensor which retained *in vitro* and *in vivo* characteristics suitable for tissue glucose monitoring (Shichiri *et al.* 1982, 1983). By applying the glucose sensor as a glucose monitoring device, a wearable artificial endocrine pancreas system enabled closed-loop glycaemic regulation in diabetic patients for more than six days (Shichiri *et al.* 1984).

23.2 The principle of glucose measurement by an intracorporeal glucose sensor

In the presence of glucose and oxygen, the glucose oxidase used in enzymatic glucose sensors catalyses the oxidation of glucose and produces gluconic acid and hydrogen peroxide. Because the physiological concentration of oxygen in blood or tissue fluid is much lower (Bartlett and Tenney 1963) than the K_M values of the enzyme (Gibson *et al.* 1964), not only glucose concentration but also oxygen tension may regulate the rate of glucose oxidation. Therefore, when a glucose sensor is implanted, output of the sensor might be non-linearly proportional to glucose concentration (Bessman *et al.* 1981). In order to solve this problem, a membrane which is more permeable to oxygen than to glucose is useful (Ikeda *et al.* 1980; Yamasaki 1984) because it limits delivery of glucose to the enzyme layer of the sensor. Thus the output of the sensor with such a membrane shows linearity over a wide range of glucose concentrations and insensitivity to fluctuation of oxygen tension.

Concerning the host response to a sensor, the size and surface configurations of the intracorporeal device are also important. Woodward (1982)

Table 23.1   Enzymatic glucose sensors used in *in vivo* monitoring

	California*	Nagoya**	Osaka***
Shape	Disc	Venous access-type	Needle-type
Size	Diameter 20 mm Depth 2 mm	—	Diameter 0.4–0.8 mm Length 20 mm
Semi-permeable membrane	—	Polypropylene	Polyurethane
Enzyme bound membrane	Nylon	Millipore nylon filter	Cellulose diacetate
Gas permeable membrane	Polypropylene	Teflon	—
Determinant	Oxygen	Oxygen	Hydrogen peroxide
Anode	Pb	Ag	Pt
Cathode	Ag	Pt	Ag
Electrolyte	KOH	NaCl	Body fluid
Response to glucose concentration (mmol/l)	0–8.3	0–38.5	0–27.5
Implanted site	sc tissue	Blood vessel	Blood vessel, sc tissue
In vivo monitoring	Rabbit, dog	Dog, human	Dog, human
Control experiment	Stz-diabetic dog	Px dog	Px dog, human diabetics

Abbreviations; stz (streptozotocine), px (pancreatectomized), sc (subcutaneous)
*   Layne *et al.* 1976; Bessman *et al.* 1981
**   Ikeda *et al.* 1980
***   Shichiri *et al.* 1982; Shichiri *et al.* 1983; Shichiri *et al.* 1984

suggested that if the sensor could be fabricated in the form of a wire or filament measuring less than about 2 mm in diameter, a minimal host response would be evoked. Therefore, a miniature needle shape is one of the ideal designs for an indwelling glucose sensor as opposed to a disc shape.

The structure and membrane design of the intracorporeal glucose sensors reported are listed in Table 23.1 along with their *in vitro* characteristics.

23.3 Preparation of a needle-type glucose sensor

A hydrogen peroxide electrode is prepared according to the method described by Hagihara *et al* (1981) modified as follows. The tip of a platinum wire (diameter 0.2 mm, length 4 cm) is melted in an oxygen natural gas flame to form a small bulb (diameter 0.3–0.7 mm), then it is sealed into a soft glass capillary by melting also in an oxygen natural gas flame. Then the tip of the electrode is polished with fine sandpaper (No. 2000) until the platinum surface (anode) is uncovered. The platinum-glass anode is inserted into a silver-plated stainless-steel tube (inner diameter 0.4 mm, length 2 cm) as the cathode of the electrode and fixed tightly by heating in an oxygen gas flame.

The electrode tip is dipped into 1% cellulose diacetate solution (Eastman Kodak Co., USA) dissolved in 50% acetone–50% ethanol solution for 5 s, and then exposed to acetone vapour for 5 min. These procedures are repeated twice. The tip is then dipped into 2.5% cellulose diacetate solution dissolved in 50% acetone–50% ethanol solution for 30 s. Then, 0.2 µl of glucose oxidase solution, in which 50 mg of glucose oxidase (from *Aspergillus niger*, type II, 17300 U/g, Sigma Chemical, Co., USA) is dissolved in 1 ml of distilled water, is dropped onto the electrode tip, the dipped end being kept upwards. For the immobilization of glucose oxidase, 0.1 µl of 2% glutaraldehyde solution (Wako Pure Chemical Industries, Ltd., Japan) is dropped onto the electrode tip. The electrode is kept in air for 2 hr at 25°C and then is exposed to acetone vapour for 5 min at 25°C. The tip is dipped into 2% polyurethane (Japan Erastran Co., Japan) dissolved in tetrahydrofuran (Wako Pure Chemical Industries, Ltd., Japan) for 2 s followed by drying in air. Then, the tip is dipped into 15% polyurethane in 50% tetrahydrofuran–50% dimethylformamide (Wako Pure Chemical Industries Ltd., Japan) for another 10 s. Finally the needle-type glucose sensor (Fig. 23.1) thus prepared is stored in the refrigerator until it is used.

23.4 *In vitro* characteristics of the glucose sensor

23.4.1 *Procedure for determining* in vitro *characteristics*

A needle-type glucose sensor polarized at a voltage of + 0.6 V is connected to the current–voltage converting amplifier (POG-200A, Unique Medical Co.,

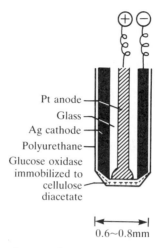

Pt anode —
Glass —
Ag cathode —
Polyurethane —
Glucose oxidase
immobilized to
cellulose —
diacetate

0.6~0.8mm

Fig. 23.1 Structure of a needle-type glucose sensor.

Ltd., Japan), which amplifies current of 1 nA to a voltage of 100 mV. A pen recorder (VP6621A, Matsushita Communication Industrial Co., Ltd., Japan) is connected to record sensor outputs.

The *in vitro* characteristics of the sensor are tested in 0.9% NaCl solution containing 7% bovine albumin (Fraction V, Miles, USA) with varying glucose concentrations in a temperature-, flow rate-, and oxygen tension-controllable chamber. The output current of the sensor is calibrated initially after a stabilization period of at least 10 min.

23.4.2 Drift and noise range of measurement

The drift of the base line and noise range of the sensor are expressed as a percentage change of the sensor output in response to 5.5 mmol/l glucose solution. The base line drift was $0.8 \pm 0.3\%$ per 24 hr and the noise range was $0.3 \pm 0.4\%$. The residual current against glucose free saline solution was $1.3 \pm 0.6\%$ (Table 23.2).

23.4.3 Dose response against glucose

The dose response pattern and rapidity of the sensor output in response to the alteration in glucose concentration were measured by infusing solutions with 0–27.5 mmol/l glucose at 37°C. The sensor output responded well to the changes in glucose concentrations. The rapidity in response shown by $T_{90\%}$ was 16.2 ± 6.2 s. Linear response was obtained in the range 0–27.5 mmol/l.

23.4.4 Effect of temperature and oxygen tension

The temperature coefficient measured by changing the temperature of the solution from 33°C to 42°C was $2.3 \pm 1.0\%/1°C$. The current

Table 23.2 Typical characteristics of a needle-type glucose sensor *in vitro*

Test	Performance
Residual current (%)	1.3 ± 0.6
Baseline drift (%/24 hr)	0.8 ± 1.3
Noise range (%)	0.3 ± 0.4
Output generated to 5.5 mmol/l glucose (nA)	1.2 ± 0.4
Range of glucose concentrations producing a linear dose response pattern (mmol/l)	0–27.5
$T_{90\%}$ response time (s)	16.2 ± 6.2
Temperature coefficient (%/1°C)	2.3 ± 1.0

Results are shown as mean $\pm$ SD for 15 sensors. The performance is expressed as percentage change of the output at 5.5 mmol/l glucose.

dependency of oxygen tension was checked by admitting varying oxygen/nitrogen gas mixtures to the solution and by monitoring the oxygen tension (15–150 mm Hg) with an oxygen sensor. The output current in response to 5.5 mmol/l of glucose concentration increased only by 0.1% per 1 mm Hg.

23.4.5 Life expectancy

The life expectancy of the glucose sensor was examined in the chamber by continuous recirculation of a solution containing glucose of 5.5 mmol/l at 37°C. Each sensor was equilibrated in this solution for 2 hr and output currents were continuously recorded for 7 days without calibration. During continuous monitoring *in vitro*, the output current gradually decreased to $76.2 \pm 6.9\%$ of the initial value at 7 days after the initiation of the monitoring.

23.5 *In vivo* characteristics of the glucose sensor

23.5.1 Procedure for determining in vivo characteristics

For *in vivo* monitoring, a needle-type glucose sensor is connected to a current–voltage converting amplifier device which was constructed by using a CMOS operational amplifier (ICU 7613, Intersil Inc., USA). A polarizing voltage in the glucose sensor is supplied by a lithium battery built in the device. The pen recorder is connected to the amplifier to monitor sensor outputs.

Each sensor's output is calibrated with a standard glucose solution in which 11 mmol of glucose is dissolved in 100 ml of sterilized 0.9% NaCl solution maintained at 37°C. Then, a glucose sensor is inserted by means of an indwelling needle (gauge no. 18) into the jugular vein or subcutaneous tissue of healthy and diabetic dogs, or into subcutaneous tissue of the forearm in healthy and diabetic volunteers. The sensor output is compared with blood glucose concentrations simultaneously measured by a bedside-type artificial endocrine pancreas system (Shichiri *et al.* 1979; Kawamori *et al.* 1980).

23.5.2 Noise range of in vivo measurement

The noise range of *in vivo* monitoring with the sensor inserted into subcutaneous tissue in generally anesthetized and unanesthetized normal dogs was $1.3 \pm 0.5\%$ ($n = 5$), and $3.1 \pm 0.8\%$ ($n = 5$), respectively. Strenuous muscular exercise in dogs produced noise in the range up to 13.4% of output.

23.5.3 Response of the sensor to blood glucose

The outputs of the sensor when kept in the jugular vein of dogs (Y) was related to the results of intravenous glucose monitoring by the bedside-type of artificial endocrine pancreas system (X) ($Y = 0.98 X + 2$, $r = 0.998$, $n = 92$). A significant relationship also existed between the glucose concentrations obtained by the needle-type glucose sensors in subcutaneous tissue (Y) and the blood glucose concentrations (X) determined by the bedside-type monitoring system in dogs ($Y = 0.85 X + 3$, $r = 0.956$, $n = 144$). In human volunteers, a high correlation ($Y = 0.79 X + 17$, $r = 0.96$, $n = 115$) was also observed (Fig. 23.2).

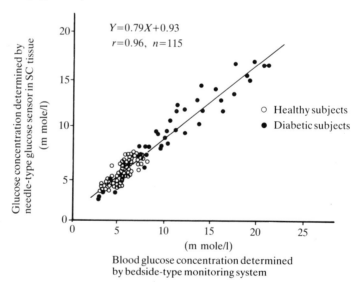

Fig. 23.2 The relationship between glucose concentration determined by a needle-type glucose sensor inserted into subcutaneous tissue and blood glucose concentration determined by a bedside-type artificial endocrine pancreas in normal and diabetic volunteers.

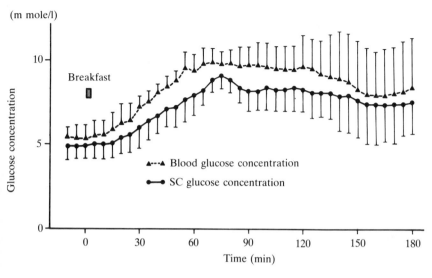

Fig. 23.3 Postprandial subcutaneous glucose concentration determined by a needle-type glucose sensor and blood glucose concentration determined by a bedside-type artificial endocrine pancreas in human diabetics ($n = 5$). Data are shown as mean $\pm$ SD.

23.5.4 *Response of the sensor to the change in blood glucose*

In order to check the sensor response to a change in blood glucose concentration, both subcutaneous glucose concentration and plasma glucose concentration were monitored in normal volunteers to whom glucose was intravenously delivered at a dose of 0.55 mmol kg^{-1} min^{-1} for 30 min. The subcutaneous glucose concentration started to rise 5–10 min after the rise in the plasma glucose concentration. Also, the subcutaneous glucose concentration showed a peak 5 min later (Fig. 23.3).

23.5.5 In vivo *effect of oxygen tension*

In normal dogs, a reference oxygen electrode was also inserted into the subcutaneous tissue 2–3 cm away from the glucose sensor to monitor background oxygen tension in the subcutaneous tissue. After monitoring the baseline for more than 30 min, the dogs inhaled 100% nitrogen gas or 95% oxygen plus 5% carbon dioxide gas. The reference oxygen electrode showed fluctuations in subcutaneous tissue oxygen tension in the range of 26–50 mm Hg. However, the glucose sensor showed stable output regardless of oxygen tension changes and the output was consistent with monitored blood glucose concentrations (Fig. 23.4).

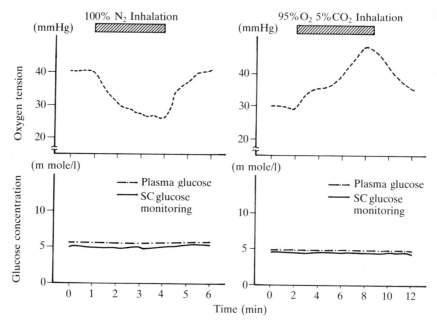

Fig. 23.4 Tissue glucose concentrations monitored by a needle-type glucose sensor. The dog inhaled 100% N_2 gas for 3 min (left panel) or 95% O_2 plus 5% CO_2 gas for 6 min (right panel). Plasma glucose concentrations were measured by discrete samplings. Tissue oxygen tension was monitored by a needle-type oxygen electrode.

23.5.6 *Life expectancy on an* in vivo *basis*

Changes in *in vitro* characteristics during continuous monitoring cannot be determined on the sensor implanted in subcutaneous tissue. Therefore, to estimate the *in vivo* sensor characteristics and the possible tissue reaction against sensor implantation, both 'relative' output current and 'relative' response time of the sensor are determined as follows: 'relative' output of the sensor kept in subcutaneous tissue for three days is calculated by comparing the sensor's output with simultaneously monitored blood glucose concentration. 'Relative' response time of the sensor is determined as the time lag between the rise in blood glucose and the rise in sensor's output after meal intake. After three days, the 'relative' output decreased to 73.5% of the initial level and the 'relative' response time increased from 5.1 min to 13.5 min. On the contrary, *in vitro* characteristics of the sensor determined after removal showed at 23% reduction in output and a 14 s delay in response (Table 23.3). Thus, reduction in *in vitro* characteristics cannot completely account for the reduction in the performance of the implanted sensor. Reduction in perfusion flow rate of interstitial fluid during the sensor's

Table 23.3 'Relative' output current and 'relative' response time of sensors inserted into subcutaneous tissue during continuous monitoring

In vitro *characteristics*

		Before application	3 days after application
Residual current	(nA)	1.0 ± 0.4	1.4 ± 1.2
Output current generated to		2.2 ± 0.5	1.7 ± 0.1
5.5 mmol/l glucose	(nA)		
$T_{90\%}$	(s)	29 ± 6	43 ± 6

In vivo *characteristics*

	Just after application	3 days after application
'Relative' output current* (%)	100	74 ± 3
'Relative' response time** (min)	5.1 ± 2.2	13.5 ± 1.5

Results are shown as mean $\pm$ SD ($n = 5$).
Sensors used in *in vivo* monitoring had a different rot number from that of the sensors examined in *in vitro* basis (Table 23.2).
*   'Relative' output current of the sensor kept in subcutaneous tissue for 3 days was calculated by comparing the sensor's output with blood glucose concentration.
** 'Relative' response time was determined as the time lag between the rise in blood glucose and the rise in sensor's output after meal intake.

implantation might result partially in the decrease in performance of implanted sensor.

23.5.7 *Scanning electron-microscope examination of the sensor's surface*
Scanning electron-microscope examinations were carried out on glucose sensors kept in subcutaneous tissue of normal dogs for 3, 7, and 14 days. Figure 23.5 shows one example of the scanning electron-microscope examinations of the membrane of the sensor. After a three-day continuous use in the subcutaneous tissue, a slight fixation of protein was observed and small pits were noted on the surface of the membrane. After seven and fourteen days of continuous use, the membrane was heavily coated with protein but the small pits on the surface were not observed. However, in these situations, fixation of fibroblasts and giant cells was not demonstrated on the surface.

Histologic changes in subcutaneous tissue around the sensor insertion area were examined on normal dogs. After a three-day application, migration of leukocytes and slight fibrin deposition was recognized in the insertion area.

23.6 *In vivo* monitoring

23.6.1 *Telemetry glucose monitoring system*
Because of the *in vivo* characteristics of the sensor, such as close linearity of

sensor output to blood glucose concentration, responsiveness to glycemic change, and long-lived stability of output, a needle-type glucose sensor is quite useful for *in vivo* monitoring. For this purpose, a telemetry glucose monitoring system has been constructed using a needle-type glucose sensor.

The system consists of a glucose sensor–transmitter and a receiver. The transmitter converts a current signal generated by a sensor to a very high frequency (VHF) audio signal. The small enclosure is packed with a current–voltage converting amplifier (ICU 7613, Intersil, Inc., USA), a voltage-frequency converter, and a lithium battery, is $4 \times 6 \times 2$ cm and weighs 50 g. The receiver demodulates the audio-frequency signal received to a voltage, and the glucose concentration calculated from the voltage is continuously displayed on the LED display. Hyperglycaemia or hypoglycaemia beyond the pre-fixed threshold sets off an alarm. This device composed of a VHF oscillator and batteries is $10 \times 12 \times 5$ cm. The receiver can detect the sensor signals from a distance of 20 meter from the transmitter.

23.6.2 Procedure for in vivo monitoring using a telemetry monitoring system

After the calibration using sterilized saline solution with and without glucose (5.5 mmol/l), a glucose sensor was inserted into subcutaneous tissue of the

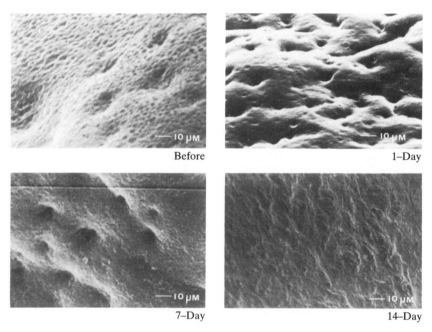

Before   1–Day

7–Day   14–Day

Fig. 23.5 Scanning electron-microscope examinations of glucose sensors kept in subcutaneous tissue of normal dogs before or after 3, 7, and 14 days of implantation.

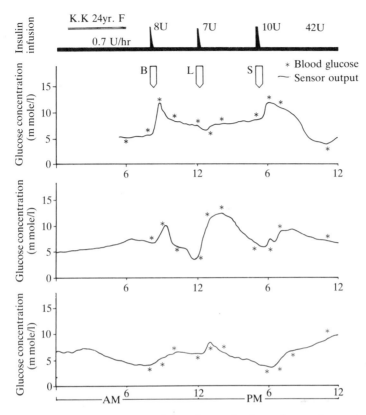

Fig. 23.6 Three days' continuous glycaemic monitoring using a telemetry glucose monitoring system in an insulin-dependent diabetic patient treated by continuous subcutaneous insulin infusion. B, L, and S denote breakfast, lunch, and supper, respectively. Asterisks indicate blood glucose concentrations determined by discrete samplings. The pattern of subcutaneous insulin infusion by the open-loop system is also depicted.

forearm of diabetic subjects by means of an indwelling needle (gauge no. 18). The sensor was fixed *in situ* with an adhesive bandage. In some patients, the sensor was replaced with a new one after three days' continuous monitoring. The transmitter was fixed to the forearm or was anchored to a waist belt.

23.6.3 In vivo *monitoring*

Figure 23.6 shows one representative case of three days' continuous record of an insulin-dependent diabetic treated with continuous subcutaneous insulin infusion. The continuous monitoring of glucose concentration disclosed a day-by-day variation of glycemia in diabetics. The subcutaneous glucose

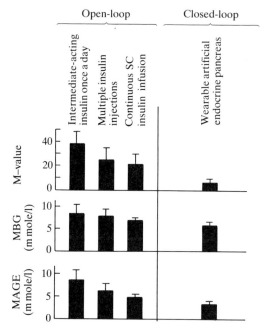

Fig. 23.7 Blood glucose regulatory indices in five insulin-dependent diabetic subjects controlled with intermediate-acting insulin injection once a day, multiple insulin injections, continuous subcutaneous insulin infusion, and wearable artificial endocrine pancreas.

concentrations determined by the sensor were consistent with the plasma glucose concentration. Results of daily glycaemic excursion demonstrated by the telemetry glucose monitoring system in diabetics treated with several insulin regimens are shown in Fig. 23.7

23.7 Application of a closed-loop glycemic control system

23.7.1 Wearable artificial endocrine pancreas

A needle-type glucose sensor provides sensor characteristics suitable for application to a closed-loop control system and allows wearability at the same time. Thus, the author developed a wearable artificial endocrine pancreas, which consists of a needle-type glucose sensor, a microcomputer system, two syringe delivery units for insulin and glucagon infusions, and lithium batteries. The total system was packed into a small unit (12 × 15 × 6 cm) weighing 400 g.

23.7.2 Computer algorithm for closed-loop insulin and glucagon infusion

Intravenous insulin and glucagon infusion algorithms in this system are the same as those of a bedside type (Shichiri *et al.* 1979; Kawamori *et al.* 1980).

Insulin infusion rate, IIR(*t*) (mU kg^{-1} min^{-1}) is expressed as follows:

$$\text{IIR}(t) = K_p \cdot \text{BG}(t) + K_d \cdot \Delta\text{BG}(t) + K_c \qquad (23.1)$$

where, BG(*t*) and ΔBG(*t*) are blood glucose concentration (mmol/l) and its rate of change (mmol l^{-1} min^{-1}) at time *t*, respectively, and K_p, and K_d are coefficients for proportional and derivative action, respectively, and K_c is a constant for basal insulin supplementation. By selecting proper parameters, ($K_p = 0.51$, $K_d = 4.89$, $K_c = -2.02$) this algorithm was proven to establish perfect glycaemic control with physiological insulinemia.

Glucagon infusion rate, GIR(*t*) (ng kg^{-1} min^{-1}) is expressed as follows;

$$\text{GIR}(t) = G_p \cdot (\text{BG}_p - \text{BG}(t\text{-}\tau)) + G_d \cdot (-\Delta\text{BG}(t\text{-}\tau)) + G_c \qquad (23.2)$$

where, BG_p is the projected value of blood glucose concentration set as 4.4 mmol/l and τ is the delay time for initiation of glucagon infusion, G_p and G_d are coefficients for proportional and derivative actions, respectively, and G_c is a constant for basal glucagon supplementation.

23.7.3 Noise reduction

The current generated by the glucose sensor is so small that noise can interfere with the output. Thus, hardware and software noise filters are built into the system. Because the sensor's signal is a direct current, low and high pass filters are effective in eliminating noises of low and high frequency waves and are used as a hardware noise filter. As a software noise filter, the computer algorithm has several program steps for noise reduction as follows: The computer calculates an average of ten samples of output current obtained every ten microseconds then the computer rejects a new data point when it shows a greater deviation from the previous 1-min of data than a pre-fixed threshold.

23.7.4 Procedure for closed-loop glycaemic control with a wearable artificial endocrine pancreas

Glycaemic control in insulin dependent diabetic patients with the wearable artificial endocrine pancreas was attempted. The parameters of insulin and glucagon infusion algorithms were; $K_p = 0.51$, $K_d = 4.89$, $K_c = -2.02$, $G_p = 3.6$, $G_d = 7.2$, $G_c = 0.4$, and $\tau = 10$. The sensor was replaced with a new one after three days' use. Glycaemic control was compared in each patient with that obtained by intensified multiple insulin injection regimens and continuous subcutaneous insulin infusion therapy.

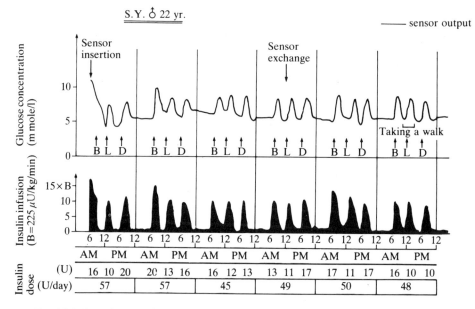

Fig. 23.8 A 6-day continuous glycaemic control in an insulin-dependent diabetic patient with a wearable artificial endocrine pancreas. The sensor was replaced on the fourth day. The patterns of insulin infusion and cumulative insulin requirement doses are also depicted. B, L, and S denote breakfast, lunch, and supper, respectively.

23.7.5 Closed-loop glycaemic control in human diabetics

The typical glycaemic control for six days in an insulin dependent diabetic patient is depicted in Fig. 23.8. In all patients studied, physiological glycaemic regulations were established. As shown in Fig. 23.7, indices of daily glycaemic excursions such as MBG (mean blood glucose), *M*-value (Schlichtkrull *et al.* 1965), and MAGE (Service *et al.* 1970) were improved significantly in diabetics controlled by the wearable artificial endocrine pancreas, compared with the patients treated with the conventional insulin therapy, multiple insulin injections therapy, and continuous subcutaneous insulin infusion therapy.

23.8 Conclusion

The successful glycaemic control in human diabetics with the artificial pancreas (Albisser *et al.* 1974; Pfeiffer *et al.* 1974; Kawamori *et al.* 1978) underlines the importance of continuous glycaemic monitoring to strict glycaemic control. However, the major obstacle to extending the term of glycaemic control on human diabetics is the development of an implantable glucose sensor with high precision in tissue glucose determination.

A needle-type glucose sensor, which is a miniature hydrogen peroxide electrode covered by a membrane with biological activity, is easy to implant and replace. The sensor has the *in vitro* and *in vivo* characteristics suitable for continuous tissue glucose monitoring.

A telemetry system using a needle-type glucose sensor is capable of monitoring glucose concentration in ambulatory diabetics. In addition, a wearable artificial endocrine pancreas, which incorporates a needle-type glucose sensor, has been devised and regulated glycaemia physiologically in human diabetics for more than six days.

Further improvements in sensor design, especially in membrane biocompatibility, might reduce the host reactions to the sensor implanted in tissue and thus extend its biological life.

References

Albisser, A. M., Leibel, B. S., Ewart, T. G., Davidovac, Z., Botz, C. K., Zingg, W., Schipper, H. and Gander, R. (1974). Clinical control of diabetes by the artificial pancreas. *Diabetes* **23**, 397-404.

Bartlett, D. Jr. and Tenney, S. M. (1963). Tissue gas tensions in experimental anemia. *J. Appl. Physiol.* **18**, 734-8.

Bessman, S. P., Thomas, L. J., Kojima, H., Sayler, D. F. and Layne, E. C. (1981). The implantation of a closed-loop artifical beta cell in dogs. *Trans. Am. Soc. Artif. Intern. Organs* **27**, 7-18.

Chang, K. W., Aisenberg, S. and Soeldner, J. S. (1972). *In vitro* tests of an implantable glucose sensor. *Proc. of 25th Ann. Conf. on Eng. in Med. and Biol.* pp. 58.

Gibson, Q. H., Swoboda, B. E. P. and Massey, V. (1964). Kinetics and mechanism of action of glucose oxidase. *J. Biol. Chem* **239**, 3927-34.

Gough, D. A., Anderson, F. L., Giner, J., Colton, C. K. and Soeldner, J. S. (1981). Effect of coreactants on electrochemical glucose oxidation. *Anal. Chem.* **50**, 941-4.

Guilbault, G. G. and Lubrano, A. (1973). An enzyme electrode for the amperometric determination of glucose. *Anal. Chim. Acta* **64**, 439-55.

Hagihara, B., Ishibashi, F., Sato, N., Minami, T., Okada, Y. and Sugimoto, T. (1981). Intravascular oxygen monitoring with a polarographic oxygen cathode. *J. Biomed. Eng.* **3**, 9-16.

Ikeda, S., Aoyama, N., Ito, K., Ohkura, K., Yamamoto, T., Ichihashi, H. and Kondo, T. (1980). Artificial pancreas — study of the new vessel access type glucose sensor. *Jpn. J. Artif. Organ* **9**, 182-92.

Kawamori, R., Shichiri, M., Goriya, Y., Yamasaki, Y., Shigeta, Y. and Abe, H. (1978). Importance of insulin secretion based on the rate of change in blood glucose concentration in glucose tolerance, assessed by the artificial beta cell. *Acta Endocrinol.* **87**, 339-51.

Kawamori, R., Shichiri, M., Kikuchi, M., Yamasaki, Y. and Abe, H. (1980). Perfect normalization of excessive glucogon responses to intravenous arginine in human diabetes mellitus with the artificial beta cell. *Diabetes* **29**, 762–5.

Layne, E. C., Schultz, R. D., Thomas, L. J., Slama, G., Sayler, D. F. and Bessman, S. P. (1976). Continuous extracorporeal monitoring of animal blood using the glucose electrde. *Diabetes* **25**, 81–9.

Pfeiffer, E. F., Thum, Ch. and Clemens, A. H. (1974). The artificial beta-cell — a continuous control of blood sugar by external regulation of insulin infusion (glucose controlled insulin infusion system). *Horm. Metab. Res.* **6**, 339–42.

Schlichtkrull, J., Munk, O., Jersild, M. (1965). The M-value, an index of blood-sugar control in diabetes. *Acta Med. Scand.* **177**, 95–102.

Service, F. J., Molnar, G. D, Rosevear, J. W., Ackerman, E., Gatewood, L. C., Taylor, W. F. (1970). Mean amplitude of glycemic excursions, a measure of diabetic instability. *Diabetes* **19**, 644–755.

Shichiri, M., Kawamori, R. and Abe, H. (1979). Normalization of paradoxic secretion of glucagon in diabetics who were controlled by the artificial beta cell. *Diabetes* **28**, 272–5.

—— Hakui, N., Yamasaki, Y. and Abe, H. (1984). Closed-loop glycemic control with a wearable artificial endocrine pancreas — Validations in daily insulin requirements to glycemic response. *Diabetes* **33**, 1200–1202.

—— Yamasaki, Y., Hakui, N. and Abe, H. (1982). Wearable-type artificial endocrine pancreas with needle-type glucose sensor. *Lancet* **2**, 1129–31.

—— Goriya, Y., Yamasaki, Y., Hakui, N., Asakawa, N. and Abe, H. (1983). Glycaemic control in pancreatectomized dogs with a wearable artificial endocrine pancreas. *Diabetologia* **24**, 179–84.

Soeldner, J. S., Chang, K. W., Aisenberg, S., Hiebert, J. M. and Egdahl, R. H. (1976). Diabetes mellitus a bioengineering approach — An implantable glucose sensor. In *Diabetes mellitus. Forgarty International Center Series on Preventive Medicine*, (ed. S. S. Fajan) Vol. 4, pp. 267–77. Dept. of Health, Education and Welfare Public Health Service, National Institutes of Health.

Updike, S. J. and Hicks, G. P. (1967). The enzyme electrode, a miniature chemical transducer using immobilized enzyme activity. *Nature* **214**, 986–8.

Woodward, S. C. (1982). How fibroblasts and giant cells encapsulate implants: Considerations in design of glucose sensors. *Diabetes Care* **5**, 278–81.

Yamasaki, Y. (1984). The development of a needle-type glucose sensor for wearable artificial endocrine pancreas. *Med. J. Osaka Univ.* **35**, 25–34.

Bioelectrochemistry
(c) Analysis of electrical impedance

24

The principles and potential of electrical admittance spectroscopy: an introduction

DOUGLAS B. KELL

24.1 Introduction and overview

In many electrochemical techniques, one applies a (clamped) DC potential to the working electrode and measures the resultant current flowing in a circuit completed by a counter electrode (e.g. Bard and Faulkner 1980; Bond 1980; Kissinger and Heineman 1984). Even in pulse voltammetric techniques, the measuring system is designed such that the potential difference between the working and reference electrodes, and the current ultimately measured, is constant for a greater or lesser period. However, the last 20 years or so have witnessed the increasing exploitation of *sinusoidal* exciting voltages in the study of electrode processes in aqueous media (e.g. Breyer and Bauer 1963; Schwan 1966; Smith 1966; Sluyters–Rehbach and Sluyters 1970; Macdonald 1977; Archer and Armstrong 1980; Bard and Faulkner 1980; Bond 1980; Gabrielli 1980; Buck 1982; Macdonald and McKubre 1982; Gabrielli *et al.* 1983), an approach which possesses two advantages in particular: (1) the sinusoid offers convenient technical and mathematical features in such systems, together with an excellent signal: noise ratio predicated upon the use of a 'steady-state' analysis (e.g. Creason *et al.* 1973; Gabrielli and Keddam 1974; Diamond and Machen 1983; Marshall 1983), and (2) the *frequency*, as well as the voltage, of the exciting wave-form may be altered, so that we may consider or use the technique as a form of spectroscopy.

To put the foregoing in another way, we may raise the idea, with which we are all familiar, that the frequency-dependent absorption of ultra-violet, visible, and infra-red light may be used in the analysis of biological (and other) materials. Yet light is only a form of electromagnetic radiation, albeit of a rather high frequency (10^{14} Hz or so), and there is thus no reason why the frequency-dependent absorption of electrical energy of *lower* frequencies might not similarly be exploited in bio-analytical devices. In such cases, at least below 30 MHz or so, one requires electrodes to act as an interface between the exciting electrical field and the sample, so that, as in the 'pure' electrochemical case above, one may study the frequency-dependent, passive electrical properties of the system consisting of the electrodes *plus* the biological sample; in other words, one may study the frequency-dependent impedance or admittance of the system.

In the following, therefore, I shall (1) outline in very elementary terms what is meant by the concepts of electrical impedance and admittance, (2) discuss the application of such measurements in (predominantly non-faradaic) electroanalysis, and (3) introduce the cognate concept of the dielectric spectroscopy of biological substances. These considerations will pave the way for (4) a discussion of the use of AC techniques, including frequency response analysis (FRA), in biosensor applications *sensu lato*. Because of the relative magnitudes of the topic and the space available, I will make no attempt to be comprehensive; my aim will be predominantly to provide, for the general reader, an introduction to a field which I believe has been widely neglected by biologists and biophysicists (despite its many spectacular successes), yet which underlies a great many present and future biosensor applications.

24.2 Electrical impedance and admittance

Let us consider a sinusoidally modulated voltage, of the form $V = V_m \sin \omega t$, where ω is the frequency in radians s^{-1} ($\omega = 2\pi f$, where f is the frequency in Hz), V_m is the maximum (peak-to-peak) voltage, and V the voltage at any given instant. If this voltage appears across the terminals of a passive circuit, device, or 'system', which may consist of pure electrical components or of a biological or chemical sample separating a pair of electrodes, the current flowing in the circuit (after any transients have died down) may be related to the voltage both by its *magnitude* and its *phase*, and is of the form $i = i_m \sin (\omega t + \theta)$. Thus (Fig. 24.1a), although the *frequency* and *sinusoidal nature* of the wave-form are unchanged by interaction with the system, the characteristics of the system are reflected in the ratio V_m/i_m and by the value of θ.

Now, systems may exhibit resistive, capacitive, and inductive properties, properties which (by definition) may be distinguished from each other by their effects upon a sinusoidal voltage. Thus, for a pure resistor (R Ohms), the current due to our exciting waveform ($V_m \sin \omega t$) is given by:

$$i = (V_m/R) \sin \omega t. \tag{24.1}$$

For a pure capacitor (C farads):

$$i = \omega C\, V_m \sin \left(\omega t + \frac{\pi}{2} \right) \tag{24.2}$$

whilst for a pure (self-) inductance of L henries:

$$i = (V_m/\omega L) \sin \left(\omega t - \frac{\pi}{2} \right). \tag{24.3}$$

Thus, for a pure resistor, there is no phase difference between V and i. In

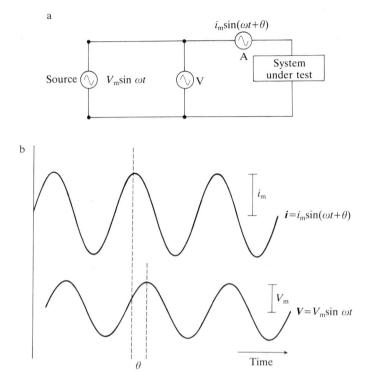

Fig. 24.1 (a), The impedimetric experiment, in which a small-amplitude pertur-bation, in the form of a sinusoidal voltage, is applied to the system of interest. The sinusoidal voltage across the system may be measured using a (high-impedance) AC vector voltmeter, V, whilst the sinusoidal current flowing in the circuit may be mea-sured by means of an AC vector ammeter A. In practice (a, b), it is found that the phase of the current differs from that of the voltage by an amount θ; in the case shown it *leads* the voltage.

contrast, for a pure capacitor, the current **leads** the voltage by $\pi/2$ radians (90°) whilst for a pure inductor the current **lags** the voltage by the same amount. Now, except in active biological systems such as nerve axons (e.g. Cole 1972; Jack *et al.* 1975; De Felice 1981), and in *certain* electrochemical systems, particularly those involving corrosion and electro-deposition (Gabrielli 1980; Macdonald and McClure 1982; Gabrielli *et al.* 1983), inductances are negligible, and we shall for the most part ignore them. We may therefore imagine intuitively (and correctly) that for a 'real' system, which possesses both resistive *and* capacitive properties (i.e. behaves as a leaky capacitor), θ takes a value between 0 and $\pi/2$, as illustrated in Fig. 24.1b.

We may then define a vector quantity **Z**, the *impedance*, with modulus

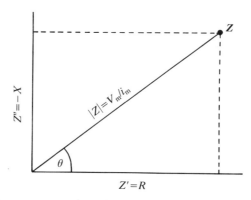

Fig. 24.2 Impedance as a complex quantity. There is a mathematical function, known as Euler's identity, which states that $Ae^{\pm j\theta} = A\cos\theta \pm Aj\sin\theta$, where $j = \sqrt{-1}$. Thus, any complex quantity may be split up into its real and imaginary part. The figure shows the manner in which this is done for the impedance function $Z = R + jX$. Simple geometrical considerations indicate (i) that $Z^2 = R^2 + X^2$, and (ii) that $R = |Z| \cos\theta$ and $X = -|Z| \sin\theta$. Thus R and X may be obtained from measurements of $|Z|$ and θ, and are known respectively as the 'in phase' and (90°) 'out-of-phase' components.

(magnitude) $|Z|$ and argument ('direction') θ, in a form analogous to that of a complex number $a + jb$ (where $j = \sqrt{-1}$) as in Fig. 24.2, where the modulus $|Z|$ of the impedance is equal to the ratio V_m/i_m. Thus, the impedance has both real and imaginary parts, and is defined as $Z = R + jX$, where the reactance $X = -1/\omega C$, and the system is treated as though it consisted of a resistance and capacitance in *series*.

We may also treat the system as consisting of an equivalent conductor (G siemens $= 1/R'$S) and capacitor (C') in *parallel*. In this case, we define an *admittance* Y, as a vector with modulus $|Y| = i_m/V_m = 1/|Z|$ and argument θ, such that $Y = 1/Z = G + jB$, where B, the susceptance, $= \omega C'$.

As succinctly stated by Falk and Fatt (1968), the distinction between the two sets of treatments is as follows: in the impedance representation, we take the impedance to represent the dependence of the voltage on the current, the terminals of the system under study (in an arrangement such as that of Fig. 24.1a) being considered as being connected to a current source of infinite resistance (i.e. open circuited). In contrast, in the admittance representation we take the admittance to represent the dependence of the current on the voltage, the terminals being considered as being connected to a voltage source of zero resistance (short-circuited).

Since the above distinctions are only distinctions in the way we *treat* the sample, it is obvious that we can move from the impedance to the admittance

Series	Parallel
Impedance	Admittance
$Z=R+jX$	$Y=\frac{1}{Z}=G+j\omega C'$

Resistance $\quad R = \dfrac{G}{G^2+(\omega C')^2}$	Conductance $\quad G= \dfrac{R}{R^2+X^2}$
Reactance $\quad X= \dfrac{-\omega C'}{G^2+(\omega C')^2} = \dfrac{-1}{\omega C}$	Susceptance $\quad B=\omega C'= \dfrac{-X}{R^2+X^2}$

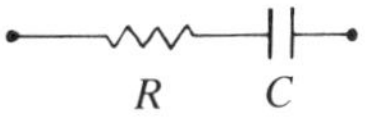

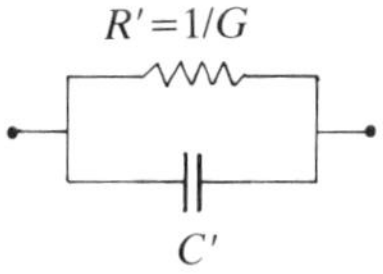

$$R'=1/G$$

Fig. 24.3 The relationships between impedance and admittance, and their real and imaginary components. For discussion, see text.

domain, and *vice versa*, by the choice of appropriate values of R, C, G, and C'. For convenience, we give the relevant equations in Fig. 24.3. In other words, regardless of the *actual* complexity of (the equivalent electrical circuit of) the system between the terminals of the measuring instrument, when we make measurements at a given frequency, we merely *treat* the system as though it consists of a single resistance (conductance) in series or in parallel with a single capacitance. For real circuits, then, the impedance $Z(\omega)$ or admittance $Y(\omega)$, and their component real and imaginary parts, are *frequency-dependent quantities*, the frequency-dependence of which may be used to describe the *actual* equivalent electrical circuits. It should be noted that, by definition, the impedance and admittance are independent of the voltage across, and current flowing in, the system under study, and this 'linear property' should be taken into account when use is made of these representations.

In general, the most convenient means by which we can extract the magnitudes and topological relationship of the components constituting the equivalent circuit is by means of complex plane diagrams, a topic to which we now turn.

24.3 Impedance diagrams

If we make measurements of the frequency-dependent impedance of an electrical circuit consisting of a 2.671 kΩ resistor in parallel with a 220.4 pF

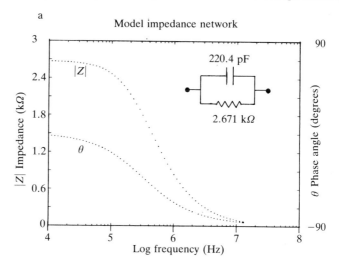

a

Model impedance network

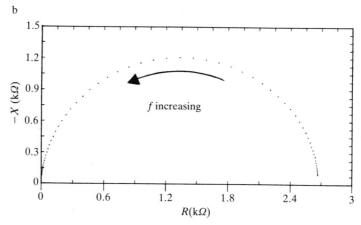

b

Fig. 24.4 The frequency-dependent impedance of a model electrical circuit. Measurements were made, and the data plotted, using the frequency-domain impedimetric system described by Harris and Kell (1983). (a) The impedance modulus and the phase angle as a function of the frequency. Note the existence of two plateau regions in frequency ranges that are respectively low and high relative to that of f_c. (b) A reactance/resistance plot, showing that the circuit has a single time constant. For further discussion, see text.

capacitor, the behaviour shown in Fig. 24.4 is obtained. (Remember that although the circuit is *actually* a parallel network, we *treat* it, in the impedance representation, as though components were connected in series.) Thus (Fig. 24.4a), as the measuring frequency is increased, we find (i) that the phase angle (θ, as defined in Fig. 24.1), decreases from approximately 0°

(purely resistive behaviour) to approximately $-90°$ (purely capacitive or reactive behaviour), and (ii) the modulus of the impedance $|Z|$ decreases from roughly 2.67 kΩ to roughly zero. The frequency at which the transition is half completed, the so-called critical or characteristic frequency f_c, may be seen, by inspection of Fig. 24.4a, to occur at approximately 300 kHz. Since the product of a resistance and a capacitance has the dimensions of time (seconds), and is equal by definition to the relaxation time τ ('time constant') for such a circuit, and since $\tau = 1/2\pi f_c$, we may also calculate τ (5.89×10^{-7} s) and f_c (270 kHz) simply from the values of the resistor and capacitor in the circuit.

Now, as shown in Fig. 24.2, we can calculate the real (R) and imaginary (X) parts of the impedance from the measured values of $|Z|$ and θ, and (since these change with frequency) plot the negative reactance against the resistance with frequency as the parameter. This is done in Fig. 24.4b, where it may be observed that the resultant plot takes the form of a semicircle, whose centre would lie on the abscissa and which has a maximal value of $-X$ which occurs (*cf.* Figs. 24.4a, 24.4b) at the characteristic frequency; further, had measurements been made over a wider frequency range, it is evident (or at least plausible) that the semicircle would have extrapolated to values of 0 and 2.67 kΩ. Thus, as discussed in many introductory textbooks of electrical circuit analysis (e.g. Bleaney and Bleaney 1976; Duffin 1980; Bobrow 1981; Brown *et al.* 1982; Harter and Lin 1982), these impedance diagrams reflect, and may be used to obtain, the values of the elements of an equivalent electrical circuit.

Using the equations given in Fig. 24.3, one may also derive from Fig. 24.4a the equivalent values of G and B pertinent to a representation in the admittance domain. In this case, a plot of B versus G (an admittance diagram) would also give a semicircle, with its centre on the abscissa and the maximum value of B when the exciting frequency $= f_c$. The production of such a plot is left as an exercise for the reader. As we shall also see when we come to consider complex conductivity and permittivity, although the information contained in each plot is the same, the relative *weightings* of the data can serve to enhance different frequency regions (Macdonald *et al.* 1982).

24.4 Impedance diagrams in electrochemical systems

For a variety of historical and other reasons, the impedance (R/X) representation has dominated the electrochemical literature, although J. R. Macdonald and his colleagues (e.g. Macdonald 1980; Macdonald *et al.* 1982) have stressed the utility of the three-dimensional perspective $R/X/\log f$ plot. Now, the general aim in studies of purely electrochemical and, in many cases, of solid-state (as opposed to biological), impedances is to gain information about the mechanisms of electrode processes, i.e. of processes occurring at the electrode/electrolyte interface. Thus, since such processes are obviously dependent upon the 'mean' potential of the working electrode, one should arrange to poise this potential at a known value, either by including both pairs of a redox couple of known E_0' in the medium (faradaic impedance) or electronically. In the latter case in particular, it is usual to use a three-electrode system (Bard and Faulkner 1980; Bond 1980; Gabrielli 1980). In such two- or three-electrode measurements, of course, one should either use identical electrodes or make the impedance of the working electrode very much greater than that of the counter electrode.

The interpretation of electrochemical impedances is a vast, detailed, and complex field, and for the present purposes I shall merely give the simplest possible description of the salient ideas. These are: (1) that the electrical double layer (e.g. Mohilner 1966; Bockris and Reddy 1970; Sparnaay 1972; Martynov and Salem 1983) at the electrode/solution interface possesses, due to its molecular thickness, a significant capacitance (of some μF per cm² actual electrode area, under typical conditions) which must be charged up before any faradaic current can flow; (ii) that the rate of the subsequent reaction may be limited by a charge transfer step, by diffusion of electro-active reactant to the reaction layer, or by both, in which latter case one finds the superposition of a straight line and a semicircle in the R/X plot; (iii) that the residual resistance at very high frequencies represents the resistance of the bulk solution between the electrodes; (iv) the diffusional impedance is often

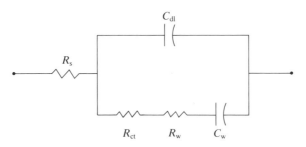

Fig. 24.5 Very general equivalent circuit for an electrochemical cell. The double layer capacitance C_{dl} is in parallel with a resistance representing the charge transfer (faradaic) step, since geometrically they occur in (essentially) the same place. This structure is in series with a 'Warburg' impedance Z_w, comprised of resistive and capacitive parts, equivalent in essence to the 'diffusion zone'. Finally, the whole arrangement is in series with the ('iR drop') bulk electrolyte solution resistance R_s. Obviously the actual magnitude of these components determines the exact frequency response of the system. The symbols used for the capacitors are to indicate the presence of some heterogeneity in the structures which they represent.

referred to as the Warburg impedance Z_w, and represented as a resistor and capacitor in series. The equivalent electrical circuit describing this behaviour, and which is usually ascribed to Randles (1947), is given in Fig. 24.5; it may be noted that we are here beginning to equate our electrical circuit components with mechanistic explanations of electrode behaviour.

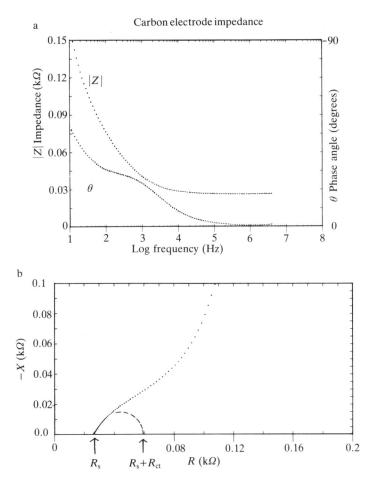

Fig. 24.6 The frequency-dependent impedance of a pair of graphite electrodes immersed in 100 mM KCl. The modulating voltage was 50 mV and measurements were performed using the apparatus described by Harris and Kell (1983). (a) Impedance modulus and phase angle versus logarithmic frequency. (b) Impedance diagram, showing how one may derive the values of R_s and R_{ct} from the semicircular portion of such a plot (Hung *et al.* 1979). In a classical Warburg-type system, the low-frequency (right hand) part of the impedance locus should make an angle of 45° with the abscissa. The characteristic frequency of the semicircular part of the plot may be used to obtain the values of C_{dl} from the relation $C_{dl} = 1/2\pi f_c R_{ct}$.

Now, it should be stressed that much more complicated behaviour than the above may be observed in practice. Nevertheless, Fig. 24.6 shows the experimentally obtained impedance diagram of a pair of cylindrical graphite electrodes (*ca.* 4 mm radius, 20 mm length, surface roughness unknown, separation 10 mm) immersed in 100 mM KCl, a diagram which, it may be observed, corresponds fairly accurately to the behaviour described above (and see Besenhard and Fritz 1983). The following points may be made with respect to this figure: (1) the semicircular locus is by no means perfect, and is poorly separated from the straight line portion, and it is not realistic to fit it such that its centre lies on the abscissa — this may be ascribed to heterogeneity in the structures underlying C_{dl} and R_{ct}; (2) the frequency dependence of the impedance extends over an enormous range — at least seven orders of magnitude in the present case; (3) there is no frequency dependence (in this range) of the impedance of the material *between* the electrodes (which is simply an ionic solution) — all the observed frequency dependence is caused by electrochemical behaviour *at the electrodes*.

Now, it is obvious that the measured resistance and reactance of our electrochemical cell is a function of the electrode size and geometry; electrodes of larger area and closer separation will, all else being equal, appear to have a lower impedance. Since, in many cases, it is the *intensive* properties of the system which are of interest, we must needs take account of this; to do so we will make use of the admittance representation (Fig. 24.7), and introduce the notions of permittivity and conductivity.

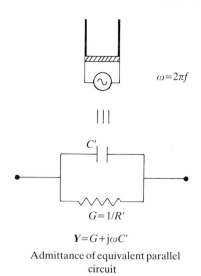

$\omega = 2\pi f$

$Y = G + j\omega C'$

Admittance of equivalent parallel
circuit

Fig. 24.7 At any given frequency, the passive electrical properties of a system may be completely described by the admittance $G + j\omega C'$ of the equivalent parallel circuit.

24.5 Permittivity, conductivity and dielectric dispersion

For a specimen held between two parallel electrodes of area A separated by a distance d, the intrinsic passive electrical properties are completely specified by the conductivity σ' and the permittivity ϵ', which are related to the measured conductance G and capacitance C' by the equations:

$$G = \sigma'(A/d) \tag{24.4}$$
$$C' = \epsilon'\epsilon_r(A/d) \tag{24.5}$$

From eqn 24.4, we find that to obtain the conductivity, we multiply the measured conductance by d/A, a factor which has the dimensions of length^{-1} (e.g. cm^{-1}) and is known as the cell constant. In eqn 24.5, ϵ_r (sometimes called ϵ_0 in the literature) is the capacitance of a cell of unit dimensions containing a vacuum, equal to 8.854×10^{-14} F/cm, so that any matter existing between the electrodes will have the effect of raising the capacitance by a factor ϵ', a factor which was formerly called the dielectric constant, but (since it is not constant) is more properly referred to as the permittivity. The permittivity of water at 25°C is approximately 78.4, so that, as may be calculated from eqns 24.4 and 24.5, a cell of cell constant 1 cm^{-1} containing water at this temperature will have a capacitance of 6.94 pF. The presence of ionic electrolytes has only a rather modest effect upon the permittivity of aqueous solutions, such that the permittivity of 1 M NaCl at 25°C is approximately 61.6 (Davies 1965).

Now, for many purposes, it is useful to make use of the complex permittivity $\epsilon^* = \epsilon' - j\epsilon''$, which, as with impedance and admittance, has both real and imaginary parts, and the imaginary part of which, the dielectric loss ϵ'', is related to the conductivity by the equation

$$\epsilon'' = \frac{\sigma' - \sigma'_L}{2\pi f \epsilon_r} \tag{24.6}$$

where σ'_L represents any DC or 'low frequency' contribution to the conductivity.

In a given frequency range, the dielectric properties of any material between the electrodes may not be constant (i.e. the material exhibits dielectric dispersion), and, as with the impedance of the model circuit in Fig. 24.4, may change between two 'plateau' values ϵ'_L and ϵ'_∞, according to the equation

$$\epsilon^* = \epsilon'_\infty + \frac{\epsilon'_L - \epsilon'_\infty}{1 + j\omega\tau} \tag{24.7}$$

where, as before, $\tau \left(= \frac{1}{2}\pi f_c \right)$ is the relaxation time. Equation 24.7 separates into

$$\epsilon' = \epsilon'_\infty + \frac{\epsilon'_L - \epsilon'_\infty}{1 + (\omega\tau)^2}, \tag{24.8}$$

$$\epsilon'' = \frac{(\epsilon'_L - \epsilon'_\infty)\omega\tau}{1 + (\omega\tau)^2}, \tag{24.9}$$

and a plot of ϵ'' versus ϵ' gives a circle whose centre is located on the ϵ' axis. However, in practice it is often observed that semicirlces result whose centre lies below the abscissa, and it was shown by Cole and Cole (1941) that this behaviour may be described by an equation of the form

$$\epsilon^* = \epsilon'_\infty + \frac{\epsilon'_L - \epsilon'_\infty}{1 + (j\omega\tau)^{1-\alpha}} \tag{25.10}$$

such that a line between the centre of the circle and the points at which the ϵ''/ϵ' locus crosses the abscissa makes an angle $\alpha\pi/2$ radians with the abscissa. Although the Cole–Cole representation is entirely empirical (it is generally taken to represent some kind of distribution of relaxation times), it is now commonplace to express data in the form of a Cole–Cole plot, such that the dispersion is characterized by the 'dielectric increment' $\Delta\epsilon' = \epsilon'_L - \epsilon'_\infty$ and by the Cole–Cole α. Many other dielectric relaxation time distributions have been suggested (reviewed by Boyd 1980 and see Marshall and Roe 1978), but they have not achieved widespread usage in biological systems, and are not discussed further here.

Complementarily, one may make use of the 'complex conductivity' plot of σ'' versus σ', where

$$\sigma'' = 2\pi f \epsilon_r (\epsilon' - \epsilon'_\infty). \tag{24.11}$$

As discussed above, the two representations have the effect of weighting the appearance of the data differently; I will illustrate this by using (in Fig. 24.8) the data (Fig. 24.6) from the carbon electrode impedance spectrum.

As Fig. 24.8a shows, the apparent permittivity of the system at low frequencies reaches truly enormous values (2×10^8 at 10 Hz), the measured capacitance at this frequency being approximately 70 μF, an effect which forms the basis of the 'electrolytic' type of capacitor used in electrical and electronic circuits. Of course, the permittivity of the electrolyte between the electrodes is only about 78, and, if we use this value for the 'high frequency'

Fig. 24.8 Admittance properties of carbon electrodes. Data were obtained as described in the legend to Fig. 24.4. (a) Conductivity and permittivity, as obtained from the measured capacitance and conductance by means of the cell constant. (b) Admittance (complex conductivity) plot, using $\epsilon'_\infty = 78.4$. The fit of the two semicircles is empirical, there being no satisfactory way (in the absence of additional knowledge) of separating overlapping dispersions. Extrapolation gives σ'_L, whence $\Delta\sigma'$ for each dispersion may be obtained. (c) Complex permittivity (Cole–Cole) plot, using the value of σ'_L obtained in b, and illustrating the estimation of the Cole–Cole α and the extrapolation (to low frequencies) by which one may obtain ϵ'_L. It may be

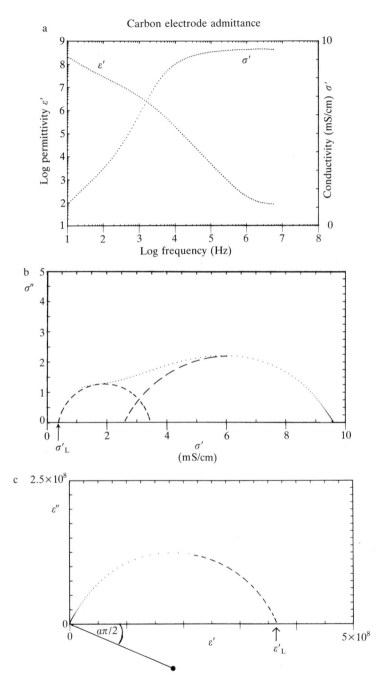

Carbon electrode admittance

noted that two dispersions are *not* discernible in this diagram, illustrating how the admittance and complex permittivity plots weight the data differently. Note that, for a given dispersion in which the Cole–Cole α is not too large, τ is given by $\Delta\epsilon'\epsilon_r/\Delta\sigma'$.

permittivity, we obtain the admittance plot shown in Fig. 24.8b; as in the impedance diagram (Fig. 24.4), two separate processes may be discerned, extrapolation of the latter to low frequencies giving the value of σ_L' (0.4 mS/cm) to be used in constructing the Cole–Cole plot in Fig. 24.8c. As stressed by Macdonald *inter alia*, the Cole–Cole plot is not really suitable for use in describing *electrochemical* impedances since permittivity and conductivity are *intrinsic* properties of materials which may be held between the electrodes, and this should be borne in mind. However, the representation in Fig. 24.8 serves to illustrate the means by which we treat data of this type, and it is hoped that this elementary exposition will assist the novice or tyro who may wish to delve further into these matters. For completeness, it should be mentioned that some literature, particularly that concerned with electrical insulators, specifies the so-called 'dissipation factor', $D = \tan \delta = \epsilon''/\epsilon'$. For materials lacking DC conductivity, $D = G/\omega C = 1/Q$, where Q is the so-called quality factor or Q-factor.

We are now more or less in a position to consider some of the mechanistic bases for the frequency-dependent electrical behaviour of systems held between electrodes and which consist not only of ionic solutions but of biological materials. However, the dielectric (passive electrical) properties of biological and chemical (Stock 1984) substances have attracted study for a great many years (e.g. Osterhout 1922), both from a scientific and an analytical standpoint. Thus, for instance, Stewart (1899a) noted that the low-frequency conductivity of blood plasma exceeded that of the whole blood from which it had been derived by an amount that was a monotonic function of the haematocrit, and derived an equation wherewith to estimate the latter by means of conductivity measurements. Since this time, a vast and increasing literature on biological impedances has accumulated, an amount far too great adequately to be reviewed herein, and what I shall therefore do is: (i) draw attention to the many excellent books, review articles, and monographs on the subject of the dielectric spectroscopy of biological substances, (ii) outline the salient observable and mechanistic features of the dielectric dispersions that have been described in biological systems, and the relationships between the dielectric increment and the effective molecular dipole moments underlying the dispersions, and (iii) describe some of the analytical methods and devices that have been used or proposed, and which have as their basis the measurement of conductivity, permittivity, or their vector sum. I shall then outline some of the technical and methodological aspects which should be borne in mind when one considers making measurements of biological impedances, and draw attention to the distinctions one may make between measurements in the time and frequency domain. This will lead us to an outline of the role of time series analysis in biosensing generally. Finally, I shall seek to bring together the ideas and facts described above in suggesting some novel approaches to the design and exploitation of biosensors.

24.6 Dielectric spectroscopy of biological susbtances

Of the many books available on the dielectric behaviour of condensed matter, those of most biological relevance, and which are especially recommended, are by Daniel (1967), Cole (1972), Hasted (1973), Grant *et al.* (1978), Schanne and Ceretti (1978) and Pethig (1979). Schwan, the doyen of biological impedance determinations, has written several excellent reviews (e.g. Schwan 1957, 1963, 1977, 1981*a, b*, 1983*a, b*; Schwan and Foster 1980; Stoy *et al.* 1982), and overviews of these matters may also be found in the review articles of Salter (1979), Pilla (1980; Pilla *et al.* 1983), Zimmermann (1982) and Pethig (1984). The latter gives an extensive discussion of measurements on proteins, which are also discussed in the reviews by Oncley (1943), Takashima (1969; Takashima and Minakata 1975), Grant and South (1972; Grant 1982, 1983), Petersen and Cone (1975), Wada (1976), Hasted *et al.* (1983), Kell and Hitchens (1983) and Kell and Westerhoff (1985). Our own work (Harris and Kell 1983; Kell 1983; Harris *et al.* 1984; Harris and Kell 1985*a*; Kell and Harris 1985*a, b*) has concentrated on microbial membranes, the latter two articles containing a fair amount of review material on this topic. Work with natural (Pauly and Packer 1960; Pauly *et al.* 1960; Falk and Fatt 1968; Irimajiri *et al.* 1979; Asami *et al.* 1980*a*, 1984) and pure phospholipid membrane vesicles (Schwan *et al.* 1970; Redwood *et al.* 1972; Asami and Irimajiri 1984; Pottel *et al.* 1984) and planar membranes (Hanai *et al.* 1964, 1965; Tien 1974; Fettiplace *et al.* 1975; Haydon *et al.* 1977; and Laver *et al.* 1984) may also be cited, whilst an entrée to the microbial literature may also be gained from the papers of Pauly (1962), Asami *et al.* (1976, 1980*b*), Clarke *et al.* (1984, 1985), Blake–Coleman *et al.* (1984), and Harris and Kell (1985*b*). Almost all charged polyelectrolytes exhibit enormous permittivities at low frequencies (e.g. Dukhin and Shilov 1974; O'Brien 1982), whilst those displayed by DNA are discussed at some length in the articles of Vreugdenhil *et al.* (1979) and Sorriso and Surowiec (1982). Most of the papers cited in this section concern work at frequencies below 100 MHz or so; the higher frequency work, with which we have not had experience to date, is discussed by Foster and Schepps (1981), Foster *et al.* 1982, Illinger (1981), Stuchly *et al.* (1981), Clegg *et al.* (1982), Kraszewski *et al.* (1982), Gabriel *et al.* (1983), Magin and Burdette (1983) and Clegg *et al.* (1984). This extensive citation list indicates very clearly the great breadth and depth of literature on biological impedance determinations. What take-home messages may one distil from this work?

In general, it has become usual to point out that biological cells and tissues exhibit three broad and more-or-less separable dielectric dispersions, centred respectively in the audio-, radio- and UHF-frequency regions and referred to as the α-, β- and γ-dispersions. Subsidiary δ- and β_1-dispersions, located between the β- and γ-dispersions, may also be noted, especially in protein solutions (Essex *et al.* 1977; Grant 1982), whilst a low-frequency μ-dispersion was described by Kell (1983), Harris *et al.* (1984), and Harris and Kell (1985a). The major mechanisms thought to underlie these dispersions are as follows: relaxation of the ion cloud tangential to charged membrane surfaces (α-dispersion); Maxwell–Wagner-type relaxation at the interface between the poorly conducting cell membranes and their adjacent aqueous solutions (β-dispersion); rotation of small charged and/or dipolar molecules (γ-dispersion); relaxation of tissue-bound water (δ-dispersion); protein rotation (β_1-dispersion) and diffusional movements of membrane-associated components (μ-dispersion). Where applicable, the superposition principle states that each of these mechanisms is independent and additive, and we would stress that *any* potential charge or dipole mobility will lead to the existence of a dielectric dispersion. In this sense, dipole rotations are electrically indistinguishable from any other motions such as the hopping of charges between different sites (Jonscher 1975; Lewis 1977; Ngai *et al.* 1979), and it is therefore obvious that a plethora of molecular mechanisms can in fact underlie the relatively broad dielectric dispersions observed in practice.

As discussed above, we can describe or characterize a dielectric dispersion by its dielectric increment, its 'mean' relaxation time and by the extent of distribution of the relaxation times as embodied in the Cole–Cole α. Now, the dielectric increment may be said to constitute the outward and visible sign of a molecular property, the dipole moment (or, for hopping of charges, etc, the *effective* dipole moment), μ. Dipole moments are traditionally measured in debyes (D), where $1D = 3.33 \times 10^{-30}$ C m; in other words, since the unit electrical charge $= 1.6 \times 10^{-19}$ C, a pair of charges of opposite sign separated by 10^{-10} m (1 Å) have a dipole moment of 4.8 D. It is the molecular dipole moment that serves to tell us what fraction of the dipoles are *actually* responding at a given field strength, according to the Langevin function (Fig. 24.9)

$$L(x) = \coth(x) - 1/x \tag{24.12}$$

where $x = \mu E_1/kT$, E_1 is the local electrical field, k is Boltzmann's constant, and T is the absolute temperature. Since, in complex biological systems especially, we are likely to know only the macroscopic field (i.e. the peak potential difference between the electrodes divided by the distance between them) rather than the local field, it is appropriate to use the former and to add an empirical constant. For the rotation of aqueous globular proteins with a permanent dipole moment, we use the factor $H = 5.8$ (obtained from a comparison between theory and experiment for the amino acid glycine) (Oncley 1943), and we have:

$$\mu = \sqrt{(9000\,kT\Delta\epsilon/4\pi NHC)} \tag{24.13}$$

where $N =$ Avogadro's number and C is the *molar* protein concentration.

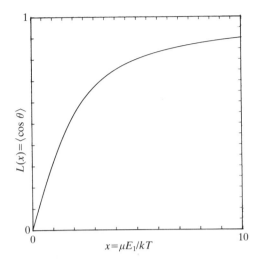

Fig. 24.9 The Langevin function. This relates the average angle between the field (at a frequency low relative to that of f_c) and the (effective) dipole of interest $<\cos\theta>$ to the field strength and effective molecular dipole moment $\mu E_1/kT$, where E_1 is the local field, k is Boltzmann's constant and T the absolute temperature. For $x (= \mu E_1/kT) <$ 1, the Langevin function reduces to $<\cos\theta>$ – $\mu E_1/3 kT$, and the dielectric increment is independent of the field strength (i.e. we are in the linear region), the number of particles *actually* moving in response to the field being proportional to E_1.

The magnitudes of the dipole moments of protein solutions observed in practice are equivalent roughly to 1–15 relative permittivity units per (g/100 ml), corresponding to roughly 5–20 D per kilodalton (e.g. Gerber *et al.* 1972; Schwan 1981*a*). One may therefore calculate that, in a typical dielectric experiment in which the field strength is most unlikely to exceed 0.5 V/cm, and is likely to be as little as 1/10 of this, the Langevin function has a very small value, such that the number of proteins *actually* rotating is in fact an extremely small fraction of the total. We shall have cause to return to this point later.

To summarize the discussions in this section as they relate to our overall considerations, we may make the following remarks: (1) there is an enormous literature indicating that all types of cells, tissues, and bio-molecules possess dielectric properties different from those of simple ionic solution; (2) especially since dielectric spectroscopy is a non-invasive tech-nique, one may exploit it to assay for the former in the presence of the latter; (3) because of the strong frequency-dependence of dielectric properties, one may assay for different substances or features by choosing different fre-quencies; (4) in such cases, a consideration of where the field lines go is likely to prove informative; (5) because of the relative insensitivity of the technique, and the breadth of the spectra obtained (which reflect relaxation rather than resonance), it is likely to be most useful in 'bulk' measurements when practised conventionally. From a bioanalytical standpoint, one must also add that, especially at low frequencies, one is likely also to be measuring the electrode properties, in addition to those of the material between the electrodes, although this does not of itself impair the potential analytical utility of the method. I would also mention that a recent and otherwise excellent book *Biological Spectroscopy* (Campbell and Dwek 1984) did not even mention the concept of dielectric spectroscopy, a rather clear indication that indeed the method is ripe for exploitation.

In this vein, therefore, I turn to a discussion of some of the articles which have sought to use the principles described herein in analytical devices.

24.7 Some bioanalytical uses of conductimetry and impedimetry

Obviously this is a vast topic as well, and I shall therefore aim for some selectivity in choosing the examples with which I shall draw attention to the use of these methods. One particular use, which is attracting increasing attention (see Firstenberg–Eden and Eden 1984; Harris and Kell 1985b), is in the exploitation of impedimetry in assessing the numbers of micro-organisms present in sparse populations, since changes in the electrical properties of microbial culture media have been known to be associated with microbial growth since the last century (Stewart 1899b). Conductimetry (e.g. Richards *et al.* 1978; Mackey and Derrick 1984), impedimetry (e.g. Cady 1978) and capacitimetry (Firstenberg–Eden and Zindulis 1984) have all been used (Firstenberg–Eden and Eden 1984); in the latter case especially, the micro-organism-dependent changes are due to effects at the electrodes (Hause *et al.* 1981), since any micro-organism-dependent changes in the bulk permittivity would here be neglible.

Since the electrical conductivity (at frequencies below that of the Maxwell–Wagner type β-dispersion) of a suspension is lower than that of the fluid in which it is suspended, one may thus detect the presence of suspended matter directly by its effects upon an electrical field. Such measurements have been made both in bulk suspension (see for example Irimajiri *et al.* 1975; Harris and Kell 1983; Lovitt *et al.* 1986) and in hydrodynamically focused lowing streams in devices based upon the principle of the Coulter Counter™ (e.g. Kubitschek 1969; Dow *et al.* 1979). Clarke and his colleagues (Blake–Coleman *et al.* 1984; Clarke *et al.* 1984, 1985) have also successfully applied impedimetry to the direct assessment of microbial biomass, and our own studies and those of others (*op. cit.*) have indeed shown that the dielectric properties of cells of a given radius scale monotonically with the volume fraction of the suspended phase.

As regards the possibilities of *distinguishing* or *identifying* cells by their frequency-dependent dielectric properties, it is certainly true that both the size and surface charge (density), *inter alia*, differ for different bacteria. For instance. Gram-positive and -negative bacteria have entirely different α-dispersions (e.g. Harris and Kell 1985*a*). However, size and surface charge depend critically on both the pH and physiological status (e.g. growth rate) of micro-organisms, and simple dielectric spectra are unlikely to contain enough information, in the absence of other tests, to be diagnostic. Similarly, in non-axenic cell suspensions, the dielectric properties of the largest cells will tend to dominate those of the suspension, so that deconvolution, already difficult, would probably be impossible in all but the most favourable cases. However, I see no reason in principle why the Coulter Counter™ method should not be extended to exploit measurements of the *frequency-dependent* electrical properties of individual cells. In particular (and see later), the magnitude of the electrical fields used would allow one to make use of the *non-linear* electrical properties of cells, properties which may be expected to be far more cell-specific than simple linear behaviour might lead one to suppose. Thus, although I do not see that the dielectric spectroscopy of microbial cell suspensions is likely to be diagnostic of the *specific* micro-organism (measurement of colonies might be more productive), the use of more advanced techniques does hold out some promise for the characterization of unknown cells. However, since published dielectric spectra of microbial cells do not cover more than ten species (of unknown physiological status) to date, much more work is required before one may make an adequate assessment of the many exciting possibilities in this area.

Other techniques exploiting the bulk permittivity, conductivity, or impedance of cells and tissues, and which have enjoyed a reasonably widespread use, include impedance plethysmography (e.g. Nyboer 1970; Wheeler and Penney 1982; Brown 1983; Anderson 1984) and pneumography (Pacela 1966; Henderson and Webster 1978), whilst measurements of the dielectric properties of excised tissue have been used in the testing of freshness (Faure *et al.* 1972; To *et al.* 1974; Kent 1975; Kent and Jason 1975), and quality (Pfutzner and Fialik 1982) of foods. As regards tissue measurements, it may also be mentioned that there are significant local decreases of skin impedance in the area of the meridian points recognized as significant in the science of acupuncture (e.g. Becker and Marino 1982; Jakoubek and Rohlicek 1982), estimations of which, it may well be argued, really constitute biosensing *sensu stricto*.

Obviously, measurements of the conductance of homogeneous solutions are widely used in environmental monitoring, and are the method of choice in estimating the salinity of the marine environment (see for example Brown 1968; Ben–Yaakov 1981; Wilson 1981). Similarly, resistivity methods have also enjoyed use in geophysical prospecting (Keller and Frischknecht 1966), although the physical and mechanistic interpretation of the data is by no means free of difficulty (Hasted 1973; Phillips 1984). It may also be mentioned that the time resolution of solution conductivity measurements may be made extremely good by using microwave frequencies (de Haas and Warman 1982). Schugerl (1984) gives a useful discussion of an elegant conductimetric method for monitoring bubble size and velocity distribution in microbial fermenters (and see later), whilst the utility of impedimetry in the monitoring of chromatographic eluents is discussed, for instance, by Alder *et al.* (1984).

As regards conductimetry in biosensors generally, Lowe (1984, 1985) and Ballot *et al.* (1984) have recently stressed that a great many of the reactions exploited in potentiometric and amperometric enzyme electrodes, for instance the urea-dependent pH and pI change in urease-containing electrodes, might be equally or better assessed conductimetrically. Similarly, Arwin and colleagues (1982) have made use of enzyme reaction-dependent changes in the double layer capacitance of symmetrical metal electrodes as a measure of enzyme or substrate activities. Workers tend to make such measurements at a single frequency, and it goes without saying that yet more selective and informative sensors might be based upon multiple-frequency methods.

Finally, we may mention the use of conductimetry in improving the response time (Powley *et al.* 1980) and selectivity (Powley and Nieman 1983) of ion-selective electrodes that are normally used in a potentiometric mode. As one would expect from the properties of electrode impedances described above, there is an optimal time (frequency) window for these measurements, in this case a delay of 0.1 ms between the stimulus and the measurement of the response being used.

Naturally one could give many, many more examples of the above type. However, what I wish to convey is that by choosing appropriate frequencies and/or analyte matrices, a great many determinants may be monitored in real time and non-invasively by the use of impedimetry in various embodiments, and that the predominant response may be due to the behaviour of the electrode, of the bulk solution, or of the interfacial region. This concept brings us to a brief discussion of some technical aspects of this type of measurement.

24.8 The realization of impedimetric systems

I have not thus far laid much stress upon the technical and instrumental considerations underlying impedimetry, since, as far as the typical user is concerned, the methods to be employed follow directly from the underlying principles. Many reviews discuss the measurement of chemical impedances (e.g. Shedlovsky 1949; Blake 1950; Reilley 1954; Loveland 1963; Thomas and Pertel 1963; Pungor 1965; Bennett and Calderwood 1971; Hollder and Enke

AC source

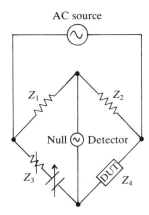

Fig. 24.10 The principle of a two-terminal impedance bridge. The device under test (DUT) forms one arm of the bridge (Z_4), which is in many ways similar to the familiar (DC) Wheatstone bridge, excet that the voltage source is a sinusoidal oscillator of variable frequency, the null detector is AC sensitive and the adjustable arm of the bridge (Z_3) contains both resistive and capacitive components. When the bridge is balanced (i.e. no current flows in the part of the circuit containing the null detector), and if $Z_1 = Z_2$, then $Z_3 = Z_4$, since, generally, $Z_1 Z_4 = Z_2 Z_3$.

1984; and see electrochemical references above) and biological impedances (Schwan 1963; Hasted 1973; Grant *et al.* 1978; Pethig 1979; Marmarelis and Marmarelis 1978; de Felice 1981) in the range up to 30 MHz or so. I use this frequency criterion because it is roughly here that the wavelength of electromagnetic radiation approaches the dimensions of the measuring system, such that at frequencies greater than this, the lumped circuit description implicit in the above ceases solely to be applicable, and one should also consider a field description based on the Maxwell equations (see for example Bleaney and Bleaney 1976; Lorrain and Corson 1979; Cheng 1981). Similarly, electrode impedances are now negligible. An entrée to the recent literature on these very high frequency methodologies may be gained from the articles by Dawkins *et al.* 1979, Burdette *et al.* 1980, Stuchly and Stuchly 1980, Athey *et al.* 1982; Foster *et al.* 1982, and Steel *et al.* 1984; we do not here discuss these matters further.

In the frequency range below 10^7 to 10^8 Hz or so, bridge methods (Fig. 24.10) remain the most widely used and are appropriate. Traditionally, manually balanced bridges were used, but modern instruments are computer-controlled and auto-balancing. Frequency response analysers provide, albeit at some loss in precision, an extremely convenient means of obtaining dielectric spectra (Morse 1974; Gabrielli 1980). The system illustrated schematically in Fig. 24.11, which is that used by the present author, measures V_m, i_m, and θ (see Fig. 24.1) by means of a vector voltmeter and ammeter,

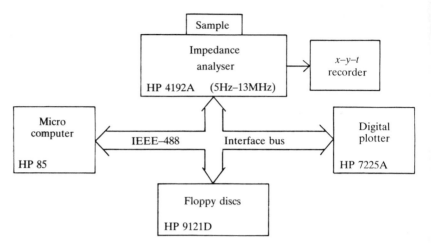

Fig. 24.11 A computer-controlled, frequency domain dielectric spectrometer, based upon commercially available components and usable in the range 5 Hz–13 MHz. The microcomputer drives the impedance analyser, stores the data obtained both in RAM and on disc, and permits the data to be plotted in a variety of forms (see Figs 24.4, 24.6, 24.8, and Harris and Kell 1983).

whence all required information may be calculated and displayed. Its implementation of the IEEE-488 standard interface makes it extremely convenient in use, and logarithmic scans may be made at a rate of 6 s (and 20 measurement frequencies) per decade. In this type of system the sinusoidal frequencies are applied one at a time, and these methods are thus called *frequency-domain* methods.

In systems of the above type, two-terminal measurements are the more common. However, this means that one is always measuring the impedance of the sample *plus* the electrodes, and, particularly at low frequencies and high conductance, the latter, which may be of no scientific or analytical interest, can dominate the measurements. In such cases, four-electrode techniques are used (Fig. 24.12), by which electrode polarization problems are in principle avoided (see for example Schwan 1963, 1966, 1968; Schwan and Ferris 1968; Nakamura *et al.* 1981), although a careful consideration of the exact location of the electrical field lines is necessary (Schwan 1955; Schwan and Ferris 1968). In such cases, the cell constant is determined by the positioning of the voltage electrodes (Tamamushi and Takahashi 1974). The minimization of electrode polarization generally, by using Pt black electrodes (e.g. Schwan 1963), and the preparation of such electrodes using electrolysis in Kohlrausch solution (Geddes 1972), are discussed elsewhere.

In recent years, time domain methods have become popular. In this type of approach, one applies a step voltage to the sample and follow, depending

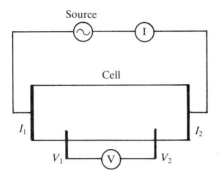

Fig. 24.12 The principle of the four-electrode technique for measuring bulk, low-frequency impedances with minimal interference from the impedance of electrode/electrolyte interfaces. Current from the AC source is measured with an ammeter and flows through the system via two current electrodes (I_1 and I_2). The voltage drop across the relevant part of the system is measured using two voltage 'pick-up' electrodes (V_1 and V_2), connected to a voltmeter of high input impedance, such that negligible current flows through them and thus no electrode polarization impedance is measured (see Schwan and Ferris 1968; Ferris 1974).

upon the frequency range, the time-dependent (dis)charging current flow, or the wave behaviour, of the equivalent *RC* circuit. Deconvolution of such data, usually by use of the fast Fourier transform (see later), gives the equivalent frequency-dependent dielectric properties. Such methods are of value at both high frequencies (see for example Cole 1975; Dawkins *et al.* 1979; Stuchly and Stuchly 1980; Burdette *et al.* 1980; Boned and Peyrelasse 1982; Steel *et al.* 1984) and low frequencies (e.g. Singh *et al.* 1979; Eden *et al.* 1980; Hart 1982; Schmukler and Pilla 1982; Mopsik 1984).

This concept, of the equivalence of the time- and frequency-domain behaviour of a system, leads us finally and naturally to the idea that we might broadly use an input wave-form of *any* shape in order to assess the passive electrical properties of a system, and this is in fact to a good approximation true. We will therefore include an introductory section on modern methods of signal analysis.

To summarize this section, we would stress again (i) that care must always be taken to be sure of the extent to which electrode polarization is contributing to the measured biological impedances, and (ii) that one should properly be aware of the pathways taken by the field lines between the electrodes.

24.9 Spectral analysis as an integral element of biosensing

The means most commonly used, in the general case, to analyse the frequency dependence of the response of a system to an input wave-form (e.g. Jenkins and Watts 1968; Priestley 1981) are the same as those used in the proper characterization of any time-dependent signal or 'time series' (e.g. Bendat and Piersol 1971; Box and Jenkins 1976; Chatfield 1984). In particular, they exploit transform techniques such as the Fourier transform (e.g. Champeney 1973; Bloomfield 1976; Bracewell 1978; Marshall 1978, 1982, 1983) and, whilst yet more advanced approaches and treatments may be mentioned (e.g. Childers 1978; Kay and Marple 1981; Chen 1982a,b; Fu 1982; Ahmed and Natarajan 1983; Geckinli and Yavuz 1983), we shall confine our short discussion to the more standard approaches that may be applied to linear, stationary, or periodic (quasi-)ergodic systems.

Any periodic signal $x(t)$ (of period T) may be represented by a Fourier series, which may be written thus:

$$x(t) = \sum_{-\infty}^{+\infty} C_n e^{j2\pi ft} \tag{24.14},$$

where

$$C_n = \frac{1}{T} \int_{-T/2}^{T/2} x(t) e^{-j2\pi ft}.dt \tag{24.15}$$

and where $j = \sqrt{-1}$ and the 'fundamental frequency' $f = 1/T$.

The Fourier series may also be written

$$\begin{aligned} S_x(f) &= F[x(t)] = X_0 + X_1(\cos 2\pi ft + j \sin 2\pi ft) \\ &\quad + X_2(\cos 4\pi ft + j \sin 4\pi ft) + \ldots\ldots \\ &\quad + X_n(\cos 2n\pi ft + j \sin 2n\pi ft) \end{aligned} \tag{24.16}$$

For non-periodic data, a continuous spectral representation must be obtained from a Fourier integral, given by

$$X(f) = \int_{-\infty}^{+\infty} x(t) e^{-j2\pi ft}.dt. \tag{24.17}$$

These equalities thus relate signals in the time domain to those in the frequency domain, and show that any signal may be represented as a sum of sinusoids of defined frequency, amplitude, and phase.

If we take an apparently 'random' signal, such as that in the top half of Fig. 24.13a, we may wish to characterize it further, and to decide, for instance, to what extent if any it may differ materially from that of another, apparently equally random, signal such as that in the top half of Fig. 24.13b. A convenient means by which this may be accomplished is by determining the autocorrelation function $R_x(\tau)$, which measures the degree to which a signal correlates with a displaced replica of itself:

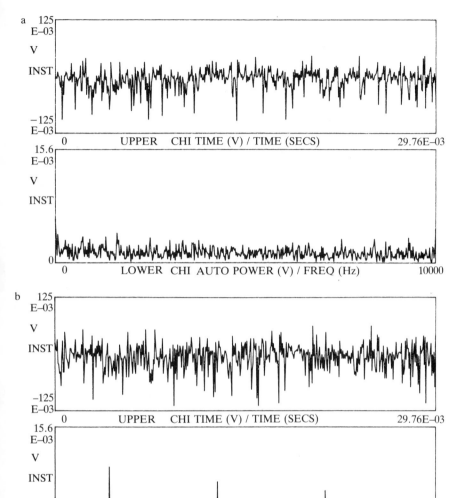

Fig. 24.13 Two 'random' signals and their autopower spectra. The upper half of each figure contains the time history of the signal, whilst the lower half is the autopower spectrum (see text) of the data. It is clear that, whilst the degree of 'randomness' in the original data is apparently similar in the two cases, the autopower spectra reveal that the signal in b has a substantial component centred at a frequency of about 1.4 kHz. In fact, the signals are constituted in each case by the output of a 'white noise' generator, that in b being mixed with the output of a sinusoidal oscillator operating at 1420 Hz. The data were analysed using a Solartron 1200 Signal Processor and plotted using a Hewlett-Packard 7470 digital plotter.

$$R_x(\tau) \;=\; \lim_{T \to \infty} \frac{1}{T} \int_0^T x(t).x(t + \tau).dt \tag{24.18}$$

At zero time displacement ($\tau = 0$), the value of $R_x(\tau)$ equals the mean square value of the signal $x(t)$. A 'purely' random signal ('white noise') has an autocorrelation function that is independent of the value of t. Such functions have found use in the on-line estimation of the time constant of electrodes (Turner and Howell 1984).

The autocorelation function is the inverse Fourier transform of the auto-power spectrum $G_x(f)$, i.e. $R_x(\tau) \;=\; F^{-1}[G_x(f)]$, and describes the general frequency composition of a time series in terms of the spectral density of its mean square value:

$$G_x \;=\; \lim_{\Delta t \to 0} \frac{1}{(\Delta f)} \left[\lim_{T \to \infty} \frac{1}{T} \int_0^T x^2(x,\, t,\, \Delta f).dt \right]. \tag{24.19}$$

(The autocorrelation function and autopower spectra thus ignore *phase* relations). Figure 24.13 illustrates the utility of the autopower spectrum in 'picking out' a periodic signal from a noisy set of data; whilst one would be hard pressed to perceive any analytical use for data as noisy as those in the time domain representations, the autopower spectra clearly show that signal b indeed contains a significant component with a frequency of 1.4 kHz or so (plus harmonics), and in this area of the spectrum the signal:noise is quite acceptable for analytical usage.

The above analyses have considered *single* signals alone. We may also define a cross-correlation function $R_{xy}(\tau)$ between signals $x(t)$ and $y(t)$, such that

$$R_{xy}(\tau) \;=\; \lim_{T \to \infty} \frac{1}{T} \int_0^T x(t).y(t + \tau).dt \tag{24.20}$$

This function tells us the extent to which one signal correlates with another, and is the inverse Fourier transform of the so-called cross-power spectrum $G_{xy}(f)$, i.e.

$$R_{xy}(\tau) = F^{-1}[G_{xy}(f)]. \tag{24.21}$$

Finally, we may use these concepts to define the transfer function of a system, $H(f)$, which serves to define the input/output relationship of a generalized transmission system. Thus, if in a test system such as that of Fig. 24.1a, the input signal $x(t)$ has an autopower spectrum $G_x(f)$, and the output signal $y(t)$ is so modified by the system that the cross-power spectrum is $G_{xy}(f)$, then

$$H(f) = G_{xy}(f)/G_x(f).$$ (24.22)

In principle, therefore, *any* input signal might therefore be used to obtain the transfer function, and hence the impedance, since in this case the transfer function may also be defined (notation as in Figs. 24.1 and 24.2) as

$$Z(f) = |Z(f)|e^{j\theta(f)}.$$ (24.23)

In practice, certain wave-forms are favoured, for reasons connected with the measuring time (Creason *et al.* 1973; Gabrielli *et al.* 1982); similarly, accuracy is improved by stressing frequency components related to the relaxation times of the system under study (one might here imagine the exploitation of an iterative system (see also Kell and Harris 1985a)). Nevertheless, despite the need to average, the 'pseudo-random' input remains popular in neurophysiological (e.g. Marmarelis and Marmarelis 1978; De Felice 1981; Fernandez *et al.* 1984) and dielectric (Nakamura *et al.* 1981) work, and is that exploited in Fig. 24.13.

We may therefore state that this type of analysis is already extremely important and useful, and will become increasingly cheap, widespread, and significant as digital electronic technology advances. (All the spectral functions are implemented in a hard-wired form and in real time in the system used to construct Fig. 24.13). Although I have included a discussion of these matters because they naturally complement the concept of admittance spectroscopy, I would stress that spectral analysis in general, i.e. what is often referred to as 'pattern recognition', should be considered as an *integral* design goal by all workers actively developing biosensing devices. Although these methods have been used for many years in photometric systems (e.g. Berne and Pecora 1976), and Fourier techniques are widely used in NMR and IR spectroscopy, etc. (e.g. Marshall 1983; Campbell and Dwek 1984), I do not as yet perceive their exploitation in biosensing systems on the wide scale that their potency merits. Therefore, and although the applicability of these techniques to fermentation technology constitutes our own main present direction, I will end by describing two possible general uses of fluctuation or spectral analysis.

24.10 Conductimetric correlation functions in the assessment of two-phase flows in bioreactors

Many systems, such as laboratory and industrial bioreactors and fermentors, exhibit highly complex and multiphase fluid dynamics (e.g. Bryant 1977). Leaving aside, for the present, particulate matter and biological cells, such systems may broadly be modelled as consisting of a heterogeneous suspension of non-conducting gas bubbles in an aqueous ionic solution. When stated thus, it is evident that conductivity (or impedimetry generally) can provide a convenient approach to the measurement of the passage of gas bubbles, on a similar principle to that employed in the Coulter Counter™ (see Harris and Kell 1985*b*). In particular, the use of more than one probe in a bioreactor allows the estimation of the cross-correlation and/or coherence functions of the conductivity fluctuations between probes, a direct indication not only of bubble size and dynamics but of bubble velocity (Buchholz and Schügerl 1979*a,b*; Schügerl 1984; Sekiguchi *et al.* 1984). Spectral analysis of pressure fluctuations has also been used to gain otherwise-unobtainable, and real-time, information on the mixing dynamics in two-phase bioreactors (Gerson 1980).

Extending such ideas, we may state (accurately) that the 'problem of scale-up' (e.g. Lilly 1983) is largely ascribable to the fact that conventional measuring practice considers only the *mean*, and not the (rapid) *fluctuations about the mean*, of signals derived from probes. It should be obvious that the proper characterization of the 'state' of a culture, by means of environmental measurements, thus requires the *full* characterization of the time-dependent behaviour of such measurements, including their fluctuations. It is our view that this area in particular represents one of the most fruitful in which future progress may be expected.

Now, whilst the type of signal analysis discussed in this section relies upon the assessment of signals generated by macroscopic probes in microbial fermentors, we wish finally and speculatively to discuss a potentially novel approach to biosensing *sensu stricto*, based upon the measurement of non-linear electrical transfer functions in relatively microscopic proteinaceous systems.

24.11 Use of the multi-dimensional dielectric spectrum of intramolecular protein motions in biosensing devices

The overwhelming majority of biosensing devices proposed or realized to date rely upon the juxtaposition of an enzyme (or protein) and either a potentiometric or an amperometric electrode. What I wish to discuss here is the possibility of exploiting the specific, *non-faradaic* and *non-linear* electrical behaviour of proteins that are bound (or adjacent) to electrodes.

It is now becoming widely recognized that the atoms of even protein crystals, let alone aqueous solutions of globular proteins, exhibit many and complex fluctuations about their mean or average positions, even when at thermodynamic equilibrium (above $0°K$) (reviews: Welch *et al.* 1982; Somogyi *et al.* 1984; Welch 1986; and references therein). Such intramolecular fluctuations are not wholly independent from each other (Kell and Hitchens 1983). Further, since proteins contain numerous charged and dipolar species, it is to be expected that the intramolecular mobilities of such groups will be (i) protein-specific and (ii) changed upon substrate (ligand) binding, enzymatic activity, or energy transduction (Welch and Kell 1985), so that a non-invasive dielectric spectroscopic assessment of protein dynamics might form the basis of an entire family of novel biosensing devices (since this principle would apply to any protein–ligand(protein) interaction). However, since the (linear) dielectric dispersions exhibited by proteins are rather broad (reflecting, presumably, the numerous underlying processes contributing to the macroscopic observables), the problem reduces to that of signal handling, i.e. to *deconvoluting* the dielectric spectra. To approach this, we propose (i) to exploit the *non-linear* dielectric properties of proteins (or indeed any other macromolecule) and (ii) to exploit two- (or multi-) dimensional analysis of the electrical transfer functions of protein–ligand systems. We shall also need to consider the appropriate frequency range for maximizing the protein-specificity of the signal.

Now, as discussed above, the fraction of charges or dipoles *actually* moving in response to an electrical field of the appropriate frequency is given by the Langevin function (see Fig. 24.9), so that, in calculating the fields necessary to drive at least say 80% of a given type of dipole to its extremal position we require that $\mu E_1/kT$ exceeds 5, a value significantly outside the linear domain (see Fig. 24.9). Since many of the effective *intramolecular* dipole moments in which our interest lies probably do not exceed say 5 charge-A (24 D), and since for $\mu E_1/kT = 5$ we require (at 298°K) a field of 6.159×10^9 V m^{-1} D^{-1} (Kell and Harris 1985a), the type of field we are likely to require is of the order of 2.5×10^8 V/m. Thus, to keep the voltages small, or at least realistic, we must use electrodes separated by as small a distance as possible, a suitable design being that of intercalated or comb electrodes (e.g. on a silicon substrate) (Fig. 24.14), as used for instance in the Eumetric™ system (Micromet Instruments Inc, Cambridge, MA 02139, USA) for low-frequency permittivity measurements.

Now, because of the protein-specific intramolecular connections of the different charged and dipolar groups, the imposition of a field (such that $\mu E_1/kT$ is greater than say 5) at one frequency will measurably affect the dielectric properties measured at another frequency. Thus, by measuring the frequency-dependent dielectric properties as a function of the frequency of a *high* electric field, we may seek to deconvulate the intramolecular electrical properties, in much the same spirit as NMR spectroscopists measure the so-called J- and NOE-connectivities or cross-relaxation pathways of NMR-active nuclei by two-dimensional techniques (e.g. Kumar *et al.* 1980; Jardetsky and Roberts 1981; Winter and Kimmich 1982; Wuthrich 1982; Campbell and Dwek 1984; Markley *et al.* 1984). In other words, one would *excite* (with a high field intensity (E_1)) at *one* frequency (f_1) and *interrogate* (with a field E_{II}) at *other* frequencies (f_2), either simultaneously ($t = 0$) or subsequently ($t > 0$), with f_1 and f_2 and/or t and perhaps also E_1 and E_{II} being varied throughout. What sort of frequencies should we consider?

To generator
and analyser

Fig. 24.14 The principle of using comb electrodes to give a high field for a reasonably low voltage, whilst covering a reasonable surface area (and thereby lowering the impedance). The alternating comb electrodes (seen here from above) are closely spaced (say 1 μm or less), and attached to the signal-generating and -analysing circuitry. The protein or biological component of interest is placed over the surface of the device, either by covalent attachment or otherwise, and the ligand-dependent change in the multi-dimensional dielectric spectrum assessed. Available variables for obtaining the multidimensional matrix include (see text) $f_1, f_2, E_\mathrm{I}, E_\mathrm{II}$, and t.

We might expect that many of the most interesting intramolecular relaxations would lie at frequencies in the more technically difficult range above 1 MHz or so, not least because simple protein rotation is likely to dominate the measured spectra below this frequency. However, increasing the local solvent viscosity, e.g. with phospholipids, or chemical cross-linking of electrode-associated enzyme molecules, would serve to lower the appropriate frequency range. Notwithstanding, at the lower frequencies a significant contribution from double layer and faradaic electrode processes would be observed, and whilst this does not affect the pattern-recognition approach *per se*, it seems likely that the biospecific signal/noise ratio of such a device will be greater the greater the contribution from the protein dynamics.

The exact features of such multi-dimensional dielectric spectra which are likely to prove of most bioanalytical value can not easily be defined at the present time. However, it is easy to predict that a difference spectrum of (protein-plus-ligand) *minus* (protein alone) is likely to give the best type of definition of the ligand-selective signal analysis required, whether the biological response *in vivo* are a function of the occupancy or the rate of occupancy of the proteinaceous receptor in question. Similarly, whilst I do not in any way underestimate the technical difficulties involved, one should state that if *proteins* recognize (bind to) ligands and each other by means of such frequency-dependent electrical processes, there is no *fundamental* reason why we should not do so as well.

The possibility of placing such a device, of the type alluded to herein, on an electrophoretic gel and therewith *identifying* a protein or nucleic acid in a band or a spot, seems sufficient justification alone to cause one further to explore the development of such a principle.

Acknowledgement

I thank the Science and Engineering Research Council for financial support, Christine Harris and Professor Gareth Morris for useful discussions, Anthony Pugh for photographic assistance, and Sian Evans for typing the manuscript.

References

Adey, W. R. (1981). Tissue interactions with nonionising electromagnetic fields. *Physiol. Rev.* **61**, 435–514.

Ahmed, N. and Natarajan, T. (1983). *Discrete-time signals and systems* Reston Publishing, Reston, Virginia, USA.

Alder, J. F., Fielden, P. R. and Clark, A. J. (1984). Simultaneous conductivity and permittivity detector with a single cell for liquid chromatography. *Anal. Chem.* **56**, 985–8.

Anderson, F. A. Jr. (1984). Impedance plethysmography in the diagnosis of arterial and venous disease. *Ann. Biomed. Eng.* **12**, 79–102.

Archer, W. I. and Armstrong, R. D. (1980). The application of A.C. impedance methods to solid electrolytes. In *Electrochemistry*, (ed. H. R. Thirsk) Vol. 7, pp. 157–202. Specialist Periodical Reports, The Chemical Society, London.

Arwin, H., Lundström, I. and Palmqvist, A. (1982). Electrode adsorption method for determination of enzymatic activity. *Med. Biol. Eng. Comput.* **20**, 362–74.

Asami, K. and Irimajiri, A. (1984). Dielectric dispersion of a single spherical bilayer membrane in suspension. *Biochim. Biophys. Acta* **769**, 370–6.

—— Hanai, T. and Koizumi, N. (1976). Dielectric properties of yeast cells. *J. Membr. Biol.* **28**, 169–180.

—— and Koizumi, N. (1980a). Dielectric approach to suspensions of ellipsoidal particles covered with a shell, in particular reference to biological cells. *Jap. J. Appl. Phys.* **19**, 359–65.

—— and Koizumi, N. (1980b). Dielectric analysis of *Escherichia coli* in the light of the theory of interfacial polarisation. *Biophys. J.* **31**, 215–28.

—— Irimajiri, A., Hanai, T. Shiraishi, N. and Utsumi, K. (1984). Dielectric analysis of mitochondria isolated from rat liver. I. Swollen mitoplasts as simulated by a single-shell model. *Biochim. Biophys. Acta* **77i**, 559–69.

Athey, T. W., Stuchly, M. A. and Stuchly, S. S. (1982). Dielectric properties of biological substances at radio frequencies. Part 1. Measurement method. *IEEE Trans. Microwave Theory Tech.* **MTT-30**, 82–6.

Ballot, C. Saizonou-Manika, B., Mealet, C., Favre–Bonvin, G. and Wallach, J. M. (1984). Conductimetric measurements of enzyme activities. *Anal. Chim. Acta* **163**, 305–8.

Bard, A. J. and Faulkner, L. R. (1980). *Electrochemical methods.* Wiley, Chichester.

Becker, R. O. and Marino, A. A. (1982). *Electromagnetism and life.* State University of New York Press, Albany.

Bendat, J. S. and Piersol, A. G. (1971). *Random data: analysis and measurement procedures.* Wiley-Interscience, New York.

Bennett, R. G. and Calderwood, J. H. (1971). Experimental techniques in dielectric studies. In *Complex permittivity* (ed. B. K. P. Scaife), pp. 112–70. English University Press, London.

Ben–Yaakov, S. (1981). Electrochemical instrumentation. In *Marine electrochemistry* (eds M. Whitfield and D. Jagner), pp. 99–122. Wiley, Chichester.

Berne, B. J. and Pecora, R. (1976). *Dynamic light scattering.* Wiley-Interscience, New York.

Besenhard, J. O. and Fritz, H. P. (1983). The electrochemistry of black carbons. *Angew. Chem. Int. Ed.* **22**, 950–75.

Blake, G. G. (1950). *Conductimetric analysis at radio-frequency.* Chapman and Hall, London.

Blake–Coleman, B. C., Calder, M. R., Carr, R. J. G., Moody, S. C. and Clarke, D. J. (1984). Direct monitoring of reactor biomass in fermentation control. *Trends Anal. Chem.* **3**, 229–35.

Bleaney, B. I. and Bleaney, B. (1976). *Electricity and magnetism*, (3rd edn). Oxford University Press, Oxford.

Bloomfield, P. (1976). *Fourier analysis of time series. An introduction.* Wiley, New York.

Bobrow, L. S. (1981). *Elementary linear circuit analysis.* Holt, Rinehart and Winston, New York.

Bockris, J. O'M. and Reddy, A. K. N. (1970). *Modern electrochemistry*, Vols. 1 and 2. Plenum Press, New York.

Bond, A. M. (1980). *Modern polarographic methods in analytical chemistry.* Marcel Dekker, New York.

Boned, C. and Peyrelasse, J. (1982). Automatic measurement of complex permittivity (from 2 MHz to 8 GHz) using time-domain spectroscopy. *J. Phys. E. Sci. Instr.* **15**, 534–8.

Box, G. E. P. and Jenkins, G. M. (1976). *Time series analysis: forecasting and control.* Revised Edition. Holden-Day, Oakland, California.

Boyd, R. H. (1980). Dielectric constant and loss. In *Methods of experimental physics* (ed. R. A. Fava) Vol. 16C, pp. 379–421. Academic Press, New York.

Bracewell, R. N. (1978). *The Fourier transform and its applications* (2nd edn). McGraw-Hill Kogakusha, Tokyo.

Breyer, B. and Bauer, H. (1963). *Alternating current polarography and tensammetry.* Wiley-Interscience, New York.

Brown, B. H. (1983). Tissue impedance methods. In *Imaging with non-ionizing radiations* (ed. D. F. Jackson), pp. 85–110. Surrey University Press, Guildford.

Brown, N. L. (1968). An *in situ* salinometer for use in the deep ocean. In *Marine sciences instrumentation* (ed. F. Alt), Vol. 4, pp. 563–77.

Brown, P. B., France, G. N. and Moraff, H. (1982). *Electronics for the modern scientist*. Elsevier, Amsterdam.

Bryant, J. (1977). The characterization of mixing in fermenters. *Adv. Biochem. Eng.* **5**, 101–23.

Bucholz, R. and Schügerl, K. (1979*a*). Bubble column reactors. I. Methods for measuring the bubble size. *Eur. J. Appl. Microbiol. Technol.* **6**, 301–13.

—— (1979*b*). Methods for measuring the bubble size in bubble column bioreactors. II. *Eur. J. Appl. Microbiol. Biotechnol.* **6**, 315–23.

Buck, R. P. (1982). The impedance method applied to the investigation of ion-selective electrodes. *Ion-Selective Electrode Rev.* **4**, 3–74.

Burdette, E. C., Cain, F. L. and Seals, J. (1980). *In vivo* probe measurement technique at VHF through microwave frequencies. *IEEE Trans. Microwave Theory Tech.* **MTT-28**, 414–27.

Cady, P. (1978). Progress in impedance measurements in microbiology. In *Mechanizing microbiology* (eds. A. N. Sharpe and D. S. Clark), pp. 199–239. Charles C. Thomas, Springfield, Illinois.

Campbell, I. D. and Dwek, R. A. (1984). *Biological spectroscopy*. Benjamin-Cummings, London.

Cartensen, E. L. and Marquis, R. E. (1975). Dielectric and electrochemical properties of bacterial cells. In *Spores VI* (eds. P. Gerhardt, R. N. Costilow and H. L. Sadoff), pp. 563–71. American Society for Microbiology, Washington, D.C.

Champeney, D. C. (1973). *Fourier transforms and their physical applications*. Academic Press, New York.

Chatfield, C. (1984). *The analysis of time series: an introduction* (3rd edn). Chapman and Hall, London.

Chen, C. H. (1982*a*) (ed.). *Digital waveform processing and recognition*. CRC Press, Boca Rabon, Florida.

—— (1982*b*) (ed.). *Nonlinear maximum entropy spectral analysis methods for signal recognition*. Research Studies Press, Chichester.

Cheng, D. K. (1983). *Field and wave electromagnetics*. Addison-Wesley, London.

Childers, D. G. (1978) (ed.). *Modern spectrum analysis*. IEEE Press, New York.

Clarke, D. J., Blake–Coleman, B. C., Calder, M. R., Carr, R. J. G. and Moody, S. C. (1984). Sensors for bioreactor monitoring and control — a perspective. *J. Biotechnol.* **1**, 135–58.

—— Calder, M. R., Carr, R. J. G., Blake–Coleman, B. C. and Moody, S. C. (1985). The development and application of biosensing devices for bioreactor monitoring and control. *Biosensors J.* **1**, 213–320.

Clegg, J. S., McClean, V. E. R., Szwarnowski, S. and Sheppard, R. J. (1984). Microwave dielectric measurements (0.8–70 GHz) on *Artemia* cysts at variable water content. *Phys. Med. Biol.* **29**, 1409–19.

—— Szwarnowski, S., McClean, V. E. R., Sheppard, R. J. and Grant, E. H. (1982). Interrelationships between water and cell metabolism in *Artemia* cysts. X. Microwave dielectric studies. *Biochim. Biophys. Acta* **721**, 458–68.

Cole, K. S. (1972). *Membranes, ions and impulses*. University of California Press.

Cole, R. H. (1975). Evaluation of dielectric behaviour by time domain spectroscopy. I. Dielectric response by real time analysis. *J. Phys. Chem.* **79**, 1459–69.

Cole, K. S. and Cole, R. H. (1941). Dispersion and absorption in dielectrics.

1. Alternating current characteristics. *J. Chem. Phys.* **9**, 341–51.

Creason, S. C., Hayes, J. W. and Smith, D. E. (1973). Fourier transform faradaic admittance measurements. III. Comparison of measurement efficiency for various test signal waveforms. *J. Electroanal. Chem. Interfacial Electrochem* **47**, 9–46.

Daniel, V. V. (1967). *Dielectric relaxation.* Academic Press, London.

Davies, M. (1965). *Some electrical and optical aspects of molecular behaviour,* pp. 96–7. Pergamon Press, Oxford.

Dawkins, A. W. J., Sheppard, R. J. and Grant, E. H. (1979). An outline computer-based system for performing time domain spectroscopy. 1. Main features of the basic system. *J. Phys. E. Sci. Instrum.* **12**, 1091–9.

De Felice, L. J. (1981). *Introduction to membrane noise.* Plenum Press, New York.

De Haas, M. P. and Warman, J. M. (1982). Photon-induced molecular charge separation studied by nanosecond time-resolved microwave conductivity. *Chem. Phys.* **73**, 35–53.

Diamond, J. M. and Machen, T. E. (1983). Impedance analysis in epithelia and the problem of gastric acid secretion. *J. Membr. Biol.* **72**, 17–41.

Dow, C. S., France, A. D., Khan, M. S. and Johnson, T. (1979). Particle size distribution analysis for the rapid detection of microbial infection of urine. *J. Clin. Pathol.* **32**, 386–90.

Duffin, W. J. (1980). *Electricity and magnetism* (3rd edn.). McGraw-Hill, London.

Dukhin, S. S. and Shilov, V. N. (1974). *Dielectric phenomena and the double layer in disease systems and polyelectrolytes.* Wiley, Chichester.

Eden, J., Gascoyne, P. R. C. and Pethig, R. (1980). Dielectric and electrical properties of hydrated bovine serum albumin. *JCS Faraday I*, **76**, 426–34.

Essex, C. G., Symonds, M. S., Sheppard, R. J., Grant, E. H., Lamotte, R., Soetewey, F., Rosseneu, M. Y. and Peeters, H. (1977). Five-component dielectric dispersion in bovine serum albumin solution. *Phys. Med. Biol.* **22**, 1160–7.

Falk, G. and Fatt, P. (1968). Passive electrical properties of rod outer segments. *J. Physiol.* **198**, 627–46.

Faure, N., Flachat, C., Jenin, P., Lenoir, J. Roullet, C. and Thomasset, A. (1972). Contribution a l'etude de la tendrete et de la maturation des viandes par la methode de la conductibilite electrique en basse et haute frequence. *Rev. Med. Vet.* **123**, 1517–27.

Fernández, J. M., Neher, E. and Gomperts, B. D. (1984). Capacitance measurements reveal stepwise fusion events in degranulating mast cells. *Nature* **312**, 453–5.

Ferris, C. D. (1974). *Introduction to bioelectrodes.* Plenum Press, New York.

Fettiplace, R., Gordon, L. G. M., Hladky, S. B., Requena, J., Zingsheim, H. P. and Haydon, D. A. (1975). Techniques in the formation and examination of 'black' lipid bilayer membranes. In *Methods of membrane biology* (ed. E. D. Korn) Vol. 4, pp. 1–75. Plenum Press, New York.

Firstenberg-Eden, R. and Eden, G. (1984). *Impedance microbiology.* Research Studies Press, Letchworth.

— and Zindulis, J. (1984). Electrochemical changes in media due to microbial growth. *J. Microbiol. Methods.* **2**, 103–15.

Foster, K. R. and Schepps, J. L. (1981). Dielectric properties of tumor and normal tissues at radio through microwave frequencies. *J. Microwave Power* **16**, 107–19.

— and Epstein, B. R. (1982). Microwave dielectric studies on proteins, tissues and heterogenous suspensions. *Bioelectromagnetics* **3**, 29–43.

Fu, K. S. (1982) (ed.). *Applications of pattern recognition*. CRC Press, Boca Raton, Florida.

Gabriel, C., Sheppard, R. J. and Grant, E. H. (1983). Dielectric properties of ocular tissue at 37°C. *Phys. Med. Biol.* **28**, 43–49.

Gabrielli, C. (1980). *Identification of electrochemical processes by frequency response analysis*. Solartron Electronic Group, Farnborough.

—— and Keddam, M. (1974). Progrès récent dans la mesure des impédances electrochemiques en régime sinusoidal. *Electrochim. Acta* **19**, 355–62.

—— and Takenouti, H. (1963). The use of A.C. techniques in the study of corrosion and passivity. In *Corrosion: aqueous processes and passive films. Treatise on materials science and technology*, (ed. J. C. Scully) Vol. 23, pp. 395–451. Academic Press, New York.

—— Huet, F., Keddam, M. and Lizee, J. F. (1982). Measurement-time versus accuracy trade-off analysed for electrochemical impedance measurements by means of sine, white noise and step signals. *J. Electroanal. Chem.* **138**, 201–8.

Geckinli, N. C. and Yavuz, D. (1983). *Discrete Fourier transformation and its applications to power spectra estimation*. Elsevier, Amsterdam.

Geddes, L. A. (1972). *Electrodes and the measurement of bioelectric events*. Wiley-Interscience, New York.

Gerber, B. R., Routledge, L. M. and Takashima, S. (1972). Self-assembly of bacterial flagellar protein: Dielectric behaviour of monomers and polymers. *J. Mol. Biol.* **71**, 317–37.

Gerson, D. F. (1980). The pressure fluctuation spectrum as a measure of mixing and emulsification in a biochemical reactor. *Eur. J. Appl. Microbiol. Biotechnol.* **10**, 59–72.

Grant, E. H. (1982). The dielectric method of investigating bound water in biological material: an appraisal of the technique. *Bioelectromagnetics* **3**, 17–24.

—— (1983). Molecular interpretation of the dielectric behaviour of biological materials. In *Biological effects of dosimetry of nonionizing radiation* (eds. M. Gandolfo, S. M. Michaelson, and A. Rindi), pp. 179–94. Plenum Press, New York.

—— and South, G. P. (1972). Dielectric relaxation of proteins in aqueous solutions. *Adv. Mol. Rel. Proc.* **3**, 355–77.

—— Sheppard, R. J. and South, G. P. (1978). *Dielectric behaviour of biological molecules in solution*. Oxford University Press, London.

Hanai, T., Haydon, D. A. and Taylor, J. (1964). An investigation by electrical methods of lecithin-in-hydrocarbon films in aqueous solutions. *Proc. R. Soc. Ser. A,* **281**, 377–91.

—— (1965). Polar group orientation and the electrical properties of lecithin biomolecular leaflets. *J. Theoret. Biol.* **9**, 278–96.

Harris, C. M. and Kell, D. B. (1983). The radio-frequency dielectric properties of yeast cells measured with a rapid, automated, frequency-domain dielectric spectrometer. *Bioelectrochem. Bioenerg.* **11**, 15–28.

—— (1985*a*). On the dielectrically observable consequences of the diffusional motions of lipids and proteins in membranes. 2. Experiments with microbial cells, protoplasts and membrane vesicles. *Eur. Biophys. J.*, **13**, 11–24.

—— (1985*b*). The estimation of microbial biomass. *Biosensors J.* **1**, 17–84.

—— Hitchens, G. D. and Kell, D. B. (1984). Dielectric spectroscopy of microbial membrane systems. In *Charge and field effects in biosystems* (eds. M. J. Allen and P. N. R. Usherwood), pp. 179–85. Abacus Press, Tunbridge Wells, UK.

Hart, F. X. (1982). The use of time domain dielectric spectroscopy to characterize the progress of wound repair. *J. Bioelectricity* **1**, 313–28.

Harter, J. H. and Lin, P. Y. (1982). *Essentials of electric circuits.* Reston Publishing Company, Reston, Virginia USA.

Hasted, J. B. (1973). *Aqueous dielectrics.* Chapman and Hall, London.

—— Husain, S. K., Ko, A. Y., Rosen, D., Nicol, E. and Birch, J. R. (1983). Excitations of proteins by electric fields. In *Coherent excitations in biological systems* (eds. H. Frohlich and F. Kremer), pp. 71–83. Springer–Verlag, Heidelberg.

Hause, L. L., Komorowski, R. A. and Gayon, F. (1981). Electrode and electrolyte impedance in the detection of bacterial growth. *IEEE Trans. Biomed. Eng.* **BME-28**, 403–10.

Haydon, D. A., Hendry, B. M., Levinson, S. R. and Requena, J. (1977). Anaesthesia by the *n*-alkanes. A comparative study of nerve impulse blockage and the properties of black lipid bilayer membranes. *Biochim. Biophys. Acta* **470**, 17–34.

Henderson, R. P. and Webster, J. G. (1978). An impedance camera for spatially specific measurements of the thorax. *IEEE Trans. Biomed. Eng.* **BME-25**, 250–54.

Holler, F. J. and Enke, C. G. (1984). Conductivity and conductimetry. In *Laboratory techniques in electroanalytical chemistry* (eds. P. T. Kissinger and W. R. Heineman) pp. 235–66. Marcel Dekker, New York.

Hung, B. N., Beard, R. B., Brownstein, M., Dubin, S. E., Niazy, N. and Miller, A. J. (1979). Correlation of linear A.C. polarization impedance studies with tissue ingrowth for porous stimulating electrodes. In *Electrical properties of bone and cartilage* (eds. C. T. Brighton, J. Black and S. R. Pollack) pp. 249–66. Grune and Stratton, New York.

Illinger, K. H. (1981). Electromagnetic-field interaction with biological systems in the microwave and far-infrared region. Physical basis. *ACS Symp. Ser.* **157**, 1–46.

Irimajiri, A., Hanai, T. and Inouye, S. (1975). Evaluation of a conductometric method to determine the volume fraction of the suspensions of biomembrane-bounded particles. *Experientia* **31**, 1373–74.

—— (1979). A dielectric theory of 'multi-stratified shell' model with its application to a lymphoma cell. *J. Theoret. Biol.* **78**, 251–69.

Jack, J. J. B., Noble, D. and Tsien, R. W. (1975). *Electric current flow in excitable cells.* Clarendon Press, Oxford.

Jakoubek, B. and Rohlicek, V. (1982). Changes of electrodermal properties in the 'acupuncture points' in men and rats. *Physiol. Bohem.* **31**, 143–149.

Jardetzky, O. and Roberts, G. C. K. (1981). Protein dynamics. In *NMR in molecular biology*, pp. 448–92. Academic Press, New York.

Jenkins, G. M. and Watts, D. G. (1968). *Spectral analysis and its applications.* Holden-Day, Oakland, California.

Jonscher, A. K. (1975). Physical basis of dielectric loss. *Nature* **253**, 717–19.

Kay, S. M. and Marple, S. L. (1981). Spectrum analysis — a modern perspective. *Proc. IEEE* **69**, 1380–1419.

Kell, D. B. (1983). Dielectric properties of bacterial chromatophores. *Bioelectrochem. Bioenerg.* **11**, 405–15.

—— and Harris, C. M. (1985a). On the dielectrically observable consequences of the diffusional motions of lipids and proteins in membranes. 1. Theory and overview. *Eur. Biophys. J.*, **12**, 181–197.

—— (1985b). Dielectric spectroscopy and membrane organisation. *J. Bioelectricity*, **4**, 317–48.

—— and Hitchens, G. D. (1983). Coherent properties of the membranous systems of electron transport phosphorylation. In *Coherent excitations in biological systems* (eds. H. Fröhlich and F. Kremer) pp. 178–98. Springer–Verlag, Heidelberg.

—— and Westerhoff, H. V. (1985). Catalytic facilitation and membrane bioenergetics. In *Organised multienzyme systems: catalytic properties* (ed. G. R. Welch) pp. 63–139. Academic Press, New York.

Keller, G. V. and Frischknecht, F. C. (1966). *Electrical methods in geophysical prospecting*. Pergamon Press, Oxford.

Kent, M. (1975). Time domain measurements of the dielectric properties of frozen fish. *J. Microwave Power* **10**, 37–48.

—— and Jason, A. C. (1975). Dielectric properties of food in relation to interactions between water and the substrate. In *Water relations of foods* (ed. R. B. Duckworth) pp. 211–231. Academic Press, London.

Kissinger, P. T. and Heineman, W. R. (1984) (eds.). *Laboratory techniques in electro-analytical chemistry* Marcel Dekker, New York.

Kraszewski, A., Stuchly, M. A., Stuchly, S. S. and Smith, A. M. (1982). *In vivo* and *in vitro* dielectric properties of animal tissues at radio frequencies. *Bioeletromagnetics* **3**, 421–32.

Kubitschek, H. E. (1969). Counting and sizing microorganisms with the Coulter counter. In *Methods in microbiology*, (eds. J. R. Norris and D. W. Ribbons), Vol. 1, pp. 593–610. Academic Press, London.

Kumar, A., Wagner, G., Ernst, R. R. and Wuthrich, K. (1980). Studies of J-connectivities and selective ^{1}H-^{1}H Overhauser effects in H_2O solutions of biological macromolecules by two-dimensional NMR experiments. *Biochem. Biophys. Res. Comm.* **96**, 1156–63.

Laver, D. R., Smith, J. R. and Coster, H. G. L. (1984). The thickness of the hydrophobic and polar regions of glycerol monooleate bilayers determined from the frequency dependence of bilayer capacitance. *Biochim. Biophys. Acta* **772**, 1–9.

Lewis, T. J. (1977). The dielectric behaviour of non-crystalline solids. *Diel. Rel. Mol. Proc.* **3**, 186–218.

Lilly, M. D. (1983). Problems in process scale-up. In *Bioactive microbial products 2; Development and production* (eds. L. J. Nisbet and D. J. Winstanley) pp. 79–89. Academic Press, London.

Lorrain, P. and Corson, D. R. (1979). *Electromagnetism*. W. H. Freeman, San Francisco.

Loveland, J. W. (1963). Conductometry and oscillometry. In *Treatise on analytical chemistry* (eds. I. M. Kolthoff and P. J. Elving), Vol. 4, pp. 2569–629.

Lovitt, R. W., Walter, R. P., Morris, J. G. and Kell, D. B. (1986). Conductimetric assessment of the biomass content of immobilised (gel-entrapped) microorganisms. *Appl. Microbiol. Biotechnol.* **23**, 168–73.

Lowe, C. R. (1984). Biosensors. *Trends Biotechnol.* **2**, 59–65.

—— (1985). An introduction to the concepts and technology of biosensors. *Biosensors* **1**, 3–16.

Macdonald. D. D. (1977). *Transient techiques in electrochemistry.* Plenum Press, New York.

—— and McKubre, M. C. H. (1982). Impedance measurements in electrochemical systems. In *Modern aspects of electrochemistry* (eds. J. O'M. Bockris and B. E. Conway) Vol. 4, pp. 61–150. Plenum Press, New York.

Macdonald, J. R. (1980). Interface effects in the electrical response of non-metallic conducting solids and liquids. *IEEE. Trans. Electr. Insul.* **EI-15**, 65–82.

—— Schoonman, J. and Lehnen, A. P. (1982). The applicability and power of complex non-linear least squares for the analysis of impedance and admittance data. *J. Electroanal. Chem.* **131**, 77–95.

Mackey, B. M. and Derrick, C. M. (1984). Conductance measurements of the lag phase of injured *Salmonella typhimurium. J. Appl. Bact.* **57**, 299–308.

Magin, R. L. and Burdette, E. C. (1983). Measurement of electrical properties of tissue at microwave frequencies: a new approach and treatment of abnormalities. In *Non-invasive measurements* (ed. P. Rolfe) Vol. 2, pp. 353–376. Academic Press, London.

Markley, J. L., Westler, W. M., Tze-Ming Chan, Kojiro, C. L. and Ulrich, E. L. (1984). Two-dimensional NMR approaches to the study of protein structure and function. *Fed. Proc.* **43**, 2648–56.

Marmarelis, P. Z. and Marmarelis, V. Z. (1978). *Analysis of physiological systems. The white-noise approach.* Plenum Press, New York.

Marshall, A. G. (1978). *Biophysical chemistry: principles, techniques and applications.* Wiley, New York.

—— (1982) (ed.). *Fourier, Hadamard and Hilbert transforms in chemistry.* Plenum Press, New York.

—— (1983). Transform techniques in chemistry. In *Physical methods in modern chemical analysis* (ed. T. Kuwana) Vol. 3, pp. 57–135. Academic Press, New York.

—— and Roe, D. C. (1978). Dispersion versus absorption: spectral line shape analysis for radiofrequency and microwave spectroscopy. *Anal. Chem.* **50**, 756–763.

Martynov, G. A. and Salem, R. R. (1983). *Electrical double layer at a metal-dilute electrolyte solution interface.* Springer–Verlag, Berlin.

Mohilner, D. M. (1966). The electrical double layer. Part 1. Elements of double layer theory. In *Electroanalytical chemistry* (ed. A. J. Bard) Vol. 1, pp. 241–409. Edward Arnold, London.

Mopsik, F. (1984). Precision time-domain dielectric spectrometer. *Rev. Sci. Instr.* **55**, 79–87.

Morse, C. T. (1974). A computer controlled apparatus for measuring AC properties of materials over the frequency rane 10^{-5} to 10^5 Hz. *J. Phys. E. Sci. Instr.* **7**, 657–62.

Nakamura, H., Hushimi, Y. and Wada, A. (1981). Time domain measurement of dielectric spectra of aqueous polyelectrolyte solutions at low frequencies. *J. Appl. Phys.* **52**, 3053–61.

Ngai, K. L., Jonscher, A. K. and White, C. T. (1979). On the origin of the universal dielectric response in condensed matter. *Nature* **277**, 185–9.

Nyboer, J. (1970). *Electrical impedance plethysmography*, (2nd edn.). Charles C. Thomas, Springfield, Illinois.

O'Brien, R. W. (1982). The response of a colloidal suspension to an alternating electrical field. *Adv. Colloid. Interf. Sci.* **16**, 281–320.

Oncley, J. L. (1943). The electric moments and the relaxation times of proteins as measured from their influence upon the dielectric constants of solutions. In *Proteins, amino acids and peptides* (eds. E. J. Cohn and J. T. Edsall) pp. 543–568. Reinhold, New York.

Osterhout, W. J. V. (1922). *Injury, recovery and death, in relation to conductivity and permeability*. J. B. Lippincott, Philadephia and London.

Pacela, A. F. (1966). Impedance pneumography — a survey of instrumentation techniques. *Med. Biol. Eng.* **4**, 1–15.

Pauly, H. (1962). Electrical properties of the cytoplasmic membrane and the cytoplasm of bacteria and of protoplasts. *IRE Trans. Biomed. Electron* **9**, 93–95.

—— and Packer, L. (1960). The relationship of internal conductance and membrane capacity to mitochondrial volume. *J. Biophys. Biochem. Cytol.* **7**, 603–12.

—— and Schwan, H. P. (1960). Electrical properties of mitochondrial membranes. *J. Biophys. Biochem. Cytol.* **7**, 589–601.

Petersen, D. C. and Cone, R. A. (1975). The electric dipole moment of rhodopsin solubilised in Triton X-100. *Biophys. J.* **15**, 1181–1200.

Pethig, R. (1979). *Dielectric and Electronic Properties of Biological Materials*. John Wiley, Chichester.

—— (1984). Dielectric properties of biological materials: biophysical and medical applications. *IEEE Trans. Electr. Insul.* **EI-19**, 453–74.

Pfutzner, H. and Fialik, E. (1982). A new electrophysical method for rapid detection of exudative porcine muscle. *Zbl. Vet. Med. A.* **29**, 637–45.

Phillips, W. J. (1984). Resonance effects in complex resistivity data and their significance in mineral exploration. *Trans. Inst. Min. Metall. (Sect. B. Appl. Earth Sci.)* **93**, B1–11.

Pilla, A. A. (1980). Electrochemical information transfer at cell surfaces and junctions; applications to the study and manipulation of cell regulation. In *Bioelectrochemistry* (eds. H. Keyser and F. Gutmann) pp. 353–396. Plenum Press, New York.

—— Sechaud, P. and McLeod, B. R. (1983). Electrochemical and electrical aspects of low-frequency electromagnetic current induction in biological systems. *J. Biol. Phys.* **11**, 51–58.

Pottel, R., Gopel, K.-D., Henze, R., Kaatze, U. and Uhlendorf, V. (1984). The dielectric permittivity spectrum of aqueous colloidal phospholipid solutions between 1 kHz and 60 GHz. *Biophys. Chem.* **19**, 233–44.

Powley, C. R. and Nieman, T. A. (1983). Bipolar pulse conductometric monitoring of ion-selective electrodes. Part 4. Interferences from electroactive species in measurements with the calcium electrode. *Anal. Chim. Acta* **155**, 1–9.

—— Geiger, R. F. Jr, and Nieman, T. A. (1980). Bipolar pulse conductance measurements with a calcium ion-selective electrode. *Anal. Chem.* **52**, 705–9.

Priestley, M. B. (1981). *Spectral analysis and time series.* 2 vols. Academic Press, New York.

Pungor, E. (1965). *Conductometry and oscillometry*. Pergamon Press, Oxford.

Randles, J. E. B. (1947). Kinetics of rapid electrode reactions. *Disc. Faraday Soc.* **1**, 11–19.

Redwood, W. R., Takashima, S., Schwan, H. P. and Thompson, T. L. (1972). Dielectric studies on homogenous phosphatidylcholine vesicles. *Biochim. Biophys. Acta.* **255**, 557–66.

Reilley, C. N. (1954). High-frequency methods. In *New instrumental methods in electrochemistry* (ed. P. Delahay) pp. 319–345. Interscience, New York.

Richards, J. C. S., Jason, A. C., Hobbs, G., Gibson, D. M. and Christie, R. H. Electronic measurement of bacterial growth. *J. Phys. E. Sci. Instrum.* **11**, 560–8.

Salter, D. C. (1979). Quantifying skin disease and healing *in vivo* using electrical impedance measurements. In *Non-invasive physiological measurements* (ed. P. Rolfe) Vol. 1, pp. 21–64. Academic Press, London.

Schanne, O. F. and Ceretti, E. R. P. (1978). *Impedance measurements in biological cells.* John Wiley, Chichester.

Schmukler, R. and Pilla, A. A. (1982). A transient impedance approach to non-faradaic electrochemical kinetics at living cell membranes. *J. Electrochem. Soc.* **129**, 526–8.

Schügerl, K. (1984). On-line process analysis and control in biotechnology. *Trends. Anal. Chem.* **3**, 239–45.

Schwan, H. P. (1955). Electrical properties of body tissues and impedance plethysmography. *IRE Trans. Biomed. Eng.* **3**, 32–46.

—— (1957). Electrical properties of tissue and cell suspensions. In *Advances in biological and medical physics* (eds. J. H. Lawrence and C. A. Tobias) Vol. 5, pp. 147–209. Academic Press, New York.

—— (1963). Determination of biological impedances. In *Physical techniques in biological research* (ed. W. L. Nastuk) Vol. VIB, pp. 323–407. Academic Press, New York.

—— (1966). Alternating current electrode polarisation. *Biophysik* **3**, 181–201.

—— (1968). Electrode polarisation impedance and measurements in biological materials. *Ann. N. Y. Acad. Sci.* **148**, 191–209.

—— (1977). Field interactions with biological matter. *Ann. N. Y. Acad. Sci.* **303**, 198–213.

—— (1981a). Dielectric properties of biological tissue and biophysical mechanisms of electromagnetic field interactions. *ACS Symp. Ser.* **157**, 109–131.

—— (1981b). Electrical properties of cells: Principles, some recent results, and some unresolved problems. In *The biophysical approach to excitable systems* (eds. W. J. Adelmann Jr. and D. E. Goldman) pp. 3–24. Plenum Press, New York.

—— (1983a). Dielectric properties of biological tissue and Cells at RF- and MW-frequencies. In *Biological effects and dosimetry and non-ionizing radiation* (eds. M. Gandolfo, S. M. Michaelson and A. Rindi) pp. 195–211. Plenum Press, New York.

—— (1983b). Dielectric properties of biological tissues and cells at ELF-frequencies. In *Biological effects and dosimetry of non-ionizing radiation* (eds. M. Gandolfo, S. M. Michaelson, and A. Rindi) pp. 549–59. Plenum Press, New York.

—— and Ferris, C. D. (1968). Four-electrode null techniques for impedance measurement with high resolution. *Rev. Sci. Instr.* **39**, 481–5.

—— and Foster, K. R. (1980). RF-field interactions with biological systems: electrical properties and biophysical mechanisms. *Proc. IEEE* **68**, 104–13.

—— Takashima, S., Miyamoto, V. K. and Stoekenius, W. (1970). Electrical properties of phospholipid vesicles. *Biophys. J.* **10**, 1102–19.

Sekoguchi, K., Takeishi, M., Hironaga, K. and Nishiura, T. (1984). Velocity measurement with electrical double-sensing devices in two-phase flow. In *Measuring techniques in gas-liquid two-phase flows* (eds. J. M. Delahaye and G. Cognet) pp. 455–477. Springer–Verlag, Heidelberg.

Shedlovsky, T. (1949). Conductometry. In *Physical methods of organic chemistry* (ed. A. Weissberger) Part 2, pp. 1651–83. Interscience, New York.

Singh, B., Smith, C. W. and Hughes, R. (1979). *In vivo* dielectric spectrometer. *Med. Biol. Eng. Comput.* **17**, 45–60.

Sluyters–Rehbach, M. and Sluyters, J. H. (1970). Sine wave methods for the study of electrode processes. In *Electroanalytical chemistry* (ed. A. J. Bard) Vol. 4, pp. 1–128. Marcel Dekker, New York.

Smith, D. E. (1966). A.C. polarography and related techniques; theory and practice. In *Electroanalytical chemistry* (ed. A. J. Bard) Vol. 1, pp. 1–155. Edward Arnold, London.

Somogyi, B., Welch, G. R. and Damjanovich, S. (1984). The dynamic basis of energy transduction in enzymes. *Biochim. Biophys. Acta* **768**, 81–112.

Sorriso, S. and Surowiec, A. (1982). Molecular dynamics investigations of DNA by dielectric relaxation measurements. *Adv. Mol. Rel. Interaction Proc.* **22**, 259–79.

Sparnaay, M. J. (1972). *The electrical double layer*. Pergamon Press, Oxford.

Steel, M., Sheppard, R. J. and Grant, E. H. (1984). A precision method for measuring the complex permittivity of solid tissue in the frequency domain between 2 and 18 GHz. *J. Phys. E. Sci. Instrum.* **17**, 29–34.

Stewart, G. N. (1899*a*). The relative volume or weight of corpuscles and plasma in blood. *J. Physiol.* **24**, 356–73.

—— (1899*b*). The changes produced by the growth of bacteria in the molecular concentration and electrical conductivity of culture media. *J. Exp. Med.* **4**, 235–43.

Stock, J. T. (1984). Two centuries of quantitative electrolytic conductivity. *Anal. Chem.* **56**, 561A–570A.

Stoy, R. D., Foster, K. R. and Schwan, H. P. (1982). Dielectric properties of mammalian tissue from 0.1 to 100 MHz: a summary of recent data. *Phys. Med. Biol.* **27**, 501–13.

Stuchly, M. A. and Stuchly, S. S. (1980). Coaxial line methods for measuring dielectric properties of biological substances at radio and microwave frequencies — a review. *IEEE Trans. Instrum. Meas* **IM-29**, 176–93.

—— Athey, T. W., Stuchly, S. S., Samaras, G. M. and Taylor, G. (1981). Dielectric properties of animal tissues *in vivo* at frequencies 10 MHz–1 GHz. *Bioelectromagnetics* **2**, 93–103.

Takashima, S. (1969). Dielectric properties of proteins. I. Dielectric relaxation. In *Physical principles and techniques of protein chemistry, Part A* (ed. S. J. Leach) pp. 291–333. Academic, New York.

—— and Minakata, A. (1975). Dielectric behaviour of biological macromolecules. In *Digest of dielectric literature* **37**, pp. 602–53. National Research Council, Washington D.C.

Tamamushi, R. and Takahashi, K. (1974). Instrumental study of electolytic conductance using four-electrode cells. *J. Electroanal. Chem.* **50**, 277–84.

Thomas, B. W. and Pertel, R. (1963). Measurement of capacity: analytical uses of the dielectric constant. In *Treatise on analytical chemistry* (eds. I. M. Kolthoff and P. J. Ewing) Vol. 4, pp. 2631–2672. Interscience, New York.

Tien, H. T. (1974). *Bilayer lipid membranes (BLM). Theory and practice*. Marcel Dekker, New York.

To, E. C., Mudgett, R. E., Wang, D. I. C., Goldbluth, S. A. and Decareau, R. V. (1974). Dielectric properties of food materials. *J. Microwave Power* **9**, 303–15.

Turner, G. and Howell, J. A. (1984). On-line estimation of the time constant of oxygen electrodes by time series analyses. *Biotechnol. Lett.* **6**, 215–20.

Vreugdenhil, Th., van der Touw, F. and Mandel, M. (1979). Electric permittivity and dielectric dispersion of low molecular weight DNA of low ionic strength. *Biophys. Chem.* **10**, 67–80.

Wada, A. (1976). The α-helix as an electric macrodipole. *Adv. Biophys.* **9**, 1–63.

Welch, G. R. (1986) (ed.). *The fluctuating enzyme*. Wiley, New York.

—— and Kell, D. B. (1985). Not just catalysts: the bioenergetics of molecular machines. In *The fluctuating enzyme* (ed. G. R. Welch), pp. 451–92. Wiley, New York.

—— Somogyi, B. and Damjanovich, S. (1982). The role of protein fluctuations in enzyme action: a review. *Progr. Biophys. Mol. Biol.* **39**, 109–46.

Wheeler, H. B. and Penney, C. (1982). Impedance plethysmography: theoretical and experimental basis. In *Non-invasive diagnostic techniques in vascular disease* (ed. E. F. Bernstein) pp. 104–116. C. V. Mosby, St Louis.

Wilson, T. R. S. (1981). Conductometry. In *Marine electrochemistry* (eds. M. Whitfield and D. Jagner) pp. 145–185. Wiley, Chichester.

Winter, F. and Kimmich, R. (1982). NMR field-cycling relaxation spectroscopy of bovine serum albumin, muscle tissue. *Micrococcus luteus* and yeast. $^{14}N^{1}H$-quadrupole dips. *Biochim. Biophys. Acta* **719**, 292–8.

Wuthrich, K. (1982). Nuclear magnetic resonance studies of internal mobility in globular proteins. *Biochem. Soc. Symp.* **46**, 17–37.

Zimmerman, U. (1982). Electric field-mediated fusion and related electrical phenomena. *Biochim. Biophys. Acta.* **694**, 227–77.

Bioelectrochemistry
(d) Silicon-based sensors

25

Micro-biosensors based on silicon fabrication technology

ISAO KARUBE

25.1 Introduction

Methods for the selective determination of organic compounds in biological fluids, such as blood, are very important in clinical analysis. Most analyses of organic compounds can be performed by spectrophotometric methods based on specific enzyme-catalysed reactions. However, these methods often require a long reaction time and complicated procedures. On the other hand, electrochemical sensors employing immobilized biocatalysts have definite advantages. Namely, an enzyme sensor possesses excellent selectivity for biological substrates and can directly determine single compounds in a complicated mixture without need for a prior separation step (Karube and Suzuki 1984, 1985). Miniaturization of the enzyme sensors is a prerequisite for medical application. This has been achieved using semiconductor fabrication technology combined with enzyme immobilization techniques to produce highly selective miniature sensors.

In this chapter, ion sensitive field effect transistors (ISFET) and micro-electrodes, prepared by silicon fabrication technology, are employed as micro-biosensor transducers. Micro-biosensors for urea, ATP (Adenosin triphosphate), glucose, and glutamate constructed from micro-transducers and immobilized enzyme thin membranes are detailed and their characteristics discussed.

25.2 FET-based sensors

25.2.1 Micro-urea sensor

The ISFET was first reported by Bergveld in 1970. Matsuo and Wise (1974) improved the ISFET properties by utilizing silicon nitride (Si_3N_4) as the gate insulator, reporting its use as a pH sensor. In 1980, Caras and Janata demonstrated that an immobilized penicillinase layer over the gate insulator of the ISFET could be used as a penicillin sensor (see Chapter 26). We have also reported an enzyme-FET sensor (Miyahara *et al.* 1983).

The assay of urea in blood and urine is a very important diagnostic test to evaluate kidney function and condition. Conventional assay methods for

471

urea are based on spectrophotometry, but involve complicated and delicate procedures. Therefore, the development of an inexpensive and miniaturized sensor that is highly selective and sensitive, yet easy to use, is extremely desirable. Realization of these goals can be achieved using the ISFET transducer.

Fabrication of the ISFET uses basically the same procedures employed for the metal-insulator-semiconductor FET (MISFET), as reported by Matsuo and Esashi (1981). The structure of the ISFET is shown in Fig. 25.1.

The gate insulator of the ISFET is composed of two layers; the lower is thermally grown silicon dioxide (SiO_2), the upper being silicon nitride (Si_3N_4), which is sensitive to H^+ ions and also has a barrier effect on ion penetration. The thickness of the SiO_2 and Si_3N_4 layers are approximately 0.1 μm. The sensor system consists of two ISFETs; one ISFET is covered with a cross-linked polyvinylbutyral membrane containing amino groups, onto which urease was immobilized through a schiff base linkage (Urea-sensitive ISFET, ENFET), and the other ISFET is only covered with a cross-linked polyvinyl-butyral resin membrane (only pH-sensitive ISFET, REFFET).

The polyvinylbutyral membrane was spread onto the gate insulator of the ISFETs by a dropping method. Approximately 0.1 g of polyvinylbutyral resin and 1 ml of 1,8-diamino-4-aminomethyloctane were dissolved in 10 ml of dichloromethane. This polymer solution was dropped onto the gate insulator of the two ISFETs and then immersed in a 5% glutaraldehyde solution at room temperature for approximately one day to advance the cross linking reaction. Urease was immobilized on the ENFET by immersing it in a

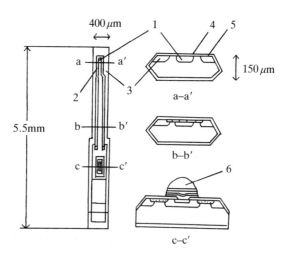

Fig. 25.1 Structure of ISFET. 1, drain; 2, gate; 3, source; 4, Si_3N_4; 5, SiO_2; 6, solder.

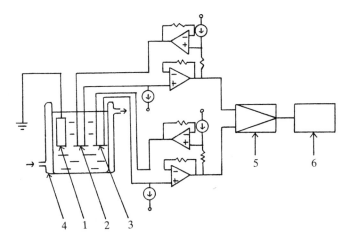

Fig. 25.2 Circuit diagram of measuring system. 1, Ag/AgCl reference electrode; 2, ENFET; 3, REFFET; 4, Cell; 5, Differential amp.; 6, Recorder.

5 mg ml^{-1} urease solution at 4°C for approximately one day.

Measurements of urea concentration were performed in a differential mode, by comparing the difference in gate output voltage of the urea-sensing gate and the reference gate. A schematic diagram of the circuit is shown in Fig. 25.2. An Ag/AgCl reference electrode was placed directly in solution with the ENFET and the REFFET, and a gate voltage applied between the Ag/AgCl reference electrode and the source of the ENFET and the REFFET. A change in solution pH affects the gate insulator surface potential, with a concomitant proportional change in the gate output voltage. 100 μl aliquots of urea were injected into a solution of 5 mM Tris-HCl buffer at 37°C $\pm$ 1°C, and the differential gate output voltage change recorded for 10–20 min.

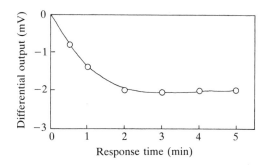

Fig. 25.3 Response curve to 1.7 mM urea. Experiments were performed at 37°C, pH 7.0.

Figure 25.3 shows a typical urea response curve of the sensor system. The differential gate output voltage reached a steady state approximately two minutes after injection of urea.

The initial rate of change of the differential gate output voltage after injection was plotted against the logarithm of the urea concentration. Figure 25.4 shows a calibration curve of the urea sensor system. A linear relationship was obtained between the initial rate of voltage change and the logarithm of urea concentration over the range 1.3 to 16.7 mM urea. An examination of the selectivity of the urea sensor system showed that it did not respond to 6.3 mM glucose, 10 mM creatinine, and 3.6 μM albumin.

The stability of the urea sensor system was also examined. The ENFET was stored at 4°C between measurements, and exhibited a response to 16.7 mM urea for at least two weeks.

25.2.2 Micro-ATP sensor

The determination of ATP (adenosine triphosphate) is important in fermentation processes and for clinical analysis. Conventional methods of ATP assay are based on spectrophotometric and bioluminescence measurements. These methods, however, require complicated and delicate procedures and a simpler and more inexpensive assay is desirable.

H$^+$-ATPase (EC 3.6.1.3) in biological membranes catalyses production or hydrolysis of ATP. Furthermore, the enzyme has many functions, such as proton transport, which could be utilized for a bio-molecular device. Several

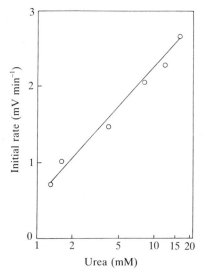

Fig. 25.4 Urea calibration curve. Experimental conditions were the same as in Fig. 25.3.

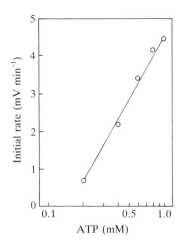

Fig. 25.5 ATP calibration curve. Experiments were performed at 40°C, pH 7.0.

studies on the properties and function of the enzyme in biological membranes have been reported by Kagawa and co-workers (Yoshida *et al.* 1977; Kagawa 1984). H^+-ATPase was prepared from a thermophilic bacterium PS3 and is classified as thermophilic F_1 (TF_1) ATP. The procedures employed in constructing the ATP sensor and measurements of gate voltage were identical to those of the urea sensor. 50 mM Tris-maleate buffer was used at 40°C $\pm$ 1°C. The differential gate output voltage reached steady state approximately 4–5 minutes after injection of ATP.

The initial rate of change of the differential gate output voltage after injection of ATP was plotted against the logarithm of the ATP concentration. Figure 25.5 shows a calibration curve of the ATP sensor system. A linear relationship was obtained between the initial rate of the voltage change and the logarithm of ATP concentration over the range 0.2 to 1.0 mM ATP.

Slight responses were obtained when 1 mM glucose, urea, and creatinine were applied to the system. The response of the system to 1 mM ATP was retained for 18 days.

25.3 Micro-electrode based sensors

25.3.1 *Glucose sensor based on a micro-hydrogen peroxide electrode*

The determination of glucose in blood samples is important in clinical fields, and the development of bioelectrochemical devices would be of considerable help in routine laboratory work.·

The development of miniaturized and implantable enzyme sensors employing micro-transducers is required in the medical field. Therefore, a

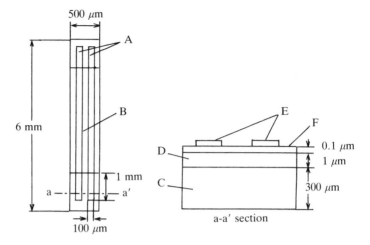

Fig. 25.6 Schematic diagram of a micro-electrode A, E, Au; B, Ta$_2$O$_5$; C, Si; D, SiO$_2$; F, Si$_3$N$_4$.

micro-hydrogen peroxide (H$_2$O$_2$) sensor has been developed utilizing the currently available integrated circuit technology. The structure of the micro-H$_2$O$_2$ sensor is shown in Fig. 25.6. Micro-Au electrodes were created on the silicon nitride surface using the vapour deposition method and partially insulated by coating with Ta$_2$O$_5$. The H$_2$O$_2$ electrode was placed in a sample solution containing H$_2$O$_2$ and the over-potential fixed at 1.1 V. The output current of the sensor immediately increased and reached a steady state value within one minute. A linear relationship was observed between the H$_2$O$_2$ concentration and the steady state current in the range 1 μM to 1 mM H$_2$O$_2$. This electrode was then employed as the transducer in a micro-glucose sensor. The procedure for glucose oxidase (GOD) immobilization onto the micro-electrode is as follows. Approximately 100 μl of γ-aminopropyl-triethoxysilane was vapourized at 80°C, 0.5 torr for 30 min onto the electrode surface, followed by 100 μl of 50% glutaraldehyde vapourized under the same conditions. The modified micro-electrodes were then immersed in GOD solution containing BSA and glutaraldehyde, the GOD becoming chemically bound to the surface of the micro-electrode by a schiff linkage. Figure 25.7 shows a typical response curve for the micro-glucose sensor. The output current increased after injection of a sample solution, steady state being reached within 5 min. Figure 25.8 shows a calibration curve for the micro-glucose sensor.

A linear relationship was observed between the current increase (the difference between the initial and steady state currents) and glucose concentration in the range 0.1 to 10 mg dl^{-1} glucose. Examination of the selectivity of

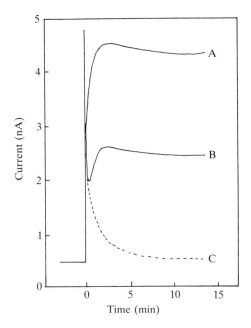

Fig. 25.7 Glucose response curves. Experiments were performed at 37°C, pH 7.0. A, 10 mg dℓ$^{-1}$ glucose; B, 5 mg dℓ$^{-1}$ glucose; C, no glucose.

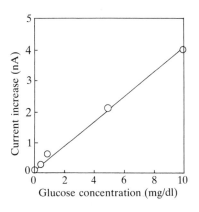

Fig. 25.8 Glucose calibration curve. Experiments were performed at 37°C, pH 7.0.

the glucose micro-sensor indicated no response to other compounds such as galactose, mannose, fructose, and maltose. Therefore, the selectivity of this sensor for glucose is highly satisfactory.

Figure 25.9 shows the effect of temperature on the current increase of the sensor system. The optimum temperature for the sensor was 55°C.

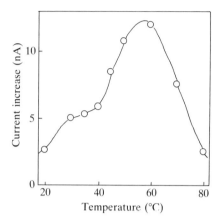

Fig. 25.9 Effect of temperature.

However, because the enzyme gradually denatures at 55°C, the stability of the sensor at this temperature is poor. Therefore, all other experiments were performed at 37°C. Continuous operation of the sensor in 10 mg dl^{-1} glucose produced a constant current output for more than 15 days and 150 assays. Therefore, this micro-glucose sensor possesses both selectivity and good stability, its potential use as a micro-glucose sensor being very good.

25.3.2 Micro-O$_2$ electrode based glutamate sensor

The determination of L-glutamic acid (L-Glu) is very important in the food industry, because large amounts of L-Glu are produced by fermentation to be used as a food seasoning. Various glutamate sensors, consisting of immobilized enzyme and an electrochemical device, have been developed for the fermentation and food industries. Glutamate oxidase catalyses the oxidation of glutamate, oxygen being consumed by the reaction. Therefore, an oxygen sensor can be employed as the transducer for a glutamate sensor. A micro-oxygen sensor was developed by modifiying the micro-H$_2$O$_2$ electrode,

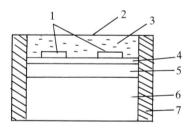

Fig. 25.10 Schematic diagram of an oxygen electrode. 1, Au; 2, Teflon membrane; 3, 0.1 M KOH; 4, Si$_3$N$_4$; 5, SiO$_2$; 6, Si; 7, silicon rubber.

prepared as previously described.

Figure 25.10 shows the structure of the micro-oxygen sensor. It consists of a gas permeable Teflon membrane, two micro-Au electrodes and 0.1 M KOH electrolyte solution. The characteristics of the micro-oxygen electrode were examined by cyclic voltammetry at various concentrations of dissolved oxygen (oxygen and nitrogen mixture was sparged through the sample solution). A peak current was observed due to reduction of oxygen, when a voltage of approximately 1.1 V was applied to the Au electrodes. A linear relationship was observed between the oxygen concentration and the peak current obtained from the cyclic voltammograms (Fig. 25.11). These results indicate that the micro-oxygen electrode can be used for oxygen concentration determination. Therefore, the micro-oxygen electrode was employed as the transducer in a micro-glutamate sensor.

Glutamate oxidase was immobilized on a cellulose triacetate membrane containing glutaraldehyde and triamine (1,8-diamino-4-aminomethyl-octane). The glutamate oxidase membrane was placed on the Teflon membrane of the micro-oxygen sensor and covered with a nylon net. Application of a glutamate sample solution to the sensor system produced a rapid drop in the current output to a steady state value, resulting from glutamate oxidation.

Figure 25.12 shows the relationship between current decrease and the glutamate concentration. When the current decrease at 5 min was used as the measure of activity, a linear relationship was observed between the current decrease and the glutamate concentration in the range 5–50 mM. The effect of temperature on the peak current decrease of the sensor was examined. The optimum temperature for the sensor was approximately 40°C, but gradual denaturation of the enzyme reduced the stability of the sensor. Therefore, all other experiments were performed at 30°C.

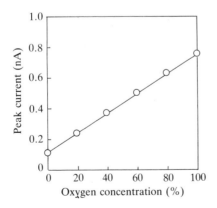

Fig. 25.11 Calibration curve of the oxygen electrode. Potential range: – 1.25 V ∼ 1 V; scan rate: 100 mV^{-1}.

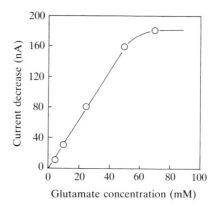

Fig. 25.12 Calibration curve of the micro-glutamate sensor. Experiments were performed at 40°C, pH 7.5.

The selectivity of the sensor for glutamate was found to be satisfactory and hence its application to fermentation process control and food analysis is very promising.

References

Bergveld, P. (1970). Development of an ion-sensitive solid-state device for neuro-physiological measurements. *IEEE Trans. on BME.* **BME–17**, 70–1.

Caras, S. and Janata, J. (1980). Field effect transistor sensitive to penicillin. *Anal. Chem.* **52**, 1935–7.

Kagawa, Y. (1984). A new model of proton motive ATP synthesis: acid-base cluster hypothesis. *J. Biochem.* **95**, 295–98.

Karube, I. and Suzuki, S. (1984). Amperometric and potentiometric determinations with immobilized enzymes and micro-organisms. *Ion-Selective Electrode. Review* **6**, 15–58.

—— (1985). Immobilized enzymes for clinical analysis, In *Enzymes and immobilized cells in biotechnology* (ed. A. I. Laskin) pp. 209–226. Benjamin/Cumming Publishing, London.

Matsuo, T. and Esashi, M. (1981). Methods of ISFET fabrication, *Sensors and Actuators* **1**, 77–96.

Matsuo, T., Wise, K. D. (1974). An integrated field-effect electrode for biopotential. *IEEE Trans. on BME.* **BME–21**, 485–7.

Miyahara, Y., Matsu, F., Moriizumi, T., Matsuoka, H., Karube, I. and Suzuki, S. (1983). Micro enzyme sensors using semiconductor and enzyme-immobilization techniques. In *Proceedings of the international meeting on chemical sensors*, Kodansha, Tokyo, pp. 501–6. Elsevier, New York.

Yoshida, M., Sone, N., Hirata, H. and Kagawa, Y. (1977). Reconstitution of adenosine triphosphatase of thermophilic bacterium from purified individual subunits. *J. Biol. Chem.* **252**, 3480–5.

26

Chemically sensitive field effect transistors

GARY F. BLACKBURN

26.1 Introduction

The chemically sensitive field-effect transistor (CHEMFET) was born out of the integration of two well developed technologies: solid state integrated circuits and ion-selective electrodes (ISE). Bergveld (1970) demonstrated the first CHEMFET which used a silicon dioxide layer to impart sensitivity to hydrogen ions upon an insulated-gate field-effect transistor (IGFET). Since that time, considerable development has taken place, especially in the area of ion-selective field-effect transistors (ISFET). The ion-selective membranes which had previously been developed for the ISE technology could be directly applied to the fabrication of ISFETs and thus their development was straight-forward. The development of CHEMFET sensors sensitive to other chemicals has also seen considerable research effort although not to the same extent as the ISFET.

The purpose of this text is not to exhaustively review the literature of the field. Rather, the purpose is to present an overview of the current areas of active research. For reviews of the literature pertaining to the CHEMFET, the reader is referred to Zemel (1975) or Janata and Huber (1980).

26.2 Theory of FET chemical sensors

To understand the operation of the chemically sensitive field-effect transistor, it is necessary to first understand the physics of the insulated-gate field-effect transistor from which the CHEMFET is fashioned. First, the electronic properties of semiconductor materials will be described in a qualitative way followed by a description of the metal-insulator-semiconductor (MIS) structure which is the precursor of the IGFET. Once the operation of the IGFET is understood, the theory can easily be extended to describe the operation of the CHEMFET. A rigorous description of semiconductor physics is beyond the scope of this book and is not required to understand the operation of CHEMFETs. The interested reader should consult either Muller and Kamins (1977) or Sze (1981) for more detailed descriptions of the physics of semiconductor devices.

It is important to note that the metal-oxide-semiconductor field-effect transistor (MOSFET), the metal-insulator-semiconductor field-effect transistor (MISFET), and the metal-nitride-oxide-semiconductor field-effect transistor (MNOSFET) are each just special cases of the IGFET.

26.2.1 Semiconductor physics

To understand the physics of semiconductor materials at a level required for the comprehension of the operation of the IGFET and CHEMFET, a description of the energy-band diagrams of semiconductor materials is required. Figure 26.1 represents the energy band diagram for silicon. Increasing energy for electrons is drawn upward while the abscissa represents distance in the silicon. The cross-hatched areas represent near continua of allowed energy levels for electrons in the silicon. The upper band is called the conduction band with its lowest energy level denoted by E_c. The lower band represents the valence band of silicon and its highest energy is usually denoted by E_v. All energy levels are referenced to the 'vacuum level', E_0, which is defined as the energy of an electron if it were just free of the influence of the given material. The energy region between E_c and E_v represents the 'forbidden' band-gap where no allowed energy levels exist for electrons. The difference in energy between E_c and E_v is called the band-gap energy, E_g, and is equal to 1.1 eV for silicon. At a temperature of absolute zero (0°K), all allowed energy levels in the valence band are filled with electrons and all levels in the conduction band are empty. Even at room temperature (300°K), the average kinetic energy of the electrons is only 0.04 eV which is less than 4% of the band-gap energy. Therefore, the number of electrons with sufficient energy to jump to the conduction band remains extremely small.

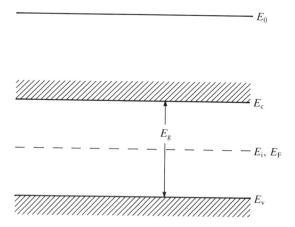

Fig. 26.1 Energy-band diagram for undoped silicon.

For electronic conduction to occur, electrons must move in the semi-conductor in response to any electric field. If the electrons move, then they must increase their kinetic energy which requires that they move to a higher, empty energy level. In undoped (intrinsic) silicon, then, conduction is insignificant because all of the valence energy levels are filled so there are no vacant energy levels for electrons to move to if they attain any additional kinetic energy. The electrons in the conduction band see a continuum of vacant energy levels to move to but because their number is extremely small, conduction in intrinsic silicon is insignificant at room temperature.

To impart conductivity on silicon, impurity atoms can be added to the crystal. Silicon is made an *n*-type semiconductor by doping the crystal with atoms from group V of the periodic table, e.g. phosphorous or arsenic. These atoms have one more valence electron than silicon and thus donate electrons to the crystal when included in the crystal lattice. Referring to the energy-band diagram in Fig. 26.2a, the impurity atoms have an energy level, E_d, which is within the band-gap and near the conduction band. At room temperature, most of the electrons at this donor energy level possess sufficient energy to jump to the conduction band. The increased concentration of electrons contributes to the electrical conductivity in the silicon. Silicon is made a *p*-type semiconductor by incorporationg impurity atoms from group III of the periodic table, e.g. boron or aluminium, into the silicon crystal. These atoms have one less valence atom than silicon and create

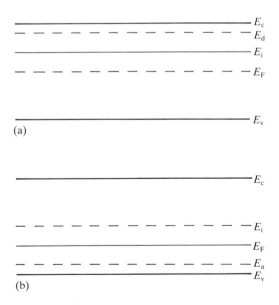

(a)

(b)

Fig. 26.2 Energy-band diagram for doped silicon. (a) *n*-type silicon, (b) *p*-type silicon.

immobile 'traps' which capture free electrons. Referring to the energy-band diagram in Fig. 26.2b, the impurity atoms have an energy level, E_a, which is near the valence band of the silicon. Most of the electrons in the valence band have sufficient energy to jump to these acceptor levels and thus nearly fully populate them. Each valence electron which populates one of the acceptor levels leaves behind a 'hole' or a vacant allowed energy level in the valence band, into which the remaining electrons may move to attain kinetic energy in response to an electric field, contributing to conductivity in the p-type silicon.

The Fermi level, E_F, of a semiconductor is defined as the energy at which the probability of occupation by an electron equals one-half. In intrinsic silicon (Fig. 26.1) the Fermi level is at the midpoint between the conduction and valence bands and is called the intrinsic level, E_i. In n-type silicon (Fig. 26.2a) the Fermi level is closer to the conduction band because the number of electrons above E_i is larger than in intrinsic silicon. For p-type silicon (Fig. 26.2b) the effect is reversed. E_F is below E_i and closer to the valence band. The concentration of added impurity atoms (dopant atoms) affects the position of E_F within the band-gap. Increasing the concentration of dopant atoms moves E_F further from the intrinsic level for either n-type or p-type silicon.

With this level of understanding of this energy-band description of semi-conductor materials, a discussion of the operation of semiconductor devices (e.g., the IGFET and CHEMFET) can be presented.

26.2.2 Metal-insulator-semiconductor structure

The physics of the IGFET are best introduced by first examining the metal-insulator-semiconductor (MIS) structure which consists of a metal electrode and a semiconductor material separated by a thin (e.g. 100 nm) insulating material such as silicon dioxide (SiO_2). This insulator is assumed to be ideal, i.e. no current can pass through the insulator. To simplify the analysis we will assume that the structure has the following 'ideal' characteristics: (1) The work function of the electrons in the metal, Φ_m, and the semiconductor, Φ_s, are equal; (2) there is no net charge anywhere in the insulator; (3) there are no mobile charged species in the insulator; and (4) there are no surface states at the interface between the semiconductor and the insulator. The analysis of the MIS structure will involve the determination of the charge and potential distribution as a function of the potential applied between the metal and semiconductor. Once the analysis of this 'ideal' MIS structure is complete, the non-ideal characteristics can be accommodated rather easily.

The energy band diagram for the ideal MIS structure with zero applied voltage is shown in Fig. 26.3. The semiconductor is assumed to be silicon doped with acceptor impurities, i.e. it is p-type silicon. The energy barrier to electron transport through the insulator is denoted $q\phi_B$. As is shown, at equilibrium the Fermi levels for the metal and silicon are equal and the

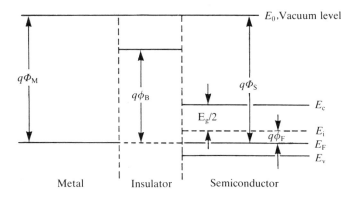

Fig. 26.3 Energy-band diagram for the ideal metal-insulator-semiconductor structure with no applied voltage.

potential and charge distributions are everywhere constant. When a potential is applied to the metal while the silicon is held at ground potential, however, the system is forced from equilibrium and the Fermi levels of the two materials separate by an amount equal to the applied potential. The system then behaves as a charged capacitor; the metal and semiconductor form the two charged plates of the capacitor.

If a negative potential is applied to the metal and the silicon is held at ground potential, then the field which is created will attract positively charged holes from the silicon to the silicon-insulator interface and, likewise, will attract electrons from the metal to the metal-insulator interface. Figure 26.4a illustrates the energy band diagram for this condition which is known as 'accumulation'. The (+) symbols near the valence band at the silicon-insulator interface represent the accumulated holes. Note that since the convention is to depict higher energy for electrons in an upward direction, the Fermi level for the metal is drawn higher than that of the silicon even though the metal is at lower energy. It would be wise at this point to consider the shape of the energy bands in the diagram. The negative applied potential effectively increases the hole concentration at the silicon-insulator interface which means that the Fermi level must move closer to the valence band at the interface. Because the charge carriers are at thermal equilibrium in the silicon (otherwise, a current would flow to bring the charge carriers to equilibrium) the Fermi level in the silicon must be flat; therefore, the valence band must curve towards the Fermi level. Since the separation between the valence band and the conduction band, E_g, is a constant for the material, the conduction band must also bend upwards near the interface. Likewise, because the position of the intrinsic Fermi level is midway between the conduction and valence bands, it must also bend upwards at the interface. In the metal,

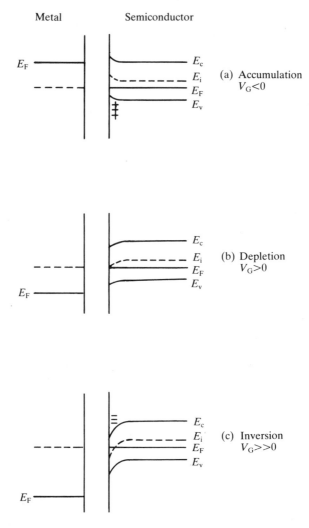

Fig. 26.4 Energy-band diagrams for the MIS structure in (a) accumulation, (b) depletion, and (c) inversion.

because the concentration of electrons and the density of vacant energy levels is so large, the Fermi level is constant up to the interface.

If a small positive potential is applied to the metal relative to the semi-conductor then the field drives the positive mobile charge carriers (i.e., the holes) away from the silicon-insulator interface resulting in a condition known as 'depletion'. Since the hole concentration in the interfacial region of the silicon is decreased, the Fermi level must move further away from the valence band. Thus, the energy bands bend downwards at the interface as shown in Fig. 26.4b. This depletion region which is created will have a net negative charge density since the negatively charged dopant atoms are immobile and cannot move in the electric field.

If the magnitude of the positive potential applied to the metal is increased, then the energy bands bend down further at the interface. At some applied potential, the intrinsic level, E_i, will bend below the Fermi level, E_F, as is depicted in Fig. 26.4c. At the point where the Fermi level is *equal* to the intrinsic level, the hole and electron concentrations will be equal. When the Fermi level bends *below* the intrinsic level, the electron concentration near the interface exceeds the hole concentration and the silicon in this region inverts from p-type to n-type. This condition is commonly referred to as the 'inversion' condition and the thin layer of n-type silicon is called the 'inversion layer'. The (–) symbols in Fig. 26.4c represent the electrons in the inversion layer.

The potential which must be applied to bring about inversion (i.e. to bend the intrinsic level to the level of the Fermi level) is shown in Fig. 26.3 as ϕ_F. For the analysis of the IGFET below, a more useful definition is that of 'strong inversion' which occurs when the band movement at the interface is equal to $2q\phi_F$. Since the electron density at the interface depends exponentially on the quantity $(E_i - E_F)$, the density of electrons in the inversion layer increases extremely rapidly beyond the point of strong inversion. As a result, the bands bend further only slightly when a potential larger than that required for strong inversion is applied. The potential which must be applied between the metal and silicon to bring about strong inversion is normally referred to as the threshold voltage, V_T, given by

$$V_r = - \frac{Q_B}{C_0} + 2\phi_F \tag{26.1}$$

where Q_B is the charge per unit area in the surface space-charge region and C_0 is the capacitance per unit area of the insulator. The first term on the right represents the portion of the applied voltage which is dropped across the insulator while the second term represents that portion which is dropped in the surface of the silicon.

Equation 26.1 applies only to the ideal MIS structure to which we have confined our discussion up to this point. Non-ideal effects generally result in band bending when zero voltage is applied between the metal and insulator. These effects are taken into account individually by altering the definition of the threshold voltage. Thus, if the effect of one of the non-ideal effects is to cause a natural upward bending of the bands at zero applied voltage, then a larger V_T must be applied in order to bend the bands down to the strong inversion condition. Each of the non-ideal effects will be dealt with in this way below.

If the work function difference between the metal and semiconductor Φ_{ms}, is not equal to zero, then at zero applied voltage, the metal and semiconductor will not be at thermal equilibrium unless electrons move from the material with the smaller work function to the material with the larger work function. This would result in a bending of the energy bands at zero applied voltage, unlike the ideal system. To bring the bands back to the 'flat-band' condition, a potential would have to be applied to counter the difference in work functions of the two materials. The threshold voltage is therefore increased by the amount Φ_{ms}

$$V_T = \Phi_{ms} - \frac{Q_B}{C_0} + 2\phi_F. \tag{26.2}$$

A non-zero charge in the insulator is handled similarly. The charge in the insulator will induce an image charge in both the metal and the silicon and will again result in band bending even with zero applied voltage. The threshold voltage can again be corrected as follows (Muller and Kamins 1977):

$$V_T = \Phi_{ms} - \frac{1}{C_0}\int_0^d \frac{x}{d}\rho(x)\mathrm{d}x - \frac{Q_B}{C_0} + 2\phi_F \tag{26.3}$$

where x is the distance from the metal-insulator interface, $\rho(x)$ is the charge density as a function of x, and d is the thickness of the insulator.

In addition to the charge dispersed in the insulator, there is also a layer of charge in the insulator next to the interface, essentially at $x = d$. This charge is generally treated separately from the disperse charge in the insulator and is usually designated Q_{ss} (charge per unit area). Considering this surface charge, the threshold voltage is given by

$$V_T = \Phi_{ms} - \frac{1}{C_0}\int_0^d \frac{x}{d}\rho(x)\mathrm{d}x - \frac{Q_{ss}}{C_0} - \frac{Q_B}{C_0} + 2\phi_F \tag{26.4}$$

The final non-ideality which must be considered is the deviation of the ideal band structure at the silicon–insulator interface where the periodic lattice structure of the silicon crystal is interrupted. This interruption of the lattice results in a nearly continuous distribution of allowed energy levels, called 'surface states', within the forbidden band-gap at the interface. The analysis of the influence of these surface states is complex and is treated elsewhere (Sze 1981). Fortunately, the annealing techniques which are currently employed in the fabrication of the MIS structure effectively reduce the number of surface states to a level where their effect is negligible, at least for the silicon/silicon dioxide system. Therefore, we will not further consider the existence of surface states.

The three terms in the threshold voltage equation (eqn 26.4) which deal with the non-idealities of the system are conveniently grouped into a single term called the 'flat-band' voltage, V_{FB}. This is the voltage which must be applied to the metal in order to bring the energy bands to a flat condition (i.e. to the ideal condition). Therefore,

$$V_T = V_{FB} + 2\phi_F - \frac{Q_B}{C_0} \qquad (26.5)$$

where

$$V_{FB} = \Phi_{ms} - \frac{Q_{ss}}{C_0} - \frac{1}{C_0} \int_0^d \frac{x}{d} \rho(x) dx. \qquad (26.6)$$

Equations 26.5 and 26.6 describe the potential which must be applied to the MIS structure in order to bring about strong inversion. These equations are also essential in describing the physics of the IGFET which, in essence, is simply an MIS structure with provisions for measuring the conductivity of the surface inversion layer.

26.2.3 Insulated-gate field-effect transistor

The structure of the IGFET shown in Fig. 26.5 is very similar to that of the MIS capacitor described in the preceding section. The gate region of the transistor consists of the p-type silicon substrate (1); the insulator, usually SiO_2 (2); and the gate metal (3); thus forming the familiar MIS structure. The structure is complicated by the addition of two n-type silicon areas known as the source (4) and drain (5). Metal contacts to the source and drain (6) permit

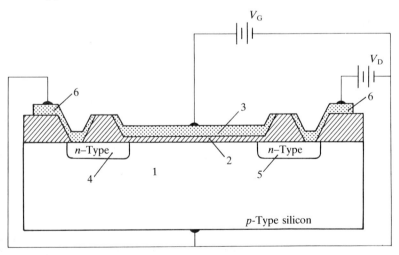

Fig. 26.5 Diagram of the IGFET. (1) p-type silicon substrate, (2) insulator, (3) gate metal, (4) n-type source, (5) n-type drain, (6) metal contacts to source and drain.

electrical contact. The source and drain allow the conductivity of the inversion layer at the surface of the p-type substrate to be measured. A voltage, V_G, is applied to the gate metal and a voltage, V_D, is applied to the drain. The substrate and the source are normally tied to ground potential. In operation, the current that flows from the drain to the source, I_D, is measured as a function of V_G and V_D.

The mechanism for operation of the IGFET can be understood rather easily, at least in a qualitative manner. With a small positive voltage V_D applied to the drain and a voltage V_G of magnitude less than the threshold voltage ($V_G < V_T$) applied to the gate metal, the surface of the silicon is either depleted or accumulated (i.e. it is not inverted and remains p-type silicon). Current cannot flow from the drain to the source under these conditions because the drain (n-type silicon) is biased positive with respect to the substrate (p-type silicon) resulting in a reverse-biased p–n junction which essentially blocks the current. When V_G is raised above the threshold voltage, however, a surface inversion layer forms and the surface of the silicon substrate becomes n-type silicon. Current can now pass from the drain to the source through the n-type inversion layer without crossing the reverse-biased p–n junction. Above the threshold voltage, the magnitude of the gate voltage modulates the number of electrons in the inversion layer and thus alters the effective conductance of the inversion layer. The resultant control of the drain current, I_D, by the gate voltage forms the basis of the transistor action of the IGFET.

Analysis of the physics of the IGFET involves the derivation of the drain current as a function of the applied voltages, V_G and V_D, and the geometry of the device. The derivation will follow the 'charge-control analysis' (Muller and Kamins 1977) which makes several simplifying assumptions but which results in a set of equations which agree well with experimental results and are easily understood.

Figure 26.6a is a schematic diagram of the IGFET showing the depletion layer (often called the space-charge region) and the inversion layer (often called the channel). The applied gate voltage, V_G, is greater than the threshold voltage (i.e. the device is in strong inversion) and V_D is assumed to be very small so that the potential in the channel does not vary strongly with position between the source and drain. In this case, the current which flows in the channel can easily be related to the charge in the channel, Q_n, and the transit time for the electron movement across the channel, T_{tr} by the equation

$$I_D = -Q_n/T_{tr}. \tag{26.7}$$

The transit time is simply the length of the channel, L, divided by the electron drift velocity, v_d, which is related to the field, V_D/L, and the electron mobility in the channel, μ_n, by the equation

$$v_d = \mu_n V_D/L. \tag{26.8}$$

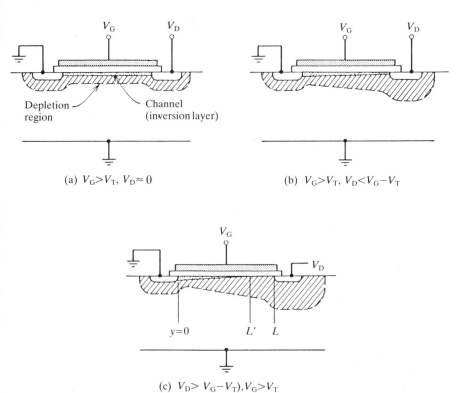

(a) $V_G > V_T$, $V_D \approx 0$

(b) $V_G > V_T$, $V_D < V_G - V_T$

(c) $V_D > V_G - V_T$), $V_G > V_T$

Fig. 26.6 IGFET cross sections showing the effects of various bias conditions on the inversion layer and depletion layer. (a) The drain voltage is very small. (b) The drain voltage is large enough to cause significant variation of the thickness of the inversion and depletion layers. (c) The drain voltage exceeds the saturation value and the effective channel length is reduced from L to L' referenced to $y = 0$ at the source (after Muller *et al.* 1977).

The transit time is therefore

$$T_{tr} = L^2 / \mu_n V_D. \tag{26.9}$$

The charge in the channel, Q_n, is simply the capacitance of the insulator, C_0, multiplied by $V_G - V_T$ (i.e. the portion of the gate voltage which created the channel). Since the insulator capacitance is expressed as a capacitance per unit area, we must multiply by the area of the gate, WL:

$$Q_n = -C_0(V_G - V_T)WL \tag{26.10}$$

where W is the width of the gate, and the threshold voltage, V_T, is given by eqn 26.5.

Substituting eqns 26.9 and 26.10 into eqn 26.7, the drain current is given by

$$I_D = \frac{\mu_n W C_0}{L}(V_G - V_T)V_D. \tag{26.11}$$

If we now consider the case with an applied drain voltage which is not negligible compared to the gate voltage, then the charge distribution in the channel and space-charge regions are altered as shown schematically in Fig. 26.6b. The electron density in the channel near the drain is now much smaller because the effective channel bias near the drain is reduced. Similarly, the thickness of the depletion region near the drain is increased because of the applied drain voltage. A first-order analysis of the charge in the channel accounting for the applied drain voltage involves approximating the average potential between the gate and channel as $\{V_G - (V_D/2)\}$. This leads to a channel charge, Q_n, different from that calculated in eqn 26.10:

$$Q_n = -C_0\{V_G - V_T - (V_D/2)\}WL. \tag{26.12}$$

The drain current therefore becomes

$$I_D = \frac{\mu_n W C_0}{L}\left(V_G - V_T - \frac{V_D}{2}\right)V_D, \quad V_D < V_{Dsat} \tag{26.13}$$

Equation 26.13 is only applicable for drain voltages less than $V_G - V_T$ (i.e. for the 'unsaturated' region of operation). When $V_D > V_G - V_T$ (i.e. the 'saturated' region of operation), the voltage applied between the gate and the channel near the drain is actually less than or equal to zero. As a consequence the channel disappears near the drain when $V_D > V_G - V_T$ as shown in Fig. 26.6c. When the IGFET is biased in the saturated region, the electrons in the channel see no energy barrier to their flow across this depletion region; rather, the region has a high electric field which accelerates the electrons to their limiting drift velocities. Consequently, the drain current is not affected by changes in the drain voltage when $V_D > V_G - V_T$. The drain current equation for the saturated region of operation is therefore obtained by substituting the drain saturation voltage, $V_{Dsat} = V_G - V_T$, into eqn 26.13:

$$I_D = \frac{\mu_n W C_0}{2L}(V_G - V_T)^2, \quad V_D > V_{Dsat}. \tag{26.14}$$

Equations 26.13 and 26.14 give rise to the set of curves shown in Fig. 26.7. While the equations are not quantitatively correct, they do contain the correct qualitative features, i.e., the saturated and unsaturated regions, the constant current above V_{Dsat}, and the dependance of V_{Dsat} on V_G and V_T.

Figure 26.8 shows the dependence of the drain current on the gate voltage, V_G, as predicted by eqn 26.13 and 26.14. In the saturated region (the curved region at low currents) the current is proportional to the square of the gate voltage while in the unsaturated region the current depends linearly upon the

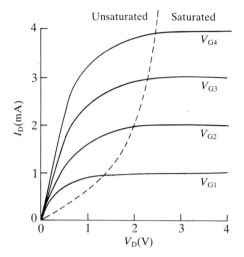

Fig. 26.7 Drain current versus drain voltage curves at several gate voltages showing the saturated and unsaturated regions of operation.

gate voltage. At higher gate voltages, however, the measured drain currents typically begin to saturate, deviating from the predicted linear curves. This deviation from predicted values arises from two separate effects. First, at large applied gate voltages, the field in the inversion layer perpendicular to the direction of current flow causes a decrease in the effective electron

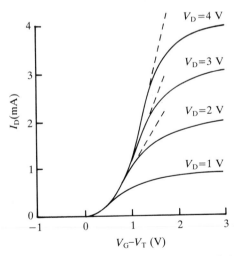

Fig. 26.8 Drain current versus gate voltage curves at several drain voltages. The dashed lines represent the theoretical linear relationship and the solid lines represent empirical curves.

mobility, μ_n, as the probability of the electron interacting with the surface increases. Second, in the typical geometrical layout of an IGFET on the silicon substrate, the bonding pads for the application of the control voltages are typically placed at the edges of the chip whereas the transistors are placed on the interior surface area of the chip. Thin metal strips or heavily doped silicon 'runners' usually connect the transistors to the bonding pads. Because these connections cannot be made resistance free, they contribute a resistance in series with the drain–source circuit of the IGFET. At high drain currents the resistive voltage drop caused by this series resistance, R_S, becomes appreciable and the actual voltage between the drain and source becomes $V_D - I_D R_S$ rather than the applied voltage V_D. The series resistance, therefore, causes the drain current to be lower than expected at high current levels.

26.2.4 The chemically sensitive field-effect transistor

The IGFET described above is transformed into a CHEMFET, conceptually at least, by replacing the metal gate with a chemically sensitive membrane. In the case of CHEMFETs sensitive to species in aqueous solution, electrical potentials are applied to the gate region through a reference electrode in the bathing solution as shown in Fig. 26.9. From a comparison of Figs 26.9 and 26.5 (CHEMFET and IGFET) it is apparent that the only difference between the electrical circuits is the replacement of the metal gate of the IGFET by the

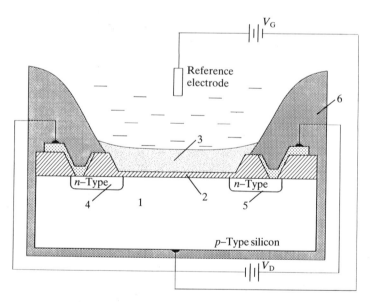

Fig. 26.9 Diagram of the CHEMFET. (1) Silicon substrate, (2) insulator, (3) chemically sensitive membrane, (4) source, (5) drain, and (6) insulating encapsulant.

series combination of the reference electrode, solution, and chemically sensitive membrane.

The equations describing the operation of the CHEMFET are derived from the analogous equations for the IGFET by taking into account the potential differences between the new elements in the circuit. In this section, a set of general equations will be developed which describe the current–voltage characteristics for the device in terms of the potential differences at the newly created interfaces but which do not describe how these potential differences depend on the chemical properties of the bathing electrolyte. Rather, the mechanism for the chemical sensitivity of each type of CHEMFET will be described independently and specific equations will be developed in the corresponding sections below.

Referring to eqns 26.13 and 26.14, V_G is the voltage applied to the gate metal and, therefore, is the potential at the surface of the insulator next to the gate metal. Analogous equations can be written for the CHEMFET by replacing V_G in these equations with the new potential at the surface of the insulator. This potential will simply be the voltage applied to the metal wire of the reference electrode, V_G, plus the sum of the potentials at the reference electrode–solution interface, E_{ref}, and the solution–membrane interface, $\phi_{sol-mem}$. The general equations for the CHEMFET in solution are, therefore,

$$I_D = \frac{\mu_n W C_0}{L}\left(V_G - V_T{}^* - E_{ref} - \phi_{sol-mem} - \frac{V_D}{2}\right)V_D \quad V_D < V_{Dsat} \quad (26.15)$$

and

$$I_D = \frac{\mu_n W C_0}{2L}(V_G - V_T{}^* - E_{ref} - \Phi_{sol-mem})^2 \quad V_D > V_{Dsat}. \quad (26.16)$$

As is evident, the threshold voltage is redefined as $V_T{}^*$ because the original definition (eqns 26.5 and 26.6) included the term Φ_{ms}, the work function difference between the metal and semiconductor. For the CHEMFET in solution, the work function difference should be divided into individual terms:

$$\Phi_{ms} = \Phi_{m-sol} + \Phi_{sol-mem} + \Phi_{mem-s} \quad (26.17)$$

where Φ_{m-sol}, $\Phi_{sol-mem}$, and Φ_{mem-s} are the work function differences between the metal and solution, solution and membrane, and membrane and semiconductor, respectively. The terms E_{ref} and $\phi_{sol-mem}$ already account for the work function differences, Φ_{m-sol} and $\Phi_{sol-mem}$ respectively so the definition of the threshold voltage must be redefined as

$$V_T{}^* = V_T - \Phi_{m-sol} - \Phi_{sol-mem} = \Phi_{mem-s} - \frac{Q_{ss}}{C_0} - \frac{Q_B}{C_0} + 2\phi_F \quad (26.18)$$

where the charge in the insulator is assumed to be negligible.

Equations 26.15 through 26.18, therefore describe the current–voltage characteristics for the CHEMFET without defining the mechanism for the generation of the potential difference at the solution–membrane interface, $\phi_{sol-mem}$. The important point is that the magnitude of the drain current is dependent upon this potential difference. The CHEMFET, therefore, acts as an extremely high impedance transducer to detect changes in this potential difference. By using membranes that develop potentials which are dependent upon the solution concentration of a particular species, the FET transducer is rendered chemically sensitive. Following sections will describe various schemes which create a field-effect transistor sensitive to a variety of different chemicals.

26.3 Sensor fabrication

The process for the fabrication of a CHEMFET sensor can be divided into two parts. The first part of the process includes the fabrication of the devices in the silicon wafer (usually a 50 or 75 mm diameter wafer). In this first phase, each process step affects every chip simultaneously (typically several hundred to thousands of chips) and is thus very cost and labour efficient. The second part of the sensor fabrication process include those steps which are taken after the wafer is diced into individual chips and includes mounting the chip on a support, making electrical connections, encapsulating the sensor, and, usually, depositing a chemically sensitive membrane. Since each sensor is treated individually, the effort per sensor can be significant.

26.3.1 Wafer micro-fabrication

Each laboratory which fabricates CHEMFET devices uses different processing sequences and procedures and thus a description of the complete process is both impractical and beyond the scope of this text. For a detailed description of semiconductor processing, the reader is referred to texts specifically devoted to the topic such as Colclaser (1980).

For an *n*-channel CHEMFET, one starts with a silicon wafer which is doped with boron, making it *p*-type. The *n*-type source and drain are then formed by masking the wafer with the proper pattern by photolithographic techniques and introducing phosphorous atoms into the surface of the silicon by either ion implantation or chemical diffusion. The silicon dioxide gate insulator (typically 50–100 nm thick) is formed by the thermal oxidation of the silicon surface at 1000–1200 °C in an oxygen atmosphere. Silicon nitride, which is often used as a second insulator on top of the silicon dioxide to provide better resistance to hydration, is typically grown by chemical vapour deposition at 600–800 °C in a nitrogen atmosphere containing silane (SiH_4) and ammonia (NH_3), again, 50–100 nm thick. Electrical contacts are made to the source, drain, and substrate by etching holes through the insulator and

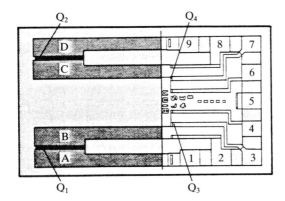

Fig. 26.10 Diagram of a typical CHEMFET chip. See text for description (after Janata and Huber 1979).

evaporating metal (generally aluminium) runners which connect these regions to bonding pads at the periphery of the chip. Upon the completion of the micro-fabrication process, the wafer is scribed with a diamond tip stylus and is then broken into individual chips.

The geometrical layout of the chips also varies among the laboratories investigating CHEMFETs. Figure 26.10 is a drawing of a chip which has been used extensively at the University of Utah (Janata and Huber 1979) and is typical of most. The chip has dimensions of 1.28×2.16 mm and contains four FET devices; Q_1 and Q_3 are CHEMFETs and Q_2 and Q_4 are conventional IGFETs. The dimensions of the gates are all 20×400 μm. A, B, C, and D are the drain and source regions for the two CHEMFETs. The numbered regions 1-9 are metal bonding pads to which electrical contacts are made to the external control circuitry. The two CHEMFET devices are placed at one end of the chip while the bonding pads are placed at the opposite end to facilitate coverage of the bonding pads, connecting wires, and edges of the chip with encapsulant while leaving the gates of the CHEMFETs uncovered.

26.3.2 Sensor packaging

Once again, each laboratory has its own techniques for packaging (supporting, wiring, and encapsulating) the CHEMFET sensors. Figure 26.11 represents the configuration used by this author for most of his research (Blackburn 1983). The support for the chip (1) is a length of 3 mm outer diameter glass tubing. Insulated copper wires (2) are threaded through the glass tubing, bent at right angles at one end and then anchored in place with epoxy (3). After curing, the surface of the epoxy is ground off and filed smooth to give a flat surface with the ends of the copper wires exposed to

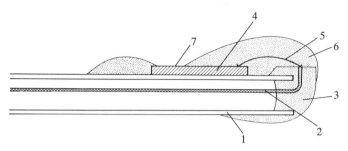

Fig. 26.11 Diagram of a typical CHEMFET sensor. (1) glass tubing, (2) copper wires, (3) epoxy encapsulant, (4) CHEMFET chip, (5) wirebond connections, (6) epoxy encapsulant, and (7) exposed gate areas of CHEMFET chip.

serve as bonding pads for the connections to the chip. The CHEMFET chip (4) is then mounted on the outer surface of the glass tubing with cyano-acrylate adhesive. Electrical connections (5) between the chip and copper wires are made with 25 μm diameter aluminium wire using an ultrasonic wire-bonder. The devices are then encapsulated with epoxy (6), covering the wire-bond wires, the copper wires, and all of the chip except the gate areas (7). The epoxy encapsulant serves to insulate the chip from the solution and must remain insulating for long periods of immersion in aqueous solutions. After curing the epoxy, chemically sensitive membranes are generally applied as described in the appropriate sections below. Most of the steps are performed under a 10–40 × stereomicroscope to aid in visualizing the small areas of the sensor.

Ho *et al.* (1983) have described a technique for packaging the CHEMFET sensor which can potentially be automated. As discussed above, automation of the encapsulation process would significantly reduce the cost of and con-comitantly enhance the commercial viability of CHEMFET sensors. Figure 26.12 depicts the packaging technique. The chip is mounted on the substrate (polyimide tape) and a second strip of polyimide tape containing a copper beam lead pattern is aligned and placed over the chip. The beam leads are then bonded to the chip's bonding pads either by ultrasonic or thermo-compression bonding. A third strip of polyimide tape containing windows is then aligned and bonded over the surface of the chip, which leaves the entire chip encapsulated except for the chemically sensitive gates of the FET. To date, the process is still performed manually under a microscope, but the process could potentially be automated.

26.4 Control and measurement circuitry

Two different operating modes are typically used in making measurements with CHEMFETs. In the first, the gate voltage is held constant and the drain

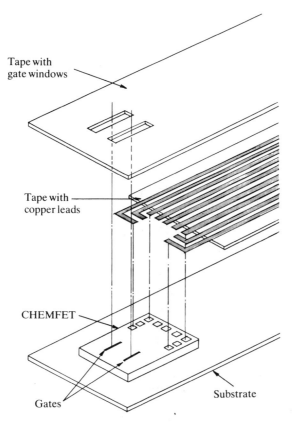

Tape with
gate windows

Tape with
copper leads

CHEMFET

Substrate

Gates

Fig. 26.12 Diagram depicting an encapsulation scheme with potential for automation utilizing polyimide tape as the encapsulant (after Ho *et al.* 1983).

current is monitored. In the second method, the gate voltage is changed as necessary by a feedback circuit to maintain a constant drain current. The analog control and measurement circuitry described below represents probably the least complex circuitry which could be employed. Although more elaborate circuits have been designed and tested and microprocessor control is straightforward, the circuits shown here provide an adequate and simple means for the operation of CHEMFET sensors.

26.4.1 Constant gate voltage operation

A simple circuit for this mode of operation is shown in Fig. 26.13 (Blackburn 1983). Constant voltages, V_D and V_G, are applied to the drain and reference electrode, respectively. The substrate and the source are shorted together on the clip and the lead is fed into an op amp which serves as a current-to-voltage converter. The output voltage of the op amp is given by the product $-R_1 I_D$.

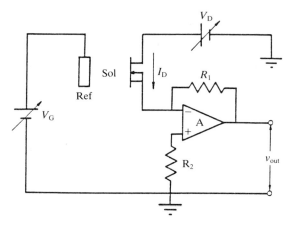

Fig. 26.13 Schematic diagram of circuit for measuring I_D at constant gate voltage. A, operational amplifier; $R_1 = 1$ kΩ; $R_2 = 470$ Ω.

Changes in the potential at the membrane–solution interface are monitored as changes in the drain current. The drain current is not a linear function of the gate voltage over its entire range, however. Thus, the relationship between the two variables must be known for every operating point to calculate the interfacial potential change from this change in drain current. The advantage of this mode of operation is that because the gate voltage is constant, several devices can be monitored simultaneously in the same solution with one reference electrode serving to bias all.

26.4.2 Constant drain current operation

A simple circuit for this mode of operation is shown in Fig. 26.14 (Blackburn, 1983). As before, the voltage applied to the drain is constant and the drain current is measured by op amp A_1. The output of the op amp, V_1, is fed into a voltage divider comprised of R_2 and R_3. The voltage at the other end of the divider is controlled by V_{set}. Since R_2 and R_3 are equal valued, the voltage between them will be the average of V_1 and V_{set}. This voltage is measured by op amp A_2. The output of this op amp is fed to the reference electrode and thus affects the drain current of the CHEMFET. The negative input of op amp A_2 is tied to ground through R_4. In operation, since the two inputs must be at the same voltage, the voltage on both inputs must be zero which requires that the output of A_1 be $- V_{set}$. Since the output of op amp A_1 is $- R_1 I_D$, I_D must be equal to V_{set}/R_1. This requirement is met by the feedback op amp A_2 which adjusts its output, V_G, to control the drain current. Thus, op amp A_2 holds the drain current constant $(I_D = V_{set}/R_1)$ by changing the voltage applied to the reference electrode. If the potential of the membrane–solution interface changes, then the feedback circuit compensates an equal and

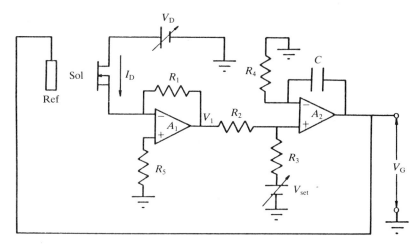

Fig. 26.14 Schematic diagram of the circuit for measuring changes in V_G at constant drain current. A_1, A_2: operational amplifiers; $R_1 = 1$ kΩ; $R_2 = R_3 = 100$ kΩ; $R_4 = 20$ kΩ; $R_5 = 470$ Ω; $C = 10$ pF.

opposite amount to maintain a constant drain current. In this way, the changes in the interfacial potential can be monitored directly.

This mode of operation has the disadvantage that only one sensor can be monitored at a time because the gate voltage for each must be independently controlled and the solution can only contain a single reference electrode. It is usually the operational mode of choice, however, because it provides a direct indication of the change in the interfacial potential.

26.5 Ion-selective field-effect transistor

The ion-selective field-effect transistor represents the marriage of the technologies of the ion-selective electrode and solid-state electronics. One of the inherent problems in the use of conventional ISE's is that the output signal from the sensor is typically rather noisy as a consequence of the high electrical impedance of the ion-selective membrane; the wires connecting the high impedance electrode to the amplifier (typically a high input impedance pH meter) serve as 'antennae,' responding to any change in the local electromagnetic field. To reduce the electrical noise problem, the wires are generally fabricated from shielded cable and their length is kept to a minimum. Even with these precautions, it is often necessary to attempt to limit the sources of interference (e.g. it is usually necessary for the operator to stand extremely still or to step away from the electrode and electronics to achieve a stable reading). The ISFET represents this solution (i.e. using shortened cables) taken to the extreme that the cable length is reduced to zero, i.e. the ion-selective membrane is placed directly on the gate of the high impedance amplifier's input transistor. To facilitate measurement, the transistor is separated from the amplifier and placed on an electrode-like support which can be placed in the sample solution. The *low impedance* output of the FET is connected to the electronics through wires of any convenient length without the need for shielding; the ISFET makes an *in situ* impedance transformation and therefore is not susceptible to interference from changes in local electro-magnetic fields.

26.5.1 Theory

The ion sensitivity of the ISFET arises from the use of ion-selective membranes as the chemically sensitive layer over the gate of the transistor. The membranes are identical to those developed for use with ion-selective electrodes as described by Freiser (1978, 1980) and Koryta (1975). The reader is referred to these sources for a thorough description of the mechanisms and thermodynamics of ion-selective membranes.

The ion-selectivity and sensitivity of a 'good' ion-selective membrane results from a very small energy barrier for the transport of one particular ion across the solution–membrane interface while a rather large energy barrier is maintained for the transport of all other ions. An interface with these properties is known in electrochemistry as 'non-polarized.' When the solution concentration of the ion of interest changes, those ions experiencing only a small energy barrier tend to diffuse down the newly changed concentration gradient across the interface. In contrast, all other ions see a large energy barrier and are unable to cross the interface. As an example, if the ion-selective membrane is selective for potassium ions and if the concentration of potassium chloride is increased in solution, then potassium ions will begin to flow from the solution into the membrane; the chloride ions, however, are unable to diffuse into the membrane because of the high energy barrier. As a result, a charge imbalance is created across the interface as ions of one charge move across the interface and their counter ions are excluded. This separation of charge creates a change in the potential across the interface which acts to force the ions in a direction opposite to that of the concentration gradient. The potential change thus slows and eventually stops the net flow of ions across the interface. The change in concentration of the particular ion therefore results in an interfacial potential change, $\Delta\phi_{\text{sol-mem}}$, which can be measured by the ISFET. An analysis of the thermodynamics of the system reveals the relationship between the potential change and the concentration of the ion.

If ion i can freely cross the interface between the solution and membrane, then at equilibrium the electrochemical potentials, $\tilde{\mu}_{i_{\text{sol}}}$ and $\tilde{\mu}_{i_{\text{mem}}}$, for the ion must be equal in the two phases:

$$\tilde{\mu}_{i_{\text{sol}}} = \tilde{\mu}_{i_{\text{mem}}} \tag{26.19}$$

the electrochemical potential for species i is defined as

$$\tilde{\mu}_i = \mu_i + z_i F\phi_i \tag{26.20}$$

where z_i is the charge of species i, F is the Faraday constant, and ϕ_i is the bulk potential in the phase in which the ions exist. μ_i is the chemical potential of species i, defined as

$$\mu_i = RT\ln(a_i) + \mu_i^0 \tag{26.21}$$

where R is the gas constant, T is the temperature (Kelvin), and μ_i^0 is the standard chemical potential for species i. a_i is the activity of species i (approximately equal to the concentration for dilute solutions). Equations 26.20 and 26.21 can be written for species i in both the membrane and solution phases. Substitution of these definitions into eqn 26.19 yields the relationship between the activity of the ion and the potential at the interface, the Nernst equation:

$$E = \phi_{\text{sol-mem}} = E^0 - \frac{Rt}{zF}\ln(a_i) \tag{26.22}$$

where a_i is now assumed to represent the activity of the ion in solution. The activity of the ion in the membrane is usually assumed to be large and constant and is therefore included in the term E^0. Equation 26.22 can now be substituted into eqns 26.15 and 26.16 to yield the ion-selective response of the ISFET to the change of activity of ion i

$$I_D = \frac{\mu_n W C_0}{L}\left\{ V_G - V_T^* - E_{\text{ref}} - E^0 + \frac{RT}{zF}\ln(a_i) - \frac{V_D}{2} \right\} V_D$$
$$V_D < V_{\text{Dsat}} \tag{26.23}$$

and

$$I_D = \frac{\mu_n W C_0}{2L}\left\{ V_G - V_T^* - E_{\text{ref}} - E^0 + \frac{RT}{zF}\ln(a_i) \right\}^2, \quad V_D > V_{\text{Dsat}}. \tag{26.24}$$

26.5.2 Ion-selective membranes for the ISFET

As stated above, the membranes which are used with ISFETs are usually identical to those used with ISEs. These two types of sensors simply represent two different schemes for the measurement of changes in the potential at the solution–membrane interface. The membranes and therefore the potential generating mechanisms are identical. Each of the three types of ion-selective membranes which have been employed in ISFETs will be discussed below.

26.5.2.1 Solid-state membranes
The first reported ISFET by Bergveld (1970) used a solid-state pH membrane of silicon dioxide (SiO_2). Shortly afterwards, Matsuo *et al.* (1971) described an ISFET which utilized a solid-

state membrane of silicon nitride (Si_3N_4). Since these early reports, SiO_2 has largely been abandoned as a pH membrane for ISFETs because it rapidly hydrates in aqueous solutions and loses its insulating properties which are essential for the operation of the CHEMFET. Solid-state pH membranes of Al_2O_3 (Abe *et al.* 1979), ZrO_2, and Ta_2O_5 (Akiyama *et al.* 1982) have also been investigated.

Solid-state membranes are particularly attractive as ion-selective membranes for ISFETs because they can be deposited using common integrated circuit fabrication techniques. In addition, the membranes are deposited on the entire wafer of sensor chips simultaneously before it is broken up into individual chips. The effort and cost per sensor are thus reduced considerably.

Of the above mentioned inorganic materials, Al_2O_3 and Ta_2O_5 demonstrate the most desirable characterisics, giving pH sensitivities of 52–58 mV/pH, a 95% response time of, at most, a few seconds, nearly negligible drift, and very little hysteresis (Abe *et al.* 1979; Akiyama *et al.* 1982).

The development of solid-state membranes for species other than the hydrogen ion have had only limited success. Many materials which are used routinely in ISEs cannot be deposited by conventional integrated circuit fabrication techniques and thus have not been exploited. Nevertheless, Buck and Hackleman (1977) developed a silver bromide solid-state membrane sensitive to bromide ions and Esashi and Matsuo (1978) developed sodium ion-selective solid-state membranes of aluminosilicate or borosilicate glass. These membranes both exhibit a sodium response of 55 mV/pNa in the range of pNa 0–3 and a measurable response down to pNa 5.

26.5.2.2 Polymer membranes The polymer membranes which are employed in the fabrication of ISFETs are identical to those used in ISEs. In general, any polymeric membrane which has been developed for ISEs can be used directly with ISFETs. Because of this significant overlap, no attempt will be made to repeat the description of all types of ion-selective membranes in this section.

The polymer membranes are normally applied to the gate region of the ISFET by solvent-casting from a volatile solvent. Multiple castings to attain membranes thicker than approximately 50 μm are usually necessary to achieve pinhole-free membranes. If pinholes are present in the membranes they act as electrical shunts through the membrane when filled with electrolyte, shorting out the electrochemical potential and rendering the ISFET useless. The most widely studied ion-selective polymer membranes coupled with ISFETs are those sensitive to potassium and calcium ions. The potassium-selective membrane contains the ionophore valinomycin in a PVC polymer matrix which is highly plasticized with dioctyladipate according to the formulation of Band *et al.* (1978). The calcium-selective membrane

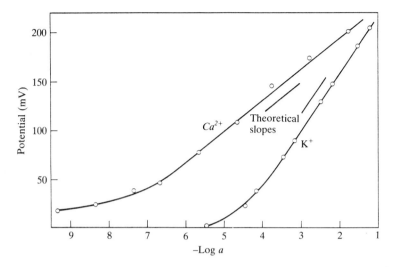

Fig. 26.15 Response of calcium and potassium ISFET with polymeric ion-selective membranes (after McBride *et al.* 1978).

utilizes tHODPP [*p*-(1,1,3,3-tetramethylbutylphenyl) phosphoric acid] as the ionophore in a similar plasticized PVC matrix according to Griffiths *et al.* (1972). The membranes are cast from a solvent mixture of 1:1 (v/v) tetrahydrofuran and cyclohexanone. Figure 26.15 shows the typical response for ISFETs using these membranes according to McBride *et al.* (1978).

26.5.2.3 Heterogeneous membranes Heterogeneous membranes were pioneered by Pungor (1967) and are of special interest for ISFETs because their use circumvents the difficulties encountered in the fabrication of many types of solid-state membranes. In general, the membranes consist of a semiconducting electrode material, usually an inorganic salt of low solubility in the form of a finely divided powder, immobilized in a polymer matrix. Shiramizu *et al.* (1979) reported the development of heterogeneous membrane ISFETs sensitive to chloride, iodide, and cyanide ions using silver salts in the elastomeric polymer, polyfluorinated phosphazine (PNF). Chloride-sensitive membranes were formulated from silver chloride powder in PNF at a weight ratio of 3:1. An improved membrane was formulated from a 4:1 mixture of silver chloride and silver sulfide. A heterogeneous membrane sensitive to both iodide and cyanide was formulated from a 3:1 mixture of 75% silver iodide and 25% silver sulfide in PNF. The response of these various ISFETs is shown in Fig. 26.16, where the Cl^-_a membrane contains both silver chloride and silver sulfide while the Cl^-_b membrane contains only silver chloride.

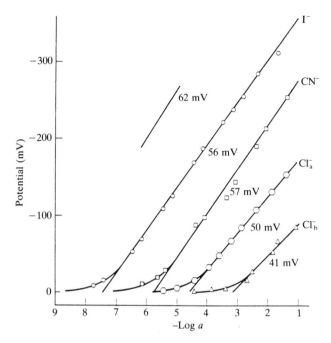

Fig. 26.16 Response of chloride, iodide, and cyanide ISFETs with heterogeneous membranes (after Janata and Huber 1980).

26.5.3 Time response

One of the primary advantages of the ISFET is that it makes an *in situ* impedance transformation, eliminating the electrical lead between the membrane and the amplifier. The parasitic capacitance of the leads is thus eliminated. As a consequence, the *RC* time constant for the response of the ISFET should be much smaller than that of conventional ISEs. McBride *et al.* (1978) reported the measurement of electrical and chemical time responses for Si_3N_4 solid-state pH membranes and for calcium-sensitive polymer membranes (see Fig. 26.17). The electrical time responses were measured by applying a square-wave voltage to the reference electrode and measuring the response of the drain current. The chemical time responses were measured by injecting a stream of solution across the membrane from a syringe containing a higher concentration of the ion. It was found that the polymer membrane exhibited a longer response time to potential changes due to the dynamic limitations of the membrane over the gate. The longer response time to changes in concentration as compared to changes in potential indicates that the response is limited by a diffusion layer at the membrane–solution interface. Thus, a shorter response time for ISFETs as compared to ISEs should not be expected.

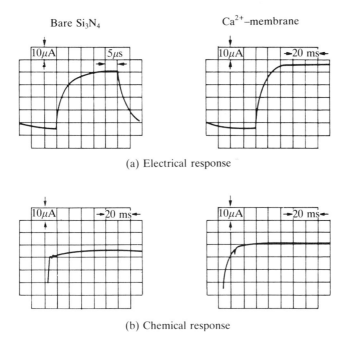

(a) Electrical response

(b) Chemical response

Fig. 26.17 Time response of silicon nitride pH-sensitive and calcium-sensitive membrane ISFET's (after McBride *et al.* 1978).

26.5.4 Suspended mesh ISFET

One of the inherent problems in the use of ISFETs with polymer ion-selective membranes is that the adhesion of the membrane to the surface of the sensor is generally very poor. In the conventional ISE, the membrane is mechanically clamped to the end of a tube so that adhesion is not a problem. In the ISFET, however, the membrane is simply cast over the gate area of the sensor and must rely on physical or chemical adhesion to the surface. This problem has been circumvented in several laboratories by applying the membrane over a large area of the sensor or by using a PVC anchoring ring embedded in the encapsulant around the perimeter of the gate area (McKinley *et al.* 1980). Others have approached the problem by changing the chemical composition of the membrane at the expense of the electrochemical performance.

The poor adhesion results in a gradual detachment of the membrane from the surrounding encapsulation and transistor surface and the development of electrolytic shunts around the membrane. The measurement of the electrochemical potential at the membrane–solution interface is thus erroneous and unpredictable. Any mechanical stress on the membrane, such as would be encountered in a high electrolyte flow situation or during *in vivo* experiments

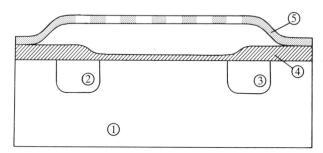

Fig. 26.18 Diagram of the suspended mesh ISFET chip before encapsulation and membrane deposition. (1) silicon substrate, (2) source, (3) drain, (4) insulator, and (5) polymer suspended mesh (after Blackburn *et al.* 1982).

when the device is inserted into tissue, usually results in complete detachment of the membrane from the device.

As a solution to the problem, Blackburn and Janata (1982) developed the suspended mesh (SM) ISFET. The device incorporates a three-dimensional structure on the surface of the FET over the sensing gates which acts to anchor the membrane. As shown schematically in Fig. 26.18, the suspended mesh consists of a polymer film suspended above the gate. The polymer film contains an array of holes through the film over the gate area of the FET. When a polymer ion-selective membrane is solvent cast over the gate area, the membrane flows under the mesh as well as over it, filling the air gap under the mesh. When the solvent evaporates, the suspended mesh becomes an integral part of the membrane, anchoring it to the surface as shown in Fig. 26.19.

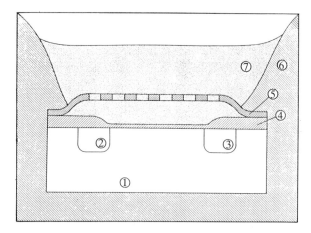

Fig. 26.19 Diagram of the suspended mesh ISFET chip after encapsulation and membrane deposition. (1) silicon substrate, (2) source, (3) drain, (4) insulator, (5) polymer suspended mesh, (6) encapsulant, and (7) ion-selective membrane (after Blackburn *et al.* 1982).

The suspended mesh is fabricated by forming the polymer film (polyimide and photoresist) over a rectangle of thin (1 μm) aluminium. The array of holes (10 μm square) is defined photolithographically and etched by conventional integrated circuit fabrication techniques. The aluminium is then etched from underneath the polymer mesh through the holes, leaving the mesh suspended approximately 1 μm above the gate insulator.

Electrical and chemical testing of the SM ISFET demonstrated that the mesh had the desired effect. The electrical characteristics of the sensor were not affected by the modification. The chemical response for two sets of potassium-selective ISFETs, one set with no means for improving the membrane adhesion and the other set with the SM modification, was monitored for several weeks. After 24 hours in solution, the first set of ISFETs all began to show the first signs of poor membrane adhesion; the potential exhibited a substantial drift after step changes in the potassium concentration. The SM ISFETs, however, all demonstrated drift-free operation for over 60 days before they failed for other reasons. Figure 26.20

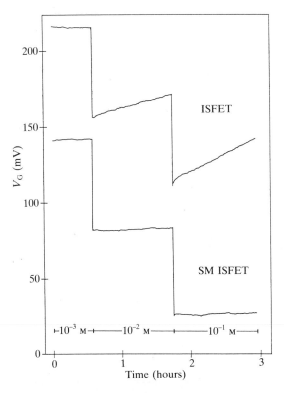

Fig. 26.20 Typical potassium standardization curves for the normal ISFET and the suspended mesh ISFET after seven days in solution (after Blackburn 1982).

shows typical response curves for a device from each set after seven days in solution.

26.6 Enzyme-based CHEMFET

Enzyme electrodes as described in this text (Chapter 1 and p. 133ff) and reviewed recently by Guilbault (1982) have generated considerable interest. They represent one of the few methods currently available for the electrochemical detection of biological molecules. The sensors generally incorporate a permeable membrane which entraps an enzyme in a thin layer over the surface of, for example, an ISE. The reaction of the enzyme with its substrate either generates products or consumes reactants whose concentrations can be monitored by the underlying ISE. The use of an ISFET as a substitute for the ISE to monitor the chemical concentrations has several distinct advantages. The enzyme-based field-effect transistor (ENFET) displays the usual advantages of the ISFET over its counterpart, the ISE. In addition, the small size and well-defined geometry of the ENFET requires only minute quantities of enzyme which has important implications when expensive enzymes are used. The configuration described by Caras *et al.* (1985*a*) also has the advantages that the thickness of the enzyme-loaded membrane can be easily controlled and the adhesion of the membrane to the surface of the ENFET is very good, eliminating the need for any type of retaining membrane as is usually necessary with conventional enzyme electrodes. A further advantage of the ENFET is that it normally has multiple transistors on the same chip, allowing a second transistor to function as a reference which responds to all electrical, chemical, and physical stimuli except the enzyme-substrate reaction. The mathematical difference between the signals from the two FETs, therefore, contains only the desired chemical information with substantially reduced extraneous signals.

Although the literature in the area of enzyme electrodes is extensive, there have been only a few reports of ENFETs. Danielsson *et al.* (1979) first reported a urea sensitive ENFET based on an ammonia gas-sensitive FET. Subsequently, Caras and Janata (1980, 1985) have developed a penicillin sensitive ENFET, Hanazoto and Shiono (1983) and Caras *et al.* (1985*a*) have developed a glucose sensitive ENFET, and Miyahara *et al.* (1983) have developed ENFETs sensitive to urea and acetylcholine (Ach).

26.6.1 Theory

The enzyme sensitive FET is fabricated from an ISFET by applying a thin layer of gel which contains the enzyme over the ion-selective membrane. Figure 26.21 is a diagram of a typical sensor. The mechanism and theory of the electrochemical response are identical to that described by Turner (Chapter 15) for the enzyme electrode and by Caras *et al.* (1985*b*) for the

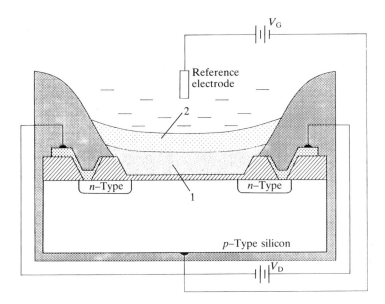

Fig. 26.21 Diagram of a typical ENFET sensor with (1) ion-selective membrane and (2) immobilized-enzyme gel layer.

ENFET. Therefore, only a qualitative presentation is offered here.

Referring to Fig. 26.21, the enzyme is immobilized in the gel layer over the ion-selective membrane. When the substrate for the enzyme is added to the solution it diffuses into the gel layer down the concentration gradient where the enzyme catalyses it's chemical modification. Either the consumed reactant or generated product is monitored by the underlying ISFET. In the case where the created products are monitored, the newly formed species in the gel layer diffuse in all directions, both toward the ion-selective membrane and out of the gel layer into the solution. Those molecules which diffuse toward the ion-selective membrane cause an increase in concentration at the surface of that membrane. A steady-state condition develops in which the concentration of the species at the interface between the gel layer and the ion-selective membrane remains constant. Since the reaction rate depends upon the substrate concentration, this steady-state concentration is determined by the solution concentration of the substrate. In the case where a reactant in the solution and gel layer is consumed by the substrate reaction, then the concentration of the monitored reagent is lowered at the membrane–gel interface, again reaching a steady state condition where this concentration is constant. The relation between the response of the ISFET and the solution concentration of the substrate is complicated and extremely difficult to solve mathematically, depending upon the rate constants for the reactions involved, the diffusion constants of each chemical, immobilized enzyme concentration, product-inhibition of the enzymatic reaction, etc. Caras *et al.* (1985*b*) have developed a model which considers most of these parameters, including the effect of a mobile buffer in the gel layer. The solution to the resulting equations is in close agreement with experimental results for ENFETs sensitive to penicillin and glucose.

26.6.2 *Practice*

With the exception of the urea sensitive ENFET developed by Daniellsson *et al.* (1979) which is based on an ammonia gas-sensitive FET, all ENFETs to date use pH-sensitive ISFETs in which the hydrogen ions are produced or consumed by an enzymatic reaction according to the equations

$$\text{Penicillin} \underset{\text{Penicillinase}}{\overset{}{\rightleftarrows}} \text{Penicilloate} + H^+$$

$$\text{Urea} + 2\,H_2O + H^+ \underset{\text{Urease}}{\overset{}{\rightleftarrows}} HCO_3^- + 2\,NH_4^+$$

$$\text{Glucose} + O_2 \underset{\text{Oxidase}}{\overset{\text{Glucose}}{\rightleftarrows}} \text{Gluconate} + H^+ + H_2O_2$$

$$\text{Ach} \overset{\text{AchE}}{\rightleftarrows} (CH_3)_3N^+CH_2CH_2OH + CH_3COO^- + H^+$$

where AchE is acetylcholinesterase.

These enzyme systems were initially chosen because the pH-sensitive ISFET does not require a polymer ion-selective membrane; the pH sensitive silicon nitride insulator is used directly. The enzyme–gel membranes are typically formed by immobilizing the enzyme in a matrix of cross-linked albumin, poly(acrylamide), or triacetylcellulose.

In practice, a dual-gate ISFET chip is normally employed so that one of the FETs can be used as a reference for the ENFET. This reference ISFET is coated with the gel membrane minus the enzyme and thus retains the same pH and temperature sensitivity as the ENFET. Because the ENFET and reference FET respond nearly identically to fluctuations in the solution potential, a stable reference electrode is not required; a wire contact to the solution is usually adequate. Thus, if the difference between the two drain currents is monitored, the signal is insensitive to changes in the solution pH, temperature, or electrical fluctuations (noise); only changes in pH within the gel membrane of the ENFET caused by the enzymatic reaction are detected.

Figure 26.22 illustrates a typical time profile of the response of a penicillin-sensitive ENFET to a step change in the substrate concentration (Caras and Janata 1980). The time response of the sensors is primarily a function of the thickness of the gel membrane since the substrate and detected species must diffuse through the membrane. For 50–100 μm thick membranes in the sited reference, 63% responses typically required 10–25 seconds. Other

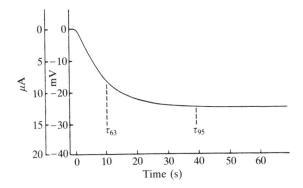

Fig. 26.22 Typical differential time response curve of a penicillin ENFET to a step change in penicillin concentration from 0 to 10 mM in 0.02 M phosphate buffer, pH 7.2; T = 25°C (after Caras *et al.* 1980).

researchers report slightly longer time constants but do not control the thickness of the gel membrane as accurately.

Figure 26.23 shows the response of the same penicillin sensitive ENFET (Caras and Janata 1980) as a function of substrate concentration. The shape of the response curve is typical for all reported ENFETs. Each type of ENFET generally demonstrates a measureable response in the concentration range of from approximately 1×10^{-4} to 1×10^{-2} M. The lifetime of the sensors is typically limited by the stability of the enzyme and thus is highly dependent on which enzyme is used and the storage conditions of the sensor. Caras and Janata (1980) and Miyahara *et al.* (1983) reported lifetimes for penicillin, urea, and acetylcholine ENFETs to be in the range of one to two months when the sensors were refrigerated between experiments.

Although to date all of the ENFETs which use ion-selective FETs as the sensor have employed the pH sensitive ISFET, there is no reason that the concept cannot be extended to other ion-selective systems as well. The sensors are simply more complicated to fabricate if a polymeric ion-selective membrane must be deposited before the gel membrane is applied. Any enzyme electrode which utilizes a macro-ISE as the sensor could realistically be adapted to utilize an ISFET in order to attain the advantages mentioned previously.

26.7 Immunochemically sensitive field-effect transistors

The size of the molecules involved in an immunochemical reaction (10 000 to 500 000 daltons) places special requirements on the electrochemical properties of the sensing membrane for any immunoelectrode. In an ordinary ion-selective electrode, the selectivity arises from the ability of only one type

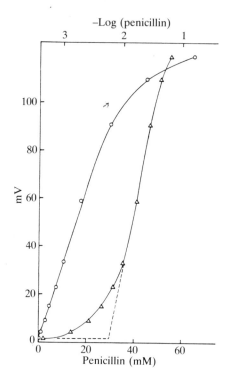

Fig. 26.23 Differential response of the penicillin ENFET. Circles are plotted according to the linear and triangles according to the logarithmic scales. $T = 37°C$, 0.02 M phosphate buffer, pH 7.2 (after Caras and Janata 1980).

of ion to permeate from the solution into the membrane with a high exchange current density. This selectivity is created by the incorporation of ionophores in the membrane which specifically bind one type of ion. It is difficult to imagine that a membrane could be designed so that it would allow specific immunochemical species to permeate easily from the solution into the membrane with a high current density while excluding the permeation of all other molecules. In other words, it is unlikely that the selectivity mechanism of ISEs could be applied in the design of an immunoelectrode. A different mechanism is required which allows the detection of the immunochemical electrochemically without requiring the movement of the immunochemical into the membrane. While it is hoped that the FET can satisfy this requirement, to date all attempts have been unsuccessful.

26.7.1 Theory

A field-effect transistor is basically a charge measuring device, i.e., any change in the excess interfacial charge at the outer insulator surface will be

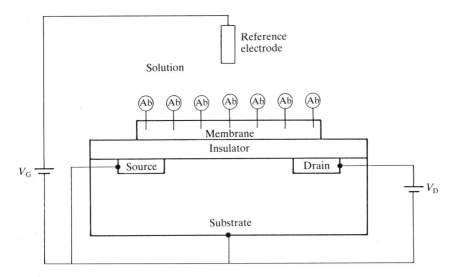

Fig. 26.24 Schematic representation of the IMFET. Ab represents antibodies immobilized at the solution-membrane interface (after Janata *et al.* 1984).

mirrored by an equal and opposite charge change in the inversion layer of the FET. If the solution–membrane interface of the CHEMFET is ideally polarized, i.e. if charge cannot cross the interface, then the CHEMFET can measure the adsorption of charged species at the interface as will be shown below. Since antibodies, antigens, and proteins are generally electrically charged molecules, then the polarized CHEMFET could be used to monitor their non-specific adsorption at the solution–membrane interface. To render the polarized CHEMFET selective for a given antigen and thus create the so-called immunochemically sensitive FET (IMFET), the specific antibody for that antigen could be immobilized on the surface of the CHEMFET as shown schematically in Fig. 26.24. The adsorption of this antigen would then be specifically enhanced over other molecules in the solution and the signal measured by the CHEMFET would be mostly due to the adsorption of that particular antigen.

This scheme for the measurement of the adsorption of charged species is feasible only if charge cannot cross the interface, which thus behaves as a perfect capacitor. The capacitance of a polarized interface is described by electrical double layer theory (Bockris and Reddy 1970) and is usually modelled as a series combination of two capacitors, C_G and C_H, where C_G is the capacitance of the diffuse Gouy–Chapman part of the double layer and C_H is the capacitance of the Helmholtz part of the double layer. The total capacitance, C_{dl}, is therefore

$$1/C_{dl} = 1/C_G + 1/C_H. \tag{26.25}$$

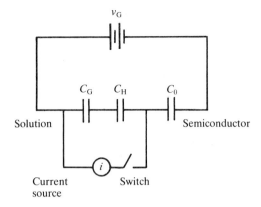

Fig. 26.25 Electrical model for the measurement of charge adsorption with the CHEMFET (after Janata *et al.* 1984).

The electrical circuit through the gate of a CHEMFET with an ideally polarized interface can be modeled, therefore, as a series combination of C_G, C_H, and C_0 as drawn in Fig. 26.25 where C_0 is the capacitance of the insulator. To the left of the Helmholtz capacitor is the bulk of the solution and to the right of the insulator capacitor is the bulk of the semiconductor. A voltage, V_G, is applied through a reference electrode between the solution and the semiconductor. The process of adsorption of charged molecules can be modeled as the transfer of a quantity of charge from the solution to the surface of the transistor as would occur if the switch were closed for a short time period allowing the current source to transfer the charge. As adsorption occurs, the charge on each plate of the capacitors will change to accommodate the new charge balance. The charge change on capacitor C_0 is the quantity of interest since it represents the charge in the inversion layer of the FET, Q_i, and will affect the drain current of the transistor. If a quantity of charge, Q_{ads}, is transferred by the adsorption of charged molecules, then the charge change on C_0, Q_i, can be represented by

$$Q_i = Q_{ads}\{C_0/(C_0 + C_{dl})\}. \tag{26.26}$$

Thus, only a fraction of the adsorbed charge will be mirrored in the transistor. When adsorption occurs, since electroneutrality must be observed in the system, an equal quantity of the opposite charge must either enter the inversion layer of the FET or enter the double layer from solution. Equation 26.26 predicts that part of the image charge will come from the solution as ions entering the double layer with the adsorbing species. This fraction of charge which is mirrored in the inversion layer of the FET will be defined as β. According to the model being considered, β is defined as

$$\beta = Q_i/Q_{ads} = C_0/(C_0 + C_{dl}). \tag{26.27}$$

In the case of a typical CHEMFET, C_0 is approximately 0.03 μF/cm^2. The double layer capacitance, C_{dl}, is approximately 10 μF/cm^2 for electrolyte concentrations of 0.1 M. Thus, according to this model, only 0.3% of the charge on the adsorbing molecules will be mirrored in the inversion layer of the FET. In more dilute solutions, however, where C_{dl} will be smaller, the fraction will be larger. In the case of the adsorption of large molecules such as immunochemicals, the adsorbed charge will not be confined to the interface but will be distributed through some distance (*ca.* 1–10 nm) away from the surface. The fraction of charge mirrored in the inversion layer of the FET will thus be even smaller; a reasonable estimate of β is probably on the order of 10^{-4}.

Referring to eqns 26.15 and 26.16 which describe the drain current of the CHEMFET as a function of the potential at the solution–membrane interface, it is clear that a relationship between the adsorbed charge and interfacial potential, $\phi_{sol-mem}$, is necessary to describe the chemical response of the IMFET. This potential is simply the charge change induced in the inversion layer divided by the insulator capacitance:

$$\phi_{sol-mem} = Q_i/C_0 = \beta Q_{ads}/C_0. \tag{26.28}$$

Substitution of this expression into eqns 26.15 and 26.16 yields the response equations for the polarized CHEMFET.

If the binding of antigen to antibody at the interface is described as

$$\text{Ab} + \text{Ag} \rightleftharpoons \text{AbAg}$$

where Ab is the antibody, Ag is the antigen, and AbAg is the complex. The reaction is characterized by the equilibrium constant K,

$$K = [\text{AbAg}]/[\text{Ab}][\text{Ag}]. \tag{26.29}$$

The total charge change at the interface due to the binding, Q_i, can be shown to be

$$Q_i = \beta Q_{ads} = \beta zF \frac{K[\text{Ag}][\text{S}]}{1 + [\text{Ag}]} \tag{26.30}$$

where z is the ionic charge of the antigen and [S] is the surface concentration of binding sites (the surface concentration of immobilized antibodies before binding). Substitution of this expression into eqn 26.28 yields

$$\phi_{sol-mem} = \frac{\beta zFK[\text{Ag}][\text{S}]}{C_0(1 + [\text{Ag}])}. \tag{26.31}$$

From this expression, the limit and range of detection for the IMFET can be predicted. If one assumes that the equilibrium constant will be in the usual range of 10^5–10^9 (Eisen 1974), that $\beta = 10^{-4}$, that the antibodies are immobilized with a surface concentration of one molecule per 10 nm^2, that the charge on the antigen is five electronic charges, and that the minimum signal measureable is 10 mV, the limit of detection would be in the range of 10^{-7}–10^{-11} M. The antigen concentration which gives 90% surface coverage can similarly be calculated to be in the range of 10^{-4}–10^{-8} M. The response range for the IMFET is thus estimated to be three orders of magnitude. If a mixture of antibodies were immobilized having a range of equilibrium constants, the response range for the sensor could be extended.

Similar equations can be derived for the case where the antigen is immobilized at the interface rather than the antibody. In this case, the IMFET would detect the concentration of specific antibodies.

Reversibility of the antigen–antibody binding reaction would determine the reversibility of the sensor. If the binding is not reversible, then the sensor could only measure immunochemical concentrations which are higher than those previously measured. This requirement would obviously limit the usefulness of the sensor for many applications such as real-time *in vivo* monitoring of immunochemical concentrations. For *in vitro* applications, however, the immunochemicals might be dissociated by some chemical treatment such as flushing with a high ionic strength solution, which would make the sensor reuseable.

Up to this point, the solution–membrane interface has been assumed to be ideal, i.e., that it behaves as a perfect capacitor with no leakage current. In reality, no interface is ideal and must be modeled as a capacitor in parallel with a resistor where the capacitor is C_{dl} and the resistance is the charge transfer resistance, R_{ct}. The consequence of this non-ideality for the IMFET is that any interfacial charge change due to the adsorption of charged species will not remain distributed amongst the model capacitors as presented above. Rather, any charge separation will leak across the solution–membrane interface, and decay in an exponential manner with a time constant equal to $R_{ct}C_{dl}$. For a typical electrolyte interface where $C_{dl} = 10\ \mu\mathrm{F\ cm}^{-2}$, R_{ct} must be at least $10^7\ \Omega\ \mathrm{cm}^2$ to attain a time constant of 100 s. Charge transfer resistances of this magnitude are rarely observed unless extreme measures are taken to eliminate any mechanism for charge transfer across the interface. The concept upon which the IMFET is based can be verified, therefore, only if a membrane material can be found which exhibits a charge transfer resistance greater than $10^7\ \Omega\ \mathrm{cm}^2$.

In principle, then, the CHEMFET with an ideally polarized interface is capable of measuring the concentrations of immunochemicals in solution, having a very low limit of detection and a broad response range. The specificity would only be limited by the specificity of the immunochemicals used in the device, a specificity which is second to none.

26.7.2 Practice

In practice, three classes of membranes have been employed in the investigation of the polarized CHEMFET (Janata and Blackburn 1984; Blackburn 1983): (1) thin conductive metals, e.g. gold and platinum; (2) thick conducting hydrophobic polymers, e.g. polyvinylchloride (PVC) and polystyrene; and (3) thin insulating membranes, e.g. Langmuir–Blodgett films of cadmium stearate. The conclusions drawn from the investigation of each of these types of membrane will be presented below.

Certain metals are routinely used in electrochemical experiments that require a polarized interface, particularly gold, platinum, and mercury. For most electroanalytical techniques, e.g. cyclic voltammetry or polarography, an electrode is considered polarized if the background current in the absence of electroactive species is small compared to the current when the electroactive species of interest is added. This requirement is much less strict than that for the polarized CHEMFET. Because the metals are electronic conductors, small concentrations of any electroactive molecule in the solution can provide a mechanism for electrons to cross the interface. To attain the charge transfer resistance necessary for the measurement of interfacial charge changes with the CHEMFET, extreme care must be taken to eliminate all electroactive species from the solution. Following such precautions, Cohen and Janata (1983) demonstrated the adsorption of iodide ion on gold-gate CHEMFETs. In solutions containing small concentrations of immunochemicals or proteins which are inherently 'contaminated' by many electroactive species, however, the charge transfer resistance was shown to be too low to allow the measurement of the adsorption of charged molecules (Blackburn 1983). Because these contaminants are ordinarily present in any solution containing immunochemicals, and because they decrease the charge transfer resistance of any metal electrode, the conclusion can be drawn that metal films are not suitable as membranes for the implementation of the IMFET.

Thick polymer membranes have been employed in several reports of immunochemical electrodes. For example, Aizawa et al. (1977) reported an immunoelectrode sensitive to the syphilis antibody with a membrane containing PVC, cholesterol, cardiolipin, and phosphatidylcholine. In the absence of an ionophore in the polymer that promotes the ion flux across the interface, it was hoped that the membrane–solution interface would be ideally polarized but the bulk would demonstrate some conductivity to allow electrical measurements.

It should be pointed out that a thick (100 μm) membrane fabricated from a polymer which is normally thought of as insulating may act as a conducting membrane when used over the gate of a CHEMFET. Since the input resistance of the transistor is approximately 10^{15} Ω, any membrane with a resistance approximately an order of magnitude smaller than this will appear conducting in the gate circuit.

Collins and Janata (1982) demonstrated that the membrane used by

Aizawa *et al.* (1977) responds to changes in the concentration of many small inorganic ions present in the solution and that DC electric current could pass through the membrane. The solution–membrane interface was therefore not polarized, by definition. Similar results have been obtained for pure polymer membranes of PVC, polystyrene, and polystyrene–polybutadiene block copolymer (Blackburn 1983). The charge transfer resistance for such membranes was shown to be between that of good ion-selective membranes and polarized electrodes. The potential at the interface is a mixed potential in which the ionic fluxes of more than one species control the potential. It is believed that the observed response to immunochemicals can be attributed to the coupling of the protein adsorption to the ion-exchange process to change the mixed potential (Collins and Janata 1982). Because the protein adsorption can be stimulated by immobilized immunochemicals, the false conclusion can be drawn that the response is due to the immunochemical reaction. Actually, the response is a secondary phenomenon; the primary response is to numerous inorganic ions. Even a minute change in the concentration of any of these ions will change the mixed potential at the interface. Thus, the very purpose of this research, the design of a highly specific immunochemical sensor, was defeated because the sensor is highly nonspecific. To date, no polymer investigated remains ideally polarized when placed in aqueous solution.

Langmuir–Blodgett films (Gaines 1965) of cadmium stearate have been investigated by Blackburn (1983) as a possible method for creating the ideally polarized interface. Langmuir–Blodgett films are formed one molecular monolayer at a time by depositing the monolayer onto a substrate from the air–water interface. The molecules are oriented by the air–water interface so that the hydrophilic end groups are situated in the water at the surface and the hydrophobic hydrocarbon chains of the molecule extend above the surface into the air, oriented away from the water at nearly a right angle. The oriented molecules are physically compressed together before deposition so that the hydrocarbon chains form a closely packed array. When deposited on a substrate, each successive monolayer is usually oriented 180° relative to the previous one, giving a head-to-tail, tail-to-head configuration. Langmuir–Blodgett films have promise as a means for creating the ideally polarized interface because of this tightly packed layer of oriented hydrocarbon chains. Each successive two monolayers of the Langmuir–Blodgett film create a layer of tightly packed hydrocarbon chains approximately 4.5 nm thick. The energy barrier for either water molecules or ions to cross such a region should be extremely large; thus, the interface should be nearly ideally polarized if the structure of the film is perfect.

Blackburn (1983) reported that Langmuir–Blodgett films of cadmium stearate on aluminum electrodes (11 monolayers, 27.5 nm thick) had the desired effect of increasing the charge transfer resistance of the interface, but

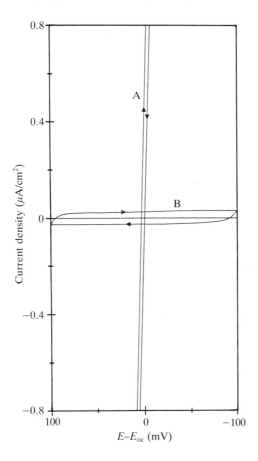

Fig. 26.26 Results of cyclic voltammetry experiments for (A) bare aluminum electrode and (B) aluminum electrode covered with 11 monolayers of cadmium stearate in 0.1 M NaCl. E_{oc} represents open circuit voltage versus Ag/AgCl reference electrode.

not to the extent necessary to create an ideally polarized interface (see Fig. 26.26). The current which could be induced to flow across the interface was attenuated by approximately three orders of magnitude but the measured slope of the current–voltage curve indicated that the resistance (a reasonable estimate for the charge transfer resistance) was only $2 \times 10^3 \ \Omega \ cm^2$, much lower than the desired $10^7 \ \Omega \ cm^2$. The conclusion was drawn that the films probably contain defects or grain boundaries that interrupt the perfect close-packed array of hydrocarbon chains, permitting the passage of charged species. This study was only a preliminary investigation of the films' properties in aqueous solution, however, and a larger effort must be undertaken to optimize the system.

It can be concluded that the failure to date to design an immunochemically sensitive potentiometric sensor (electrode or FET) is a consequence of the failure to find the ideally polarized interface. Numerous reports of immuno-chemical potentiometric sensors should be regarded as experimental artifacts that can be explained on the basis of electrode kinetics, i.e., changes in the mixed potential at non-ideally polarized interfaces. Janata and Blackburn (1984) state that, in their opinion, while there is still hope for a potentiometric immunochemical sensor, it is highly unlikely that an interface with a charge transfer resistance as high as 10^7 Ω cm^2 will be found. It is this fact that causes the creation of such a sensor to be somewhat improbable.

26.8 Gas sensitive field-effect transistor

26.8.1 Hydrogen sensitive palladium gate IGFET

The first FET sensor sensitive to gaseous species was reported by Lundstrom *et al.* (1975). The device was of the conventional IGFET configuration, i.e., with a metal gate deposited between the drain and source of the transistor over the insulator. The design of the IGFET was novel in that the gate metal consisted of a catalytic metal, palladium. Particular transition metals such as palladium and platinum are unique for two reasons: first, they catalyse the decomposition of hydrogen molecules, H_2, to hydrogen atoms at the metal–gas interface where the atoms then adsorb and, second, the hydrogen atoms are soluble in palladium and platinum permitting them to diffuse from the metal–gas interface into the bulk of the gate metal as depicted in Fig. 26.27. Lundstrom (1981) and Lundstrom and Soderberg (1981/82) have shown that some of the hydrogen atoms which dissolve in the gate metal

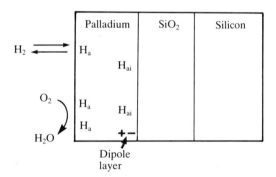

Fig. 26.27 Schematic representation for the mechanism of hydrogen and oxygen sensitivity of palladium-gate IGFET. H_a represents adsorbed hydrogen atoms, H_b represents hydrogen atoms dissolved in the bulk of the palladium, and H_{ai} represents hydrogen atoms adsorbed at the metal–insulator interface, contributing to the dipole layer.

spontaneously adsorb at the metal–insulator interface. The adsorbed hydrogen atoms' induced dipole moment contribute to a change in the work function of the metal gate. Referring to eqn 26.13 and 26.14, the drain current of the IGFET is sensitive to the difference in work functions between the gate metal and semiconductor. The change in the work function of the platinum or palladium gate metal therefore induces a change in the drain current of the transistor; changes of the drain current, therefore, are directly related to the concentration of hydrogen molecules in the gas ambient around the gate area of the transistor.

In the presence of oxygen (or other 'oxidizing' gases) chemical reactions can occur with the adsorbed hydrogen atoms, depleting the surface of hydrogen atoms as shown in Fig. 26.27. Since the hydrogen atoms adsorbed at the metal–insulator interface are in equilibrium with the atoms adsorbed at the metal–gas interface, the introduction of oxygen into the system decreases the magnitude of the dipole layer potential. In this manner the hydrogen sensitive IGFET can be used as an oxygen sensor if the ambient hydrogen pressure is held constant (Lundstrom 1981).

Figure 26.28 shows a typical response for a Pd-MOS transistor in air (Lundstrom *et al.* 1977) in air. The temperature of the transistor was maintained at 120°C, a condition which is necessary to attain reasonable response time for the sensors. The minimum detectable limit for hydrogen as reported

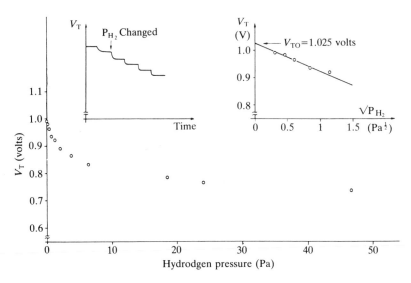

Fig. 26.28 Response of a Pd-gate IGFET which was exposed to different concentrations of hydrogen in air. V_{TO} represents is the threshold voltage with the Pd film completely discharged of hydrogen. The temperature of the transistor was maintained at 120°C (after Lundstrom *et al.* 1977).

by Lundstrom (1981) is approximately 3×10^{-5} Pa in an inert atmosphere and 5×10^{-4} Pa in air. The higher value in air is caused by the decrease in adsorbed hydrogen as a consequence of reactivity with atmospheric oxygen.

Palladium gate IGFETs have also been demonstrated to be sensitive to other molecules containing hydrogen such as ammonia and hydrogen sulfide (Lundstrom 1981) as well as to methane and butane (Poteat and Lalevic 1982). It is believed that the metal catalyses the decomposition of these molecules to hydrogen atoms and other species. For each of these gases, the detection scheme involves the formation of a dipole layer of hydrogen atoms at the metal–insulator interface, which is identical to the scheme for hydrogen gas sensitivity. The selectivity of the sensors for hydrogen-containing gases is a result of the high solubility of hydrogen in palladium and the low solubility of all other molecules.

Several researchers have reported palladium gate IGFETs which are sensitive to carbon monoxide gas. In order to attain sensitivity to gases other than hydrogenous species it is necessary to create a gate metal structure with 'holes' so that the metal–insulator interface is accessible to the gas molecules; for non-porous metals, the only mechanism to reach the interface requires solubility in and diffusion through the metal. Lundstrom *et al.* (1981/82) described a porous palladium gate IGFET and Krey *et al.* (1982/83) have described a gate structure with lithographically defined holes through the palladium which allow the gas molecules access to the metal–insulator interface. Figure 26.29 shows a cross section through the Pd-gate hole structure IGFET sensor. The CO sensitivity of the sensor is approximately 75 mV at 0.1 torr with a maximum signal of about 150 mV. The sensor is also sensitive to hydrogen, methane, butane, and other hydrogen-containing gases as expected. Krey *et al.* (1982/83) have shown, however, that the hydrogen sensitivity can be reduced by at least an order of magnitude by covering the

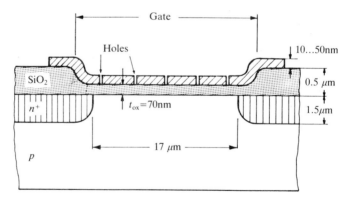

Fig. 26.29 Cross section of a palladium-gate IGFET with photolithographically defined holes (after Krey *et al.* 1982/83).

palladium with a 20 nm thick film of aluminum. The modification also reduces the CO sensitivity, but only by a factor of two. The aluminum apparently inhibits the diffusion of the hydrogen into the palladium.

26.8.2 Suspended gate GASFET

The transition metal gate FET sensors discussed above are selective for hydrogen-containing molecules because only hydrogen is appreciably soluble in the gate metal. Unfortunately, such selectivity for other gases using different gate metals has not been demonstrated. To generate a sensitivity and selectivity to other gases, a gate structure is required which allows the gases access to the metal–insulator interface and which could potentially be made selective by surface modification of these interfaces.

Stenberg and Dahlenback (1983) described an IGFET structure in which a portion of the insulator under the poly-silicon gate is etched away, creating an air gap between the gate and the silicon over a small portion of the gate.

Blackburn *et al.* (1983) described a 'suspended-gate' GASFET with a platinum gate suspended over the entire gate region of the transistor as shown in Fig. 26.30. An array of holes in the platinum gate allows the ambient gas access to the air gap between the metal and insulator. The structure is similar to that of the suspended mesh ISFET described in section 5.4., above.

The gap between the metal and insulator can be viewed as an additional insulator with a permittivity close to 1. When gaseous molecules with a dipole moment diffuse into the gap, the permittivity of the air gap is changed imperceptibly. However, when the molecules adsorb either on the metal surface or the insulator surface with some preferred orientation a dipole potential is created, contributing to the surface potential χ:

$$\chi = \frac{1}{\epsilon_0} \sum_i N_i \mu_i \tag{26.32}$$

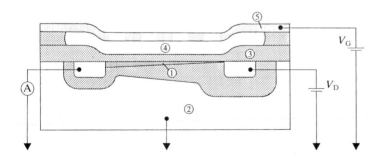

Fig. 26.30 Cross section through the suspended gate GASFET. (1) inversion layer, (2) silicon substrate, (3) insulator, (4) air gap, and (5) suspended platinum gate (after Blackburn *et al.* 1983).

where N_i is the density of adsorbed molecules i, μ_i is the vertical component of their dipole moment (not to be confused with the chemical potential having the same symbol), and ϵ_0 is the permittivity of free space. This potential can be considered as a voltage source in series with the applied gate voltage, V_G. A change in the density of adsorbed dipoles will, therefore, give rise to a change in the overall electric field and alter the drain current. Using the constant current mode of operation, this change in surface potential can be monitored directly.

The suspended metal mesh is formed on a silicon wafer upon which an array of FETs without any gate metallization has already been fabricated. The suspended mesh is formed by fabricating the array of holes in a platinum film over a layer of aluminum. The aluminum is then etched from underneath the platinum through the array of holes, leaving the mesh suspended over the gate of the FET. The initial aluminum layer is typically 100 nm thick so the resultant air gap is approximately the same dimension. The holes are 5 μm in diameter and spaced 10 μm apart. A detailed description of the fabrication process is given by Blackburn *et al.* (1983).

The chemical response has been preliminarily tested under flowing conditions by injecting 5 μl of tested substance into a 5 ml evaporation chamber from which it was flushed out in exponential fashion past the GASFET. The response curves are shown in Fig. 26.31. The lack of response to pentane and

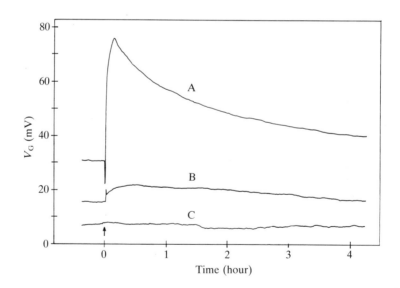

Fig. 26.31 Response of the suspended gate GASFET to addition of 5 μl of (A) methanol, (B) methylene chloride, and (C) *n*-heptane to a flowing stream of nitrogen (after Blackburn *et al.* 1983).

other non-polar molecules confirms the concept of the change in surface potential. The initial, fast response signal followed by the strong, slow response which was obtained upon addition of methanol or methylene chloride could be due to different kinetics of adsorption and/or orientation of these molecules on the platinum and/or insulator (silicon nitride) and is the subject of present studies. The long time required for the signal to return to its preinjection value results from the slow desorption from the walls of the gas delivery system; subsequent experimentation with the sensor attached at the exit of a gas chromatograph column have given much faster response times.

The suspended gate GASFET is an important development because the sensor's selectivity is not limited to only one species as it is for the palladium gate GASFETs. Indeed, in its present state, the suspended gate sensor is sensitive to most polar molecules. Chemical modification of the surfaces of the gate structure is being investigated and will hopefully impart some selectivity to this new class of gas sensors.

26.9 Conclusion

This chapter has presented the theory and implementation of several types of chemically sensitive field-effect transistors. The purpose was not to provide an exhaustive review of the literature, but rather to provide an overview of the different areas of interest of investigators in the field.

The ion-selective FET has seen the greatest development effort of the various types of CHEMFET sensors. This is due, in part, to the availability of ion-selective membranes which have seen considerable scientific development for application in ISEs. The ISFET should be viewed as a compliment to the ISE which may have distinct advantages in particular applications. The *in situ* impedance transformation eliminates the need for cumbersome shielded cables while maintaining a desireable low noise level in the measured signals. This advantage, combined with the small size of the sensor itself makes the ISFET ideal for applications such as *in vivo* monitoring of electrolytes where the small size of both the sensor and cable is essential. The solid-state construction of the sensors (in particular, the elimination of the internal filling solution of ISEs) makes the ISFET small, lightweight, and rugged. Because the size of each FET on the surface of the chip can be very small, the potential exists for the development of sensors which monitor many different chemicals simultaneously. This development awaits a membrane deposition method which allows many small membranes to be reliably deposited close to one another on a single chip. Because the sensors are fabricated on a semiconductor substrate, additional signal processing circuitry can easily be added to the chip thereby providing such functions as multiplexing and analog-to-digital signal conversion. Finally, because the chips are fabricated thousands at a time in silicon wafers, the cost of production can potentially be very small. This reduction in cost and effort, however, awaits the development of techniques for automatic encapsulation and membrane deposition.

The chemically sensitive field-effect transistor is also an exciting development in that it makes possible the detection of many chemicals using mechanisms which are previously either difficult or impossible to demonstrate. In particular, the polarized CHEMFET opens up the possibility of measuring changes in interfacial charge which can be induced by specific surface interactions of immunochemicals. Unfortunately, the requirement for a nearly ideal polarized interface may not allow the development of this class of sensors. The development of gas sensors using FET devices represents another area where new sensing mechanisms are being developed which could not have been conveniently explored previously.

Although the field of chemically sensitive field-effect transistors is still in its infancy and considerable work has yet to be accomplished, this class of sensors shows considerable promise for creating chemical sensors which have advantages over their existing counterparts. In addition, the CHEMFET provides new mechanisms to conveniently measure many chemicals which were not previously possible.

References

Abe, H., Esashi, M. and Matsuo, T. (1979). ISFET's using inorganic gate thin films. *IEEE Trans. Electron Devices* **ED–26**, 1939–44.

Aizawa, M., Kato, S. and Suzuki, S. (1977). Immunoresponsive membrane I. Membrane potential change associated with an immunochemical reaction between membrane-bound antigen and free antibody. *J. Membrane Sci.* **2**, 125–32.

Akiyama, T., Ujihira, Y., Okabe, Y., Sugano, T. and Niki, E. (1982). Ion-sensitive field-effect transistors with inorganic gate oxide for pH sensing. *IEEE Trans. Electron Devices* **ED–29**, 1936–41.

Band, D.M., Kratochvil, J., Poole Wilson, P.A. and Treasure, T. (1978). Relationship between activity and concentration of plasma potassium. *Analyst* **103**, 246–51.

Bergveld, P. (1970). Development of an ion-selective solid-state device for neurophysiological measurements. *IEEE Trans. Biomed. Eng.* **BME–17**, 70–1.

Blackburn, G.F. (1983). Molecular adsorption measurement with chemically sensitive field effect transistors. Ph.D. Dissertation, University of Utah, USA.

—— and Janata, J. (1982). The suspended mesh ion selective field effect transistor. *J. Electrochem. Soc.* **129**, 2580–4.

—— Levy, M.L. and Janata, J. (1983). Field-effect transistor sensitive to dipolar molecules. *Appl. Phys. Lett.* **43**, 700–1.

Bockris, J.O'M. and Reddy, A.K.N. (1970). *Modern electrochemistry* Vol. 2. Plenum Press, New York.

Buck, R.P. and Hackleman, D.E. (1977). Field effect potentiometric sensors. *Anal. Chem.* **49**, 2315–21.

Caras, S.D. and Janata, J. (1980). Field effect transistor sensitive to penicillin. *Anal.*

Chem. **52** 1935-7.

—— (1985). pH based enzyme potentiometric sensors. Part 3. Penicillin sensitive field effect transistor. *Anal. Chem.* **57**, 1924-5.

—— Petelenz, D. and Janata, J. (1985*a*). pH based enzyme potentiometric sensors. Part 2. Glucose sensitive field effect transistor. *Anal. Chem.* **57**, 1920-3.

—— Janata, J., Saupe, D. and Schmitt, K. (1985*b*). pH based enzyme potentiometric sensors. Part 1. Theory. *Anal. Chem.* **57**, 1917-20.

Cohen, R. M. and Janata, J. (1983). Measurement of excess charge at polarized electrodes with field effect transistors, Part 1. Direction determination of the Esin–Markov coefficient. *J. Electroanal. Chem.* **151**, 33-9.

Colclaser, R. A. (1980). *Microelectronics: processing and device design.* John Wiley, New York.

Collins, S. and Janata, J. (1982). A critical evaluation of the mechanism of potential response of antigen polymer membranes to the corresponding antiserum. *Anal. Chim. Acta.* **136**, 93-99.

Danielsson, B., Lundstrom, I., Winquist, F. and Mosbach, K. (1979). On a new enzyme transducer combination: the enzyme transistor. *Anal. Lett. B.* **12**, 1189-99.

Eisen, H. N. (1974). *Immunology, an introduction to molecular and cellular principles of the immune response.* Harper and Row, New York.

Esashi, M. and Matsuo, T. (1978). Integrated micro-multi-ion sensor using field effect of semiconductor. *IEEE Trans. Biomed. Eng.* **BME–25**, 184-92.

Freiser, H. (ed.) (1978). *Ion-selective electrodes in analytical chemistry* Vol. 1. Plenum Press, New York.

Freiser, H. (ed.,) (1980). *Ion-selective electrodes in analytical chemistry* Vol. 2. Plenum Press, New York.

Gaines, G. L. (1965). *Insoluble monolayers at liquid–gas interfaces.* Interscience Publishers, New York.

Griffiths, G. H., Moody, G. J. and Thomas, J. D. R. (1972). An investigation of the optimum composition of poly(vinyl chloride) matrix membranes used for selective calcium-sensitive electrodes. *Analyst* **97**, 420-7.

Guilbault, G. G. (1982). Immobilized enzymes as analytical reagents. *Appl. Biochem. Biotechnol.* **7**, 85-98.

Hanazoto, Y. and Shiono, S. (1983). Bioelectrode using two hydrogen sensitive field effect transistors and a platinum wire pseudo reference electrode. In *Proceedings of the international meeting on chemical sensors*, Fukuoka, Japan, September 19-22, 1983, 513-518. Elsevier, New York.

Ho, N. J., Kratochvil, J., Blackburn, G. F. and Janata, J. (1983). Encapsulation of polymeric membrane-based ion-selective field effect transistors. *Sensors and Actuators* **4**, 413-21.

Janata, J. and Blackburn, G. F. (1984). Immunochemical potentiometric sensors. *Annals of the New York Academy of Sciences* **428**, 286-92.

—— and Huber, R. J. (1979). Ion sensitive field effect transistors. *Ion-Sel. Electrode Rev.* **1**, 31-78.

—— (1980). Chemically sensitive field effect transistors. In *Ion-selective electrodes in analytical chemistry* (ed. H. Freiser), pp. 107-74. Plenum Press, New York.

Koryta, J. (1975). *Ion-selective electrodes.* Cambridge University Press.

Krey, D., Dobos, K. and Zimmer, G. (1982/83). An integrated CO-sensitive MOS transistor. *Sensors and Actuators* **3**, 169–77.

Lundstrom, I. (1981). Hydrogen sensitive MOS-structure Part 1: Principles and applications. *Sensors and Actuators* **1**, 403–26.

—— and Soderberg, D. (1981/82). Hydrogen sensitive MOS-structures Part 2: Characterization. *Sensors and Actuators* **2**, 105–38.

—— Shivaraman, M. S. and Svensson, C. (1977). Chemical reactions on palladium surfaces studied with Pd-MOS structures. *Surface Science* **64**, 497–519.

—— and Lundqvist, L. (1975). A hydrogen sensitive MOS field-effect transistor. *Appl. Phys. Lett.* **26**, 55–7.

Matsuo, T., Esashi, M. and Iinuma, K. (1971). Biomedical active electrode utilizing field-effect of solid state device (1). *Digests of Joint Meeting of Tohoku Sections of I.E.E.J.,* October 1971.

McBride, P. T., Janata, J., Comte, P. A., Moss, S. D. and Johnson, C. C. (1978). Ion-selective field-effect transistors with polymeric membranes. *Anal. Chim. Acta.* **101**, 239–45.

McKinley, B. A., Saffle, J., Jordan, W. S., Janata, J., Moss, S. D. and Westenskow, D. R. (1980). *In vivo* continuous monitoring of K$^+$ in animals using ISFETs. *Med. Instrum.* **14**, 93–7.

Miyahara, Y., Matsu, F. and Moriizumi, T. (1983). Micro-enzyme sensors using semiconductor and enzyme-immobilization techniques. In *Proceedings of the international meeting on chemical sensors*, Fukuoka, Japan, September 19–22, 1983, 513–518. Elsevier, New York.

Muller, R. S. and Kamins, T. I. (1977). *Device electronics for integrated circuits.* John Wiley, New York.

Poteat, T. L. and Lalevic, B. (1982). Transition metal-gate MOS gaseous detectors. *IEEE Trans. Electron Devices* **ED-29**, 123–9.

Pungor, E., Toth, K. and Havas, J. (1966). Theory and application of heterogenous rubber membrane electrodes in the determination of some ions. *Mikrochim. Acta* **1966**, 689–98.

Shiramizu, B. T., Janata, J. and Moss, S. D. (1979). Ion-selective field effect transistors with heterogeneous membranes. *Anal. Chim. Acta* **108**, 161–7.

Stenberg, M. and Dahlenback, B. I. (1983). Surface-accessible FET for gas sensing. *Sensors and Actuators* **4**, 273–81.

Sze, S. E. (1981). *Physics of semiconductor devices* (2nd edn). John Wiley, New York.

Zemel, J. N. (1975). Ion-sensitive field effect transistors and related devices. *Anal. Chem.* **47**, 255A–66A.

27

Biosensors based on semiconductor gas sensors

BENGT DANIELSSON and FREDRIK WINQUIST

27.1 Introduction

In this chapter we will describe some biological applications of semi-conductor gas sensors based on PdMOS-components developed by Lundström *et al.* (1975). These are primarily hydrogen sensitive field effect transistors fabricated by metal oxide semiconductor technique (PdMOSFET) although they could display a certain sensitivity towards small hydrogen containing molecules, such as ammonia and hydrogen sulphide. Indeed, in our first study in this field, Danielsson *et al.* (1979) demonstrated the feasibility of using an ammonia-sensitive PdMOSFET as a transducer in an 'enzyme transistor' utilizing the enzymes urease and creatinine imino-hydrolase. After this preliminary study we started investigations of the use of hydrogen-sensitive PdMOS components for monitoring hydrogen producing systems including the enzyme hydrogenase (EC 1.12.1.2) (Danielsson *et al.* 1983). Following the discovery of techniques for reproducible enhancement of the ammonia-sensitivity of PdMOS-devices by Winquist *et al.* (1983), attention was again directed towards the combination of this group of sensors with biological systems. Recent studies show that such ammonia sensors can be used in highly specific and sensitive biosensors (Winquist *et al.* 1984*a,b*; 1985).

Biotechnology today is receiving tremendous political, economical, scientific, and general world-wide interest as one of the most promising field for future development. Biosensors, in particular, have been recognized as a concept bearing much promise for the future, both as a biotechnology product and especially as useful sensors for measurements in biotechnology, in complex media, fermentation broths and *in vivo*. For such measurements the sensor must be rugged, have good operational stability, and withstand clogging, fouling, and interfering compounds. In many cases, it must also have high sensitivity and small dimensions. In this context, we have had very good experiences with our biosensors based on gas sensors, in which the detector is separated from the sample solution by a gas permeable membrane with only the biological component of the biosensor directly exposed to the sample. We are generally using small columns containing an immobilized

531

preparation of the biocatalyst, which ensures high operational stability. In most cases, a large excess of catalytic activity can be employed resulting in virtually unchanged performance of the reactor despite variations in sample composition, buffer capacity, pH, ionic strength, colour, turbidity, temperature, denaturing, and even, to some extent, to inhibitor concentration.

This is in contrast to biosensors based on ISFETs (ion sensitive field effect transistors) which are operated in the sample solution and consequently, will have their response affected by pH, buffer capacity, and the concentration of interfering ionic species similar to the measured compound.

Semiconductors, in general, have the advantage of cheap fabrication by common semiconductor technology, resulting in small size and the possibility to develop multifunctional devices as well as the direct integration with electronics for signal processing — 'smart sensors'. These features are especially attractive for *in vivo* sensors as it would allow for miniaturized biosensors with several enzyme patches on a single chip, either for different analyses or with several parallel channels for increased reliability. A four-function CHEMFET for simultaneous measurement of potassium, sodium, calcium, and hydrogen ions has been described by Sibbald *et al.* (1984). A further advantage of the semiconductor sensors is their low-impedance connection to associated electronics, which makes the signal leads less sensitive to electrical disturbances.

An interesting aspect of using a gas detector to follow a biochemical reaction that occurs in solution is that the measured compound will be present in a relatively higher concentration in the gas phase than in the liquid phase since the detector can be placed in a comparatively small gas volume. This is reflected by the fact that a sensitivity for NH_4^+ in aqueous solution of 0.1 μM can easily be obtained with a sensor having only 1 ppm NH_3 (g)-sensitivity. Similar results are obtained with the hydrogen sensors.

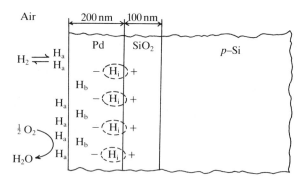

Fig. 27.1 Schematics of the chemical reactions occurring at a palladium interface.

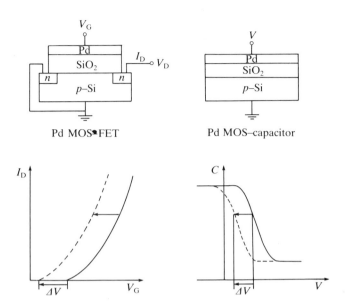

Fig. 27.2 Left: Schematic illustration of a PdMOS field effect transistor and the corresponding I_D-V_G characteristics. Right: Schematic illustration of a PdMOS-capacitor and the corresponding $C(V)$-curve. Exposure to hydrogen will shift the characteristics to the left as indicated by the dotted lines.

In the following we will describe theory, fabrication, and measurement techniques involving H_2- and NH_3-sensing semiconductor structures. Application examples include the use of hydrogenase as a hydrogen producing system, recycling systems, and various ammonia producing enzymes, such as urease, creatininase, and amino acid deaminases.

27.2 Physical background

Hydrogen-detecting PdMOS-structures are made by evaporating a non-porous, 100–200 nm thick Pd-film on a p-silicon chip with a thermally grown 100 nm thick oxide layer (Fig. 27.1). The sensors can be fabricated as capacitors with an aluminum film as back contact, or as field effect transistors (Fig. 27.2). In the latter case, a temperature controlled heating circuitry is included on the same chip. (Fig. 27.3). The capacitors, which are easier to make and therefore are the component type of choice for exploring studies, e.g. of film composition, are placed on a small temperature controlled metal plate when used. The size of the components is of the order of 1 mm².

The reactions constituting the hydrogen sensitivity of PdMOS-structures

Active gate

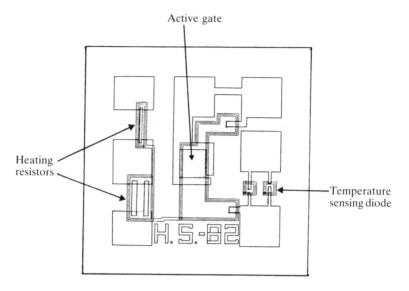

Heating
resistors

Temperature
sensing diode

Fig. 27.3 A 2.5×2.5 mm^2 chip containing a PdMOSFET with integrated temperature control. The chip can be mounted in a TO-18 package.

occur on the surface and inside of the Pd layer. As indicated in Fig. 27.1, hydrogen molecules in the surrounding gas are dissociated on the surface and some of the adsorbed hydrogen atoms diffuse into the Pd layer where they become polarized in the electrical field over the component. The dipole layer thus formed will cause a voltage drop in the electric field, which in turn will shift the I_D-V_G characteristics of a transistor or the $C(V)$-curve of a capacitor along the voltage axis (Fig. 27.2). The voltage drop is related to the ambient hydrogen pressure following the equation:

$$\Delta V = C_1 \times (P_{H_2})^{0.5} \text{ for } P_{H_2} \leqslant 50 \text{ ppm} \tag{27.1}$$

where C_1 is a constant. C_1 depends on the properties of the Pd layer, film thickness, size of the active area, etc. A typical value of C_1 is 27 mV/ppm. Hydrogen atoms leave the Pd layer on recombination to hydrogen molecules or on combination with oxygen (if present) to water. Consequently, the sensitivity will be considerably higher in the absence of oxygen, ~ 0.01 ppm, than in the presence of oxygen, ~ 1 ppm. The recovery time will also be much shorter in the presence of oxygen, although it can be reduced by increasing the working temperature of the sensor to 100–150°C, which is the normal working temperature of a PdMOSFET. This temperature also prevents water molecules from sticking to the sensor surface. The response time is about 1 min at low concentrations of hydrogen. PdMOS devices were thoroughly described by Lundström (1981).

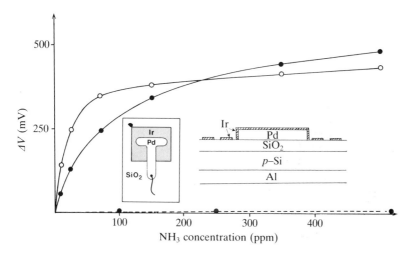

Fig. 27.4 Steady state response for different modifications of a PdMOS-structure in comparison with that of an unmodified device. (—•—) Ir modified device; (—○—) Pt modified device; (----) unmodified device. The inserts show a schematic drawing and the cross-section of a PdMOS-capacitor modified with a thin Ir-film.

27.2.1 Increased ammonia gas sensitivity

Normal PdMOS devices have only a low NH_3-sensitivity. As shown by Winquist and co-workers (1983), the NH_3-sensitivity can be considerably enhanced by incorporating a second submonolayer of a suitable catalytic metal such as Ir or Pt (Fig. 27.4). Ir has usually been chosen in the following studies since it gives a high NH_3-sensitivity at the same time as the H_2-sensitivity is comparatively low. Hitherto, devices in the form of capacitors have been used with an Ir layer with a nominal thickness of 3 nm resistively evaporated through a metal mask over a T-shaped Pd film as shown in the insert of Fig. 27.4.

NH_3-sensors will now also be available as MOSFETs with integrated temperature control. In contrast to the H_2-sensors, our NH_3-sensors are usually operated at room temperature or at a slightly higher temperature, 35°C, to prevent water condensation. This means that in a biosensor, the biochemical component can be placed very close to the sensing area. The maximum NH_3-sensitivity is 1 ppm. At low NH_3 concentrations ($\leqslant 50$ ppm) the response follows the equation

$$\Delta V = C_2 \times (P_{NH_3})^a \tag{27.2}$$

where C_2 and a are constants (typical values are $C_2 = 24$ mV/ppm and $a = 0.55$). Furthermore, Winquist *et al.* (1984b) have shown that if an IrMOS is exposed to NH_3 for only a short time, Δt, at low concentration

($\leqslant 50$ ppm) then the maximum voltage shift for an ammonia pulse is

$$\Delta V = k \times P_{NH_3} \times \Delta t, \text{ where } k \text{ is a constant.} \qquad (27.3)$$

A similar linear relation applies to H_2-sensitive PdMOS devices as well. Normally $\Delta t \leqslant 60$ s, which is short enough to achieve linearity, but a sufficiently long time for reliable measurements.

27.3 Experimental

For gaseous samples the experimental arrangement can be quite simple. It has turned out to be advantageous to work with rather short sample pulses as this gives linear response for low concentrations (eqn 27.3) and makes the determination less affected by any base line drift. The sample can be introduced via a (timer-controlled) miniature solenoid valve that is normally open to the air but can open for the sample for a short period, e.g. 10 s. At continuous monitoring this can be automatically repeated by the timer, e.g. every 10 min. The samples are conveniently drawn through the valve to the sensor with a peristaltic pump (~ 1 ml/min). Due to the relatively high sensitivity a dilution of the sample usually has to be made. Immediately after the pump the sample stream is therefore mixed with a stream of air of nitrogen controlled by a needle-valve or a flow-controller to give a suitable dilution factor. The combined gas stream is then led through a small flow cell in which the gas sensor is mounted. The dilution gas also efficiently flushes the cell between samples.

With aqueous samples the compound to be measured must be transferred to the gas phase in a controlled fashion in relation to its concentration. This can be done with the equipment shown in Fig. 27.5, in which the separation is accomplished with a porous, gas-permeable Teflon membrane (Fluoropore, Millipore, USA) with a pore diameter of 0.2 to 5 μm. A membrane area of 1–3 cm² suffices for the flow rates normally employed, i.e. a fluid stream of

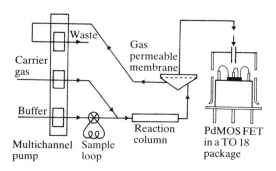

Fig. 27.5 Flow system for the determination of hydrogen in solutions.

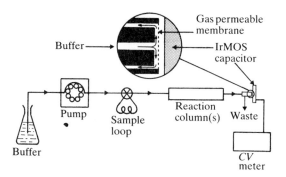

Fig. 27.6 Experimental set-up for the flow injection analysis of ammonia with an IrMOS-capacitor.

0.5–1 ml/min mixed with 2.5 ml/min of air or nitrogen. From the other side of the membrane a gas stream of 1 ml/min leads to the detector cell. Samples are introduced via a sample injection valve with 0.5 ml loop. It is convenient to use a multichannel peristaltic pump (for instance a Minipuls H8, Gilson, France) for administering the different flow streams. The pump can also be used for any additions or dilutions required. At high concentrations, requiring more extensive dilutions, this set-up could be combined with the apparatus described above.

For work with NH_3-sensitive IrMOS capacitors a somewhat different approach can be used since the capacitors are mounted in such a way that the sensing area is very close to the gas permeable membrane. Over such short distances gas transport by diffusion is satisfactory, obviating the need for a carrier gas. (See Fig. 27.6.) A peristaltic pump is used to pump buffer and sample at a flow rate of 0.4 ml/min past the membrane (porous Teflon with 5 μm pore size, diameter 4 mm) which is placed 0.2 mm above the sensor. In order to increase the pressure over the membrane a tubing 0.5 m × 0.2 mm internal diameter is attached to the outlet of the flow-cell. Samples are introduced through an injection valve with a 0.2 ml loop. If necessary, it is simple to raise the pH of the effluent of the enzyme column or of the NH_4^+ solution by mixing with an alkaline solution in order to increase the proportion of NH_3. However, remarkably high sensitivity is obtained even at rather low pH. Figure 27.7 compares the response obtained with NH_4^+ samples at pH 7.7 and 12.7. It should be noted that ammonia producing enzymic reactions normally have rather high pH-optima (pH > 8).

An alternative, enzyme electrode-like design was recently developed by Winquist and co-workers (1984a). Here, the enzyme probe consists of an enzyme layer placed directly on the gas-permeable membrane, which in turn is placed in close proximity to the IrMOS capacitor (see below).

PdMOSFETs and equipment for hydrogen determination are available

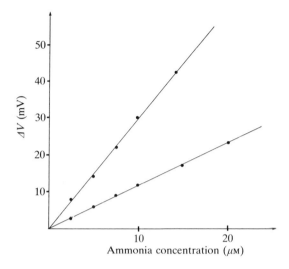

Fig. 27.7 Calibration graphs obtained from 0.2 ml ammonia-N standards at pH 7.7 and 12.7, respectively, with the flow injection system for ammonia-N determination.

from Sensistor AB, Linköping, Sweden, IrMOSFETs will soon be available for NH_3-determinations with the same equipment. The experiments described here involving NH_3 were carried out with a capacitance meter and temperature controller assembled at the Applied Physics Laboratory at the University of Linköping.

27.3.1 Preparation of immobilized hydrogenase

Hydrogenase (EC 1.12.1.2) is a key enzyme for dehydrogenase assays utilizing a PdMOSFET, which becomes evident upon examination of the reaction catalysed by hydrogenase (HDH):

$$NAD(P)^+ + H_2 \overset{HDH}{\rightleftharpoons} NAD(P)H + H^+ \tag{27.4}$$

We have used an HDH isolated from *Alcaligenes eutrophus* H 16 and immobilized on controlled pore glass (CPG) following procedures described by Winquist *et al.* (1986*b*).

27.4 Results

27.4.1 Hydrogen gas determination

The hydrogen gas sensor produced by the Sensistor Co. is primarily intended for use as a hydrogen leak detector. As an example, hydrogen can be used as a cheap, non-poisonous test gas for localization of damage to underground electricity or telecommunication cables. Hydrogen is introduced at one end of the cable and any leakage can easily be localized as hydrogen readily leaks through the soil.

Many important routes lead to hydrogen evolution or consumption and hydrogen is produced by many micro-organisms under anaerobic conditions. Furthermore, various hydrogenase systems are attracting considerable interest since they are involved in microbial or photosynthetic hydrogen production as a future energy source of great potential. We have previously demonstrated that a PdMOSFET in the set up shown in Fig. 27.5 can be conveniently used for monitoring microbial hydrogen production (Winquist *et al.* 1982). In this study we particularly studied *Clostridium acetobutylicum* immobilized in alginate beads, with the effluent after dilution fed to the apparatus shown in Fig. 27.5.

Cleland *et al.* (1984) used a PdMOS sensor in a study of the hydrogen evolution from an *E. coli* cultivation. Hydrogen is produced only under anaerobic conditions and this was clearly demonstrated as hydrogen evolution sharply increased when the oxygen level fell to zero. The hydrogen production rapidly decreased when oxygen was admitted as a consequence of the inhibitory effect of oxygen on the hydrogenase system. It was suggested that the PdMOS sensor could be used to detect inhomogeneity of mixing, e.g. in scale-up studies of bioreactors, because any 'partial anaerobiosis' would lead to hydrogen evolution that would readily be detectable with the highly sensitive hydrogen detector.

The susceptibility of *Enterobacteriaceae* to ampicillin was investigated by Hörnsten *et al.* (1985) using a hydrogen sensitive PdMOSFET. A large number of isolates of enterobacteria from urinary tract infections were cultured in sealed tubes and the amount of hydrogen produced was measured by injecting a 2 ml gas sample into a measuring cell housing the PdMOS-sensor. Molecular hydrogen is an end product of mixed acid fermentation by *Enterobacteriaceae*, and therefore the degree of inhibition of hydrogen evolution is a measure of ampicillin susceptibility. In all but a few cases it could be established within five hours whether the cells were viable or not in the presence of ampicillin. The results agreed well with common, routine disc-diffusion results. In conclusion, assay of hydrogen production promises to become a useful, quick and simple technique for establishing antibiotic susceptibility.

In a recent study, Hörnsten *et al.* (1986*a*) investigated the ampicillin susceptibility of an *E. coli* strain causing urinary tract infection using a PdMOSFET sensor for determining hydrogen production (Hörnsten *et al.* 1986*b*) in comparison with three other parameters: heat production (as measured with use of an enzyme thermistor unit (Danielsson 1986; see also Chapter 29)), intracellular ATP-level, and acid/base production. Hydrogen evolution, heat production, and acid/base production were measured on-line

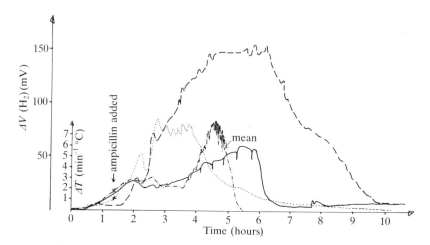

Fig. 27.8 Hydrogen and heat production by *E. coli* under anaerobic conditions with and without ampicillin added at minimal inhibitory concentration (MIC = 4 mg/l): —·—·—, thermogram with and ——, without ampicillin; ·····, hydrogen concentration with and ----, without ampicillin.

from fermentations in various media of 2–2.5 l of *E. coli* suspensions with different additions of ampicillin. Hydrogen was sampled by a peristaltic pump through a timer-operated solenoid valve and mixed with an air-stream for proper dilution as described above (Section 27.3). All four methods were found to give valuable information. The use of two of the methods in parallel evidently facilitates correct conclusions. Hydrogen monitoring during fermentations gives rapid indication of antibiotic susceptibility and requires only rather simple techniques and equipment. Figure 27.8 compares two different runs with and without ampicillin added.

27.4.1.1 Hydrogenase Small reaction columns containing about 1 ml of HDH immobilized on CPG were inserted in the analytical system shown in Fig. 27.5 for quantification of NAD$^+$ and NADH. Samples of NADH (0.5 ml) were directly introduced into the stream of Tris-HCl buffer, pH 8.0, and the hydrogen produced by the HDH catalysed reaction was monitored with a PdMOSFET. The calibration curve was linear up to 0.5 mM NADH (C_{NADH} (μM) = 0.1 × ΔV (mV)) with a detectability of 0.03 mM. At least ten samples per hour could be analysed (Danielsson *et al.* 1983).

The same system could be used for determination of NAD$^+$ based on the reversed HDH reaction in which H$_2$ is consumed. In this case the working buffer was supplemented with 100 ppm of H$_2$ and 0.1 mM NADH. The calibration curve was linear over the range 0.05–0.6 mM. Furthermore, we have studied combinations of various dehydrogenases and HDH to extend the applicability of hydrogen sensors. For instance, ethanol could be quantified using the following reaction sequence:

$$C_2H_5OH + NAD^+ \xrightarrow[- CH_3CHO]{ADH} NADH + H^+ \xrightarrow{HDH} NAD^+ + H_2 \quad (27.5)$$

An interesting approach to the analysis of volatile dehydrogenase substrates directly in gaseous samples is possible through the use of co-immobilized dehydrogenase/HDH in a 'moist' column saturated with buffer and coenzyme. The sample is introduced into a carrier gas stream that transports the hydrogen produced in the reaction column to the PdMOS-detector. Encouraging results have been obtained in preliminary tests with alcohol and aldehyde vapours.

As immobilized HDH is comparatively stable, it offers an attractive way of coenzyme regeneration, since the reaction solution is not polluted by any other substrates/products than H_2/H^+. We have demonstrated the feasibility of such a system using co-immobilized alanine dehydrogenase/HDH for the formation of alanine from pyruvate accompanied by continuous regeneration of NADH (Danielsson *et al.* 1982):

$$\begin{array}{c} \text{Pyruvate} + NH_3 \xrightarrow{\text{L-Alanine-dehydrogenase}} \text{L-Alanine} \\ \overbrace{NADH \qquad\qquad NAD^+} \\ H^+ \longleftarrow \underbrace{\qquad\qquad\qquad} H_2 \\ HDH \end{array} \quad (27.6)$$

It can be anticipated that this type of coenzyme regenerative system could find use for signal amplification in combination with PdMOS-sensors in a similar way as described by Scheller and co-workers (1985) using substrate amplifying systems together with an enzyme thermistor. This should make very sensitive determinations possible.

27.4.2 Measurements involving NH₃

Ammonium is a weak acid with $pK_a = 9.25$, which means that ammonium ions are in equilibrium with ammonia in the pH range 6–12. In measurements of ammonia in aqueous solutions with the flow system based on the IrMOS-capacitance the fraction of NH_3 is measured. Consequently, the pH of the solution is an important parameter that must be carefully controlled. If the pH is raised, formation of $NH_3(g)$ will be favoured and the sensitivity will be higher. Maximum sensitivity is obtained for pH values above 11. For determination of ammonia in inorganic samples, such as rain and river water, we have worked at pH 12.5. With biological samples the pH could not be raised so far, because NH_3 could be released from labile nitrogen compounds under strong alkaline conditions. For blood samples the pH is not allowed to exceed 8.5.

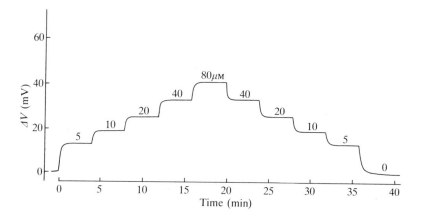

Fig. 27.9 Recording from a continuous monitoring of the ammonium concentration in buffer, pH 7.7. The ammonium concentration was changed stepwise every 4 min.

The concentration of ammonia-N (total amount of ammonia and ammonium ions) in aqueous solutions can be determined with the flow injection system depicted in Fig. 27.6 with the reaction column omitted. The linear calibration graphs obtained with 0.2 ml samples at pH 7.7 and 12.7 respectively, are displayed in Fig. 27.7. The lower limit of detection (at S/N = 3) was 0.4 μM at pH 7.7 and 0.2 μM at pH 12.7 and the graphs were linear up to 50 μM. The high sensitivity makes it possible to perform determination of ammonia-N in only 20 μl samples of blood or blood serum, even after ten-fold dilution. The expected concentration range is 10–70 μM. This method would be useful for pediatric samples due to the small sample volume needed and it should be noted that the technique works equally well with whole blood since the colour or turbidity of the sample will not interfere.

To give an idea of the performance of the sensor a continuous and a pulse-wise recording of ammonia-N in buffer pH 7.7 is given in Fig. 27.9. The concentration was changed stepwise every 4 min.

A disadvantage of the present IrPdMOS sensor is that some low molecular weight amines as well as H_2 interfere with the NH_3 determination. Table 27.1 lists the response obtained with some amines in comparison with ammonia at pH 7.7. It was found that the response for amines was even higher for gaseous samples (Winquist *et al.* 1984*b*). This indicates that the phase separation step and the membrane properties are important factors to consider in any efforts to bring down the interferences. It may also be possible to change the catalytic properties of the sensor surface. Another possibility is to use scavenger (enzyme) columns or to make differential measurements. In the applications studied to date, however, we have not found that interferences would be a serious problem in practice.

Table 27.1 Response of an IrMOS-capacitor for various amines (50 μM) at pH 7.7 in relation to the response for 50 μM ammonia-N

Compound	Relative sensitivity %
Ammonia-N	100
Methylamine	10
Ethylamine	5
Butylamine	0
Diethylamine	2
Ethanolamine	2
Ethylenediamine	1

27.4.2.1 Urea determinations Urea was determined by the flow system shown in Fig. 27.6 using a 40 × 2 mm Eupergit C (polyacrylic beads from Röhm–Pharma GmbH, Darmstadt, West Germany) column with 40 IU of urease. Urease produces two molecules of NH_3 per urea molecule:

$$(NH_2)_2CO + H_2O \xrightleftharpoons{\text{Urease}} CO_2 + 2NH_3 \qquad (27.7)$$

Due to the large amount of enzyme on the column, 100% conversion and unchanged performance was achieved for at least one month (Winquist *et al.* 1984*a*) despite unfavourable pH of the working buffer. The assay was

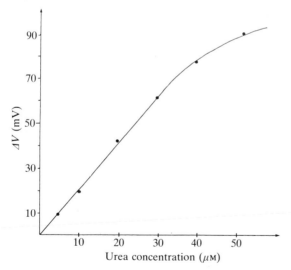

Fig. 27.10 Calibration curve for 0.2 ml urea standards at pH 8.1 using a reaction column containing 40 I.U. of urease.

made in 0.05 M Tris-HCl, pH 8.1, while the pH optimum for urease activity is 7.0. The calibration curve for 0.2 ml samples was linear up to 40 μM with a lower limit of detection of 0.2 μM (Fig. 27.10). Twenty 500-fold diluted serum samples could be assayed per hour with a precision of about 2%. The sampling rate evidently is too low for large collections of samples and should be increased. One possibility would be to use several parallel sensors (and may enzyme columns) in an automatically switching arrangement. The present flow system is, however, excellent for a limited number of samples and is a suitable back-up system due to its high operational stability and short start-up time.

27.4.2.2 Determination of L-asparagine Several enzymes are available which more or less selectively deaminate various amino acids. An example is L-asparaginase (EC 3.5.1.1):

$$\text{L-Asparagine} + H_2O \xrightarrow{\text{L-Asparaginase}} \text{L-Aspartate} + NH_4^+ \quad (27.8)$$

For assays of samples that normally contain ammonia, such as blood and serum samples, an ammonia scavenging column of L-glutamate-dehydrogenase can be used to remove the ammonia prior to the analysis of other ammonia producing compounds:

$$NH_4^+ + NADH + \alpha\text{-Oxoglutarate} \xrightarrow[\text{dehydrogenase}]{\text{L-Glutamate-}} NAD^+ + \text{L-Glutamate} \quad (27.9)$$

The use of a scavenger column can be illustrated by an assay proposed for the determination of L-asparagine in blood (serum) (Winquist *et al.* 1986*b*). Twenty units of L-glutamate-dehydrogenase and five units of L-asparaginase, respectively, were bound to Eupergit C and packed in two consecutive Teflon columns (32 × 2 mm) connected to the flow system shown in Fig. 27.6. The working buffer was 0.05 M Tris-HCl, pH 8.2, containing 1 mM NADH, 0.5 mM α-oxoglutaric acid, and 3 mM NaN$_3$. Under the conditions at room temperature the L-glutamate-dehydrogenase column was capable of completely removing up to 0.5 mM ammonia-N in 0.2 ml samples at a flow rate of 0.4 ml/min, which gives good margins for diluted blood samples. The calibration graph for L-asparagine was linear up to 40 μM; the voltage shift was 0.8 mV/μM. After every 20 samples, columns and tubings were washed for 5 min with 0.1 M K-phosphate, pH 7.0, containing 0.8 M NaCl.

27.4.2.3 Creatinine determinations A method for determination of creatinine in serum and urine was recently developed by Winquist *et al.*

(1986*a*). Ammonia, released by creatinine iminohydrolase (EC 3.5.4.21) immobilized on oxirane acrylic beads (Eupergit C),

$$\text{Creatinine} + H_2O \xrightarrow{\text{Creatininase}} \textit{N}\text{-Methylhydantoin} + \textit{NH}_3$$
(27.10)

was measured with an IrMOS-capacitor. The creatininase column was preceded by a L-glutamate dehydrogenase column for removal of endogeneous ammonia-N. The working buffer was 0.05 M Tris-HCl, pH 8.5 and the procedure was the same as for determination of L-asparagine. With 6 IU of creatininase (obtained from Aalto Bio Reagents Ltd., Dublin, Ireland) in a 0.1 ml column, the sensor response was linear up to 30 μM for 85 μl samples with a detection limit of 0.2 μM. Very satisfactory results were obtained in comparison with conventional methods; 25-fold diluted serum and 1000-fold diluted urine samples were analysed with a precision of about 3% without any serious interferences. Thus, the sample consumption was very low, which makes this method well suited for pediatric samples, although the relatively low sample throughput (15 samples/h) is a hindrance for larger series of samples to be processed.

27.5 Concluding remarks

The flow system equipped with an enzyme reactor (Fig. 27.6) has been used for a number of enzyme–substrate combinations. If the activity of the reactor is large enough for complete substrate conversion, a given amount of substrate will give the same amount of ammonia irrespective of enzyme–substrate combination. This is shown in Table 27.2 where the

Table 27.2 Responses obtained with an IrMOS-capacitor for different enzyme–substrate combinations. Buffer: 0.05 M Tris-HCl, pH 8.5. Substrate concentration: 10 μM during 30 s

Substrate	Enzyme	Product	Voltage shift (mV)
Urea	Urease	CO_2 + $2NH_3$	16
L-Asparagine	Asparaginase	Aspartate + NH_3	8
L-Aspartate	Aspartase	Fumarate + NH_3	8
L-Glutamate	Glutamate dehydrogenase	α-oxoglutarate + NADH + NH_3	8
Adenosine	Adenosine deaminase	Inosine + NH_3	8
Creatinine	Creatinine iminohydrolase	$\textit{N}$-Methylhydantoin + NH_3	8
NH_3	—	NH_3	8

responses for various such combinations are compared under identical conditions. Urea gives twice the voltage shift as compared to the other substrates because it produces two ammonia molecules. Detection ranges for some NH_3-producing systems under the operating conditions described in the previous section are summarized in Table 27.3.

Table 27.3   Operating ranges for NH_3 and some enzyme–substrate systems with a flow injection system according to Fig. 27.6. Sample volume: 0.2 ml; Flow rate: 0.4 ml/min

Substrate	Enzyme	pH_{exp}	Linear range (μM)*
NH_3	—	7.7	0.4–50
NH_3	—	12.7	<0.2–50
L-Asparagine	Asparaginase	8.2	0.2–40
Creatinine	Creatinine imminohydrolase	8.5	0.2–30
Urea	Urease	8.1	0.2–40

* The first number corresponds to the lower limit of detection ($S/N = 3$).

In the introduction we discussed advantages and disadvantages of the present sensor design that must be operated in the gas phase. In many applications the measuring procedure would be greatly simplified if the transducer could be placed directly in the sample solution. This would be of special value in probes intended for *in vivo* monitoring. Work is in progress at the Linköping laboratory to modify the PdMOS-structures for operation in electrolyte solutions. These experiments reveal that the approach is possible, but no attempts have been made as yet to combine these sensors with enzymes. Slow responses to changes in the hydrogen concentration presently is a problem. In particular, the recovery time is much longer in electrolytes than in gases.

The membrane used for phase separation in the biosensor designs described in this chapter can, however, be placed very close to the sensor surface. Thus we have recently prepared a probe-like construction with relatively small dimensions which rather easily could be further reduced, if desired (Winquist *et al.* 1985). Figure 27.11 shows the design and the responses for urea and ammonia of a urease probe based on an IrMOS-capacitor. The sensor is embedded with a polyester resin in a small tube leaving only the porous Teflon membrane (3 mm²) exposed to the solution. About 200 IU of urease were applied onto the membrane and cross-linked with glutaraldehyde. This bio-probe has a rather high sensitivity, although its response is slower than that of the NH_3-detecting flow system. The sensitivity for urea is higher than for $NH_4{}^+$, since each urea molecule produces two ammonia molecules. By using one probe with active urease and one with

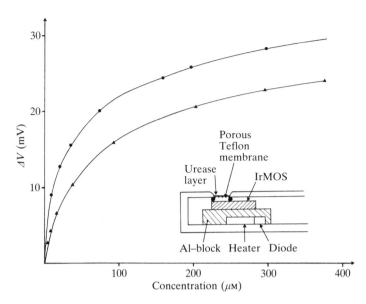

Fig. 27.11 Stead state response for urea (•) and NH_4^+ (▲) of a urease probe. The insert shows a cross-section of the probe.

inactivated enzyme it was possible to determine urea concentrations in samples containing endogeneous ammonia. Future developments could further bring down the dimensions of the probes and also combine several sensor elements for incorporation of a reference or for the simultaneous measurement of several components.

The H_2S-sensitivity of PdMOS-sensors was early demonstrated by Shivaraman (1976). It is of the same order as that of NH_3 and H_2. No attempts have been made to date to exploit this property, but there should be many interesting biological applications, both with pure enzyme systems for detection of sulphur-containing metabolites and with micro-organisms.

There is no doubt that future developments along the lines described here will bring semiconductor sensors closer to useable *in vivo* sensors, multi-component sensors, 'smart sensors', and maybe also towards the biochip concept.

References

Cleland, N., Hörnsten, G., Elwing, H., Enfors, S.-O. and Lundström, I. (1984). Measurement of hydrogen evolution by oxygen-limited *E. coli* by means of a hydrogen sensitive Pd-MOS sensor. *Appl. Microbiol. Biotechnol.* **20** 268–70.

Danielsson, B. (1986). Enzyme thermistor devices. *Methods in Enzymol.* In press.

—— Lundström, I., Mosbach, K. and Stiblert, L. (1979). On a new enzyme transducer combination: The enzyme transistor. *Anal. Lett.* **12**, 1189–99.

—— Winquist, F., Malpote, J.-Y. and Mosbach, K. (1982). Regeneration of NADH

548   *Biosensors based on semiconductor gas sensors*

with immobilized systems of alanine dehydrogenase and hydrogen dehydrogenase. *Biotechnol. Lett.* **4**, 673–8.

—— Mosbach, K. and Lundström, I. (1983). Bioanalytical applications of hydrogen- and ammonia-sensitive palladium gate MOS devices. In *Proc. int. meeting on chemical sensors* in Fukuoka, Kodansha, Tokyo, pp. 507–512. Elsevier, New York.

Hörnsten, G., Elwing, H., Kihlström, E. and Lundström, I. (1985). Determination of molecular hydrogen in investigations of the susceptibility of *Enterobacteriaceae* to ampicillin. *J. Antimicrob. Chemother.* **15**, 695–700.

—— Danielsson, B., Nilsson, L. and Lundström, I. (1986*a*). Physiological studies of *Escherichia coli* under ampicillin stress and anaerobic conditions. Submitted.

Hörnsten, G., Danielsson, B., Elwing, H., and Lundström, I. (1986*b*). Sensorized on line determinations of molecular hydrogen in *Escherichia coli* fermentations. *Appl. Microbiol. Biotechnol.* **24**, 117–21.

Lundström, I. (1981). Hydrogen-sensitive MOS-structures. Part I: Principles and applications. *Sensors and Actuators* **1**, 403–26.

—— Shivaraman, S. and Svensson, C. (1975). A hydrogen sensitive Pd-gate MOS-transistor. *J. Appl. Phys.* **46**, 3876–81.

Scheller, F., Siegbahn, N., Danielsson, B. and Mosbach, K. (1985). High-sensitivity enzyme thermistor determination of L-lactate by substrate recycling. *Anal. Chem.* **57**, 1740–3.

Shivaraman, S. (1976). Detection of hydrogen sulfide with palladium-gate MOS field-effect transistors. *J. Appl. Phys.* **47**, 3592–3.

Sibbald, A., Whalley, P. D. and Covington, A. K. (1984). A miniature flow-through cell with a four-function ChemFET integrated circuit for simultaneous measurements of potassium, hydrogen, calcium and sodium ions. *Anal. Chim. Acta* **159**, 47–62.

Winquist, F., Lundström. I. and Danielsson, B. (1986*a*). Determination of creatinine by an ammonia-sensitive semiconductor structure and immobilized enzymes. *Anal. Chem.* **58**, 145–8.

—— Danielsson, B., Lundström, I. and Mosbach, K. (1982). Use of hydrogen-sensitive Pd-MOS materials in biochemical analysis. *App. Biochem. Biotechnol.* **7**, 135–9.

—— (1986*b*). The use of hydrogen and ammonia sensitive semiconductor structures in analytical biochemistry — 'Enzyme transistors'. *Methods in Enzymol.* In press.

—— Spetz, A., Lundström, I. and Danielsson, B. (1984*a*). Determination of urea with an ammonia gas-sensitive semiconductor device in combination with urease. *Anal. Chim. Acta* **163**, 143–9.

—— (1984*b*). Determination of ammonia in air and aqueous samples with a gas-sensitive semiconductor capacitor. *Anal. Chim. Acta* **164**, 127–38.

—— Armgarth, M., Nylander, C. and Lundström, I. (1983). Modified palladium metal-oxide-semiconductor structures with increased ammonia gas sensitivity. *Appl. Phys. Lett.* **43**, 839–41.

—— Lundström, I. and Danielsson, B. (1985). Biosensors based on ammonia sensitive metal-oxide-semiconductor structures. *Sensors and Actuators.* **8**, 91–100.

Mechanical and acoustic impedance

28

Principles and potential of piezo-electric transducers and acoustical techniques

DAVID J. CLARK, BARRIE C. BLAKE-COLEMAN, and MICHAEL R. CALDER

28.1 Introduction

Acoustical methods have become highly sophisticated particularly through audio engineering and developments in naval instrumentation (e.g. echo sounding and acoustic signatures of vessels). Accompanying such developments have been significant advances in piezo-electric transducer technology, particularly at the upper ultrasonic frequency limits and in the development of piezo-electric polymers. However, exploitations of acoustical techniques in the biological sciences have remained relatively few and dispersed until recently. Most notable are advances in acoustic microscopy, surface mass detecting sensors, acoustic resonance densitometry, and acoustic impedance of inhomogeneous systems. The principles and application of such techniques are discussed.

28.2 Piezo-electric transducers

Piezo-electric transducers are central to most acoustic techniques. Piezo-electricity was discovered in 1880 by the Curie brothers as a phenomenon where electric dipoles (developing a potential difference) are generated in anisotropic natural crystals subjected to mechanical stress (Curie and Curie 1880). Such materials also exhibit the converse effect in suffering dimensional change under the influence of an electric field. Some piezo-electric materials are also pyro-electric, electric polarization resulting from thermal absorption by the material (Cady 1946). All materials exhibiting an anisotropic effect, such as piezo-electricity, have no centre of symmetry in their crystal structure. All such crystals belong to one of 32 point groups (crystal classes), 20 of the 32 classes exhibit piezo-electric effects and ten of these pyro-electric effects. A few naturally abundant crystals (e.g. quartz, tourmaline, and Rochelle salt) are piezo-electric (Cady 1946). Although manmade ceramic piezo-electrics are most widely applied (van Randeraat and Setterington 1974), more recent piezo-electric polymers (Kocharyan *et al.* 1967) are finding increasing exploitation. Since polymeric materials are not usually obtained as single crystals of appreciable size, piezo-electric effects in these materials are usually observed in the uniaxially oriented state. According to the state of orientation, four types of symmetry are found (Fukada 1974). Certain anisotropic biological structures (e.g. DNA, proteins) can also be considered to be piezo-electric and pyro-electric (Fukada 1968, 1974), a point which could well prove important in molecular biosensor research.

28.2.1 Ceramics

The existence of a polar axis in natural piezo-electric crystals gives rise to an inherent polarization, before any electric field is applied. The highly polar structure of quartz crystals under different conditions of loading is outlined in Fig. 28.1a. Man-made piezo-electric ceramics have improved piezo-electric properties and are polycrystalline in structure (e.g. barium titanate and various lead zirconate-titanates). The individual crystallite domains possess polar axes which are randomly alligned and do not have piezo-electric properties in their original state. Polarization in intense electric fields at elevated temperatures (above the Curie point) aligns the polar axes of the individual crystallite domains (Fig. 28.1b). Ceramics are highly chemically stable and mechanically rigid, and can be sintered into a wide variety of shapes and sizes (van Randeraat and Setterington 1974).

28.2.2 Polymers

Kocharyan *et al.* (1967) first identified that the high polarity of the unit cells of polytrifluoroethylene, plasticized, and rigid polyvinyl chloride yielded their high piezo-electric activities. Polyvinylidene fluoride (PVDF) was later shown to be susceptible to still higher levels of poling (Kawai 1969). PVDF is an approximate equal mixture of amorphous and crystalline polymer, the latter principally having a non-polar alpha form and a highly polar beta form, where the hydrogen and fluorine atoms are arranged to give maximum dipole moment per unit cell (Fig. 28.2a). These are randomly oriented along the polymer chain until poled (Fig. 28.2b). Commercial processes also exploit uniaxial or biaxial mechanical stretching of the extruded or cast polymer to ensure that the beta form predominates. Unlike ceramics, PVDF films are highly compliant. Apart from their chemical resistance, they are more sensitive transducers of mechanical to electrical energy than ceramics or quartz crystals.

28.2.3 Modes of transduction

Dipoles are largely poled normal to the major plane of the piezo-electric material. Piezo-electrics are anisotropic, their electrical, mechanical, and electromechanical properties differing for electrical or mechanical transduction along their respective axes. Convention uses numbered subscripts to identify the vector and tensor directions (Fig. 28.3). The first subscript iden-

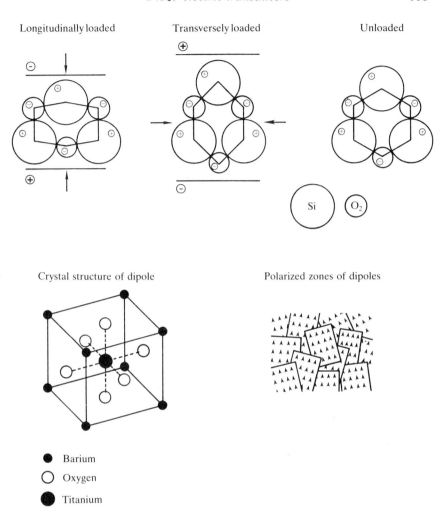

Fig. 28.1 Crystal and domain structures of piezo-electric ceramics. (a) Crystal structure of quartz showing changes in dipole moment underloading. (b) Barium titanate ceramic structure.

tifies the polarization and direction of field, the second the mechanical stress or strain axis (see Fukada 1974). Generally, polarization is along the y axis (subscript 3), when force can be applied along the x (subscript 1), y, or z (subscript 2) axes. Fig. 28.3 summarizes these conventions for the piezo-electric constant (d). Mechanical stress or strain (g), compliance ratio (s), dielectric constant (ϵ), etc. are similarly described (Fukada 1974). Thus transducer plates can be length, width, or thickness expanders (Fig. 28.3). Similarly, discs can be radial (d_{31}) or thickness expanders (d_{33}) and hoops or tubes,

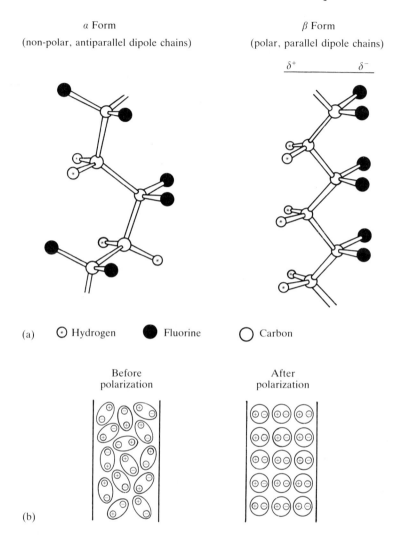

Fig. 28.2 Molecular structure and domain structure of polyvinylidene fluoride piezo-electric film. (a) Molecular structure of polyvinylidine fluoride. (b) Orientation of dipoles in polyvinylidine fluoride film.

length (d_{31}) or thickness expanders (d_{33}). Piezo-electric layers are often applied to non-piezo-electric materials to manufacture shear plates (e.g., d_{15} to achieve x and z plane stress). Laminates (multimorphs) of piezo-electric material, arranged serially or in parallel, can be manufactured to allow bending. Further, manufacturing processes are capable of altering the relative magnitudes of electrical, mechanical, and electromechanical properties

	Poled	Field axis	Stress or strain axis	Free axis	Piezo-electric constants
Length expander	↓	↕	↔	↗	d_{31}
Width expander	↓	↕	↗	↔	d_{32}
Thickness expander	↓	↕	↕	↗	d_{33}

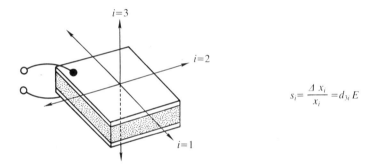

$$s_i = \frac{\varDelta x_i}{x_i} = d_{3i} E$$

Fig. 28.3 Anisotropy of mechanical, electrical, and electromechanical parameters in typical piezo-electric materials where the relative deformation (s_i) of the body in the x_i direction at a certain electrical field strength (E) is related to the piezoelectric strain constant (d_{3i}) shown in the table (above).

of the piezo-electric material itself to suit particular applications. Consequently, considerable attention is required in selecting the appropriate piezoelectric for any application. Similarly, mounting piezo-electric transducers in enclosed probes requires attention to design models (e.g. Krimholtz *et al.* 1970). The nature of transducer backing structure and materials, together with the nature, properties, and structure of the coupling materials separating the piezo-electric material from the external medium under study, affect probe performance significantly (Tamura *et al.* 1975; Silk 1980; Bainton and Silk, 1980; Bainton *et al.* 1981).

28.3 Discrete biosensor devices using piezo-electric transducers

Despite the existence of a wide range of piezo-electric materials and accompanying measurement principles, virtually all reported exploitations of. piezo-electric transducers in discrete sensor devices have used specially coated, oscillating quartz crystals as sensitive detectors of changes in surface mass (gravimetric sensors). This principle has been widely used in volatile and gas phase analysis (Guilbault 1970; Alder and McCallum 1983), but application to liquid phase measurements has proved problematical.

28.3.1 Principles of electrogravimetric sensors

Industrially grown, rather than natural, quartz crystals are used almost exclusively for electrogravimetric sensors because of their higher purity. Although transducer thickness is the principal determinant of oscillator frequency of piezo-electrics, special 'Y' cut quartz crystals oscillating in shear mode can be used to overcome harmonic and overtone interference. However, temperature coefficient and oscillator frequency also varies with the angle of rotation (Lack *et al.* 1934). AT (+ 35°15′) and BT (− 49°00′) cut crystals have minimal temperature coefficients (Lack *et al.* 1934; Heising 1946). Other performance criteria are well studied (e.g. Heising, 1946). The majority of electrogravimetric sensors use crystals cut along the AT plane into thin (10–15 mm) plates or discs with the electric field being applied along the *y* axis. These oscillate in the thickness shear mode, parallel to the major axis, and yield antimodally displacing surfaces (Heising 1946; Guilbault 1980; Alder and McCallum 1983). Crystals are placed in an oscillator circuit and the resonant frequency measured using conventional electronic techniques (Fig. 28.4). The frequency of oscillation largely depends on the combined mass of the crystal and its coatings, as described for a AT crystal microbalance (Sauerbrey 1959; Stockbridge 1966). The change in resonant frequency (Δf) resulting from adsorption of detected analyte can be calculated (Guilbault 1980; Alder and McCallum 1983) as providing extremely high sensitivity (approx. 500 to 2500 Hz/μg) sensors with pg detection limits for commercially available quartz crystals,

$$\Delta f = -2.3 \times 10^6 f^2 \frac{\Delta m}{A}$$

where f is the frequency (Hz) of the crystal, Δm (g) the mass of adsorbed material, and A (cm) is the adsorbing or sensing area.

28.3.2 Gravimetric biosensors

King (1964, 1965) first reported use of piezo-electric crystals as detectors for gas chromatography. Guilbault (Hlavay and Guilbault, 1977; Guilbault 1980, 1982) and Alder and McCallum (1983) have provided excellent reviews

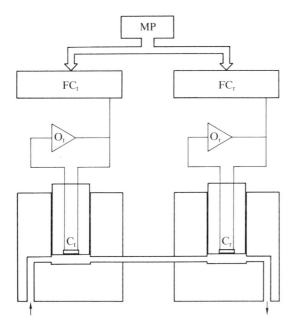

Fig. 28.4 Typical system for electrogravimetric sensor analyses incorporating reference (C_r) and test (C_t) crystal sensors, individually held in oscillating circuits (O_r and O_t, respectively) serviced with separate frequency counters (FC$_r$ and FC$_t$, respectively), interfaced to a common microprocessor.

of the development and application of piezo-electric crystals in analytical chemistry by coating crystals with compounds which selectively adsorb analytes of interest. The majority of work concerns detection of gases (e.g. sulphur dioxide, carbon monoxide, hydrogen chloride) or volatile species (aromatic and aliphatic hydrocarbons) and, in so much, does not have significant biological applications. Most require relative humidity to be low and held constant. However, ammonia sensors using a variety of chemical, biochemical, and polymer coatings (Karmarker and Guilbault 1975; Karmarker *et al.* 1976; Hlavay and Guilbault 1978; Edmonds *et al.*, 1982) and a dissolved carbon dioxide sensor using didodecylamine or dioctadecylamine coated crystals separated from the solution with a Teflon membrane (Schuman and Fogelman 1976), could well be useful in fermentation monitoring (Clarke *et al.* 1984, 1985). King (1970) has also reported a methane sensor, which although effective is perhaps less useful for monitoring bioconversion of wastes to methane than other hydrocarbon sensors (Clarke *et al.* 1984, 1985). Volatile organoleptic compounds are important in many biological processes (e.g. fermentation and food). It is conceivable that sufficiently selective coatings could be developed for these substances to replace

GCMS monitoring and other spectrometric analyses. In a similar manner to ion-selective electrode analyses (Clarke *et al.* 1982), it has been suggested that multicomponent analysis/interference correction could be carried out to improve the practical selectivity of coated crystals (Alder and McCallum 1983).

King (1972) first suggested use of similar surface adsorption principles in biological fluids; the problems of achieving a practical device were quickly pointed out by Richardson (1972). Subsequently Downes (1979) failed to monitor the growth rate of micro-organisms through their interactions with crystals, apparently, for reasons of slow growth rates and the possibility of ultrasonic disruption of the cells. Although using a sensitive diaphragm microphone Hill (1983) analysed noise (using Fourier transform techniques) from cilia and flagellae, whose motion is rapidly sensitive to the energy state of cells.

Viscous damping of oscillation, medium temperature fluctuations, and the greater likelyhood of non-specific adorptions are envisaged as the major problems of such applications. Nomura has been particularly active in applying piezo-electric crystals in fluids for a number of reasons. The change in oscillation frequency on immersing crystals in solvent solutions was expectedly found to depend principally on the density (ρ) and viscosity (η) of the solution (Nomura *et al.* 1981; Nomura and Okuhara 1982), according to the following empirical relationship,

$$\Delta f = a\rho^{\frac{1}{2}} + b\eta^{\frac{1}{2}} - c$$

where a, b, and c are constants. Further, the resonant frequency also decreased with increasing electrolyte concentration and specific conductivity, as would be expected, largely through their proportionality with solution density. However, some curious (Alder and McCallum 1983) effects of solution concentration were noted (Nomura and Maruyama 1983), where linearity with specific conductivity was noted up to approximately 2 mM of metal phosphate solutions, when significant deviations from linearity due to viscosity and density were reported. At concentrations in excess of 20 mM, the solution was reported as short circuiting the quartz crystal causing dramatic changes in resonant frequency. Many compounds can be determined by their electrodeposition on electrodes. Iodide determination was achieved through its deposition on the Pt-Ag/AgCl coating of the gold electrode of a quartz crystal (Nomura and Mimatsu 1982). Many metal ions also adsorb onto surfaces from solution. Such tests were similarly arranged for determination of iron III, lead II, and aluminium III through adsorption of their phosphate salts onto a thin glass slide (to prevent electrodeposition) virtually contiguous with the crystal surface (i.e. electrode), producing relatively linear sensors in the concentration range 10 to 100 μM (Nomura and Maruyama 1983). Similar principles have been exploited in attempts to develop an electrogravimetric immunosensor (Roederer and Baastians 1983). In this case, ST cut SAW (surface acoustic wave) crystals consisting of inter-digitized (in the manner of plate condensers) nickel transducers. Areas between electrodes were etched prior to silanization and attachment of anti-body (goat antihuman IgG). Significant decreases in resonant frequency were noted on immersion in buffer solutions, which were dependent on the volume presented to the devices. The responses to buffer alone to antibody modified and non-modified (reference) crystals should be the same (Konash and Baastians 1980). The observation that they were not was apportioned to dif-ferences in non-specific binding due to the absence of protein modification on the reference sensor. However, a major problem was insufficient sensi-tivity and improvements in detection limits of about three orders of mag-nitude would be required to achieve a clinically useful device (e.g. for gravimetric immunosensors). These improvements are being sought through blocking non-specific adsorption sites, increasing the density of coverage with immobilized antibody, immobilizing inert protein on the reference crystal and using more sensitive crystals (Roederer and Baastians 1983), when significant improvements in performance appear to be possible (Baastians, unpublished). In a similar manner to those workers now considering closer and more exclusive coupling between the detecting principle (not only the detector) and sensing ligand principle (see Clarke *et al.* 1985 for a review), piezo-electric biosensors could be similarly improved. Further, use could well be made of the natural piezo-electric properties of biopolymers and their aggregates/structures, rather than concentrating solely on surface binding.

Damping of crystal resonance in fluid media has been overcome by the rather simple procedure of allowing adsorption to take place in solution and then air drying the sensor prior to measurement of the resonant frequency. This was demonstrated by immersing crystals in chloroform extracted 8-quinolinate lead chelate (Nomura *et al.* 1982). Rather than relying on non-specific adsorption and/or retention prior to drying of the extracted lead, the chelator (and other sensor ligands) could be immobilized onto the crystal surface in a similar manner to other types of sensors (see Clarke *et al.* 1985 for a review).

28.4 Acoustic wave propagation and acoustic impedance

There exists sophisticated analyses of the passage of acoustic waves through low viscosity and visco-elastic materials. The natural complexity and inherent dynamic behaviour of solutions, suspensions, or pellets of bio-logical materials would be expected to present significant difficulties in achieving specific or biologically meaningful measurement from such analyses. Simultaneous multiparameter monitoring and multicomponent analyses would be expected to overcome many of these drawbacks. Despite the potential significance of this area, relatively few biological studies have been forthcoming, perhaps disproportionately restricting our attention to the area.

28.4.1 Basic principles

Most methods of acoustic and ultrasonic analysis are long established, although the significant benefits of modern signal handling instrumentation are now available. In general, acoustic waves are introduced into the signal modifying medium and either received by the same or a separate transducer. Other monitoring techniques (e.g. optical) are occasionally used.

In low viscosity liquids, shear stiffness is considered negligible in comparison to the compressional stiffness and reverberation methods can be applied at low frequencies. Quantities of interest are the complex bulk modulus $(K = K' + jK'')$ and the imaginary component of the complex shear modulus $(G = G' + G'')$. Both shear components must be considered in visco-elastic materials, requiring further measurements (e.g. longitudinal wave amplitude measurements and shear mechanics). Although in certain cases low viscosity liquid parameters can be measured directly, in most cases, multiple measurements (introduced into some form of model) are required. The predominating loss mechanisms and thermal effects cause attentuation to vary as the square of frequency, such that losses are so small at low KHz range frequencies as to require use of resonance techniques and/or use of large volumes of liquid. Ceramic piezo-electrics can be used to excite single radial modes and to monitor signal decay when excitation is switched off after achievement of steady state (Mulders 1948). Since at higher frequencies, high overtone modes can be difficult to identify, the simultaneous induction of multiple modes by frequency modulation is preferred. Decay patterns can then be similarly monitored (Lawley and Reed 1955).

Acoustic interferometry is a long established technique for monitoring wave velocities and attenuation, most often configured by causing the wave to be reflected back across a variable distance, towards a single transducer (Del Grosso *et al.* 1954). Alternatively the reflector can be replaced with an identical piezo-electric, when the received signal will progress through maxima and minima as the distance is varied (Fry 1949). Fixed path interferometers can also be used (Carstensen 1954).

Perhaps one of the most useful techniques for determining attenuation and velocity was introduced by Pellam and Galt (1946). A piezo-electric transducer radiates a short train of waves, subsequently acting as a receiver for the reflected signal (the 'pulse echo' technique). Transit time provides velocity and loss is determined from the attenuation of the waves over various reflected distances. Wave diffraction is significant in such methods, particularly at low frequencies. Although velocities can be determined from direct delay measurements, phase comparison techniques are similarly useful (McSkimin 1960).

The Debeye and Sears (1932) photo-acoustic effect has allowed determination of wave velocities and attenuations. The alternate compressions and rarefactions accompanying the passage of a sound wave in fluids, effectively produces a diffraction grating for light and diffraction angles can be used to determine the sound wavelength and therefore velocity. Measurement of the intensity of the diffracted orders provides measurements of loss. Such methods are not to be confused with photo-acoustic spectroscopy, relying on the acoustic wave accompanying the generation of a thermal wave through absorption of modulated light (e.g. Cahen *et al.* 1980; Yip and Yeung 1983). This method has been particularly useful for infrared and visible spectroscopy of optically dense biological samples (e.g. Carpenter *et al.* 1983*a*, *b*).

28.4.2 Applications

Generally, molecular acoustics has played a relatively small role in studying homogeneous solutions of biological molecules. Measurement of ultrasonic velocities can supply information about the inter- and intramolecular interactions of macromolecules (Passynski 1938; Jacobson, 1950; Stuher & Yeger, 1965). Ultrasonic absorption spectroscopy has provided a means of studying the kinetics and thermodynamics of proton transfer, since relaxation times (< 100 ps) lie within the time constants of achievable ultrasound frequencies. Such techniques require precise methods or measuring propagation velocity (Eggers and Funck 1973; Sarvazyan and Kharakov 1977) such that the compressibility and hydration of macromolecules can be analysed (Sarvazyan *et al.* 1979). Ionizable groups tend to be a principal influence on the absorption spectra of amino acids and corresponding pK values could be identified. Similar influences on the absorption spectra of protein solutions (metmyoglobin) were noted. A velocity change due to protein denaturation was also identified (see also Cho *et al.* 1985; Jurgens and Baumann 1985).

Acoustical analysis of inhomogeneous fluids (i.e. particles suspended in electrolyte solutions, e.g. microbial cultures) is particularly difficult. Measurement of sludge concentration of wastewaters has been achieved ultrasonically (Hayakawa and Kori 1972). Growth of a yeast (and other) cultures has been monitored ultrasonically using a flexible piezo-electric membrane transducer consisting of a polyacetal resin, chlorinated polyethylene, and lead zirconate titanate (Ishimori *et al.* 1981). The measurement cell consisted of two piezo-electric membranes (each 2.5 × 1.5 cm and 0.2 mm thick) separated by 2.5 mm of culture fluid. The oscillation frequency of the transmitting membrane was fixed at 40 KHz such that approx 20–100 mV peak to peak amplitudes were generated at the receiving membrane. Although output voltage should increase with increasing medium concentration (Stuehr and Yeager 1965), little increase in amplitude (approx. 5 mV) was observed over the concentration range 10 mM to 500 mM. Similarly, increase in sound velocity with temperature (Stuehr and Yeager, 1965) was slight in this system over the range 25 to 40°C. Since culture medium density often changes during growth of cultures, the response of the sensor to various glycerol concentrations (from densities of 1 to 1.10) was monitored. Changes in amplitude again were small. Conversely, introduction of populations of bacteria and yeast provoked significantly greater responses (amplitudes varying from 20 mV to 50–80 mV (approx.) for variations in numbers of 10 to 10 per ml). Output was relatively linear with cell number up to 10 cells/ml and appeared to provide better growth curve data than culture conductivity measurements (e.g. Cady 1978). Although the transducer could withstand a small number of steam sterilization cycles, eventual cracking of the piezo-membrane proved to be a problem. The precise underlying principles of the method are unclear, except that suspension compressibility appeared to play a greater role in the measurement than sound velocity and density (Ishimori *et al.* 1981).

Significant advances in understanding the propagation of ultrasonic waves in inhomogeneous suspensions (of non-biological particles) has been achieved, particularly through the work of Chivers and Anson (Chivers 1980; Anson and Chivers, 1981*a, b*; Chivers and Anson 1982). Table 28.1 outlines the main parameters of interest for modelling the acoustic interactions of the medium and suspended particle components of inhomogeneous systems. Although these would be expected to result in complex formulations, particularly when the dynamics of microbial cultures and attendent gas bubbles are considered, a wide range of measurements could be applied (Table 28.1) to multicomponent analysis methods. This would require extension of the

Table 28.1   Some analytically useful measurements for multicomponent analysis of the various influences on acoustic wave propagation in inhomogeneous suspensions of particles in electrolyte media

Some analytically useful parameters	Homogeneous medium	Suspended particles
Attenuation	Density	Density
Specific absorption (resonance)	Longitudinal wave absorption	Longitudinal wave absorption
Propagation delay	Viscosity	Surface shear attenuation
Wave shape (Fourier analysis)	Bulk modulus	Elasticity
Scatter and coherency	Thermal expansion	Thermal expansion
Scatter direction	Specific heat	Specific heat

above models for more biological suspensions. Despite their complexity, biologically meaningful measurements could result.

Ultrasound fields have also been used to polarize and aggregate cell populations. One important exploitation of these effects has been in electro-acoustic cell fusion procedures (Vienken *et al.* 1985; see also Coakley 1985; Coakley *et al.* 1986). When cell suspensions are exposed to ultrasound fields, two forces can operate to bring cells close together. In a standing wave situation, the first force operates to move cells close to the velocity maxima in the sound field. The other operates to bring cells into contact perpendicular to the direction of the velocity amplitude in the absence of the cells. Their combined effects will move cells to preferred areas of the sound field, where the aggregation forces will be at a maximum (e.g. Vienken *et al.* 1985).

28.5 Acoustic microscopy

Although acoustic microscopy cannot be considered to be a biosensing technique, recent developments are worthwhile considering because of the capabilities likely to be offered to the biologist. Not only are resolutions comparable to the resolution of optical microscopes, but the penetration of acoustic waves through solid material is usefully exploited in resolving structural information at various depths (for reviews see Attal 1983; Wickramansinghe 1984 Wiczkowski 1984). Further, the extensive developments undertaken over the last decade have significantly improved broader understanding in a number of relevant areas.

Lemons and Quate (1974; see also Quate *et al* 1979) first demonstrated scanning acoustic microscopy (SAM), as first suggested by Sokolov's (1949) realization that GHz acoustic waves in water had similar wavelengths to visible light.

Figure 28.5 jointly outlines the respective configurations of transmission and reflective acoustic microscopy. In the former configuration, identical sapphire lens-piezo-electric transducer (lithium niobate below 150 MHz and zinc oxide at higher frequencies) configurations are used, whereas the reflective configuration employs a single lens-transducer configuration alternately switched between excitation and receiver modes. Exciting radio-frequency (RF) signals are applied to the transmitting lens which excites longitudinal waves in the sapphire rod. These are focused to a diffraction limited beam waist by the subsequent lens. In the transmission configuration, the receiver lens is confocal with the transmitter, collecting and collimating the acoustic signal prior to its reconversion into an electrical signal. Resolution in such a configuration is principally defined by the beam waist. The spot diameter can approach 0.7λ, using a high quality wide aperture lens ($f/0.7$). It is conceivable that the theoretical resolving power of acoustic microscopy could be increased further by data analysis techniques. Walker (1983) has

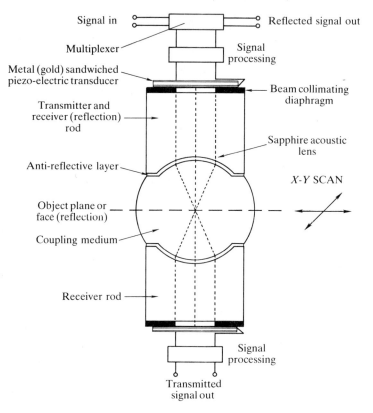

Fig. 28.5 Schematic configuration of a scanning acoustic microscope illustrating transmission and reflection modes of operation (see text for further details).

experimentally demonstrated that imaging resolutions greater than the Rayleigh criterion should be achievable using an iterative spectral extrapolation algorithm based on the Gerchberg method.

Many of the imaging modes of optical microscopy (*viz.* stereo imaging, dark field contrast, phase contrast, and differential phase contrast) have counterparts in acoustic microscopy (Wickramansinghe 1984). The piezo-electric transducers generate coherent waves when excited with a RF signal, which are converted back to a coherent RF signal in the receive mode. Consequently, at each pixel point of the scan, it is possible to measure phase as well as amplitude. Stereo imaging has been demonstrated by taking two images at different scan plane angles and dark field by replacing the transmitter with a plane wave transducer and introducing a zero order stop at the aperture centre of the receiver lens. Photo-acoustic spectroscopy principles have also been incorporated into acoustic microscopes. Quantitative acoustic measurements have also been made at each pixel point.

Biological materials have high acoustic contrast without resort to staining techniques. Living red blood cells and chick fibroblasts have been studied using scanning acoustic microscopy (see Wickramansinghe 1984). Clearly many more interesting applications await this highly developed tool.

28.6 Acoustic resonance densitometry (ARD)

The idea of mass determination by the mass damping of a vibrating resonant body can be attributed to Rayleigh (1870, 1875). Although vibrating visco-meter devices were reported in the 1930s (e.g. Philipoff 1934), use of mass damping in mechanically resonating bodies as sensitive measures of mass change are due mainly to Kratky and Leopold (1968).

The tubular (see Fig. 28.6) or spherical sample chamber of ARD instruments encloses a fixed test volume. It should be elastically self-supporting and possess a low temperature coefficient (e.g., by using a silica, stainless steel, or nickel alloy construction) to minimize thermal expansion, stress, and loading. Resonance is initially excited and sustained by applying to the sample chamber a pair of solenoids connected within a closed oscillatory circuit using a fixed gain AC amplifier. The amplifier ensures resonant displacement of the sample chamber within its linear range, preventing non-harmonic oscillations (radial and longitudinal) and ensuring the almost exclusive transverse displacements required for tubular sample chamber configurations (Fig. 28.6). When such conditions are maintained there exists

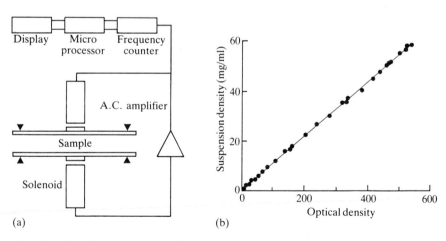

Fig. 28.6 Monitoring of microbial biomass by acoustic resonance densitometry (ARD). (a) Configuration of ARD apparatus. (b) Correlation of ARD measurement of microbial suspension density with conventional optical density measurement (see text for details).

a direct relation between the density of the sample and the square of the oscillation frequency, which excludes parameters such as sample viscocity. A simple approach has been to hold the sample chamber at constant temperature and convert the frequency (period, τ) to density (ρ) using two calibration constants (A and B),

$$\rho = \frac{1}{A}(\tau^2 - B).$$

Alternatively, measured temperature corrections can be incorporated into such formulations.

It is surprising that the precise (4–6 digit) density measurements afforded by such instruments have not found biological exploitation to any significant extent. However, it has been recently demonstrated (Blake-Coleman and Clarke 1984*a*, *b*; Blake-Coleman *et al.* 1984, 1986), that ARD can operate as a linear monitor of microbial biomass over an extremely wide range of culture density (Fig. 28.6). Application in harvested culture processing as well as monitoring culture growth should thereby be afforded (Blake-Coleman *et al.* 1986). The transducer is robust and does not suffer adverse effects on steam sterilization. The natural resonance of the sample chamber tends to discourage microbial fouling and the incorporation of sonic (or steam flushing) cleaning cycles can be arranged. Since most micro-organisms have a higher density than their suspending medium, increase in their numbers provides a linear relation with density. Cultures treated by a variety of cell breakage procedures maintain the same density (Blake-Coleman *et al.* 1986), illustrating that true bulk mass per unit volume changes are involved, rather than some more subtle mass rearrangement within the cell structure. The medium density *per se* also changes throughout the course of growth of some cultures. Consequently, in such cases, medium density changes must be simultaneously monitored and these values subtracted from the measured composite culture density changes (Blake-Coleman *et al.* 1984, 1986). Although this can be achieved aseptically using dual sample chamber configurations, one of which is supplied by a tangential flow filtration assembly, instrumental methods of achieving precise correction for dynamic changes in medium density are currently being developed (Blake-Coleman and Clarke 1984*a*, *b*; Clarke and Blake-Coleman 1985).

28.7 Conclusions and future potential

Although acoustical techniques have not found application comparable to other biosensing techniques, a number of principles and techniques are now developing which can tackle the complexities of biological measurements. However, our understanding of the acoustical properties of biological materials are only partially developed, and further developments will require sophisticated measurement, modelling and data analysis techniques. Considerable attention has been devoted to the development of piezo-electric sensors with chemical sensitivity. Similar attention to biochemical specificities would be expected to provide a number of piezo-electric biosensors. However, in common with other biosensing principles, close attention needs to be devoted to achieving more direct, close, and exclusive coupling between the biosensing and detector materials.

References

Alder, J. F. and McCallum, J. F. (1983). Piezo-electric crsytals for mass and chemical measurements. *The Analyst* **108** (1291), 1169–89.

Anson, L. W. and Chivers, R. C. (1981*a*). Frequency dependence of the acoustic radiation force function (Yp) for spherical targets of a wide range of materials. *J. Acoust. Soc. Am.* **69**, 1618–22.

—— (1981*b*). The use of absorbing polymeric materials for suspended sphere ultrasonic radiometry. *Acoust. Letts.* **4**(4), 74–80.

Attal, J. (1983). La microscopie acoustique. *La Recherche* **14** (Mai), 664–667.

Bainton, K. F. and Silk, M. G. (1980). Some factors which affect the performance of ultrasonic transducers. *Brit. J. of N. D. T.* **22**, 15–21.

—— Hillier, M. J. and Silk, M. G. (1981). An easily constructed broad bandwidth ultrasonic probe for research purposes. *J. Phys. E* (*Sci. Instrum.*) **14**, 1313–9.

Blake-Coleman, B. C. and Clarke, D. J. (1984*a*). Coil geometry and ARD apparatus. Brit. Pat. Appl. No. 84085/27.

—— (1984*b*). Determination of biomass using ARD. Brit. Pat. Appl. No. 84085/28.

—— Calder, M. R., Carr, R. J. G., Moody, S. C. and Clarke, D. J. (1984). Direct monitoring of reactor biomass in fermentation control. *Trends in Anal. Chem.* **3**(9), 229–32.

—— Clarke, D. J., Calder, M. R. and Moody, S. C. (1986). Determination of reactor biomass by acoustic resonance densitometry. *Biotechnol. & Bioeng.* **28**(8), 1241–7.

Cady, P. (1978). Progress in impedance measurements in microbiology. In *Mechanizing microbiology* (eds. A. N. Sharpe, D. S. Clark and A. Balows) p. 199. John Wiley, New York.

Cady, W. G. (1946). *Piezo-electricity*. McGraw Hill, New York and London.

Cahen, D. G., Garty, M. and Becker, S. (1980). Photoacoustic calorimetry of concentrated fluorescent solutions. *J. Phys. Chem.* **84**, 3384–9.

Carpenter, R., Larue, B. and Leblanc, R. M. (1983*a*). Photoacoustic spectroscopy of *Anacystis nidulans* I. *Arch. Biochem. & Biophys.* **222**(2), 403–10.

—— (1983*b*). Photoacoustic spectroscopy of *Anacystic nidulans* II. *Arch. Biochem. & Biophys.* **222**(2), 411–5.

Carstensen, E. L. (1954). Measurement of dispersion velocity of sound in liquids. *J. Acoust. Soc. Am.* **26**, 858–91.

Chivers, R. C. (1980). Acoustic wave fluctuations in inhomogeneous media. *J. Phys. D* **13**, 1947–51.

—— and Anson, L. W. (1982). Choice of target and accuracy of measurement in suspended sphere ultrasonic radiometry. *J. Acoust. Soc. Am.* **72**, 1670–95.

Cho, K., Leung, W. P., Mok, H. Y. and Choy, C. L. (1985). Ultrasonic absorption in myoglobin and other globular proteins. *Biochem. Biophys. Acta* **830**, 36–44.

Clarke, D. J. and Blake-Coleman, B. C. (1985). Improvements in filters. Brit. Pat. Appl. No. 8514899.

—— Kell, D. B., Burns, A. and Morris, J. G. (1982). The role of ion-selective electrodes in fermentation control. *I. S. E. Reviews* **4**, 75–133.

—— Blake-Coleman, B. C., Calder, M. R., Carr, R. J. G. and Moody, S. C. (1984). Sensors for bioreactor monitoring and control — a perspective. *J. Biotechnol.* **1**, 135–58.

—— Calder, M. R., Carr, R. J. G., Blake-Coleman, B. C., Moody, S. C. and Collinge, T. A. (1985). The development and application of biosensor devices for bioreactor monitoring and control. *Biosensors* **1**(3), 213–320.

Coakley, W. T. (1985). Interfacial instability and cell membranes. *APSM Bulletin* **5**, 16–18.

—— Hewison, L. A. and Tilley, D. (1986). Interfacial instability and the agglutination of erythrocytes by polymers. *Studia Biophysica* In press.

Curie, J. & Curie, P. (1880). Development, par pression, de l'electricite polarise dans les crystaux hemiedries et faces inclines. *Comp. Rend.* **91**, 294–7.

Debeye, P. and Sears, F. W. (1932). Scattering of light by sound. *Proc. Natl. Acad. Sci. (U. S. A.)* **18**, 410–15.

Del Grosso, V. A., Smura, J. A. and Fougere, P. F. (1954). Ultrasonic investigations in liquids. Naval Res. Lab. Reports NRL-4439.

Downes, J. (1979). Monitoring of microbial growth using piezoelectric crystals. Internal Report, Imperial College, London, UK.

Edmonds, T. E., Fraser, S. M. and West, T. S. (1982). Polyvinylpyrrolidone coated piezoelectric quartz crystals as an ammonia sensor. Poster at Roy. Soc. of Chem. Int. Conf. on 'Detection and Measurement of Hazardous Substances in the Atmosphere', City Univ., London, 20–22 December 1982.

Eggers, F. and Funck, Th. (1973). Ultrasonic measurements with millilitre liquid samples in the 0.5 to 100 MHz range. *Rev. Sci. Instrum.* **44**(8), 969–73.

Fry, W. J. (1949). The double crystal acoustic interferometer. *J. Acoust. Soc. Am.* **21**, 17–21.

Fukada, E. (1968). Piezoelectricity in polymers and biological materials. *Ultrasonics* October 1968, 229–330.

—— (1974). Piezoelectric properties of biological macromolecules. *Adv. in Biophys.* **6**, 121–55.

Guilbault, G. G. (1980). Use of piezoelectric crystal detector in analytical chemistry. *I.S.E. Reviews* **2**(1), 4–15.

—— (1982). Piezoelectric crystal detectors in analytical chemistry. *Anal. Proc.* **19**, 68–79.

Hayakawa, N. and Kori, A. (1972). Ultrasonic probe for monitoring the concentration of wastewater sludge. *Mizu Shori Gijutsu* **13**, 57–63.

Heising, R. A. (1946). *Quartz crystals for electrical circuits* p. 24. Van Nostrad, New York.

Hill, R. J. (1983). The frequency dependent emission of low frequency sound by motile cultures of the ciliate *Tetrahymena thermophilia. Biochem. Biophys. Res. Commun.* **117**(1), 190–5.

Hlavay, J. and Guilbault, G. G. (1977). Application of the piezoelectric crystal detector in analytical chemistry. *Anal. Chem.* **49**, 890-2.

—— (1978). Applications of piezoelectric crystal detectors in analytical chemistry. *Anal. Chem.* **50**, 1044-8.

Ishimori, Y., Karube, I. and Suzuki, S. (1981). Determination of microbial populations with piezoelectric membranes. *Applied & Environ. Microbiol.* **42(4)**, 632-7.

Jacobson, B. (1950). On the adiabatic compressibility of aqueous solutions. *Ark. Kemi.* **2**, 177-81.

Jurgens, K. D. and Baumann, R. (1985). Ultrasonic absorption studies of protein-buffer interactions. *Eur. J. Biophys.* **12**, 217-22.

Karmarkar, K. H. and Guilbault, G. G. (1975). The determination of ammonia and nitrogen dioxide at the parts per billion level with coated piezoelectric crystal detectors. *Anal. Chim. Acta* **75**, 111-15.

—— Webber, L. M. and Guilbault, G. G. (1976). Measurement of sulfur dioxide in automobile exhausts and industrial stack gases with a coated piezoelectric crystal detector. *Anal. Chim. Acta* **81(2)**, 265-71.

Kawai, H. (1969). The piezoelectricity of poly(vinylidene fluoride). *Jap. J. Appl. Phys.* **8**, 975-9.

King W. H. Jr. (1964). Piezoelectric sorption detector. *Anal Chem.* **36**, 1735-9.

—— (1965). Piezoelectric sorption detector. U.S. Patent 3, 164, 004 (Jan 5), 1965.

—— (1970). Monitoring of hydrogen, methane and hydrocarbons in the atmosphere. *Environ. Sci. & Technol.* **4(12)**, 1136-40.

—— (1972). Chemical analysis using piezoelectric crystal detectors. *Bull. N. Y. Acad. Sci.* **48**, 459-69.

Kocharayan, N. M., Pachadzhyan, B. and Tivriktsyan, Zh. (1967). 'Induced' piezoelectric effect in some polymers. *Dokl. Akad. Nauk. Ann. S. R. R.* **44(3)**, 111-6.

Konash, P. L. and Baastians, G. J. (1980). Piezoelectric crystal detectors in liquid chromatography. *Anal. Chem.* **52**, 1929-32.

Kratky, O. and Leopold, H. (1968). Acoustic resonance densitometry. Austrian Patent No. 2704.

Krimholtz, R., Loedom, D. and Matthaei, G. (1970). New equivalent circuits of elementary piezoelectric transducers. *Electron Letts.* **6**, 398-402.

Lack, F. R., Willard, G. W. and Farni, Z. E. (1934). Angle of rotation of quartz crystals. *Bell Syst. Tech. J.* **13**, 453-6.

Lawley, L. E. and Reed, R. D. C. (1955). A reverberation method for the measurement of the adsorption of ultrasonics in liquids. *Acoustica* **5**, 316-19.

Lemons, R. A. and Quate, C. F. (1974). Integrated circuits as viewed with an acoustic microscope. *Appl. Phys. Letts.* **24**, 163-6.

McSkimin, H. J. (1960). Performance of high frequency barium titanate transducers for generating ultrasonic waves in liquids. *J. Acoust. Soc. Am.* **32**, 1401-5.

Mulders, L. E. (1948). Ultrasonic reverbation measurements in liquids. *Appl. Sci. Res.* **B1**, 149-52.

Nomura, T. and Maruyama, M. (1983). Effect of metal ions on a piezoelectric quartz crystal in aqueous solution and the adsorptive determination of iron III as its phosphate. *Anal. Chim. Acta* **147**, 365-9.

—— and Mimatsu, T. (1982). Electrolytic determination of traces of iodide in solution with a piezoelectric quartz crystal. *Anal. Chim. Acta* **143**, 237-41.

—— and Okuhara, M (1982). Frequency shifts of piezoelectric quartz crystals immersed in organic liquids. *Anal. Chim. Acta* **142**, 281–5.

—— Yamashita, T. and West, T. S. (1982). Determination of lead by adsorption of the extracted 8-quinolinolate on the electrodes of a piezoelectric quartz crystal. *Anal. Chim. Acta* **143**, 247.

—— Okuhara, M., Murata, K. and Hattori, O. (1981). Behaviour of a piezoelectric quartz crystal in organic solvents. *Bunskei Kagaku* **30(6)**, 417–21.

Passynski, A. (1938). Compressibility of electrolytes. *Acta Physiochem U.R.S.S.* **8**, 385–9.

Pellam, J. R. and Galt, J. K. (1946). Ultrasonic propagation in liquids. I Application of pulse techniques to velocity and absorption measurements at 15 megacycles. *J. Chem. Phys.* **14**, 608–12.

Philipoff, W. (1934). Dynamische untersuchungen an kolloiden systemen. *Physik Zeitschr.* **35**, 884–905.

Quate, C. F., Atlar, A. and Wickramansinghe, H. K. (1979). Acoustic microscopy with mechanical scanning. *Proc. I. E. E.* **67**, 1092–6.

Rayleigh, Baron (alias Strutt, J. W.) (1870). On the theory of resonance. *Philos. Trans.* **161**, 77–9.

—— (1875). Vibrations of a liquid in a cylindrical vessel. *Nature* **12**, 251.

Richardson, P. D. (1972). The operation of piezoelectric crystal detectors in fluids. *Bull. N. Y. Acad. Med.* **48**, 465–9.

Roederer, J. E. and Baastians, G. J. (1983). Microgravimetric immunoassay with piezoelectric crystals. *Anal. Chem.* **55**, 2333–6.

Sarvazayan, A. P. & Khorakov, D. P. (1977). *Molecular and cellular biophysics.* p. 93. Nakau, Moscow.

—— and Hemmes, P. (1979). Ultrasonic investigation of the pH dependence solute-solvent interactions in aqueous solutions of amino acids and proteins. *J. Phys. Chem.* **83**(13), 1796–9.

Sauerbrey, G. Z. (1959). Use of a quartz vibrator for weighing thin layers on a micro-balance. *Z. Physik.* **155**, 206–10.

Schuman, M. S. and Fogelman, W. W. (1976). Nature of analysis for inorganics in water. *J. Water Pollut. Control Fed.* **49**(6), 901–5.

Silk, M. G. (1980). The effect of constructional variations on ultrasonic probe performance. *U. K. Atomic Energy Res. Est. Reps.* AERE-R9, 761–5.

Sokolov, S. (1949). An acoustic microscope. *Dokl. Akad. Nauk.* **64**, 333–6.

Stockbridge, C. D. (1966). Hydrostatic pressure on quartz crystal resonators. *Vac. Microbalance Tech.* **5**, 193–7.

Stuehr, J. and Yeager, E. (1965). *Physical acoustics* (ed. W. P. Mason), Vol. 2, Part A, 211–49.

Tamura, M., Yamaguchi, T., Oyaba, T. and Yoshimi, T. (1975). Electroacoustic transducers with piezoelectric high polymer films. *J. Audio. Eng. Soc.* **23**, 21–5.

Van Randeraat, J. and Setterington, R. E. (1974). *Piezoelectric ceramics.* Mullard Ltd.

Vienken, J., Zimmermann, U., Zenner, H. P., Coakley, W. T. and Gould, R. K. (1985). Electro-acoustic fusion of erythrocytes and of myeloma cells. *Biochem. Biophys. Acta* **820**, 259–64.

Walker, J. G. (1983). Optical imaging with resolution exceeding the Rayleigh criterion. *Optica Acta* **30**(4), 1197–202.

Wickramansinghe, H. K. (1984). Acoustic microscopy: present and future. *I. E. E. Proc. 131*, Part A, No. 4, 282–91.

Wiczkowski, J. (1984). Son et lumiere. *Lab Practice* October 1984, 15–20.

Yip, B. C. and Yeung, E. S. (1983). Photoacoustic spectroscopy in gases based on wavelength modulation. *Anal. Chem.* **55**, 978–87.

Calorimetry

29

Theory and application of calorimetric sensors

BENGT DANIELSSON and KLAUS MOSBACH

29.1 Introduction

In recent years experience gained in the field of enzyme immobilization has led to the development of bio-analytical devices in which the 'sensing' enzymes are placed in close proximity to the actual measuring part, the transducer. The best known example of such a combination of enzyme and transducer is the enzyme electrode. Various other combinations have been described, including the enzyme thermistor and other thermal bio-analysers. These devices are based on a general detection principle, the measurement of the heat of reaction. Enzymic reactions, in particular, are accompanied by a considerable heat evolution, generally in the range of 25 to 100 kJ/mol (Table 29.1), which makes enzyme calorimetry a highly versatile technique. The lack of specificity due to the general detection principle is adequately compensated for by the use of specific, immobilized biocatalysts, such as enzymes. Other common advantages associated with the use of an immobilized biocatalyst proximal to the transducer include repeated use of the biocatalyst, higher sensitivity, quicker response time, possibility of continuous flow operation, and probable stabilization of the biocatalyst.

Although many applications of calorimetry in biochemical analysis have been reported (Johansson et al. 1976; Martin and Marini 1977; Grime 1980), calorimetry has not gained widespread use in routine bio-analysis and might be attributed to the high cost and complexity of available instruments and tedious, time-consuming operation. Several research groups have attempted to develop simple and less expensive calorimeters for routine use with immobilized enzymes. A 'small volume calorimeter', in which the enzyme was attached to a thin aluminium foil placed on the surface of a Peltier element as a temperature sensor (Pennington 1976), was one of the first instruments developed. A drop of the sample was applied on the enzyme layer with the amount of substrate detected as a very small temperature change. The sensitivity, however, was poor and continuous flow operation was not possible.

A most straightforward approach was used in the thermal enzyme probes (TEP) (Cooney et al. 1974; Mosbach et al. 1974; Weaver et al. 1976) in which the enzyme was directly attached to the temperature transducer, a thermistor,

Table 29.1 Molar enthalpies of enzyme catalysed reactions

Enzyme	Substrate	$-\Delta H$ (kJ/mol)	References
Catalase	Hydrogen peroxide	100	Rehak and Young 1978
Cholesterol oxidase	Cholesterol	53	Rehak and Young 1978
Glucose oxidase	Glucose	80	Schmidt et al. 1976
Hexokinase	Glucose	28 (75)*	McGlothlin and Jordan 1975
Lactate dehydrogenase	Na-pyruvate	62	Brown 1969
NADH-dehydrogenase	NADH	225	Poe et al. 1967
Penicillinase	Penicillin G	67 (115)*	Grime and Tan 1979
Trypsin	Benzoyl-L-arginineamide	29	Brown 1969
Urease	Urea (phosphate buffer, pH 7.5)	61	Grime 1985
Uricase	Urate	49	Rehak and Young 1978

* The ΔH values in parenthesis include protonation of Tris (-47.5 kJ/mol (Rehak and Young 1978)).

by either cross-linking or entrapping the enzyme in a dialysis bag enclosing the thermistor. Unfortunately, the major part of the heat evolved in the enzymic reaction was lost to the surrounding solution without being detected by the thermistor. Consequently, the sensitivity was low and even if this advantage to some extent was alleviated in later designs (Tran-Minh and Vallin 1978; Rich *et al.* 1979), the TEP concept was primarily intended for batch operation.

A considerably more efficient detection of the reaction heat was possible in systems employing small columns with enzyme bound to support particles, as in the 'enzyme thermistor' (Mosbach and Danielsson 1974; Mosbach *et al.* 1975) and in the 'immobilized enzyme flow-enthalpimetric analyser' (Bowers *et al.* 1976). The combination of a flow-enthalpimeter of commercial design with a thermostated, immobilized enzyme column has also been described (Kiba *et al.* 1984). In these cases the heat was transported by the liquid passed through the column to or along the temperature sensor that was mounted at the top of the column or at its outlet.

The possibility for continuous analysis is an additional advantage when using flow-through arrangements. Most of these closely related devices have rather similar performances. As established from reactions of known enthalpy (Table 29.1) or electrical calibration (Danielsson *et al.* 1979), as much as 80% of heat evolved in such 'semi-adiabatic' instruments can be registered as a temperature change. For a given substrate present at a concentration of 1 mmol/l and with a molar enthalpy change of 80 kJ/mol, a peak height corresponding to 10^{-2}°C or higher will be expected, and a temperature resolution of 10^{-4}°C is required in order to give 1% accuracy in the measurement. As previously mentioned, most enzymic reactions are accompanied by considerable heat production in the range of 25 to 100 kJ/mol; therefore, measurements of concentrations as low as 0.1 mmol/l should not present any problems.

29.2 Experimental

29.2.1 Apparatus

The enzyme thermistor developed in the authors' laboratory has previously been described (Danielsson *et al.* 1981*a*). A recent design of the apparatus is schematically shown in Fig. 29.1. Figure 29.2 shows all the instruments needed for performing enzyme thermistor analysis. Inside a temperature-controlled (25, 30, or 37°C) aluminium cylinder placed in a polyurethane foam insulated casing is another aluminium cylinder separated by a thin air-space that provides a certain degree of thermal insulation. Heat is transported between the two blocks mainly by convection and by the fluid pumped from the main heat exchanger in the outer cylinder to the short, secondary heat exchanger in the inner cylinder. The columns will therefore be

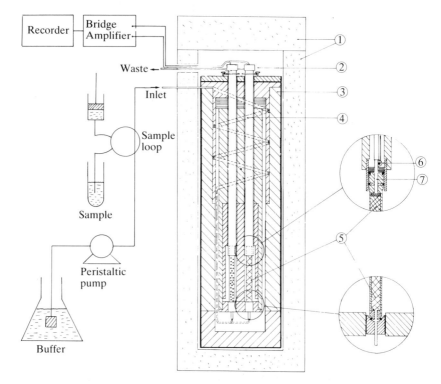

Fig. 29.1 Schematic cross-section of an enzyme thermistor with aluminium constant temperature jacket in a typical set-up: (1) Polyurethane insulation, (2) plexiglas tube/thermistor probe for column insertion, (3) thermostatted aluminium cylinder, (4) heat exchanger, (5) enzyme column, (6) thermistor attached to a gold capillary, (7) column outlet. There are two identical column ports that can be used independently or one of the ports can be used as a reference channel (split-flow).

surrounded by an environment with a very stable temperature.

The major part of the heat produced in the enzyme column is transported out of the column by the flow stream. The temperature at the outlet of the column is measured with a small thermistor mounted on a short gold capillary tube. A dual bead isotherm thermistor (type A395, Victory Engineering Corp., Springfield, N. J., USA) with a resistance of 16 kΩ at 25°C and a temperature coefficient of—3.9%/°C is commonly used. In addition, a reference thermistor mounted in the inner block for differential measurements is also utilized which results in increased baseline stability.

Temperature registration is made by a DC-coupled Wheatstone bridge equipped with a chopper-stabilized amplifier and wire-wound precision resistors with a low temperature coefficient. At maximum sensitivity this bridge produces a 100 mV change in the recorder signal for a temperature

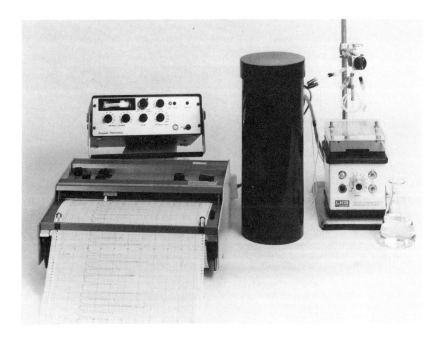

Fig. 29.2 Enzyme thermistor equipment for manual operation.

change of 0.001°C. The lowest practical useful range, mainly dictated by temperature fluctuations created by friction and turbulence in the column, is usually higher, typically 0.01°C. It should be noted that a substrate concentration of 0.5 mmol/l to 1 mmol/l in many reactions gives a temperature change of 0.01°C. Over the past five years more than 15 devices as shown in Figure 29.2 have been produced at our institute and utilized in various laboratories.

29.2.2 Enzyme column

Changing columns is very easy since the column is simply inserted into the end of a plastic tube (containing the outlet tubing and the temperature sensor) by which it is fitted into the apparatus. Columns of different diameters (maximum internal diameter 7 mm) and bed heights (maximum 30 mm) can be used. Nylon tubing wound around a special adaptor which fits into the column holder and connects the tubing to the flow system can also be used as enzyme support. (Nylon tubing is advantageous for analysis of crude samples containing particulates (Mattiasson *et al.* 1981) but suffers from low enzyme loading capacity). Thus, the carrier material usually used is CPG (controlled pore glass) that offers high enzyme-coupling capacity, good mechanical, chemical and microbial stability, as well as relatively simple coupling procedures. Other materials have also been used (Danielsson *et al.* 1981*a*; Mosbach and Danielsson 1981). Different carrier materials can show considerable variation in their adsorption of sample constituents depending for instance on the actual surface distribution of ionic or hydrophobic groups. Since such adsorption almost certainly will give rise to non-specific heat and may even affect the enzymic reaction, the choice of enzyme support material could be rather crucial. Using CPG with pore sizes in the range of 500 Å to 2000 Å and with a particle size usually around 80 mesh has given good results. When using either untreated CPG or alkyl(propyl)amino-derivatized CPG obtained from different suppliers, glutaraldehyde activation of the glass and subsequent binding of the enzyme almost invariably gives good results. It should be noted that a rather large excess of enzyme (often 100 units) is generally applied to an enzyme thermistor column. This procedure ensures good operational stability and unchanged performance of the system over a long series of samples or extended periods of continuous monitoring. The column should be functional for several months.

29.2.3 Procedure

The instrumental arrangement for enzyme thermistor analysis permits the inclusion of an inactive reference column for compensation of non-specific heat. The split-flow arrangement (Mattiasson *et al.* 1976) has proven valuable in many situations involving crude samples (e.g. for determination of triglycerides (Satoh *et al.* 1981)), but in most cases it is possible to avoid non-specific effects by careful design of the procedure, so that variations in solvent composition (mixing and solution heats) are avoided and adsorption of macromolecules or micro-organisms is prevented.

Buffer is continuously pumped through each functioning channel at a flow rate of 0.5 to 3 ml/minute. Samples are generally introduced as short pulses through a chromatography valve equipped with 0.1 to 1 ml loop. Thermal steady state will not be obtained for short sample pulses, but the enzymic reaction will generate a temperature peak, the height of which is normally taken as a measure of the substrate concentration (Danielsson *et al.* 1981*a*).

The linear range of the relationship between temperature peak height and substrate concentration is usually at least 10^{-5} to 10^{-1} mol/l when not limited by reactant concentrations (as oxidases are by the supply of oxygen) or by other factors. The maximum number of samples that can be analysed by the present system is 15 to 60 per hour with the stated sample volumes. The latter figure is obtained by decreasing the sample volume to 0.1 ml and increasing the flow rate to 2 to 3 ml/minute. In order to demonstrate simplified sample handling, a sample changer for an Auto Analyzer system (Technicon Instruments Corp., Tarrytown, New York, USA.) was modified and interfaced with a small desktop computer that also controls the sampling valve. This system can be left unattended, for instance, overnight. If the sample series has also included calibration standards, the computer is programmed to calculate the concentration of each sample based on peak heights or peak areas. When the sample pulse length is sufficiently increased to more than 1 to 5 minutes, the temperature response will eventually reach a constant value proportional to the concentration. Consequently, the concentration of an enzyme substrate can be continuously monitored.

29.2.4 Amplification

A number of 'tricks' can be applied to amplify heat formation. (Although many enzymic reactions have sufficiently high molar enthalpies, permitting determinations with devices such as the enzyme thermistor with a sensitivity as low as 10^{-5} mol/l, some reactions, such as enzymic hydrolysis of esters, produce very little heat). For example, hydrolysis of acetylcholine by choline esterase has an enthalpy change close to zero. Nevertheless, this reaction can be detected calorimetrically because the hydrolytic step produces a proton which can protonate a suitable buffer (Tris) with high protonation enthalpy (e.g. Tris, $\Delta H = -47.5$ kJ/mol (Rehak and Young 1978)) making the total process strongly exothermic. In another example, the response of an enzyme thermistor charged with immobilized trypsin was studied in Tris as well as in phosphate buffer ($\Delta H = -4.7$ kJ/mol) (Mosbach and Danielsson 1974).

Sensitivity can also be increased by co-immobilizing sequentially operating enzymes. Each reaction step will contribute to the temperature signal registered and represent the sum of the reaction enthalpies. Determination of glucose, for example, with glucose oxidase (Glucose + O_2 $\xrightarrow{\text{Glucose oxidase}}$ Glucono-δ-lactone + H_2O_2) could be made about twice as sensitive by including catalase (H_2O_2 $\xrightarrow{\text{catalase}}$ ½ O_2 + H_2O) in the enzyme thermistor column. At the same time, half of the oxygen consumed in the glucose oxidase reaction is regenerated thereby increasing the upper concentration limit for linearity from about 0.45 to 0.7 mmol/l. Co-immobilized, sequentially operating multi-step enzyme systems may offer further advantages, such as faster substrate conversion as compared with the situation where the enzymes are immobilized on separate polymer beads and better efficiency at low substrate concentrations (Danielsson *et al.* 1977).

When the first reaction is only weakly exothermic, the corresponding enzyme may be placed in a precolumn outside the enzyme thermistor, leaving only the subsequent enzyme(s) inside the calorimeter. This allows for an increased flexibility and improves the overall performance since more efficient enzyme columns can be used, especially in the first step. Determination of cellobiose using β-glucosidase (Danielsson *et al.*, 1981c) and determination of lactose using β-galactosidase (Mattiasson and Danielsson 1982) were made in this manner. Because the hydrolytic steps have a very low enthalpy, the actual thermal measurements were performed on the glucose formed by hydrolysis, using a glucose oxidase/catalase enzyme thermistor.

The sensitivity of a calorimetric assay can be greatly increased by substrate recycling, for instance with an oxidase and a dehydrogenase acting on the same substrate/product pair. It was recently demonstrated that a 1000-fold increased sensitivity for lactate or pyruvate could be obtained with use of lactate oxidase and catalase co-immobilized with lactate dehydrogenase (Scheller *et al* 1985). While passing through the column, lactate is repeatedly oxidized by the lactate oxidase and the pyruvate reduced to lactate by the lactate dehydrogenase with simultaneous consumption of NADH. The total enthalpy charge will be approximately the same as for the oxidation of NADH by oxygen, which is a highly exothermic reaction (cf. Table 29.1). Lactate or pyruvate concentrations as low as 10 nM could be determined with this technique using a 0.8 ml column with 0.5 ml samples at a flow rate of 1 ml/min. Under similar conditions the detectability for NAD(H) could be increased up to 80-fold by co-enzyme recycling using the co-immobilized enzyme couple lactate dehydrogenase and glucose 6-phosphate dehydrogenase.

29.3 Applications

Highly promising results have been obtained with enzyme thermistors and similar devices in many areas of bio-analysis including clinical analysis, process control, fermentation analysis, and environmental control. The application to chromatographic monitoring was recently described demonstrating the possibility of specific detection of a particular enzyme in a complex mixture. In addition, a flow system for immunoassay based on the enzyme thermistor has been developed. Table 29.2 summarizes a number of the many analyses that have been studied with the enzyme calorimeters presented, although some of these studies are of a rather early date showing detection ranges that probably could be considerably improved with modern equipment.

29.3.1 Thermometric enzyme-linked immunosorbent assay (TELISA)

The enzyme thermistor can also be applied to a growing area of immunochemical analysis: antigen/antibody determination. For this alternative procedure, the authors have suggested the name 'thermometric enzyme-linked immunosorbent assay' (TELISA) (Mattiasson *et al.* 1977). In principle, the column of the enzyme thermistor is filled with immunosorbent, such as antibodies immobilized on Sepharose CL-4B. The antigen to be determined and an enzyme (e.g. catalase)-labelled antigen are introduced into the flow; the amount of catalase-bound antigen remaining bound to the column is a function of the content of antigen. The less antigen that is present in the sample, the more catalase-labelled antigen will be found in the column and thus evolve more heat after the subsequent introduction of hydrogen peroxide, the substrate of catalase, into the flow stream. Sensitivities as low as 10^{-13} mol/l have currently been obtained with the TELISA technique. After the determination, the immunosorbent is readily regenerated by a glycine wash at low pH and a complete measuring cycle will only take 10–15 minutes to perform. The advantage of this technique is that occasional samples can be rapidly and sensitively analysed in a very simple procedure. For use in biotechnology, for instance for monitoring the production of hormones and proteins by genetically engineered micro-organisms, we have automated the TELISA procedure (Birnbaum *et al.* 1986). The sample valve and valves for substrate and wash solutions are then operated by a program-mable controller. The cycle time is 15 minutes and the samples can be taken from the process stream or from a sample changer.

29.3.2 Applications in clinical chemistry

Several routine methods based on immobilized urease for the determination of urea in serum have been described (Tran-Minh and Vallin 1978; Rich *et al.* 1979; Bowers *et al.* 1976; Fulton *et al.* 1980; Danielsson *et al.* 1976). We found that a remarkable wide range of linearity could be achieved; typically 0.01 to 200 mmol/l (Danielsson *et al.* 1976). Since serum samples were diluted 10-fold, most samples fell within the 0.3 and 10 mmol/l range. Consequently, there was a considerable margin for enzyme inactivation; i.e. the operational stability could be expected to be high. An enzyme column could be used for several months or for several hundreds of determinations of serum samples. The time required per sample (about two to three minutes) is acceptable for a short series of samples and the precision with a relative standard deviation of about 1% is good.

For determining glucose concentrations, either hexokinase or glucose oxidase (with catalase) have been used. Soluble hexokinase was used in a direct-injection enthalpimetric assay for glucose samples in the range of 0.5 to 50 mmol/l (McGlothlin and Jordan 1975). Immobilized hexokinase was used in a similar system in the range of 0.5 to 25 mmol/l (Bowers and Carr 1976). The throughput of 40 samples/hour, the accuracy, the precision, in addition to the long-term stability and reproducibility of the latter system make it very acceptable as a routine clinical instrument for determining glucose concentrations.

The use of glucose oxidase instead of hexokinase was preferred due to better enzymic stability and no cofactor requirements (Danielsson *et al.* 1977). A disadvantage when using glucose oxidase is, however, that linearity is obtained up to 0.45 mmol/l glucose or 0.7 mmol/l with co-immobilized glucose oxidase and catalase. This limitation can be overcome by diluting samples 50- to 100-fold, or by injecting small serum volumes (5 to 20 μl) directly into the buffer stream entering the enzyme thermistor. The precision of the determinations was high. A 0.6% relative standard deviation for samples was determined in the course of a day, both with the single-column and split-flow apparatus. Glucose concentrations determined by the enzyme thermistor agreed well with the values obtained from a conventional, spectro-photometric, enzymic technique used in routine hospital diagnosis. The operational stability of the system was at least as good as that of the urease thermistor. Similar results were obtained by Schmidt and co-workers (1976), who also used glucose oxidase co-immobilized with catalase, and in a study (Marconi, 1978) where these enzymes were fibre entrapped, resulting in a broader range of linear response (up to 5 mmol/l glucose), although at the expense of sensitivity and probably also with lower operational stability.

By employing an alternative electron acceptor to oxygen, benzoquinone, the linear range of glucose oxidase can be considerably extended. Addition of 45 mM benzoquinone to the working buffer resulted in a linear range of 0.1 to 70 mM (Kiba *et al.* 1984).

A glucose oxidase/catalase thermistor in combination with a disaccharide splitting enzyme can be applied for the determination of disaccharides containing glucose (e.g. cellobiose (Danielsson *et al.* 1981c) and lactose (Mattiasson and Danielsson 1982)). In addition, sucrose has been measured directly with the enzyme invertase (EC 3.2.1.26) in the range of 0.05 to 100 mmol/l (Mattiasson and Danielsson 1982). This example illustrates one of the advantages of the enzyme thermistor since this reaction can be followed directly without any coupled reaction which is not possible with other techniques, such as colorimetry. Galactose oxidase (EC 1.1.3.9) can be used for galactose assays and ascorbate oxidase (EC 1.10.3.3) can be used for vitamin C assays with linearity between 0.05 and 0.6 mmol/l (Mattiasson and Danielsson 1982).

Triglyceride determination (Satoh *et al.* 1981) is a current example of enzyme calorimetry employing a single enzyme, where in most other tech-niques several enzymes have to be used. Lipoprotein lipase (EC 3.1.1.34) was immobilized on CPG having a pore size of 2000 Å. The assay was performed with a split-flow apparatus in 0.1 M Tris buffer, pH 8.0, containing 0.5% Triton X-100. A linear temperature response was obtained for 0.05 to 10 mmol/l of tributyrin and for 0.1 to 5 mmol/l of triolein (Fig. 29.3). The triglyceride concentration in serum samples could be directly determined after two-fold dilution (up to a concentration of 3 mmol/l) with the Tris buffer. The results correlated well with those obtained with conventional spectrophotometric enzymic methods.

Another example of lipid assay comes from a recent study of phospholipid determination employing three consecutively acting enzymes: phospholipase D, choline oxidase, and catalase (Satoh *et al.* 1986). Of these enzymes soluble phospholipase D (36 I U) was added directly to 0.05 ml sample, which was then injected into the buffer stream (1 ml/min. of 0.1 *M* Tris-HC1, pH 8.0, containing 15 mM $CaCl_2$ and 0.5% Triton X-100), whereas the enzyme

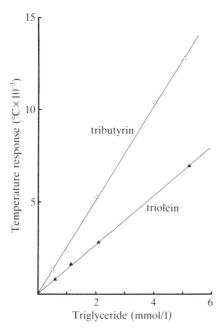

Fig. 29.3 Calibration curves for a split-flow enzyme thermistor containing lipoprotein lipase bound to CPG.

column was charged with only choline oxidase and catalase co-immobilized on CPG. The linear range was between 0.03 and 0.19 mM and serum samples could be directly analysed after 10-fold dilution and with good correlation with conventional methods. Co-immobilization of all three enzymes involved resulted in rather low operational stability, but the proposed technique permitted eight weeks of operation or at least 1600 analyses with each column.

The authors' current studies on applications of the enzyme thermistor in biotechnology include determination of lactate in fermentation broth. This metabolite is also of clinical interest. Using lactate 2-monooxygenase (EC 1.13.12.4) bound to CPG, lactate concentrations in aqueous standards as well as in biological samples can be determined with high sensitivity and stability from 0.005 mmol/l up to 3 mmol/l, with a linear response up to about 0.5 to 1 mmol/l. A comparison between calorimetric and electrochemical determination of lactate showed that the enzyme thermistor gave a higher sensitivity than a polarographic oxygen electrode in a flow cell combined with a lactate oxidase column of the same type as used in the enzyme thermistor (B. Danielsson, I. Satoh, and B. Mattiasson, unpublished results).

Furthermore, an oxidase from *Pediococcus pseudomonas* (EC 1.1.3.2) is now available and has been used particularly in the recycling system

Table 29.2 Substances analysed with enzyme thermistors

Substance	Immobilized biocatalyst	Concentration range (mmol/l)	References
Clinical analysis			
Ascorbic acid	Ascorbic acid oxidase	0.05–0.6	*a*
ATP	Apyrase	1–8	*b*
Cholesterol	Cholesterol oxidase	0.03–0.15	*c*
Cholesterol esters	Cholesterol esterase + cholesterol oxidase	0.03–0.15	*c*
Creatinine	Creatinine iminohydrolase	0.01–10	*c*
Glucose	Glucose oxidase + catalase	0.002–0.8	*d, e, f, g*
Glucose	Hexokinase	0.5–25	*h*
Lactate	Lactate 2-monooxygenase	0.005–2	*c, i*
Oxalic acid	Oxalate oxidase	0.005–0.5	*j*
Oxalic acid	Oxalate decarboxylase	0.1–3	*c*
Triglycerides	Lipoprotein lipase	0.1–5	*k*
Urea	Urease	0.01–500	*l, m, n, o, p*
Uric acid	Uricase	0.05–4	*c*
Soluble enzyme analysis			
Urea	Urease (soluble)	0.1–100 U/ml	*q*
H_2O_2	Catalase (soluble)	0.1–100 U/ml	*q*
Glucose + ATP	Hexokinase (soluble)	0.1–2.5 U/ml	*r*
Immunological analysis, TELISA			
Albumin (antigen)	Immobilized antibodies + enzyme-linked antigen	10^{-10}–	*s*
Gentamicin (antigen)	,,	0.1– μg/ml	*c*
Insulin (antigen)	,,	0.1–1.0 U/ml	
		0.1–50 μg/ml	*t*
Fermentation analysis and process control			
Cellobiose	β-glucosidase + glucose oxidase + catalase	0.05–5	*u*
Cephalosporin	Cephalosporinase	0.005–10	*c*
Ethanol	Alcohol oxidase	0.01–2	*v*
Galactose	Galactose oxidase	0.01–1	*a*
Lactose	Lactase and glucose oxidase + catalase	0.05–10	*a*
Penicillin G	Penicillinase	0.05–500	*x, y*
Sucrose	Invertase	0.05–100	*a*

a. Mattiasson and Danielsson 1982	*m.* Rich *et al.* 1976
b. Mosbach and Danielsson 1974	*n.* Bowers *et al.* 1976
c. Danielsson *et al.* 1981*a*	*o.* Fulton *et al.* 1980
d. Schmidt *et al.* 1976	*p.* Danielsson *et al.* 1976
e. Kiba *et al.* 1984	*q.* Danielsson and Mosbach 1979
f. Danielsson *et al.* 1977	*r.* Danielsson *et al.* 1981*c*
g. Marconi 1978	*s.* Mattiasson *et al.* 1977
h. Bowers and Carr 1976	*t.* Birnbaum *et al.* 1986
i. Danielsson *et al.* unpublished	*u.* Danielsson *et al.* 1981*b*
j. Winquist *et al.* 1985	*v.* Guilbault *et al.* 1983
k. Satoh *et al.* 1981	*x.* Mattiasson *et al.* 1981
l. Tran-Minh and Vallin 1978	*y.* Decristoforo and Danielsson 1984

described above (Scheller *et al.* 1985), resulting in an extremely high sensitivity (10 nM). This enzyme can, of course, also be used, preferably together with catalase, in the common type of enzyme thermistor assay, then with a performance similar to that of the glucose oxidase/catalase system.

A calorimetric assay for determining oxalic acid content in urine and in serum has also been developed. The enzyme oxalate oxidase (EC 1.2.3.4) has become available (Boehringer Mannheim). Very promising results have been obtained with this preparation and with the authors' preparations from barley seedlings. The oxalic acid concentration can be determined directly in 5- to 10-fold diluted urine in the range of 0.01 to 0.5 mmol/l (Winquist *et al.* 1985). This assay is also useful with food samples.

Rapid enzymic determination of ethanol is of interest in clinical chemistry as well as in biotechnology. In a recent study, enzyme electrode assays, based on a polarographic oxygen electrode, and enzyme thermistor alcohol assays were compared using the alcohol oxidase from *Candida boidinii* (EC 1.1.3.13) (Guilbault *et al.* 1983). The stability of the CPG-bound enzyme in the enzyme thermistor was drastically improved by co-immobilizing catalase. Catalase continuously removes the deleterious hydrogen peroxide formed and simultaneously recovers half of the oxygen consumed, and the reaction approximately doubles the heat formation. Both methods were found to give quite adequate sensitivities for blood ethanol determination. With the thermistor probe, as little as 0.2 mmol/l (with linearity up to 2 mmol/l) could be assayed with a precision of 1.5%. In addition to ethanol, methanol, propanol, and butanol were found to give good responses with both techniques.

29.3.3 Enzyme activity determination

With a minor modification of the flow system, the enzyme thermistor allows for determination of soluble enzyme activity. The sample solution containing the enzyme and an appropriate substrate solution containing a substrate to the enzyme in excess are each passed through a heat exchanger prior to being mixed and rapidly passed through one of the short, inner heat exchangers to eliminate heat generated on mixing, before entering a reaction chamber. The reaction chamber (about 1 ml volume) replaces the enzyme column normally used in the apparatus and consists of either an inactive column or a piece of Teflon tubing forming a 'reaction coil'. The temperature at the outlet of the reaction chamber is continuously measured with one of the thermistor probes as described in the experimental section (29.2). Linear correlation has been found between temperature response and enzyme activity for a variety of enzymes (Danielsson and Mosbach 1979). The sensitivity is in the order 0.01 to 0.1 IU/ml depending on the enzyme. Determination of soluble enzyme activities by calorimetry could be of interest in the clinical area, as well as for monitoring enzyme purification processes. Although the absolute sensitivity of this technique is rather low, it has the advantage of being a direct, continuous flow method that can be used on crude samples with inexpensive substrates (no need for expensive substrates to produce coloured products).

29.3.4 Calorimetric monitoring of chromatography

The enzyme thermistor has been successfully applied as an instrument for the specific monitoring of gel filtration, ion exchange chromatography, and affinity chromatography (Danielsson *et al.* 1981*b*). Since the enzyme thermistor can be used for continuous monitoring of enzymic activities directly on crude samples, it provides possibilities for direct identification and localization of a specific component in a complex chromatogram, for instance, in the initial steps of an enzyme purification scheme (Fig. 29.4). Furthermore, elution in affinity chromatography is frequently accomplished with co-enzymes having

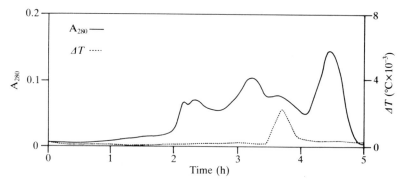

Fig. 29.4 Gel filtration of 1 ml crude yeast extract on an Ultrogel AcA 44 column eluted with 0.2 M Tris-HCl, 0.0133 M MgCl$_2$, pH 7.8, at a flow rate of 0.75 ml/min. For enzyme thermistor assay of hexokinase (dotted line) the effluent was mixed with substrate solution containing 0.54 M glucose, 0.011 M ATP, flow rate 0.2 ml/min (Danielsson *et al.*, 1981b). Reproduced with permission from the publisher Academic Press, Inc., Orlando, Florida, USA.

a strong ultraviolet absorbance, thereby often precluding on-line assay of a particular enzyme either by UV-monitoring or by spectrophotometric monitoring of changes in NAD(P)H concentration. Thus, calorimetric detection of the eluted enzyme activity should have definite advantages for monitoring this type of affinity chromatography.

29.3.5 Process control and fermentation analysis

One of the most promising application fields for thermal bio-analysers appears to be in process control and fermentation analysis. As biotechnology advances, a growing interest can be expected in direct methods for on-line determination of specific components formed or consumed in processes. With the exception of methods for determining physical variables, such as pH, pO_2, and pCO_2, most analytical techniques currently used for process control are discontinuous, off-line procedures. In contrast, continuous on-line methods reduce the costs of sample handling and personnel and give more information, making them more suitable for process control. Much of the knowledge gained in this field is directly applicable to medical areas, for instance to *in vivo* monitoring systems. The suitability of the enzyme thermistor for continuous monitoring and control was investigated. In one model study, the authors used an enzyme thermistor to control the effluent composition of an enzyme reactor containing β-galactosidase (Danielsson *et al.* 1979). Lactose present in whey from cow's milk pumped through the reactor was hydrolysed to glucose and galactose and the glucose level in the effluent was measured with use of a glucose oxidase/catalase loaded enzyme

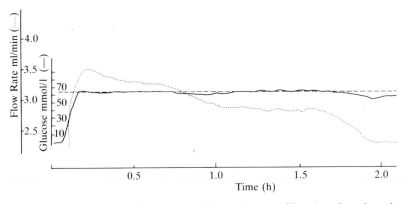

Fig. 29.5 Glucose concentration measured by a glucose oxidase/catalase thermistor (——) and pump speed (·····) upon pumping whey (150 M in lactose) through a plug-flow reactor containing Sepharose-bound lactase. The glucose concentration was set to 63 M (-----) (Danielsson *et al.* 1979). Reproduced with permission from the publisher John Wiley & Sons, Inc., New York, N.Y., USA.

thermistor (Fig. 29.5). The heat signal registered by the thermistor unit was used via a proportional/integral-controller to regulate the flow of substrate through the reactor. Thus, it was possible to keep the product composition (e.g. glucose) in the effluent constant, despite clogging occurring in the column.

As discussed, specific, continuous flow assays for several sugars have been devised. Different types of process control involving such sugars (Mattiasson *et al.* 1983; Mandenius *et al.* 1985) are being investigated by the authors. The experiments indicate that the enzyme thermistor is stable enough to monitor and control a process over several days without any need for change of enzyme cartridge or recalibration. It is advisable to check the baseline once a day. The system is also fast enough to respond to sudden changes (1 to 3 minutes) and has been used with analogue controllers and digital computers. In principle, the same approach could be used to control the blood glucose level in a patient by dosing insulin in response to the signal from an enzyme thermistor which continuously measures the glucose concentration.

In another study penicillin present in fermentation broth was analysed with a unit containing immobilized penicillinase (β-lactamase) (Mattiasson *et al.* 1981). With CPG as enzyme matrix, the useful linear range was found to be at least 0.01 to 100 mmol/l. This study provides a comparison between CPG-bound and nylon tubing-bound penicillinase. In Fig. 29.6 some penicillin G determinations in samples made up in fermentation broth are plotted in

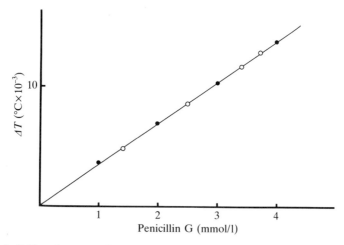

Fig. 29.6 Calibration curve for penicillin G in 0.3 M sodium phosphate buffer, pH 7.0 (•), with samples containing known amounts of penicillin G in 10-fold diluted fermentation broth plotted in the same diagram (○). The sample volume was 1 ml, flow rate 1 ml/minute, and the enzyme thermistor column contained CPG-bound penicillinase.

relation to a calibration curve for the lower concentration range. The coefficient of correlation between analytical results obtained with the calorimetric method and those from conventional assays was 0.997 for broth samples. Penicillin determination by the enzyme thermistor in the antibiotics industry has proven superior to commonly used methods such as high performance liquid chromatography (HPLC) and colorimetric procedures. Several instruments have been installed to replace the latter techniques (Decristoforo and Danielsson 1984).

Most fermentation analyses are complex systems containing particulate matter. Methods to prevent entry of these particles must be devised in order to prevent clogging of the analytical device. This can be accomplished either by the insertion of a dialysis membrane (of the type Technicon is using in its Auto Analyzer system (Danielsson *et al.* 1981*c*) or by employing enzymes bound to the inside of nylon tubing instead of using regular columns. With the former arrangement, the important requirement for sterility in fermentation process can also be met. Since the nylon tubing has a more limited binding capacity than that of CPG, the linear range will also be limited. In addition, the sensitivity of the CPG-system is high enough to permit higher degree of dilution, which is a third way of reducing the problem of clogging. With the enzyme thermistor unit, it is possible not only to continuously monitor a product (e.g. penicillin as it is formed in a fermentation process) as well as substrates (e.g. glucose being consumed), but also to simultaneously register the overall thermal behaviour of such a microbial process, yielding a thermogram (power-time curve) which provides valuable information (Danielsson *et al.* 1981*a*). In this case the micro-organism suspension is mixed with a substrate solution and the temperature increase after appropriate reaction time is measured. The procedure is similar to that of thermal enzyme activity determination.

29.3.6 Environmental analysis

Thermal analysis can also be applied to both discontinuous and continuous environmental control analysis (Danielsson *et al.* 1981*a*); in the latter case acting as a kind of toxi-guard. If detection of a specific toxic compound is required, a limiting amount of an enzyme that is inhibited by the compound can be immobilized in the enzyme column of an enzyme thermistor. Heavy metals, for instance Hg^{2+} in concentrations down to 0.2 ppb, could be determined due to the inhibitory action on immobilized urease (Danielsson *et al.* 1981*a*). The heavy metal concentration of a sample was determined by comparison of the temperature response to a substrate pulse (containing an excess amount of urea) before and after introduction of the sample. A special washing step completely restored the original urease activity permitting repeated analysis with the same enzyme column. In some instances there are enzymes available that act directly on the substance to be measured. Such is the case of cyanide, that can be determined with a sensitivity of 10^{-5}M using the enzyme rhodanese (Danielsson *et al.* 1981*a*). Even for pesticides and acetylcholine esterase inhibitors a direct approach can be envisaged (Danielsson *et al.* 1981*a*). Alternatively, one may utilize immobilized, intact cells, organelles, or multi-enzyme systems placed in the column in case a more general detection of poisonous material is required. With such a system a larger number of potentially toxic compounds would be detected as these affect the overall metabolism, leading to decreased heat generation.

29.4 Conclusion

Despite many attractive properties, surprisingly few immobilized enzyme probes have yet been applied in commercial instruments. To date only a very limited number of enzyme-electrode based systems have been introduced. The rapidly growing importance of biotechnology will lead to an increasing demand for flow stream analysers to be used in process control, fermentation monitoring, and downstream analysis. In this field immobilized enzyme probes will certainly find their applications as they allow for highly specific continuous flow analysis. The use of immobilized enzymes cuts down enzyme costs and increases the operational stability. Thermal flow analysers appear to be particularly attractive due to the possibility of analysing turbid, particulate, or coloured samples. Furthermore, they are based on the most general detection principle, the detection of the heat of reaction, which makes them directly applicable to most enzymic reactions. The heat formed by the primary enzymic reaction is usually sufficient for reliable measurements thus obviating the need for auxiliary enzymic reactions generally required in other analytical procedures (often involving expensive co-enzymes — especially disadvantageous in continuous flow analysis). The prospects are also good for applications of thermal flow analysers in medical instruments, for instance in flow analysers for metabolite monitoring. Parallel with the development of highly sophisticated, high-capacity multichannel laboratory systems there is a development of small dedicated single-channel instruments, such as creatinine and glucose analysers. Excellent flow stream analysers of this type could be based on enzyme thermistors as section 29.3 above indicated, for example in an oxalate analyser.

References

Birnbaum, S., Bülow, L., Danielsson, B., Hardy, K. and Mosbach, K. (1986). Rapid automated analysis of human proinsulin produced by *Escherichia coli. Anal. Biochem.* **157**. In press.

Bowers, L. D. and Carr, P. W. (1976). Immobilized-enzyme flow-enthalpimetric analyzer: application to glucose determination by direct phosphorylation catalyzed by hexokinase. *Clin. Chem.* **22**, 1427–33.

—— Canning, L. M., Sayers, C. N. and Carr, P. W. (1976). Rapid flow-enthalpimetric determination of urea in serum with use of an immobilized urease reactor. *Clin. Chem.* **22**, 1314–8.

Brown, H. D. (1969). Calorimetry of enzyme catalyzed reactions. In *Biochemical microcalorimetry* (ed. H. D. Brown) p. 149. Academic Press, New York.

Cooney, C. L., Weaver, J. C., Tannenbaum, S. R., Faller, D. V., Shields, A. and Jahnke, M. (1974). The thermal enzyme probe — a novel approach to chemical analysis. In *enzyme engineering* (eds. E. K. Pye and L. B. Wingard, Jr.) Vol. 2, p. 411–7. Plenum. New York.

Danielsson, B. and Mosbach, K. (1979). Determination of enzyme activities with the enzyme thermistor unit. *FEBS Lett.* **101**, 47–50.

—— Mattiasson, B. and Mosbach, K. (1981*a*). Enzyme thermistor devices and their analytical applications. *Appl. Biochem. Bioeng.* **3**, 97–143.

—— Gadd, K., Mattiasson, B. and Mosbach, K. (1977). Enzyme thermistor determination of glucose in serum using immobilized glucose oxidase. *Clin. Chim. Acta* **81**, 163–75.

—— (1976). Determination of urea with an enzyme thermistor using immobilized urease. *Anal. Lett.* **9**, 987–1001.

—— Mattiasson, B., Karlsson, R. and Winquist, F. (1979). Use of an enzyme thermistor in continuous measurements and enzyme reactor control. *Biotechnol. Bioeng.* **21**, 1749–66.

—— Bülow, L., Lowe, C. R., Satoh, I. and Mosbach, K. (1981*b*). Evaluation of the enzyme thermistor as a specific detector for chromatographic procedures. *Anal. Biochem.* **117**, 84–93.

—— Rieke, E., Mattiasson, B., Winquist, F. and Mosbach, K. (1981*c*). Determination by the enzyme thermistor of cellobiose formed on degradation of cellulose. *Appl. Biochem. Biotechnol.* **6**, 207–22.

Decristoforo, G. and Danielsson, B. (1984). Flow injection analysis with enzyme thermistor detector for automated determination of β-lactams. *Anal. Chem.* **56**, 263–8.

Fulton, S. P., Cooney, C. L. and Weaver, J. C. (1980). Thermal enzyme probe differential temperature measurements in a laminar flow-through cell. *Anal. Chem.* **52**, 505–8.

Grime, J. K. (1980). Biochemical and clinical analysis by enthalpimetric measurements — a realistic alternative approach? *Anal. Chim. Acta* **118**, 191–225.

—— (1985). Application of solution calorimetry to biochemical and clinical analyses. In *Analytical solution calorimetry* (ed. J. K. Grime) p. 345. Wiley-Interscience, New York.

—— and Tan, B. (1979). The determination of some selected penicillins by enzymatic enthalpimetry. *Anal. Chim. Acta* **107**, 319–26.

Guilbault, G. G., Danielsson, B., Mandenius, C. F. and Mosbach, K. (1983). A comparison of enzyme electrode and thermistor probes for assay of alcohols using alcohol oxidase. *Anal. Chem.* **55**, 1582–5.

Johansson, Å., Mattiasson, B. and Mosbach, K. (1976). Immobilized enzymes in microcalorimetry. *Methods in Enzymol.* **44**, 659–67.

Kiba, N., Tomiyasu, T. and Furusawa, M. (1984). Flow enthalpimetric determination of glucose based on oxidation by 1.4-benzoquinone with use of immobilized glucose oxidase column. *Talanta* **31**, 131–2.

Mandenius, C. F., Bülow, L., Danielsson, B. and Mosbach, K. (1985). Monitoring and control of enzymic sucrose hydrolysis using on-line biosensors. *Appl. Microbiol. Biotechnol.* **21**, 135–42.

Marconi, W. (1978). Biomedical applications of enzymatic fibres. In *Enzyme engineering* (eds. G. B. Broun, G. Manecke, and L. B. Wingard, Jr.) Vol. 4, p. 179–86. Plenum Press, New York.

Martin, C. J. and Marini, M. A. (1977). Microcalorimetry in biochemical analysis. *CRC Crit. Rev. in Anal. Chem.* **8**, 221–86.

Mattiasson, B. and Danielsson, B. (1982). Calorimetric analysis of sugars and sugar derivatives with aid of an enzyme thermistor. *Carbohydr. Res.* **102**, 273–82.

—— and Mosbach, K. (1976). A split-flow enzyme thermistor. *Anal. Lett.*, **9**, 867–89.

—— Borrebaeck, C., Sanfridsson, B. and Mosbach, K. (1977). Thermometric enzyme linked immunosorbent assay: TELISA. *Biochim. Biophys. Acta* **483**, 221–7.

—— Danielsson, B., Winquist, F., Nilsson, H. and Mosbach, K. (1981). Enzyme thermistor analysis of penicillin in standard solutions and in fermentation broths. *Appl. Environ. Microbiol.* **41**, 903–8.

—— Mandenius, C. F., Axelsson, J. P., Danielsson B. and Hagander, P. (1983). Computer control of fermentation with biosensors. *Ann. N. Y. Acad. Sci.* **413**, 193–6.

McGlothlin, C. D. and Jordan, J. (1975). Enzymatic enthalpimetry, a new approach to clinical analysis: glucose determination by hexokinase catalyzed phosphorylation. *Anal. Chem.* **47**, 786–90.

Mosbach, K. and Danielsson, B. (1974). An enzyme thermistor. *Biochim. Biophys. Acta* **364**, 140–5.

—— and Danielsson, B. (1981). Thermal bioanalyzers in flow streams–enzyme thermistor devices. *Anal. Chem.* **53**, 83A–94A.

—— Borgerud, A. and Scott, M. (1975). Determination of heat changes in the proximity of immobilized enzymes with an enzyme thermistor and its use for the assay of metabolites. *Biochim. Biophys. Acta* **403**, 256–65.

—— Mattiasson, B., Gestrelius, S., Srere, P. A. and Danielsson, B. (1974). Theoretical and practical aspects of immobilized multi-step enzyme systems. In *Enzyme engineering* (eds. E. K. Pye and L. B. Wingard, Jr.) Vol. 2, p. 151. Plenum, New York.

Pennington, S. N. (1976). A small volume microcalorimeter for analytical determinations. *Anal. Biochem.* **72**, 230–7.

Poe, M., Gutfreund, H. and Estabrook, R. W. (1967). Kinetic studies of temperature changes and oxygen uptake in a differential calorimeter: The heat of oxidation of NADH and succinate. *Arch. Biochem. Biophys.* **122**, 204–11.

Rehak, N. N. and Young, D. S. (1978). Prospective applications of calorimetry in the clinical laboratory. *Clin. Chem.* **24**, 1414–19.

Rich, S., Ianiello, R. M. and Jespersen, N. D. (1979). Development and application of a thermistor enzyme probe in the urea-urease system. *Anal. Chem.* **51**, 204–6.

Satoh, I., Danielsson, B. and Mosbach, K. (1981). Triglyceride determination with use of an enzyme thermistor. *Anal. Chim. Acta* **131**, 255–62.

—— Ogawa, T. and Danielsson, B. (1986). Calorimetric phospholipid determination. Submitted.

Scheller, F., Siegbahn, N., Danielsson, B. and Mosbach, K. (1985). High-sensitivity enzyme thermistor of L-lactate by substrate recycling. *Anal. Chem.* **57**, 1740–3.

Schmidt, H.-L., Krisam, G. and Grenner, G. (1976). Microcalorimetric methods for substrate determinations in flow streams with immobilized enzymes. *Biochim. Biophys. Acta* **429**, 283–90.

Tran-Minh, C. and Vallin, D. (1978). Enzyme-bound thermistor as an enthalpimetric sensor. *Anal. Chem.* **50**, 1874–8.

Weaver, J. C., Cooney, C. L., Fulton, S. P., Schuler, D. and Tannenbaum, S. R. (1976). Experiments and calculation concerning a thermal enzyme probe. *Biochim. Biophys. Acta* **452**, 285–91.

Winquist, F., Danielsson, B., Malpote, J.-Y., Persson, L. and Larsson, M.-B. (1985). Enzyme thermistor determination of oxalate with immobilized oxalate oxidase. *Anal. Lett.* **18**, 573–88.

Photometry

30

Optical sensors based on immobilized reagents

W. RUDOLF SEITZ

30.1 Introduction

This chapter will deal with devices involving an immobilized reagent phase on the end of a single optical fibre or a fibre bundle. Interaction of the component being measured (i.e. the analyte) with the immobilized reagent phase causes a change in the optical properties of the reagent phase which is measured through the optical fibre. An example would be a pH sensor prepared by placing an immobilized acid-base indicator on the end of an optical fibre bundle.

These sensors involve the synthesis of two ideas. One is the use of optical fibres to bring light from a spectrometer to a sample and back. The other is the use of immobilization as a means of allowing a chemical reagent to be used on a continuous rather on a one-time basis. While both ideas have been applied individually for many years, their combination is relatively new and presents exciting possibilities that are just beginning to be realized. The use of optical fibres effectively permits scientist to 'bring the spectrometer to the sample', while the use of immobilized reagent phases makes it possible to do chemistry on the sample *in situ*.

D. W. Luebbers and co-workers were the first to use immobilized indicators for continuous measurements in biological fluids (Luebbers and Opitz 1975). They used the term 'optode' for their devices in analogy to 'electrode'. Subsequently, T. Hirshfeld and co-workers have introduced the term 'optrode'. Since the 'r' belongs to the root word, electrical, 'optode' is the grammatically correct term. However, because 'optode' suggests a kind of small wart-causing amphibian, the more euphonious 'optrode' may become the accepted term. In this chapter both terms will be avoided in favour of 'optical sensors'.

30.1.1 Scope of chapter

This chapter will review the advantages and limitations of optical sensors relative to electrodes. The instrumentation required for an optical sensor system will be briefly described. The ways in which the immobilized reagent phase can interact with analyte will be described and illustrated with specific devices. The chapter will confine itself to devices which respond on a continuous basis and will not consider systems where the immobilized reagent is used on a one-time basis. It will, however, include systems where immobilized reagents have been used for continuous optical measurements without fibre optics, since these reagents could easily be adapted for use with optical fibres.

Prior reviews have considered biomedical applications of all types of fiber optic sensors (Peterson and Vurek 1984) and general characteristics of chemical sensors based on fibre optics (Seitz 1984).

30.2 Advantages and limitations

Because most optical sensors reported to date respond to analytes that can also be sensed electrically, electrochemical sensors have provided the frame of reference for evaluating the performance of optical sensors. A general comparison must be treated with caution, however. Since optical sensors are based on very different principles than electrical sensors, the relative merit of the two will depend on both the particular analyte being measured and the demands of a particular application. In general, optical sensors offer the following advantages relative to electrodes:

1) No 'reference electrode' is required. (However, as discussed below, it is good practice to measure the signal of interest relative to a reference intensity of some sort. This can involve the addition of a reference compound to the reagent phase.)

2) Because the signal is optical, it is not subject to electrical interference. This advantage is particularly important for sensors operated in electrically noisy environments.

3) The immobilized reagent phase does not have to be in physical contact with the optical fibre. This simplifies the development of sensors in which the immobilized reagent phase can be conveniently discarded and replaced. This is likely to be important in practice because it will be difficult to develop reagent phases with sufficient stability to be useful on an indefinite basis.

4) Optical devices are inherently safer than electrical devices when used for *in vivo* biomedical measurements because there is no danger of electrical shock.

5) Certain analytes, most notably oxygen, can be sensed on an equilibrium basis optically but not electrochemically. Because, once equilibrium is reached, 'equilibrium' sensors do not require a steady state supply of analyte to the sensor surface, they are inherently less sensitive to fluctuations in temperature and flow conditions in the sample than amperometric electrochemical sensors.

6) Optical sensors can be highly stable with respect to calibration. This

will be particularly true if the sensor involves the measurement of the ratio of intensities at two different wavelengths. For example, a highly stable pH sensor can be prepared if one optically measures the amounts of both the acid and base forms of an indicator and relates pH to the ratio of the two.

7) Optical sensors that simultaneously respond to more than one analyte can be prepared using multiple immobilized reagents with different wavelength characteristics. For example, a sensor responding simultaneously to O_2 and CO_2 has been reported (Opitz and Luebbers 1976).

8) Multiwavelength measurements can be used to monitor any change in the optical properties of the immobilized reagent phase which might indicate decomposition of the reagent or some other process affecting the ability of the immobilized reagent phase to respond accurately. This information could be used to decide when to replace the reagent phase.

The last three advantages of optical sensors reflect the fact that optical sensors have the potential for higher information content than electrical sensors because there is a complete spectrum of information available. In addition, in luminescence-based sensors there is further information that can be acquired by measuring luminescence lifetimes. The challenge for the chemist is to design immobilized reagent phases that exploit this potential. *If appropriate reagent phases can not be developed, then the advantages of optical sensors will not be realized in practice.*

In general, optical sensors have the following limitations relative to electrical sensors:

1) They are subject to background from ambient light. This can be eliminated by excluding light and/or modulation techniques.

2) Compared to some electrical sensors, optical sensors have limited dynamic ranges. For example, the pH electrode has a dynamic range of greater than 10^{12} compared to a typical range of 10^2 for an optical pH sensor.

3) Optical sensors are 'extensive' devices. The signal depends on the amount of reagent. Thus miniaturizing the sensor causes a decrease in the magnitude of measured intensities which in turn complicates the technology of the measurement.

4) Long-term stability of immobilized reagents subjected to incident light is likely to be a problem. The stability of a particular reagent will depend on several factors involving both the intrinsic reactivity of the reagent and operating parameters of the sensor such as temperature and the intensity and duration of incident light. While it is reasonable to expect development of reagent phases that are stable for days and weeks, it will be

difficult at best to find reagent phases that can be used reliably for longer time periods.

5) Response times for some optical sensors may be slow because there must be mass transfer of analyte to or from the reagent phase before constant response is reached. While response times can be reduced by making the reagent phase smaller, this is accompanied by a decrease in the amount of reagent and the magnitude of the optical signal.

30.3 Instrumental considerations

The instrumentation required for optical sensors depends on the intended application. Fortunately, most biomedical applications do not require that the signal be transmitted for long distances through optical fibre. This means that the degree of signal attenuation in the fibre is relatively small and successful sensors can be designed using conventional continuum sources rather than requiring the greater intensity available only with lasers. This not only reduces instrumentation costs but also allows greater flexibility in choice of immobilized reagent phases since there are fewer limitations on available wavelengths. The majority of biomedical applications reported to date as well as the first commercial chemical sensor system based on fibre optics (Cardiovascular Devices Inc.) involve incandescent sources and interference filters. Measurements at more than one wavelength can be accomplished by arrangements for sequentially inserting different filters into the optical path or by splitting the beam after it returns from the immobilized reagent phase.

In some applications an argon laser has been used as a source (Milanovich *et al.* 1984; Schultz *et al.* 1982). The high intensity available from the laser makes it possible to miniaturize the sensor while maintaining acceptable intensities. It is particularly well suited for immobilized reagents based on fluorescein derivatives because the 488 nm laser line efficiently excites fluorescein fluorescence.

While, unlike electrodes, optical sensors do not require a separate reference sensor, the response characteristics of optical sensors are generally improved by comparing the analytical signal relative to a reference intensity. This can be accomplished in several ways. The simplest is to directly measure source intensity at the analytical wavelength to compensate for source fluctuations. A more attractive approach is to use a reference intensity which follows an optical path through the immobilized reagent since this will compensate for any changes in the optical properties of the reagent phase, (e.g., changes in scattering by the reagent phase due to variation in refractive index of the sample with time). Back-scattered excitation radiation has been used as a reference in an oxygen sensor based on fluorescence (Peterson *et al.* 1984). Alternatively, a fluorophor that is insensitive to analyte can be incorporated into the reagent phase to provide a reference signal. Where feasible, the best approach is to incorporate the reference signal into the immobilized reagent itself. For example, in a pH sensor based on an indicator with acid and base forms that fluoresce at different wavelengths, the measured parameter can be the ratio of fluorescence for the two forms (Zhujun and Seitz 1984*a*). This type of reference compensates not only for instrumental fluctuations and variations in reagent phase optical properties but also for changes in the amount of immobilized indicator due to slow decomposition or some other process.

The type of optical fibre used influences the cost and performance of optical sensors. Plastic has the lowest cost and is the safest, but is limited to wavelengths above about 450 nm. Glass fibers are somewhat more expensive but are suitable for measurements down to about 380 nm. Because measurements below 380 nm require arc lamp sources and considerably more expensive fused silica fibre, there is a significant cost incentive to use immobilized reagent phases that change optical properties in the visible region of the spectrum. Fibre diameters have typically been in the range from 50 to 200 micrometers.

Optical sensors can be configured in several ways, some of which are illustrated in Fig. 30.1. Figure 30.1a shows a bifurcated device in which separate

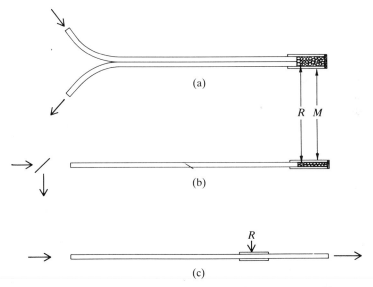

Fig. 30.1 Optical Sensor Configurations. M, membrane permeable to analyte; R, immobilized reagent phase. The arrows represent the direction in which light is travelling. (a) Bifurcated sensor in which separate fibres carry light to and from the immobilized reagent. (b) Sensor in which the same fibre(s) carry light to and from the reagent, and a beam splitter is used to redirect emerging light to a detection system. (c) Sensor in which the reagent phase is coated on the outside of the fibre.

fibres are used to transmit light to and from an immobilized reagent phase. The reagent is immobilized on solid substrate particles represented as spheres in the figure. A tubular membrane slipped over the two fibres serves to hold the reagent in place. Analyte diffuses through the membrane to interact with the reagent. A cap at the end of the tubular membrane blocks the incident radiation from directly interacting with the sample, avoiding a potential source of interference. In addition to serving as the immobilization substrate, the solid particles scatter the incident radiation so that some of it is redirected into the second fibre which leads to a detection system. The arrangement in Fig. 30.1a has been successfully employed in sensors designed for bio-chemical measurements of pH and oxygen (Peterson *et al.* 1980; Peterson *et al.* 1984). The reagent phase is a typically few millimeters long in this type of sensor.

The arrangement in Fig. 30.1b differs from that in Fig. 30.1a only in that a single fiber is used to transmit light both to and from the reagent phase. This arrangement is suitable for sensors based on changes in fluorescence because the fluorescence of interest is readily distinguished from scattered excitation radiation on the basis of wavelength.

In Fig. 30.1c the cladding is removed from part of the optical fibre and replaced by the reagent phase. This arrangement takes advantage of the fact that light transmitted through the optical fibre penetrates a small distance into the cladding. Changes in the refractive index and/or the absorptive properties of the reagent phase will modify the intensity of light transmitted through the fibre. Furthermore, it is possible to excite fluorescence from reagents on the surface of fibre. This optical configuration has been used for immunoassay (Sutherland *et al.* 1984; Sutherland *et al.* 1984), an application which is described in more detail in Chapter 33. However it is unsuitable for many applications because a relatively long length of fibre has to be coated with reagent.

The immobilized reagent phase of an optical sensor is generally not a well defined medium for spectroscopy. If the reagent is immobilized on a solid phase, there will be considerable scattering of the incident radiation. This is particulary true if the reagent phase consists of solid particles as shown in Fig. 30.1a and b. Because the immobilized reagent phase is used on a conti-nuous basis, the effect of optical inhomogeneities on the measured signal can be accounted for by calibration. However, the calibration procedure will be simpler and more reliable if the relationship between the optical signal and the measured parameter is known. In sensors based on fluorescence, it has generally been assumed that fluorescence intensity is directly proportional to the concentration of fluorophor. While this is probably a good assumption in most cases, it should be recognized that there may be significant inner filter effects due to absorption of the excitation radiation by the immobilized reagent. If changes in fluorophor concentration are accompanied by changes in absorption by the reagent phase, then the magnitude of the inner filter effect on fluorescence will vary with fluorophor concentration and the measured intensity will no longer be proportional to concentration. For example, using equations reported in the literature (Zhujun and Seitz 1984*a*), it can be calculated that the response of a fluorescent indicator to pH will show substantial shifts when there are large inner filter effects.

In sensors based on colour changes, the problem of developing a theoretical relationship between concentration of absorber and measured intensity is considerably more difficult. The first problem is that there is no way to measure the reference intensity at the same wavelength in the absence of absorber. Instead the reference intensity has to be measured at a different wavelength where the incident radiation is not absorbed or through a separate optical path which bypasses the reagent phase. The second problem is that the interaction of the incident radiation with the coloured reagent will involve both reflection and absorption. While optical sensors based on colour changes have been shown to respond linearly to analyte over relatively small concentration ranges (Peterson *et al.* 1980), the difficulty in developing a quantitative relationship between signal and analyte concentration remains a problem. In addition to optical convenience, this is another reason why sensors based on changes in fluorescence are preferred where feasible.

30.4 Reagent considerations

The immobilized reagent phase of an optical sensor can interact with analyte in a variety ways which are considered below.

30.4.1 Indicator

The reagent can act as an indicator, reversibly reacting with the analyte to form a product that has different optical properties from the uncombined reagent. Where feasible, this approach is attractive because the measured signal involves an equilibrium. The majority of optical sensors reported to date involve reagents acting as indicators. An example would be a pH sensor where the reagent can be considered to be the base form of an indicator, the analyte is hydrogen ion and the product is protonated indicator.

The interaction of an indicator reagent with analyte may be represented;

$$A + R <\longrightarrow> AR \tag{30.1}$$

where A = analyte, R = reagent, and AR = combined reagent. If the indicator reaction is 1:1, then the equilibrium constant, K_e, will be

$$K_e = AR/[A]R \tag{30.2}$$

where R and AR are the moles of free and combined reagent molecules in the immobilized phase, respectively. It is assumed that activity effects in the immobilized phase are equivalent for R and AR and thus cancel.

AR and R vary with analyte concentration as follows:

$$AR = K_e[A]C_r/(1 + K_e[A]) \tag{30.3}$$
$$R = C_r/(1 + K_e[A]) \tag{30.4}$$

where C_r is the sum of free and combined reagent:

$$C_r = AR + R. \tag{30.5}$$

C_r is necessarily fixed since there will be a constant number of moles of reagents in the immobilized phase.

If the measured optical parameter is proportional to AR, then response is proportional to [A] at low concentrations ($[A] \ll 1/K_e$) and shows saturation behaviour reaching a limiting value as [A] increases to values $\gg 1/K_e$.

If the measured parameter is proportional to R, then the signal decreases with added analyte. In this case, a linear working curve is obtained based on a rearranged form of eqn 30.4,

$$C_r/R = 1 + K_e[A]. \tag{30.6}$$

The ratio of signal in the absence of added analyte to the signal in the presence of analyte is the measured parameter. This situation is commonly encountered in sensors based on fluorescence quenching. In this case K_e is not a true equilibrium constant. Instead it is a measure of the fluorescent reagent's susceptibility to quenching and depends on the rate of quenching relative to the rates of other excited state processes.

The dependence on C_r, the amount of immobilized indicator, can be eliminated if one can measure both AR and R, since the ratio of the two is directly proportional to analyte concentration,

$$AR/R = K_e[A]. \tag{30.7}$$

Where feasible, this is the preferred situation. Effectively, the measurement of R serves as the reference for the measurement of AR, since the measured ratio is independent of instrumental fluctuations and any changes in reagent phase optical properties.

Because the reagent is serving as an indicator, the response necessarily depends on K_e. For a reagent to be useful for an optical sensor, it must not only have suitable optical characteristics but must also have a K_e appropriate to the range of concentrations to be measured. (For example, the range of pHs measured by an optical pH sensor depends on the pK_a of the immobilized indicator.) Any uncontrolled variable that influences K_e is a potential source of error. For example, because the activity of charged reagents depends on ionic strength, variations in ionic strength can be a source of error. In addition to direct effects on K_e, there can also be indirect effects. For example, variations in temperature and/or ionic strength can affect the immobilization matrix (e.g. by causing it to swell) thereby influencing K_e. Problems of this sort are likely to be identified as optical sensors reach the point where they are evaluated for long term response characteristics in practical contexts.

The above analysis assumes that the amount of analyte combining with or released by the immobilized reagent is small relative to the amount of analyte in the sample. If this is not the case, systematic errors can arise when the concentration of analyte changes.

30.4.2 Competitive binding

The concept of sensors based on competitive binding was first proposed by Schultz and Sims (1979). In this type of sensor, the immobilized reagent phase includes both a selective reagent and a 'ligand' which binds to the reagent. Added analyte displaces the ligand from the reagent,

$$A + LR < \longrightarrow > L + AR \tag{30.8}$$

where L = ligand. For this reation to occur, the ligand or the reagent must be in solution. Whichever of the two is in solution must be larger than the analyte so it can be immobilized by confinement behind a size-selective membrane which is permeable to analyte.

The measured optical parameter is based on the ligand–reagent interaction. The first reported competitive binding sensor was developed for glucose. In this device, the reagent, concanavalin A, is immobilized on the inside surface of a hollow fibre permeable to glucose (Schultz *et al.* 1982). When the end of the optical fibre is placed inside the hollow fibre, the immobilized concanavalin A is out of the optical path. As a consequence fluorophor-labelled ligand fluorescein-labelled dextran, is not excited when bound to concanavalin A. Added glucose displaces the dextran allowing it to diffuse into the optical path where fluorescence is excited. Therefore, increasing glucose levels are accompanied by increases in the observed fluorescence signal. Because the dextran is too large to pass through the hollow fibre, it remains immobilized.

In ongoing work in the author's laboratory, competitive binding sensors are being developed using fluorescence energy transfer. In this case the ligand is labelled with a donor and the reagent with an acceptor (or vice versa). The excitation wavelength is set to selectively excite the donor. When ligand is bound to reagent the distance between the donor and acceptor is short so that energy transfer from the donor to the acceptor occurs. When analyte binds to reagent displacing ligand, the distance between the donor and acceptor increases so that energy transfer does not occur. This leads to an increase in donor emission and a decrease in acceptor emission. The measured parameter is the ratio of emission intensities for donor and acceptor fluorescence.

The use of two wavelengths for the measurement effectively provides a convenient reference intensity.

In addition to the glucose sensor (Schultz *et al*. 1982) the competitive binding approach can potentially be applied to many other reactions. In addition to providing access to analytes that cannot be sensed directly, it has the attractive feature that the range of analyte concentrations that are sensed can be controlled to some degree by varying the ligand concentration.

The major limitation of the competitive binding approach is likely to be the rate of response. A strong association between ligand/analyte and reagent inherently means that the rate of dissociation is slow. Since dissociation of ligand/analyte from the reagent is necessary for the sensor to respond, this means a slow response time.

The competitive binding approach to sensing is described in more depth in Chapter 32.

30.4.3 Catalyst

The immobilized reagent can catalyse transformation of an analyte to a product with different optical properties. For example, a sensor has been reported based on the use of immobilized alkaline phosphatase to catalyse the hydrolysis of *p*-nitrophenylphosphate to *p*-nitrophenoxide (Arnold 1985). The measured signal is the steady-state absorbance of product under conditions where the rate of product generation is balanced by the rate of product diffusion away from the sensor. This approach can potentially be applied using other enzymes and thus lead to a whole class of new devices.

Catalyst-based sensors require careful control of conditions. Factors affecting both the rate of the catalysed reaction and the efficiency of mass transfer to and from the sensor surface will affect the steady state signal. While the approach warrants further study, it remains to be demonstrated whether or not these sensors will prove to be practical.

30.4.4 Chemiluminescence

In general it is not possible to develop continuous sensing devices using a reagent phase which reacts irreversibly with analyte to form a product (unless there are provisions for removing the product and renewing the reagent). Instead, these devices would act as integrating sensors since the amount of product formed would be proportional to the amount of analyte that has contacted the sensor since it was first placed in operation. In some cases the product can be removed by exposing the immobilized reagent phase to a different medium (Sutherland *et al*. 1984). In this case the sensor is 'rechargeable' and can be used for multiple measurements on an integrating basis.

Devices based on chemiluminescence and bioluminescence represent an exception to the above generalization. The reason for this is that chemi/bioluminescence is proportional to the rate at which product is generated rather than being proportional to the concentration of product. The measured parameter is steady-state light emission as analyte diffuses into the reagent phase and reacts. Once formed the product does not contribute further to the observed signal. The rate of the light-producing process will slow down as reagent is consumed. This problem can be minimized, however, if the amount of reagent is large relative to the rate of reagent consumption. A sensitive oxygen sensor based on tetrakis-alkyaminoethylene chemiluminescence has been reported (Freeman and Seitz 1981; MacDonald and Seitz 1982).

Sensors based on chemi/bioluminescence have the attractive feature that no excitation source is required since the analytical reaction generates its own light. However, because the measured signal involves a steady state, it is inherently sensitive to parameters influencing either the supply of analyte to the sensor surface or the rate of the light producing process. The possibilities of such sensors are discussed in more detail in the chapter by McCapra (Chapter 31).

30.4.5 Adsorbent

The reagent phase can be an adsorbent of some sort that selectively concentrates an optically detectable analyte in the field of view of the optical fibre. In effect this involves the combination of a separation with direct spectroscopy. A sensor for polyaromatic hydrocarbons based on this principle has been reported (Kawahara *et al.* 1983). However, while there has been interest in direct *in vivo* measurement of optically detectable analytes (Sepaniak *et al.* 1983), there are as yet no examples of biological applications of this approach.

30.5 Applications

30.5.1 pH

Because optical sensors offer the prospect of improved stability relative to electrodes with respect to calibration, considerable effort has been devoted to the development of an optical pH sensor suitable for continuous *in vivo* measurement. Various indicators have been used, each with its own set of advantages and disadvantages. Phenol red changes adsorption characteristics with pH at wavelengths longer than 450 nm and thus can be used with plastic optical fibres (Peterson *et al.* 1980). The covalently immobilized indicator has a pK_a of 7.6 compared to the solution pK_a of 7.9. The measured parameter is the ratio of intensity reflected/transmitted by the reagent phase at 558 nm where the base form of the indicator absorbs to the intensity at 600 nm where neither form of the indicator absorbs. The sensor measures pH to 0.01 pH unit in the range from 7.0 to 7.4. It is stable with respect to calibration for hours. It responds exponentially to changes in pH with a response time of 0.7 minute to reach (1–(1/e) or 63% of the final value. The limitation of this sensor is that it is based on a change in absorbance/reflectance rather than fluorescence.

4-Methylumbelliferone has the attractive feature that the acid and base forms fluoresce at different wavelengths making it possible to relate pH to the ratio of intensities for the two forms of the indicator (Chen 1968; Luebbers *et al.* 1977). However, because 4-methylumbelliferone is excited in the ultraviolet region of the spectrum (318 nm), it requires relatively expensive instrumentation, i.e. an arc lamp source and fused silica optical fibre.

The trisodium salt of 8-hydroxy-1,3,6-pyrenetrisulfonic acid (HPTS) is another fluorescent indicator that has attracted considerable attention. In a study of solution indicators, it was judged the most suitable for physiological pH measurements (Wolfbeis, *et al.* 1983). The spectral features of HPTS are shown in Fig. 30.2. The base form of the indicator is specifically excited at 470 nm while the acid form is selectively excited at 405 nm. In a buffered medium over the physiological pH range, the acid form of HPTS undergoes excited state deprotonation more rapidly than it fluoresces. As a consequence, emission from the base form of the indicator is observed even when the ground state indicator is in the acid form. The ratio of fluorescence intensities excited at 405 nm and 470 nm is the measured parameter related to pH.

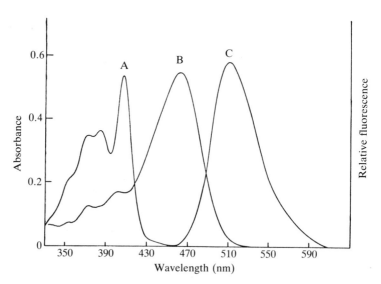

Fig. 30.2 Spectral Properties of HPTS. A is the absorption spectrum of the acid form of HPTS, B is the absorption spectrum of the base form of HPTS and C is the fluorescence emission spectrum of the base form of HPTS. At neutral pH's the fluorescence of the base is observed even when the indicator is in the ground state acid form.

HPTS provides a ratio measurement like 4-methylumbelliferone but can be used with glass optical fibre and an incandescent source.

Because of the three sulfonate groups the solution pK_a of HPTS has a strong dependence on ionic strength. In fact, the difference in pH as measured with 4-methylumbelliferone from the pH measured with HPTS has been proposed as an optical indicator of ionic strength (Opitz and Luebbers 1983, 1984). HPTS has been immobilized both covalently and by ion exchange (Zhujun and Seitz 1984*a*). Immobilization changes and can even reverse the ionic strength dependence of the pK_a. If HPTS can be immobilized on a substrate that keeps the ionic strength dependence of the pKa at an acceptable level it is likely to prove to be the indicator of choice for physiological pH measurements. (It should be noted that the author has stated in a paper that the pH measured by HPTS immobilized on an ion exchange membrane is independent of ionic strength (Zhujun and Seitz 1984*a*). This was meant only to imply that the use of an intensity ratio measurement eliminates the effect of variations in fluorescence efficiency as a function of ionic strength and not the pK_a is independent of ionic strength when HPTS is immobilized on the membrane.)

Fluorescein and its derivatives can be also be used as fluorometric pH indicators (Milanovitch *et al.* 1984; Saari and Seitz 1982). They have the advantage that they can be efficiently excited by an argon ion laser.

Optical sensors for pH have a working range of 1 to 2 pH units centred around the pK_a of the indicator. Although there has been considerable effort directed towards finding indicators that are suitable for the physiological pH range, relatively little has been done with pH indicators that respond outside this range. A series of immobilized colorimetric indicators that respond at a variety of pHs has been evaluated for reflectance based pH sensing (Kirkbright *et al.* 1984*a*, *b*).

30.5.2 pCO₂

Optical CO_2 sensors are analogous to the Severinghaus CO_2 electrode. An optical pH sensor is placed in contact with a reservoir of bicarbonate solution and covered with a CO_2 permeable membrane, usually silicone. The CO_2 partial pressure determines the concentration of carbonic acid in the internal filling solution which in turn determines the pH of the carbonic acid/bicarbonate buffer system. The range of CO_2 partial pressures sensed depends on the bicarbonate concentration and on the pH sensitivity of the optical pH sensor. Optical sensors that respond to physiological pHs are suitable as the internal sensing element for sensors that respond to CO_2 partial pressures in the range of physiological interest. The pH sensors that have received extensive evaluation for physiological applications have also been used as the internal sensing element in pCO_2 sensors (Vurek *et al.* 1983; Zhujun and Seitz 1984*b*; Luebbers and Opitz 1975, 1983).

CO_2 sensors are actually simpler than pH sensors. Because the internal filling solution is isolated from the sample by a hydrophobic gas-permeable membrane, variation in the ionic strength of the sample is less of a problem. Furthermore, the indicator can be dissolved in the internal filling solution rather than having to be immobilized on a solid substrate. The major problem in developing optical CO_2 sensors is to achieve a short response time since the time to reach equilibrium in the internal filling solution is added to the intrinsic response time of the pH sensor. The solution to this problem lies primarily in engineering the sensor to minimize the distance that CO_2 has to diffuse in solution for the device to reach equilibrium.

30.5.3 Oxygen

Most optical oxygen sensors reported to date are based on fluorescence quenching. Because they involve an equilibrium measurement, they are inherently less sensitive to variations in temperature and flow conditions than the widely used polarographic oxygen electrode. The fluorescent reagent can be in solution separated from the sample by a hydrophobic oxygen permeable membrane or it can be incorporated into or onto a solid phase. In general the susceptibility of the reagent to oxygen quenching depends both on the fluorophor and the medium. Linear calibration curves with an intercept of 1.00 are observed plotting I_{fo}/I_f *vs* partial pressure of oxygen where I_{fo} is the fluorescence intensity in the absence of oxygen and I_f is the intensity in the presence of oxygen (eqn 30.6 assuming fluorescence intensity is proportional to unquenched reagent). Because curves are linear, a one-point calibration is possible.

A variety of reagent phases have been used in optical oxygen sensors. Pyrenebutyric acid has been used both in solution (Luebbers and Optiz 1975, 1983) and immobilized on a solid substrate (Wolfbeis *et al.* 1984). Because pyrenebutyrate has a long fluorescence lifetime, it has time to interact with oxygen and is therefore more susceptible to quenching than most fluorophors. However, pyrenebutyric acid requires excitation in the ultraviolet (342 nm). Perylenedibutyrate adsorbed on a hydrophobic matrix was selected as the reagent for an optical oxygen sensor after a screening study involving 70 dyes (Peterson *et al.* 1984). Because perylenedibutyrate is excited at 468 nm and emits at 514 nm, it can be used in a sensor with plastic optical fibre. A sterilizable oxygen sensor based on a fluorophor cast directly into a silicone membrane has been reported (Kroneis and Marsoner 1983). Response times for optical oxygen sensors can be shorter than one second.

Because the reagent phases used for optical oxygen sensors are confined by a hydrophobic membrane, they are only subject to interference from volatile components of the sample. Certain anaesthetics such as halogenated hydrocarbons interfere by quenching fluorescence (Peterson *et al.* 1984). When a hydrophilic substrate was used for fluorophor immobilization, adsorbed water was found to reduce the susceptibility of the fluorophor to quenching (Peterson *et al*. 1984). The reference intensity for oxygen sensors has been the source intensity at the excitation wavelength measured either directly or as backscattered by the reagent phase. An alternative approach is to add a reference fluorophor that is not susceptible to oxygen quenching and emits at a different wavelength from the oxygen-susceptible fluorophor.

For oxygen measurements based on a change in intensity rather than a shift in spectrum, any change in response due to reagent degradation or changing susceptibility to quenching can only be determined by recalibrating the sensor. (This differs from the situation in optical pH sensors where the ratio of acid to base is the measured parameter.) The problem of reagent degradation can be dealt with by measuring the fluorescence lifetime rather than the fluorescence intensity. The ratio of the fluorescence lifetime in the absence of quencher to the lifetime in the presence of quencher is equivalent to I_{fo}/I_f. The lifetime approach to oxygen measurement will be easier to implement if a fluorophor or phosphor can be found with a relatively long lifetime so that the instrumental requirements for accurate lifetime measurements are simplified.

Another approach would be to base an oxygen sensor on a reagent that changes colour while reversibly binding oxygen. For example, an oxygen sensor can be based on changes in the absorption/reflection spectrum of immobilized haemoglobin. The problem with this approach is that reagents which reversibly bind oxygen tend to be subject to slow irreversible oxidation. Fot it to be viable a reagent phase which is sufficiently stable with respect to oxidation must be developed. The attractive feature of this approach is that it creates the possibility of measuring the ratio of the amount of reagent combined with oxygen to the amount of reagent not combined with oxygen.

30.5.4 Metal ion sensors

Metal ion sensors have been reported based on immobilized ligands that form fluorescent complexes (Saari and Seitz 1983; Seitz *et al*. 1985). In general any ligand that changes optical properties, either colour or fluorescence, upon complexation can potentially be used as an indicator in the reagent phase of a metal ion sensor. Just as the response range of a pH sensor depends on the pK_a of the immobilized acid-base indicator, the range of metal concentration that can be sensed with an immobilized ligand as the reagent depend on the formation constant for complex formation. One of the problems inherent in designing metal ion sensors is that complex formation often involves the displacement of one or more protons by the metal ion. When this happens, response depends on a conditional formation constant which depends on pH. Thus pH control is required for metal sensing.

30.5.5 Halide sensors

Two different types of optical sensors for halide ions have been reported. One type is based on halide quenching of fluorescence from an immobilized organic cation (Urbano *et al* 1984). Because heavy atoms are better quenchers than lighter atoms, the sensitivity of the sensor follows the order $I^- > Br^- > Cl^-$. The other approach is based on silver fluoresceinate as a reagent (Hirschfield *et al*. 1983). The effect of added halide is pull the silver away from the fluorescein rendering it fluorescent. This sensor follows the same sensitivity order as the first sensor. However, in the case of the second sensor the sensitivity order is determined by the relative solubilities of the various silver halide salts.

30.5.6 Other sensors

Sensors for glucose and for antigens based on competitive binding have been referred to earlier in the chapter and are described in detail in other chapters. As sensors for pH, CO_2, oxygen and other analytes are developed to a higher degree of refinement, one can expect that they will be coupled to other biological reagents to make sensors for new analytes. Already, an optical oxygen sensor has been coupled with immobilized oxidase enzymes to make sensors responding to the oxidase substrates (Voelkl *et al*. 1980; Uwira *et al*. 1984).

References

Arnold, M. A. (1985). Enzyme-based fiber optic sensor. *Anal. Chem.* **57**, 565–6.

Chen, R. F. (1968). Fluorescent pH indicators: Spectral changes of 4-methylumbelliferone. *Anal. Lett* **1**, 423–8.

Freeman, T. M. and Seitz, W. R. (1981). Oxygen probe based on tetrakis(alklylamino)ethylene chemiluminescence. *Anal. Chem.* **53**, 98–102.

Hirschfield, T, Deaton, T., Milanovich, F. and Klainer, S. (1983). Feasibility of using fiber optics for monitoring groundwater contaminants. *Opt. Eng.* **22**, 527–31.

Kawahara, F. K., Fiutem, R. A., Silvus, H. S., Newman, F. M. and Frazar, J. H. (1983). Development of a novel method for monitoring oils in water. *Anal. Chim. Acta* **151**, 315–27.

Kirkbright, G. F., Narayanaswamy, R. and Welti, N. A. (1984*a*). Studies with immobilised chemical reagents using a flow-cell for the development of chemically sensitive fibre-optic devices. *Analyst* **109**, 15–17.

—— (1984*b*). Fibre-optic pH probe based on the use of an immobilised colorimetric indicator. *Analyst* **109**, 1025–8.

Kroneis, H. W. and Marsoner, H. J. (1983). A fluorescence-based sterilizable oxygen probe for use in bioreactors. *Sensors and Actuators* **4**, 587–92.

Luebbers, D. W. and Opitz, N. (1975). The pCO_2-/pO_2-optode. New probe for measurement of partial pressure of carbon dioxide or partial pressure of oxygen in fluids and gases. *Z. Naturforsch., C: Biosci.* **30c**, 532–3.

—— (1983). Optical fluorescence sensors for continuous measurement of chemical concentration in biological systems. *Sensors and Actuators* **4**, 641–54.

—— Speiser, P. P. and Bisson, H. J. (1977). Nanoencapsulated fluorescence indicator molecules measuring pH and pO_2 down to submicroscopial regions on the basis of the optode principle. *Z. Naturforsch.* **32c**, 133-4.

MacDonald, B. F. and Seitz, W. R. (1982). Tetrakis *N*-dimethylaminoethylene is an extraordinarily sensitive reagent for oxygen. *Anal. Lett.* **15(A1)**, 57-66.

Milanovich, F. P., Hirschfield, T. B., Wang, F. T. and Klainer, S. M. (1984) Clinical measurements using fiber optics and optrodes. *Proc. SPIE*-Int. Soc. Opt. Engl **494**, 18-24.

Opitz, N. and Luebbers, D. W. (1976). Simultaneous measurement of blood gases by means of fluorescence indicators. *Pfluegers Arch.* **362**, R52.

—— (1983). New fluorescence photometrical techniques for simultaneous and continuous measurements of ionic strength and hydrogen ion activities. *Sensors and Actuators* **4**, 473-9.

—— (1984) A correction method for ionic strength-independent fluorescence photometric pH measurement. *Adv. Exp. Med. Biol.* **169**, 907-12.

Peterson, J. I. and Vurek, G. G. (1984). Fiber optic sensors for biomedical applications. *Science* **224**, 123-127.

—— Fitzgerald, R. V. and Buckhold, D. K. (1984). A fiber-optic pO_2 sensor for physiological use. *Anal. Chem.* **56**, 62-7.

Peterson, J. I., Goldstein, S. R., Fitzgerald, R. V. and Buckhold, D. K. (1980). Fiber optic pH probe for physiological use. *Anal. Chem.* **52**, 864-9.

Saari, L. A. and Seitz, W. R. (1982). pH sensor based on immobilized fluoresceinamine. *Anal. Chem.* **54**, 821-3.

—— (1983). Immobilized morin as fluorescence sensor for determination of aluminium (III). *Anal. Chem.* **55**, 667-70.

Schultz, J. S. and Sims, G. (1979). Affinity sensors for individual metabolites. *Biotechnol. Bioeng. Symp.* **9**, 65-71.

—— Mansoure, S. and Goldstein, I. J. (1982). Affinity sensor: A new technique for developing implantable sensors for glucose and other metabolites. *Diabetes Care* **5D**, 245-53.

Seitz, W. R. (1984). Chemical sensors based on fiber optics. *Anal. Chem.* **56**, 16A.

—— Saari, L. A., Zhujun, Z., Pokornicki, S., Hudson, R. D., Sieber, S. C. and Ditzler, M. A. (1985). Metal ion sensors based on immobilized fluorogenic ligands. In Advances in Luminescence Spectrometry (eds. L. J. Cline Love and D. Eastwood) pp. 63-77. ASTM Pub. no. 863, Philadelphia.

Sepaniak, M. J., Tromberg, B. J. and Eastham, J. F. (1983). Optical fiber fluoroprobes in clinical analysis. *Clin. Chem.* **29**, 1678-82.

Sutherland, R. M., Daehne, C. and Place, J. F. (1984*a*). Preliminary results obtained with a no-label homogeneous, optical immunoassay for human immunoglobulin G. *Anal. Lett.* **17**, 43-53.

—— and Ringrose, A. S. (1984*b*). Optical detection of antibody-antigen reactions at a glass-liquid interface. *Clin. Chem.* **30**, 1533-8.

Urbano, E., Offenbacher, H. and Wolfbeis, O. S. (1984). Optical sensor for continuous determination of halides. *Anal. Chem.* **56**, 427-9.

Uwira, N., Opitz, N. and Luebbers, D. W. (1984). Influence of enzyme concentration and thickness of the enzyme layer on the calibration curve of the continuously measuring glucose optode. *Adv. Exp. Med. Biol.* **169**, 913-21.

Voelkl, K. P., Optiz, N. and Luebbers, D. W. (1980). Continuous measurement of concentrations of alcohol using a fluorescence-photometric enzymatic method. *Fres. Z. Anal. Chem.* **301**, 162–3.

Vurek, G. G., Feustel, P. J. and Severinghaus, J. W. (1983) A fiber optic pCO_2 sensor. *Annals of Biomed. Eng.* **11**, 499–510.

Wolfbeis, O. S. Fuerlinger, E., Kroneis, H. and Marsoner, H. (1983). Fluorimetric analysis. 1. A study of fluorescent indicators for measuring near neutral ('physiologiucal' pH-values. *Fres. Z. Anal. Chem.* **314**, 119–24.

Wolfbeis, O. S., Offenbacher, H., Kroneis, H. and Marsoner, H. (1984). A fast responding fluorescence sensor for oxygen. *Mikrochimica Acta* 153–8.

Zhujun, Z. and Seitz, W. R. (1984*a*). A fluorescence sensor for quantifying pH in the range from 6.5 to 8.5 *Anal. Chim. Acta* **160**, 47–55.

—— —— (1984*b*). A carbon dioxide sensor based on fluorescence. *Anal. Chim. Acta* **160**, 305–9.

31

Potential applications of bioluminescence and chemiluminescence in biosensors

F. MCCAPRA

31.1 Introduction

It is obvious from discussions of the concept of biosensors, especially as presented in this monograph, that there are several possible definitions. The use of biologically derived entities such as whole cells, enzymes, or immuno-globulins in primary contact with the analyte is almost universal. Problems associated with the application of these are common to all biosensor techniques and will not be discussed here. On the other hand, signal handling methods are very well developed, often only needing miniaturization or other adaptation to the specific purpose. In the middle, presenting many oppor-tunities for invention and imagination are the transducers, translating bio-chemical events into electronic effects or electrical signals. Sensitivity is at a premium here, together with an ability to operate in biological fluids without undue interference.

Recently both bioluminescent and chemiluminescent reactions have been shown to provide sensitivity second to none, especially when used in conjunc-tion with the very best photon counting equipment. However their use in con-venient devices has been relatively unexplored. The purpose of the present article is to describe the principles of luminescent reactions, their success as rivals to established enzyme and immuno-assay methods, and to provide indications of the ways in which their special properties may be exploited. Although their use in biosensors is only at a preliminary stage, there is an extensive literature on analytical uses. (DeLuca 1978; Kricka and Carter 1982; Kricka *et al.* 1984.)

31.2 Bioluminescence

The emission of light from reactions of organic molecules in solution is an interesting and by now reasonably well understood phenomenon. Biolu-minescent organisms such as fireflies, glow-worms, angler-fish, and those responsible for the phosphorescence of the sea are often familiar. How-ever there are very many organisms, particularly marine, such as squid, shrimp and deep sea fish which show even more dramatic effects. Their biochemistry, where known, is as interesting and almost wholly unexploited. An excellent modern survey of all aspects of bioluminescence, with particular reference to be biological aspects is available (Herring 1978).

Various biochemical sequences are used to produce light, but the simplest in terms of its components, and having an accepted reaction mechanism, is that of the little ostracod crustacean *Cypridina hilgendorfii* (Tsuji 1978). It provides the basic description of light emission in luminescent organisms.

$$\text{Luciferin + Luciferase} \xrightarrow[\text{H}_2\text{O}]{\text{O}_2} \text{Oxyluciferin*}$$

$$\text{Oxyluciferin*} \longrightarrow \text{Oxyluciferin + Light}$$

In the simplest cases, the luciferin is a small heterocyclic organic molecule whose enzyme catalysed oxidation leads to the formation of the product, oxyluciferin, in a singlet excited state. Radiation from this state is identical to that of fluorescence, which can be produced by irradiating the oxyluciferin in the usual way.

Several of the enzymes (luciferases) involved use common cofactors in the reaction. These cofactors are often central to metabolic processes in general, and the light emitting reaction can thus be coupled to many reactions of biological significance. Foremost among this type of bioluminescent reaction is that found in the firefly (ATP as cofactor), Renilla (PAPS as cofactor), luminous bacteria (NADH or NAD(P)H and FMN as cofactors) and the jelly-fish *Aequorea* (Ca^{2+}). Other less well understood organisms such as the rare boring clam *Pholas dactylus* and the earthworm *Diplocardia* have had brief examination as potential analytical tools. A very good review in the series *Methods in enzymology* of all of the above types is available (DeLuca 1978). A further volume in the series is in preparation.

It is not appropriate to discuss the detailed chemistry and biochemistry of bioluminescence, but it would be helpful to give an outline of the two most used systems since an understanding of the principles underlies any possible application.

31.2.1 Firefly bioluminescence

This is the most studied and best understood of the luminous organisms. Its chemistry, biochemistry, and biology are all well reviewed (McCapra 1976, 1982; DeLuca 1978; Herring 1978). It was also the first organism which allowed the demonstration of the power of light detection in analysis (Strehler 1968).

Although the luciferin is readily synthesized, the luciferase is naturally only obtainable from the firefly itself. Several other related members of the *Coleoptera* also use the same light system, but these organisms are relatively rare and have not been exploited. Methods for the synthesis of luciferin and the extraction and purification have been published (DeLuca 1978; Lundin 1982). The luciferase is a moderately stable enzyme, readily obtainable at various levels of purification. Potent inhibitors of the enzyme such as dehydroluciferin (found as an impurity in commercial preparations), pyro-phosphate, and the products of the reaction, oxyluciferin and adenosine mono-phosphate, must be removed for maximum sensitivity. The avoidance of their effects on the analysis has been discussed (Lundin 1982).

The luciferase catalyses all of the reactions in the sequence shown below. For ease of understanding the chemical events are shown separately. Indeed the chemical reactions can be performed without enzyme with a reduction in efficiency to about 25% of that of the enzymic reaction (White, *et al.* 1975; McCapra *et al.* 1968). This chemiluminescent reaction does not require ATP and thus loses contact with the assay under discussion. It is analogous to che-miluminescent systems discussed later.

Luciferin + Luciferase + Mg^{2+} + ATP → Luciferyl adenylate L-AMP
L-AMP-luciferase + O_2 → Oxyluciferin*-Luciferase
Oxyluciferin*-Luciferase → Oxyluciferin-Luciferase + Light (562 nm)

The overall efficiency, measured as the quantum yield ϕ (see later) is a remarkable 88% (Seliger and McElroy 1960).

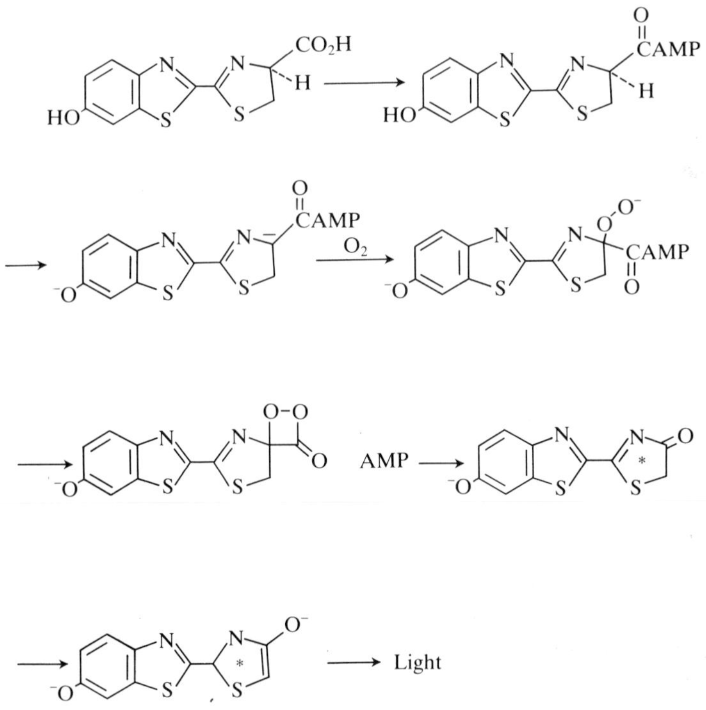

31.2.2 Firefly luciferase in ATP analysis

Since ATP occupies such a central place in the biochemistry of all living systems, it is not surprising to find that there is a very large number (over 1000 papers) of applications. There is little point in giving a description of these since the most significant references have been collected, and the methods described (DeLuca 1978; Kricka *et al.* 1984). They include biomass determinations, detection of bacterial infection (not species specific), antibiotic assay, and any enzymic reaction either producing or utilising ATP.

Although it is possible to produce the materials for these assays as required (DeLuca 1978), the need for good, consistent quality reagents has made the use of commercially available reagents (e.g. from Sigma or LKB-Wallac, Turku, Finland) very attractive.

This historically important technique is however not well suited to biosensor applications in view of its complexity unless ATP is the specific target. High sensitivity can be more readily achieved by the much more flexible chemiluminescent systems described later. Nevertheless the co-immobilization of luciferase and other analytically useful enzymes is being explored with some success (DeLuca 1984). The clinically important enzyme creatine kinase (in heart disease) can be measured at the 1 femtomole level, and the successful addition of automated flow systems suggests that convenient sensing devices are possible (Wienhausen *et al.* 1982; Kricka, *et al.* 1983).

31.2.3 Bacterial luminescence

Luminous bacteria (e.g. *Photobacterium phosphoreum, Vibrio harveyi*) are found in almost all marine environments, as saprophytes, free living organisms, and symbionts. Many fish use the light of colonies of such bacteria for purposes such as mating, shoaling, and attracting prey. They are easily cultured and a large amount is known about their biochemistry (Hastings 1978; Hastings and Nelson 1977). One very attractive feature is the large amount of easily purified luciferase (up to 5% of the cellular contents) that can be obtained. There is no luciferin in the same sense as in the firefly. The light emitting species seems to be a complex of luciferase, reduced flavin (FMNH), and a long chain fatty aldehyde. Although the chemical mechanism of light emission is not fully established, the outline shown is accepted. The bacterial luciferase sold commercially contains the necessary NAD(P)H:FMN oxidoreductase in varying amounts but contamination by other enzymes severely limits its usefulness. Isolation of both enzymes from a cultured cell paste in sufficient purity for analytical purposes is relatively easy. (Hastings *et al.* 1978; Jablonski and DeLuca 1977)

$$NAD(P)H + FMN \xrightarrow[\text{reductase}]{\text{Oxido}} FMNH_2 + NAD(P)$$

$$FMNH_2 + Luciferase + O_2 \rightarrow FMNH(OOH) \cdot luciferase$$
$$FMNH(OOH) \cdot luciferase + RCHO \rightarrow FMN + R \cdot CO_2H + Luciferase$$
$$+ H_2O + Light$$

31.2.4 Applications of bacterial bioluminescence

Mention has already been made of the use of the firefly system in ATP analysis, and there is little doubt that it is the method of choice for this ubiquitous substance. Immobilization of the enzyme has been achieved. A more versatile immobilized enzyme, and one that is very accessible, is the bacterial luciferase. The number of assays of enzymes which can be coupled to either the production or consumption of NADH and NAD(P)H is very large. Many of these have been listed (Jablonski and DeLuca 1982). Some examples and the assay limit are NADH (0.1 fmol), glucose (0.5–6 pmol), malate (20–250 pmol), testosterone (0.2–5 nmol), TNT (30 fmol). The analysis of TNT for example was achieved by inducing a TNT reductase which used NADH as cofactor. This technique could obviously be extended to other reduceable compounds for which enzymes may be induced.

Detailed descriptions of the methods used for the immobilization of the reductase and luciferase have been given (Jablonski and DeLuca 1978). Glass rods were coated by cementing arylamine glass beads using epoxy adhesive, and the enzyme coupled to the beads by diazotization.

The active rod can be used over 100 times without loss of activity although the specific activity of the enzymes may be reduced by about a thousand-fold. Light detection is carried out by placing the rod in the buffer–analyte solution in front of a phototube. Considerable retention of substrates, particularly NADH at high concentrations, necessitates extensive washing which can reduce activity still further.

Improvements to this system are being continuously made and cyanogen bromide activated *Sepharose* (DeLuca 1984) and nylon-6 (Roda, Girotti, Ghini, Grigolo, Carrea and Bovara 1982) are effective carriers. Some 25 different enzymes have been immobilized with excellent retention of enzyme activity in both the 'analysing' enzyme and the light emitting components. NAD(P)H can be measured at the 6 fmol level using a flow system.

31.2.5 Other bioluminescent systems

The only other prominent uses of the many bioluminescent organisms concern the jellyfish *Aequorea*, the hydroid *Obelia*, and the sea pansy *Renilla*.

Renilla luciferin is stored in the organism as an enol sulfate (Cormier 1978) and is released by a sulfokinase. The reaction sequence shown below shows how 3′, 5′-phosphoadenosine phosphate (PAP) and the product of the transfer 3′-phosphoadenosine-5′-phosphosulfate (PAPS) can be coupled to the light reaction and analysed at the 10 to 100 pmol level. The significance of the metabolites is not great at present and the example is more illustrative of the value to analysis of continued research into bioluminescence.

$$\text{Luciferyl sulphate + PAP} \xrightarrow{\text{Sulphokinase}} \text{Luciferin + PAPS}$$

$$\text{Luciferin + O}_2 \xrightarrow{\text{Luciferase}} \text{Oxyluciferin + CO}_2 + \text{Light}$$

The central role of Ca^{2+} in cellular processes makes it an attractive target for quantitation (Ashley and Campbell 1979). It is even possible to localize the source of Ca^{2+} within large cells since image intensification devices (Reynolds 1978, 1979) allow microscopic visualization with a resolution of about 2 μM. The technique depends on the fact that certain coelenterates (principally *Aequorea* and *Obelia*) store the luciferin as a peroxide (1) bound to the luciferase, making a single entity called a photoprotein. Isolation of this photoprotein is achieved in the presence of a high concentration of EDTA to inactivate endogenous calcium ion. Cytoplasmic Ca^{2+} can be detected at about the 10^{-7} M level on micro-injection of the photoprotein (called aequorin).

1

Serum levels of Ca^{2+} are too high for direct examination by this technique, causing saturation (Campbell 1982). Again this specialized use of luminescence serves more as an indicator of future possibilities than as a practical biosensor, since the technique is among the more difficult to master. Nevertheless it is not unreasonable to suggest that the chemist may eventually mimic the triggering event which gives rise to the easily detected light signal. A variety of synthetic compounds whose light emission is catalysed by an ion or other ligand can be envisaged suggesting an important research goal.

The ostracod crustacean *Cypridina hilgendorfii* generates light by the same chemical mechanism as the firefly in spite of the very different structure of the luciferin (2). A related luciferin (3) first characterized from the sea pansy *Renilla reniformis* has subsequently been found in a remarkably wide variety of organisms, including fish, shrimp, squid, and very many coelenterates (e.g. the jellyfish *Aequorea aequorea*) (Cormier 1973).

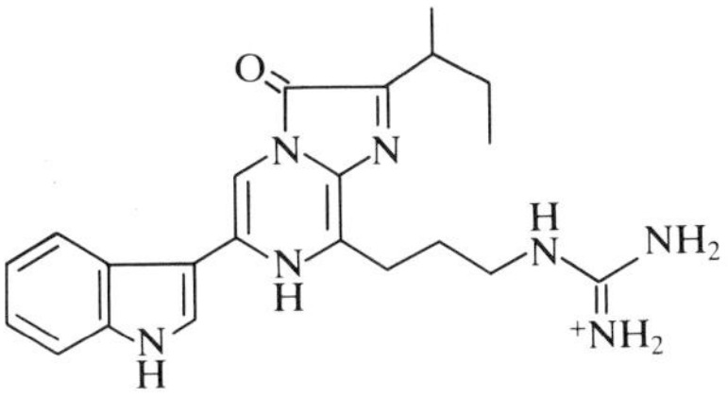

2

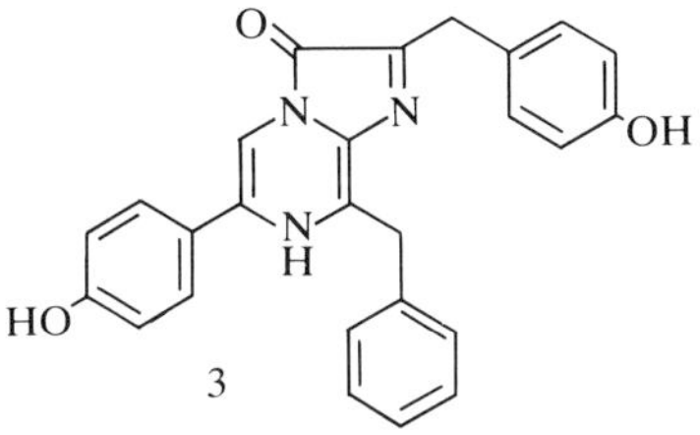

3

The chemical mechanism proposed for these luciferins is closely related to that of several efficient, purely chemical, systems, representing a notable success of interpretative organic chemistry (McCapra 1976).

Other luciferins for which no mechanism exists for light emission are those of the fresh water limpet *Latia neritoides* (4), the earthworm *Diplocardia longa* (5) and the dinoflagellate *Pyrocystis lunula* (6).

The luciferase from *Diplocardia longa* is a copper protein, and has peroxidase activity. Its value in assays for H_2O_2 and some oxidases has been assessed (Muilkerrin and Wampler 1978). As will be seen later, peroxidase reactions make excellent chemiluminescent analyses and assays. Another,

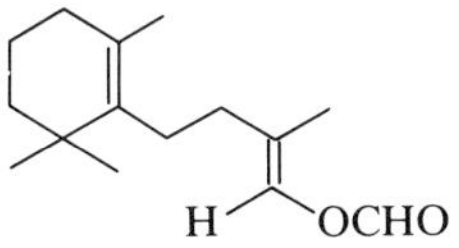

4

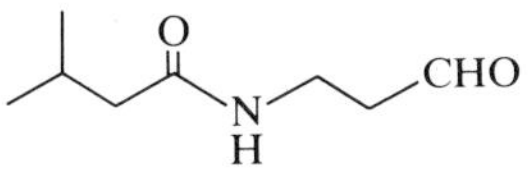

5

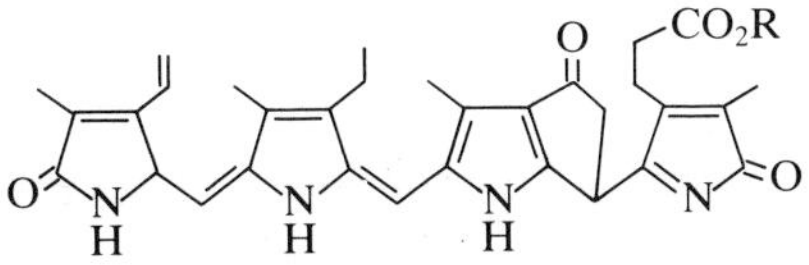

6

much more active but exceedingly scarce, peroxidase system is that isolated from the clam *Pholas dactylus* (Michelson 1978).

31.3 Chemiluminescence

Although the fundamental mechanisms underlying light emission from biological and chemical reactions must be the same, the two fields developed independently until about 15 years ago. Fully convincing detailed mechanisms are available only for the firefly, *Cypridina*, and coelenterate systems, but very many more organic compounds react by well understood mechanisms.

Chemiluminescence in solution is almost invariably an oxidative reaction. Molecular oxygen and hydrogen peroxide are most often involved. A very wide range of chemical structure can be found (McCapra 1973; Gundermann 1968) and a few chemiluminescent compounds are shown below to illustrate the diversity.

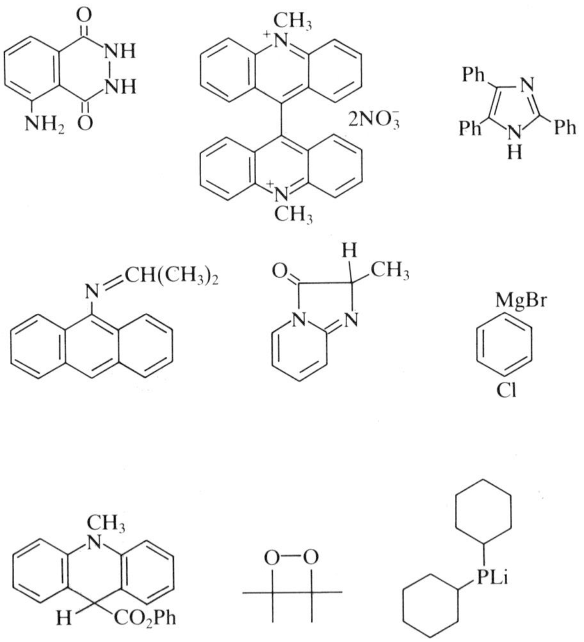

The efficiency of light emission is measured in terms of the number of photons produced per molecule reacting, stated in terms of a quantum yield ϕ. This in turn depends on three factors,

$$R \xrightarrow{\phi_C \phi_E} P^*, \quad P^* \xrightarrow{\phi_F} P + h\nu,$$
$$\phi_{CL} = \phi_C \times \phi_F \times \phi_E.$$

A high chemical yield ϕ_C of excited product P* is obviously required, and the fluorescence yield ϕ_F should be as near unity as possible. The third term ϕ_E denotes the proportion of molecules entering the excited state, and this depends intimately on the reaction mechanism. The *in vitro* firefly reaction is the most efficient known with $\phi_{CL} = 0.88$ (Seliger and McElroy 1960) but the simple chemical reaction of a derivative of firefly luciferin can almost match this with $\phi_{CL} = 0.33$ (White *et al.* 1975). Other quantum yields range from 1 $\times 10^{-8}$ for Grignard compounds up to 0.25 for the reaction of active oxalates with suitable fluorescers (Rauhut 1979).

A variety of solvents can be used for the reactions, with aqueous conditions being the least suitable for high quantum yields. Exceptions to this observation are the reactions of the cyclic hydrazides such as luminol, acridinium salts and to a certain extent, special active oxalate esters.

For maximum detectability, the electronically excited molecule formed in the reaction should be in the singlet state. This is because the alternative triplet state is much longer lived, and subject to quenching by other molecules present, particularly oxygen. The light observed is thus a chemically produced fluorescence.

The best known chemiluminescent compound is undoubtedly luminol (7). Much is known about its properties and those of a large number of analogues (Roswell and White 1978; Gundermann 1968). The fact that there is no agreed mechanism for the actual light emitting step for this most studied of molecules has not hindered extensive application. It is not the most efficient hydrazide known, partly because the excited product, the diphthalate ion (8), is not particularly fluorescent. Under the best conditions the chemiluminescence quantum yield is only about 1%.

The mechanism as already indicated is not well understood. This is particularly true of the catalysed reaction which has been of greatest use in analysis. It is not possible to do other than outline the reaction scheme in this context.

In aqueous solution catalysts and hydrogen peroxide are both essential for strong light emission, although base and oxygen alone are sufficient in dipolar aprotic solvents such as dimethylsulfoxide.

31.3.1 Mechanisms of chemiluminescence

Only a very brief account is necessary here, although it is an interesting and important area, an understanding of which can be expected to improve the application of the phenomenon. Concentration on the best understood reactions will give a useful basis, even if it does beg many questions. Compounds may react with oxygen, usually in the form of a carbanion or electron rich species to produce a peroxide. A closely related peroxide can also be produced if the structure of the compound invites attack by hydrogen peroxide, which is a very powerful nucleophile in aqueous solution. The purpose of the metal catalysis in the luminol reaction is to produce an intermediate derived from luminol which will react with H_2O_2 or its oxidation product $O_2 \cdot ^-$, superoxide ion. The acridinium salts and acridans can be used to demonstrate both routes.

In this case the fluorescent product (9) is directly derived from the reactant. In the very flexible active oxalate series, the reactant gives an intermediate which is not fluorescent, but can react with a large variety of added fluorescers, resulting in very high light yields. Incidentally, this reaction demonstrates what is believed to be the nature of the actual excitation step involving electron transfer (McCapra 1973; Schuster 1979). The group Ar must be strongly electronegative, the most common being dinitrophenyl and trichlorophenyl although many others are possible. Some of these are particularly suitable for use in aqueous systems (Tseng and Rauhut 1981).

$$\underset{\substack{\\ \text{O} \quad \text{O} \\ \| \quad \| }}{\text{Ar—O—C—C—OAr}} + H_2O_2 \rightarrow \underset{\substack{\\ \text{O} \quad \text{O} \\ \| \quad \| }}{\text{H—O—O—C—C—OAr}} \rightarrow$$

$$+ \text{Fluorescer} \rightarrow [\text{Fluorescer}]^{\overset{\bullet}{+}} CO_2^{\overset{\bullet}{-}} + CO_2$$
$$\rightarrow \text{Fluorescer*} + CO_2 \rightarrow \text{Fluorescer} + \text{Light}$$

Lastly, mention must be made of dioxetans such as (10) and (11). These are isolable compounds which on mild heating give light, with no other reagent or intermediate involved (Wilson 1976).

$$\underset{\substack{| \quad | \\ \text{CH}_3\text{CH}_3 \\ \\ 10}}{\underset{\substack{\text{O—O} \\ | \quad |}}{\text{H}_3\text{C—C—C—CH}_3}} \xrightarrow{\text{heat}} (CH_3)_2\overset{*}{\text{C}}\text{O} + (CH_3)_2\text{CO}$$

Me$_2$N⟨ ⟩—(O—O / O O)—⟨ ⟩NMe$_2$

11

Simple dioxetans such as (10) give almost exclusively triplet states, but others such as (11) give high yields of singlet states.

31.3.2 Chemiluminescent immunoassays

Use of the bioluminescent systems in bio-analysis has the advantages of an inbuilt specificity since the luciferases and associated enzymes are naturally specific. However by labelling either antibody or antigen (occasionally both) with a chemiluminescent compound, all the advantages of enzyme- and radio-immunoassays are obtained with none of the disadvantages. Sensitivity can be higher than RIA (Weeks *et al.* 1984), stability of the label is excellent, measurement is both flexible and easy, and the instrumentation is simple and relatively cheap (Kricka *et al.* 1984; Kricka and Carter 1982).

31.3.2.1 Types of assay
In spite of the relatively short time in which chemiluminescent immunoassays have been studied, several different sorts of assay have been developed. The simplest is the direct replacement of ^{125}I by the luminescent compound. Many such applications have been reported, using cyclic hydrazides such as isoluminol (Schroeder *et al.* 1978), luminol itself (Maier 1978), acridinium phenyl esters (Weeks *et al.* 1983), dioxetans (Wynberg *et al.* 1981) to label haptens or small peptides.

The methods of labelling are very similar to those developed for attaching

$$H_2N(CH_2)_4N \overset{Et}{} \quad \overset{O}{\underset{O}{\parallel}} \; NH \atop NH$$

ABEI

fluorescent compounds to proteins or tyrosine (for subsequent iodination) to haptens. Isothiocyanate, *N*-hydroxysuccinimidyl ester and imido-ethers have all been used. A favourite label first applied by Schroeder *et al.* in 1978 is 6-[*N*-(4-aminobutyl)-*N*-ethyl]amino-2, 3-dihydro-1,4-phthalazine-1,4-dione (ABEI). Thyroxine was labelled by this and other hydrazides. Various steroidal assays have been similarly developed. (Salerno *et al.* 1984; Kohen *et al.* 1984). Reactions such as these require injection of the reagents and give an easily quantified, but brief, emission of light. Excellent results in the quantification of protein and peptide hormones such as hCG (human chorionic gonadotrophin, Kohen *et al.* 1984) TSH (thyrotropin) (Weeks *et al.* 1984) and α-fetoprotein (Weeks *et al.* 1983) have been achieved. Acridinium salts are particularly useful in this area.

As already noted the reactions which emit the detectable light are usually fast. This has advantages in sensitivity but enzyme labelling of antigen or antibody, coupled to light emission provides a much longer lived emission, and could thus be used in principle for continuous monitoring. Peroxidases in conjunction with luminol are the best developed systems of this sort. For example horseradish peroxidase has been coupled to all the components necessary for complete thyroid-function analysis, including both proteins and haptens (Thorpe *et al.* 1984). Such techniques while successful are still in their infancy. Improvements, as demonstrated by the use of synergistic enhancements of sensitivity (Whitehead *et al.* 1983) can be reasonably expected as investigation proceeds. This approach is very similar to that of the well-known enzyme immunoassays, but has two very significant advantages of potential use in biosensor design. The light level is directly proportional to analyte concentration (there is no build up in intensity as in a colorimetric assay) and the detectability is very much higher.

31.3.2.2 Homogeneous assay　All of the assays outlined above are separation assays. Continuous monitoring of biologically significant compounds in a biosensor requires both a continuing signal and a direct response to changing concentrations of analyte without resort to separation of the materials being analysed. Homogeneous immunoassay methods have recently been developed, using two very different phenomena.

The essential requirement of course is to distinguish bound from unbound ligand, and the influence of the protein on ligand properties is a feature that luminescence possesses, whereas radioactivity does not. Luminescence from the luciferins in bioluminescence, both *in vivo* and *in vitro* is much affected with regard to wavelength and efficiency on binding to proteins or on being placed in an otherwise non-aqueous environment (Ward and Cormier 1979; McCapra and Manning 1973; Goto and Fukatsu 1969; McCapra *et al.* 1973).

These effects have been exploited in a model biotin-avidin system in which the light intensity increases 10-fold on the binding of the attached luminol (Schroeder 1976). Several homogeneous steroidal assays make use of the adventitious enhancement of light from the reaction of the attached iso-luminol which results when the steroid is bound to the antibody (Kohen *et al.* 1979, 1981; Salerno *et al.* 1984).

A more fundamental investigation has recently demonstrated a potentially very important technique (Patel *et al.* 1983; Campbell and Patel 1983). The system is based on transfer of the original electronic excitation of the chemi-luminescent product to a fluorescent energy acceptor. Such a phenomenon is well known in spectroscopy and photochemistry (Lamola and Turro 1969).

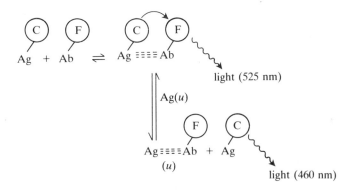

The ligand (e.g. cAMP or progesterone) is covalently attached to the chemiluminescent compound (ABEI) and the antibody made fluorescent by attachment of fluorescein. The transfer of energy is governed by the Förster equation, requiring a close approach (*ca* 50 Å) of donor and acceptor (Lamola and Turro 1969). Thus the bound fraction emits green light and the unbound, the unaltered blue emission of isoluminol. Various filters can be used (the emission bands are broad) with the ratio at 460/525 nm producing the best results. In general the principle can be described thus where Ag (the antigen) is labelled with a chemiluminescent compound (C) and Ab (the antibody) is labelled with a fluorescent acceptor (F). When Ag-C is displaced by the analyte of unknown concentration Ag(u), the distance between C and F is too great for energy transfer, so that bound and unbound are readily distinguished.

31.3.3 Light measuring techniques

Chemiluminescent reactions respond to variables such as pH and catalysts in a number of ways. From some luminescent systems it is possible to obtain a flash with a duration of milliseconds or a prolonged lower light level lasting some hours. Bioluminescent reactions are less easily manipulated, but similar characteristics are obtainable. Thus detection can be arranged for maximum sensitivity or convenience. It is obvious that for a given number of photons maximum sensitivity is obtained by arranging light emission in the shortest possible time. This has its drawbacks because mixing errors are at a maximum in the initial phases. Enzyme turn-over (as in the peroxidase reactions) provides amplifications which results in prolonged, relatively high intensity emission since the luminescent compound is in excess and not stoicheometrically linked to the analyte. Peak sensing, integration of the light and monitoring changes in the rate of reaction are also possible. The various possibilities are shown diagrammatically in Fig. 31.1.

31.3.4 Kinetic measurements

All luminescent reactions are subject to variations in rate. This is a potentially powerful means of analysis since the high detectability of light emission gives opportunities for rapid sampling of small portions of a reaction sequence.

31.3.5 Light measuring devices

Photomultiplier tubes are the most powerful and most common light

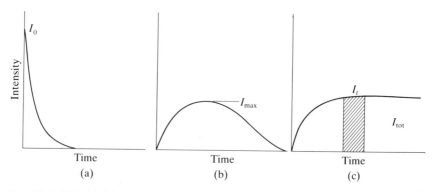

Fig. 31.1 (a) Initial intensity, I_o, provides maximum sensitivity, but may give a lesser, still acceptable precision.
(b) Peak sensing devices provide automatic quantification. The peak I_{max} can be produced by variation of the reaction characteristics so as to produce optimum sensitivity consistent with reproduceability.
(c) Devices similar to those used in (b) can integrate for a variable time after a variable delay (I_t). Alternatively the light signal can be integrated for as long as is convenient to produce the necessary sensitivity.

detector. The associated electronics are well developed and basic easily constructed sensitive systems have been described (Anderson *et al*. 1982; Stimson 1974). Modern photon (pulse) counting instrumentation increases sensitivity by lowering noise levels and is increasingly used in commercially available luminometers. Photomultiplier tubes are most noise free when sensitive in the blue region of the spectrum, (350 to 450 mm), and are thus suitable, if not ideal, for the great majority of chemiluminescent reactions. Only the firefly system is seriously disadvantaged since its peak emission occurs at a fairly long wavelength (560 mm). The very robust, cheap and adaptable light sensitive diodes are less sensitive than photomultiplier tubes, particularly in the blue region. Photosensitive film, especially modern enhanced sensitivity types can also be used. The merits of each of these has been discussed (Carter *et al*. 1979). In favourable cases, with sufficient light available, photodiode based systems provide cheap portable devices, with a variety of commercially available ATP detectors being available for simple field-testing for bacterial infection. This and some thirty other commercial luminometers have been described (Stanley 1982). A portable prototype using photodiodes for glucose analysis has been developed in the author's laboratory.

Light measurement in the homogeneous energy transfer assay previously mentioned provides certain challenges and advantages. For example, the measurement of a ratio of wavelengths provides an intrinsic improvement in precision since some variations in signal must cancel. Two separate photo-tubes may be used, with an appropriate filter for each (Campbell and Patel 1983; Patel 1983). The use of a single phototube with rotating filters frequency locked to phase sensitive amplifiers provides a more elegant and potentially less noisy detecting system (Richardson 1985).

31.4 Possible biosensor applications

If we were to define biosensors in their ideal form, capable of implantation, continuous monitoring, uniquely sensitive, and free from interference, then luminescence methods have a long way to go. However, it is abundantly clear that as a method of translating the presence in tiny amounts of biological compounds into an easily processed signal, they are successful.

They also possess characteristics such as sufficient sensitivity and an ability to sample without separation that strongly suggests that there is considerable potential. Existing configurations are on the whole, classical, in that a prepared sample is placed in a cell or cuvette and light emission detected by placing it in front of a photomultiplier tube. Recently however there have been developments which suggest that the manufacture of convenient devices is on the horizon.

A device which may well prove to be a model for others based on the reactions described in this chapter utilizes a ⅛ inch diameter fibre optic.

(Freeman and Seitz 1978; Seitz, this volume Chapter 30.) Peroxidase is immobilized in a clear polyacrylamide gel and used to measure the concentration of hydrogen peroxide in a buffer solution using luminol both in the gel and solution. Concentrations down to 10^{-6} M were detectable by a photomultiplier tube at the other end of the two foot long fibre. It was pointed out that unlike other enzyme electrodes, there is no need to have the product of the enzymic reaction diffuse to the surface of the electrode. Thus response time is very short at about four seconds. A major problem noted was that the response was mass transfer limited. Use of a simple form of light guide has supported this idea as a convenient and workable configuration (Brolin *et al.* 1984). The major problems in pursuing this approach are probably those associated with enzyme immobilization. In the case of an immunosensor of course the difficulty presented by the slow rate of the ligand–antibody binding equilibrium itself looms large. Nevertheless the high sensitivity of light detection and independence from electrode phenomena make further research seem very worthwhile.

The availability of the luciferases has been considered a threat to the development of analytical devices based on bioluminescence. Recently however there have been some encouraging advances which suggest that this is no longer a problem. Bacterial luciferase (Baldwin *et al.* 1984) and the photoprotein aequorin (Charbonneau *et al.* 1985) have been cloned. There is now the prospect that the rarity of the organism will no longer inhibit attempts to devise new analyses based on their very desirable characteristics. Some problems remain to be solved before unusual luciferases are made available in quantity, but attention will increasingly turn to bioluminescence with this restraint removed.

As with all devices based on the use of enzymes, the question of stability arises. A fair amount of experience has already been gained on the use of luciferases immobilized on various supports. Firefly luciferase has not yet been found to be sufficiently stable as to prove suitable for sensor applications, but bacterial luciferase has shown a steady improvement in stability as an understanding of the best methods of immobilizing it has increased. It can now undergo several hundreds of reuse cycles and there is every hope that these enzymes will be no different than many others. Whether they will prove as durable as the relatively few stalwarts in common use remains a matter for future research.

Another problem facing chemiluminescence and bioluminescence in sensor applications is the need for reagent replenishment. If the easy detectability and high sensitivity of light emission are to be exploited, the configuration of the device must take this into account. It must be understood that the phenomenon requires the irreversible oxidation of the substrate–the luciferin in the case of bioluminescence–and the readily available small organic molecule in chemiluminescence. Many of the reactions described in this article can be made limiting with respect to the analyte only. At present the only way in which this flexibility can be utilized is by having the luminescent compound present in excess. Such 'buffering' by the reagent presents no problems in ordinary analytical work, but considerable ingenuity will have to be depolyed to produce the same effect within the restrictions of a sensor with severely limited volume. However, with the very reasonable assumption that the analytes to be examined by this technique will themselves be at the lowest end of the concentration range (made extremely likely by the unrivalled sensitivity) this should not prevent the design of suitable devices. An interesting natural example of the longevity of a luciferin supply is provided by the firefly itself. The organism emerges from the pupa with all the luciferin required for a lifetime (about one month) of almost continuous nightly flashing! Given the very much reduced need for photons that photomultipliers have as compared to the intense firefly flash, it should be possible to estimate the length of time over which the sensor may operate. Until the attempt is made, no precise answer to the question can be given, but in the best cases this may well be not too different from the presently available lifetime of the enzymes employed in existing biosensors. Chemiluminescent compounds will function as solids or pastes, and semi-permeable membranes in conjunction with suitably altered and thus sequestered compounds can be envisaged.

Finally, the question of interference must be considered. It is difficult to discuss this in general since there are many different reactions which lead to luminescence. However there are several compounds available that can be used to overcome particular problems. For example, luminol is oxidized with the emission of light as a result of the catalytic effect of iron compounds such as haem. Its use for other purposes in the presence of whole blood is thus precluded. We have developed the use of acridinium esters for glucose measurement in whole blood with excellent results–identical to those in aqueous buffer and serum. In conclusion, no claim can be made at present that luminescent reactions are ready for incorporation into a robust sensor, but their advantages of easy detectability and extreme sensitivity make further investigations worth pursuing.

References

Anderson, J. M., Faini, G. J., Wampler, J. E. and Stimson A. (1974). *Photometry and radiometry for Engineers*. Interscience, New York.

Ashley C. C. and Campbell A. K. (eds.) (1979). *Detection and measurement of free calcium in cells*. Elsevier-North Holland, Amsterdam.

Baldwin, T. O., Johnson, T. C. and Swanson, R. (1984). Recent progress in bioluminescence: Cloning of the structural genes encoding bacterial luciferase, analysis of the encoded sequences and crystallisation of the enzyme. In *Flavins and Flavoproteins* (eds. R. C. Bray, P. C. Engel, and S. G. Mayhew) pp. 345–58. de Gruyter, Berlin.

Brolin, S. E., Berggren, P. O. and Naeser P, (1984). Application of light guides for enhancement of signal to noise ratios at low levels of luminescence detectability. In *Analytical applications of bioluminescence and chemiluminescence* (eds. L. J. Kricka, P. E. Stanley, G. H. G. Thorpe, and T. P. Whitehead) p. 479. Academic Press, London.

Campbell, A. K. and Patel, A. (1983). A homogeneous immunoassay for cyclic nucleotides based on chemiluinscence energy transfer, *Biochem. J.* **216**, 185–194.

Carter, T. J. N., Kricka, L. J., Bullock, D. G., Bunce, R. A. and Whitehead T. P. (1979). Optimisation of luminescence instrumentation. In *Proc. International Symposium on Analytical Applications of Bioluminescence and Chemiluminescence* (eds. E. Schram and P. Stanley.) pp. 637–51. State Printing and Publishing, Westlake Village, CA, USA.

Charbonneau, H., Walsh, K. A., McCann, R. O., Prendergast, F. G., Cormier, M. J. and Vanaman, T. C. (1985). Amino acid sequence of the calcium-dependent photoprotein aequorin. *Biochem.*, **24**, 6762–71.

Cormier, M. J. (1978). Comparitive biochemistry of animal systems. In *Bioluminescence in action* (ed. P. J. Herring) pp. 75–108. Academic Press, London.

—— Hori, K. Karkhanis, Y. D., Anderson, J. M., Wampler, J. E., Morin, J. G. and Hastings, J. W. (1973). Evidence for similar biochemical requirements for bioluminescence among the coelenterates, *J. Cell. Physiol.* **81**, 291–7.

DeLuca, M. (ed.) (1978). *Bioluminescence and chemiluminescence, Methods in enzymology* Vol. 57, Academic Press, New York.

DeLuca, M. (1984). Bioluminescence assays using co-immobilised enzymes. In *Analytical applications of bioluminescence and chemiluminescence* (eds. L. J. Kricka, P. E. Stanley, G. H. G. Thorpe, and T. P. Whitehead) pp., 111–23. Academic Press, London.

Freeman, T. M. and Seitz, W. R. (1978). Chemiluminescence fiber optic probe for hydrogen peroxide based on the luminol reaction. *Anal. Chem.* **50**, 1242–6.

Goto, T. and Fukatsu, H. (1969). Cypridina Luminescence. Chemiluminescence in micelle solutions — a model system for cypridina bioluminescence. *Tetrahedron Letters* 4299–302.

Gundermann, K.-D. (1968). *Chemilumineszenz organischer verbindungen.* Springer-Verlag, Berlin.

Hallett, M. B. and Campbell, A. K. (19XX). Applications of coelenterate luminescent proteins. In *Clinical and biochemical luminescence.* (eds. L. J. Kricka and T. J. N. Carter) pp. 89–133. Dekker, New York.

Hastings, J. W. (1978). Bacterial and dinoflagellate luminescent systems. In *bioluminescence in action* (ed. P. J. Herring). pp. 129–70. Academic Press, London.

—— and Nealson, K. H. (1977). Bacterial bioluminescence, *A. Rev. Microbiol.* **31**, 549–95.

—— Baldwin, T. O. and Nicoli, M. Z. (1978). Bacterial luciferase: Assay, purification and properties. In *Methods in enzymology* (ed. M. DeLuca) Vol. 57, pp. 135–52. Academic Press, New York.

Herring, P. J. (ed.) (1978). *Bioluminescence in action*, Academic Press, London.

Jablonski, E. G. and DeLuca, M. (1977). Purification and properties of the NADH and NADPH specific FMN oxidoreductases from *Beneckea harveyi. Biochem.* **16** 2932–6.

—— (1982). Analytical applications of bioluminescence: Marine bacterial system. In *Clinical and biochemical luminescence* (eds. L. J. Kricka and T. J. N. Carter) pp. 75–87. Dekker, New York.

Kohen, F., Bayer, E. A., Wilchek, M., Barnard, G., Kim, J. B., Collins, W. P., Beheshti, I., Richardson, A. P. and McCapra, F. (1984). Development of luminescence based assays for haptens and protein hormones. In *Analytical applications of bioluminescence and chemiluminescence* (eds. L. J. Kricka, P. E. Stanley, G. H. G. Thorpe, and T. P. Whitehead) pp. 149–58. Academic Press, London.

Kricka, L. J. and Carter, T. J. N. (eds.) (1982). *Clinical and biochemical luminescence*, Dekker, New York.

—— Stanley P. E., Thorpe, G. H. G. and Whitehead, T. P. (eds.) (1984). *Analytical applications of bioluminescence and chemiluminescence.* Academic Press, London.

—— Wienhausen, G. K., Hinkley, J. E. and DeLuca, M. (1983). Automated bioluminescence assays for NADH, glucose 6-phosphate, primary bile acids and ATP. *Anal. biochem.* **129**, 392–401.

Lamola, A. A. and Turro, N. J. (1969). Energy transfer and organic photochemistry. In *Technique of organic chemistry* (ed. A. Weissberger) Vol. 14. Wiley, New York.

Lundin A. (1982). Analytical applications of bioluminescence: the firefly system. In *Clinical and biochemical luminescence* (eds. L. J. Kricka and T. J. N. Carter) pp. 43–74. Dekker, New York.

Maier, C. L. (1978). Assay of pharmacologically, immunologically and biochemically active compounds in biological fluids. U.S. Patent 4,104,029.

McCapra, F. (1973). The chemiluminescence of organic compounds. In *Progress in Organic Chemistry*, (eds. W. Carruthers and J. K. Sutherland) Vol. 8, pp. 231–77. Butterworths, London.

—— (1975). The chemistry of bioluminescence. *Acct. Chem. Res.* **9**. 201–8.

—— (1982). The chemistry of bioluminescence. *Proc. R. Soc. Lond. B.* **215**, 247–72.

—— and Manning, M. (1973). Bioluminescence of coelenterates: chemiluminescent model compounds, *Chem. Commun.* 467–8.

—— Chang, Y. C. and Francois, V. (1968). The chemiluminescence of a firefly luciferin analogue. *Chem. Commun.* 22–3.

—— Roth, M., Hysert, D. and Zaklika, K. A. (1973). Model compounds in the study of bioluminescence. In *Chemiluminescence and bioluminescence* (eds. M. J. Cormier, D. M. Hercules, and J. Lee) pp.313–23. Plenum Press, London.

Michelson, A. M. (1978). Purification and properties of *Pholas dactylus* luciferin and luciferase. In *Methods in enzymology.* Vol. 57 (ed. M. DeLuca), pp. 385–406. Academic Press, New York.

Mulkerrin, M. G. and Wampler, J. E. (1978). Assaying hydrogen peroxide using the earthworm system. In *Methods in enzymology.* Vol. 57 (ed. M. DeLuca) pp. 375–81. Academic Press, New York.

Patel, A. (1983). The development of homogeneous chemiluminescence immunoassay, Ph. D. Thesis, the University of Wales, Cardiff, Wales, UK.

—— Campbell, A. K. and McCapra, F. (1983). Chemiluminescence energy transfer: a new technique applicable to the study of ligand–ligand interactions in intact cells. *Anal. Biochem.* **129**, 162–9.

Rauhut, M. M. (1979). Chemiluminescence. In *Kirk-Othmer encyclopedia of chemical technology*, Vol. 5, p. 416.

Reynolds, G. T. (1978). Applications of photosensitive devices of bioluminescence studies, *Photochem. Photobiol.* **27**, 405.

—— (1979). Localisation of free ionised calcium in cells by means of image intensification. In *Detection and Measurement of Free Calcium Ions*, (eds. C. C. Ashley and A. K. Campbell) p. 227. Elsevier — North Holland, Amsterdam.

Richardson A. P. (1985). Novel chemiluminescence immunoassays, D. Phil. Thesis, University of Sussex, England.

Roda, A., Girotta, S., Ghini, S., Grigola, B., Carrea, G. and Bovara,   (1984). Development of a continuous-flow analysis for serum and salivary bile acids using bacterial bioluminescent enzymes immobilised on nylon coil. In *Clinical and biochemical luminescence* (eds. L. J. Kricka and T. J. N. Carter) p. 129. Dekker, New York.

Roswell, D. F. and White, E. H. (1978). Chemiluminescence of luminol and related hydrazides, In *Methods in enzymology*, 57,(ed. M. Deluca) p.409. Academic Press, New York.

Salerno, R. Moneti, G., Magini, A., Tomasi, A. and Pazzagli, M. (1984). Evaluation of luminescent immunoassay methods for urinary steroids. In *Analytical applications of bioluminescence and chemiluminescence* (eds. L. J. Kricka, P. E. Stanley, G. H. G. Thorpe, and T. P. Whitehead) p. 179. Academic Press, London.

Schroeder, H. R., Boguslaski, R. C., Carrico, R. J. and Buckler, R. T. (1978). Monitoring specific protein binding reactions with chemiluminescence. In *Methods in enzymology* 57, (ed. M. DeLuca) pp. 424–45. Academic Press, New York.

Schuster, G. B. (1979). Chemiluminescence of organic compounds: conversion of ground state reagents to excited state products by the CIEEL mechanism. *Acct. Chem. Res.* **12**, 366–73.

Seliger, H. H. and McElroy, W. D. (1960). Pathways of energy transfer in bioluminescence. *Radiation Res.* Suppl. 2, 528–38.

Stanley, P. E. (1982). Instrumentation. In *Clinical and biochemical luminescence* (eds. L. J. Kricka and T. J. N. Carter) pp. 219–260. Dekker, New York.

Strehler, B. L. (1968). Bioluminescence assay: principles and practice. *Methods Biochem. Anal.* **16**, 99–181.

Tseng, S. and Rauhut, M. M. (1981). Europ. Pat. Appl. No. 811 003 69.8.

Tsuji, F. I. (1978). Cypridina luciferin and luciferase. In *Methods in Enzymology 57* (ed. M. DeLuca) pp. 364–72. Academic Press, New York.

Ward, W. W. and Cormier, M. J. (1979). An Energy transfer protein in coelenterate bioluminescence. *J. Biol. Chem.* **254**, 781–88.

Weeks, I., Campbell, A. K. and Woodhead, J. S. (1983). Two-site immunochemiluminometric assay for human alpha-fetoprotein *Chin. Chem.* **29**, 1480–3.

—— Beheshti, I., McCapra, F., Campbell, A. K. and Woodhead, J. S. (1983). Acridinium esters as high specific activity labels in immunoassay. *Chin. Chem.* **29**, 1474–9.

——, Sturgess, M. Siddle, K. Jones M. K. and Woodhead, J. S. (1984). A High sensitivity immunochemiluminometric assay for human thyrotropin. *Clin. Endocrinol.*

20, 489–95.

White, E. H., Miano, J. D. and Umbreit, M. (1975). On the mechanism of firefly luciferin luminescence. *J. Am. Chem. Soc.* **97**, 198–200.

Wilson, T. (1976) Chemiluminescence in the liquid phase, *Int, Sci, Rev.* **9**. 265–322.

Wienhausen, G. K., Kricka, L. J., Hinckley, J. E. and DeLuca, M. (1982), Properties of bacterial Luciferase/NADH-FMN oxidoreductase and firefly luciferase immobilised onto sepharose. *Appl. Biochem. Biotech.* **7**, 463–72.

Wynberg, H., Meijer, E. W. and Hummelen, J. C. (1981). 1.2-Dioxetanes as chemiluminescent probes and labels. In *Bioluminescence and chemiluminescence* (eds. M. DeLuca and W. D. McElroy) pp. 687–9. Academic Press, New York.

32

Design of fibre-optic biosensors based on bioreceptors

JEROME S. SCHULTZ

32.1 Introduction

The use of optical fibre wave guides for miniaturization of spectrophoto-metric methods to monitor samples on the order of 0.1 lambda in volume has taken on special significance in recent years due to the ready availability of a variety of optical fibres and opto-electronic devices for light sources and detectors (Chabay, 1982). Optical fibres have been used to fabricate micro-calorimeters and micro-fluorimeters (Vurek and Brown 1969). However, it is only recently that optical fibres and detector elements have been coupled to biochemical reactions for the purposes of developing miniaturized biosensors.

There have been adequate demonstrations of fibre-optic based analytical devices for physical properties such as temperature and simple analytes such as pH, CO_2, O_2 (Lubbers and Opitz 1983; Peterson *et al.* 1980; Saari and Seitz 1982). Some recent reviews of developments in optical biosensors have been published by Seitz (1984; Chapter 30) and Peterson and Vurek (1984).

Schultz and Sims (1979) introduced an approach to measure biochemicals based on competitive binding between specific receptors and fluorescently labeled analogue-analytes. The system was miniaturized by using a single hollow dialysis fibre as a microscopic 'test tube', and by inserting a single optical fibre into this reaction chamber spectrophotometric changes can be monitored. An important characteristic of this system is that it is reagentless, i.e. since the reactions are reversible and the reagents are retained within the dialysis chamber by utilizing macromolecular derivatives, the systems is self-contained and does not need to be regenerated.

32.2 Optical fibres

The basic construction of an optical fibre is shown in Fig. 32.1. It consists of a core material which has a higher refractive index than the cladding material (Lacey 1982). The result of this construction is that light that enters the fibre is totally internally reflected at the interface between the two transparent materials and is guided along the length of the fibre. Modern materials for

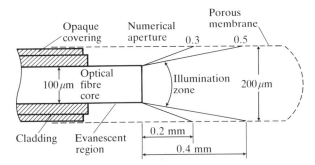

Fig. 32.1 Basic construction of an optical fibre illustrating the two mechanisms of light exchange, i.e. an illumination cone from the end of the fibre, and an evanescent wave from a decladded portion of the fibre. In usual practice only one of these modes is utilized in a given application.

optical fibres are highly purified so that the extent of attenuation due to absorption or scattering is relatively insignificant for fibre lengths on the order of several meters, which would be the case for most analytical systems of interest here.

For the purposes of using fibre optics in biosensor applications, there are two principle mechanisms by which light interacts with the external environment. Primarily, light emanates from the end of the core. If the light source is a laser, then the exit beam will be highly columniated with a diameter about equal to that of the incident laser beam. This cylindrical beam is of particular importance in the 'separation' techniques described below. If the light source is a focused beam from a typical lamp, then the light leave the core and diverges in a cone of illumination as shown in Fig. 32.1. The dispersion of the cone of light (called the numerical aperture of the fibre) depends on the difference in refractive indices between the core material and the external fluid. Regions of illumination for typical commercially available fibres are shown in this figure. The active biochemical constituents of a biosensor are often sheltered from the external environment by one or more membrane layers that cover the end of the optical fibre. The characteristics of these membranes are selected for particular functions in different analyses.

Light intensity diminishes as the region of illumination widens with distance from the end of the cleaved fibre. Also, the fraction of light emitted by fluorescence that returns to the optical fibre and is transmitted to the detection system falls off rapidly with distance. Some idea of the geometrical considerations for detection are shown in Fig. 32.2 for an axial beam of light. The total amount of light that re-enters the fibre is the sum of all these point sources in the region of illumination, but for practical purposes, only a zone

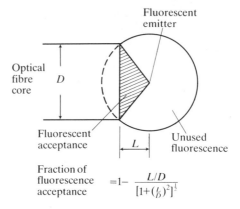

Fraction of
fluorescence $=1-\dfrac{L/D}{[1+(\frac{L}{D})^2]^{\frac{1}{2}}}$
acceptance

Fig. 32.2 Geometric considerations of the light gathering power of an optical fibre. The shaded region is the cone of light from a point emitter on the axis that enters the optical fibre.

of about ten fibre diameters in length provides useful signals back to the detector. Thus as shown in Fig. 32.3. for fibres on the order of 200 microns in diameter, the effective sensor zone is about 2 mm in length.

Another mechanism for allowing light to penetrate the outside environment is to remove the cladding from the central core. Provided the refractive index of the core is still higher than the external fluid, the light will still be

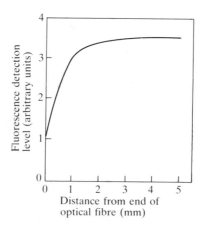

Fig. 32.3 Effect of chamber length on total amount of fluorescence detected by an optical fibre.

transmitted down the fibre, but a small portion will escape into the external phase. This evanescent wave of light energy decreases exponentially with distance from the core surface, and for all practical purposes is only effective for distances on the order of 100 angstroms.

32.3 Biosensors based on bioreceptors

In this chapter, we restrict our discussion to biosensors that are based on the reversible binding between analytes and specific receptors. The most common form of this type of assay in biology are the immunoassay procedures based on specific antibodies developed for low molecular weight haptens (i.e. in this context, analytes). Although the original implementation of immunoassays utilized radioactive tracers to monitor the extent of binding, over the last few years the use of fluorescent labels has become of increasing interest because of the elimination of possible radiation hazards (Smith *et al.* 1981). Fortunately, most of the technology that has been developed for fluoro-immunoassays can be readily adapted for biosensor development.

In addition to the availability of antibodies as receptor candidates for biosensors, there are several other classes of proteins that have the desired characteristics of reversible selective binding. For example, lectins have specific binding characteristics for different sugars (Goldstein and Hayes 1978); membrane binding proteins with specificities for different amino acids and sugars have been isolated and described (Landich and Oxender 1982); and enzymes have non-reactive binding sites for allosteric effectors (Lehninger 1970).

The technology associated with affinity chromatography can provide a wealth of information and materials for 'affinity-pairs'. Many combinations of receptors and ligands have been evaluated in the context of purification of proteins by affinity chromatography (Chaiken *et al.* 1984). Some of these systems could be adapted for use in a biosensor, e.g. flavin and flavin-binding protein.

The design of biosensors based on reversible binding to biological receptors will be discussed in two categories — direct and indirect methods.

32.3.1 Direct method

The direct method involves only the reversible reaction of the analyte and receptor species:

$$\text{Analyte} + \text{Receptor} \rightleftharpoons \text{Analyte:receptor} \qquad (32.1)$$

In order to use this reaction directly, there must be a spectral change in at least one of these three species. For example, if the absorption spectrum of the receptor changes when the analyte is bound, then monitoring this change would provide a direct measure of the extent of binding and thus a measure of analyte concentration. A classical case is the spectral change that occurs when oxygen binds to haemoglobin. Although this colour change has been used primarily to monitor the percent oxygenation of haemoglobin, the effect could be turned around for the estimation of the partial pressure of oxygen colorimetrically.

Of course since the binding of oxygen to haemoglobin is sensitive to pH, carbon dioxide, and temperature, this reaction would not be the first choice for constructing an oxygen sensor. But, it does remind one that for a sensor one needs to evaluate the effect of environmental conditions on binding behavior.

Another, and somewhat more prevalent optical effect that has been used to measure the extent of reaction is the quenching of fluorescence when the analyte binds to the protein. Most proteins fluoresce when excited in the green due to the residues of tryptophan in the molecule. This fluorescence can be quenched when the analyte binds to the protein if the absorption spectrum of the analyte overlaps the emission spectrum of tryptophan. An example of clinical importance is the fluorescent assay of aminoglycoside antibiotics as described by Shaw *et al.* (1977) for gentamicin.

It should be noted that for direct systems, it is not necessary to have a membrane separating the chemical constituents of the sensor from the sample fluid if the receptor is conserved by immobilizing it to the surface of the optical probe. However it may be desirable to use a membrane anyway, to protect the receptor protein from other constituents of the sample fluid, e.g. enzymes.

32.3.2 Indirect method

If neither the analyte nor receptor exhibit a spectral change on binding, then one must resort to the use of analyte-analogues that have some measurable response. In these indirect methods the general chemical equation are:

$$\text{Analyte} + \text{Receptor} \rightleftharpoons \text{Analyte:receptor} \tag{32.2}$$

$$\text{Analogue–analyte} + \text{Receptor} \rightleftharpoons \text{Analogue–analyte:receptor} \tag{32.3}$$

Where the analogue-analyte either has an inherent measurable optical characteristic, or induces some optical change on binding to the receptor. If one can monitor the extent of the second reaction then, indirectly, one can estimate the concentration of the analyte since changes in analyte concentration will alter the extent of the second reaction. Some possibilities for implementing this concept in the design of biosensors are discussed below.

32.3.2.1 Spatial separation techniques
As mentioned in the description of optical fibre-characteristics, the emanating beam from an optical fibre is

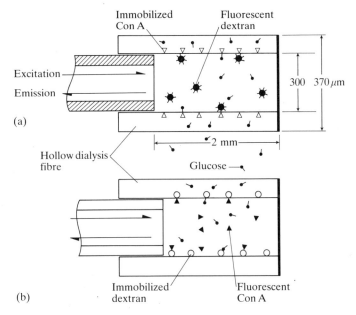

Fig. 32.4 Configurations for a glucose biosensor based on the 'separation' principle, i.e. the measurement of only the unbound fluorescently labeled macromolecule.
(a) Glucose sensor utilizing immobilized Con A as the bioreceptor and fluorescently labeled dextran as the freely mobile analogue-analyte (Schultz *et al.* 1982).
(b) An alternative scheme for a glucose sensor where the analog-analyte, i.e. dextran, is immobilized and the bioreceptor, i.e. Con A, is fluorescently labeled and freely mobile.

focused to some extent, depending on the illumination source and numerical aperture of the optical fibre. This property can be used to advantage to independently monitor individual constituents if one of the components of the system is immobilized out of the field of view of the optical fibre. Figure 32.4a shows one arrangement to accomplish this task.

Here the receptor protein is immobilized to the interior surface of a hollow dialysis fibre that defines the transducer chamber. This configuration was used successfully for a prototype glucose sensor (Schultz *et al.* 1982; Mansouri and Schultz 1984). Concanavalin A provided the specific receptor for sugars and high molecular weight (70 000), fluorescently labeled dextran (FITC-dextran) was chosen as the analogue-analyte. Con A was covalently immobilized to the cellulose hollow fibre (Sirinivasan *et al.* 1986), essentially out of the view of the optical fibre.

In the absence of sugar, a signal equivalent to about 20% of the maximum fluorescence was measured. Through a variety of tests (Mansouri 1983) it was

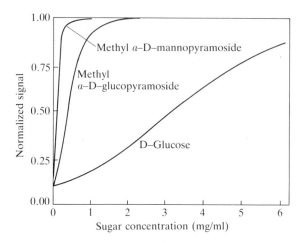

Fig. 32.5 Typical sugar calibration curves for a Con A based biosensor (Mansouri 1983).

estimated that about three quarters of this baseline signal was from free FITC-dextran and the balance from dextran bound to Con A on the dialysis tube. As the sensor is placed in solutions of increasing sugar concentration, increasing amounts of fluorescent dextran are displaced from the wall into the field of view of the optical fibre. Eventually, at high sugar concentrations, all the dextran is free and no further increase in fluorescence is obtained. The saturation-type of calibration curves shown in Fig. 32.5 are typical of the response from systems involving receptor binding. Simplified mathematical models for these response curves are discussed below.

The response for three different sugars are shown in Fig. 32.5 to illustrate that the sensitivity of the method is directly related to the binding constant between the analyte and receptor. The sensor is more than ten times more sensitive to methyl mannoside than to glucose, with a mid-range response of about 100 micrograms per ml for the mannose derivative. These curves also show that if a solution contained a mixture of sugars, then the sensor output would provide some weighted mean level of the sugars present. Fortunately, if the sensor is used to monitor glucose in blood, there are no other sugars of consequence present in blood to compete with glucose for the binding sites. The ultimate sensitivity of this device is related to the lowest fluorescein concentration that can be measured, this was to be on the order of 100 nanograms of fluorescein per ml.

It should be pointed out that an alternative labeling scheme with essentially equivalent characteristics as the above case would be to label Con A with

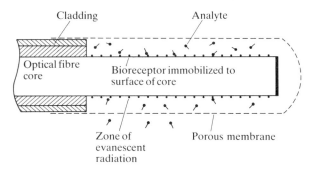

Fig. 32.6 Configuration for a biosensor based on the use of the evanescent wave for detection of the bound bioreceptor-analogue-analyte complexes.

fluorescein and immobilize the dextran (unlabeled) to the hollow dialysis fibre. This situation which is depicted in Fig. 32.4b could have some advantages if it were easier to label Con A with fluorescein or if one could obtain a higher density of immobilized dextran than immobilized Con A.

Instead of monitoring the free fluorescent species, the fluorescence of the immobilized fraction could be measured as well. There are a number of optical techniques for doing this, but perhaps the most elegant is the use of the evanescent wave approach introduced by Kronick and Little (1975). In this method, the receptor would be bound to the core of a decladed optical fibre as shown in Fig. 32.6. Since the extent of penetration of the evanescent wave into the fluid is only on the order of 100 angstroms, the primary volume sampled will be the absorbed layer of receptor molecules and bound fraction of analyte. Andrade *et al.* (1985) have demonstrated the feasibility of using the evanescent wave in this fashion.

The sensitivity of these methods may be increased by the use of time resolved fluorimetry (Soini and Hemmila 1979). In this technique, fluorescent moieties are chosen that have relatively long lifetimes (persistence after excitation on the order of microseconds rather than nanoseconds, as is typical for fluorescein). This allows one to measure fluorescent emission after turning off the excitation beam. An advantage of this approach is that interferences from background scattering of the excitation beam and background fluorescence due to impurities (usually short-time in nature) are eliminated.

Typically rare-earth chelate fluorophores have been found to have the appropriate properties for time-resolved fluorimetry. For example, Leung (1977) has shown that a 'bifunctional' chelation agent can be used to covalently attach heavy metal chelates to albumin, allowing measurement down to the micromolar level. Special gated fluorimeters for this purpose have been designed (Soini and Kojola 1983).

32.3.2.2 Homogeneous techniques   There are a number of other optical techniques that can be used with the indirect method and that have the additional advantage that no immobilization chemistry is required.

Fluorescent energy transfer.
Ullman (Ullman *et al.* 1976) introduced the concept and proved the utility of fluorescent excitement energy transfer immunoassays. The essence of the approach can be represented as follows:

$$Ag-F + Ab-R \rightleftharpoons Ag-F:Ab-R \tag{32.4}$$

where F = fluorescein, R = rhodamine, Ag = antigen, and Ab = antibody (receptor). Thus, light of the appropriate frequency is used to excite the fluorescence of fluorescein. When the antigen (Ag-F) is in the free form (left side of the equation) emitted light is detected by the optics. On the other hand, when the fluorescein moiety is in close proximity to rhodamine (that has an absorption spectrum that overlaps the Ag-F fluorescence spectrum) about 70% of the emitted light is quenched by direct energy transfer from fluorescein to rhodamine. Thus an optical biosensor can be constructed on this principle:

$$Analyte + Receptor-R \rightleftharpoons Analyte:receptor-R \tag{32.5}$$

$$Analogue-analyte-F + Receptor-R \rightleftharpoons Analog-analyte-F:receptor-R \tag{32.6}$$

$$\text{(fluorescent)} \qquad\qquad \text{(quenched)}$$

The measurement of fluorescence quenching gives an indirect estimate of the unlabeled analyte concentration through the competitive binding mechanism.

A particular advantage of this technique is that neither the receptor nor the analogue-analyte needs to be immobilized, since the quenching occurs is solution. Furthermore, one has more complete control of the concentration of receptor and analogue-analyte in the transducer compartment and can more easily optimize the conditions for maximum assay sensitivity. Also, the choice of membrane materials for the hollow fibre would be expanded because one is not limited to materials that can be easily activated for immobilization and the strength of the hollow fibre would not be compromised by the immobilization chemistry.

A least two physical configurations are possible in this case, either a single fibre arrangement as shown in Fig. 32.7a, or a fibre bundle arrangement as

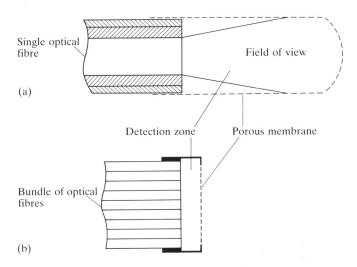

Fig. 32.7 Configurations for biosensors based on spectral changes in homogeneous reactions. (a) Single optical fibre, (b) use of a bundle of optical fibres, with a detection chamber of thickness t.

shown in Fig. 32.7b. The latter type has some advantages in that there is more light gathering power with multiple fibres, as a result the chamber thickness (dimension t in the figure) can be made very small, which will decrease the diffusion path length and increase the response rate of the system.

Fluorescence depolarization

An alternative to energy transfer is the method of fluorescence depolarization introduced by Dandliker (Dandliker and Saussuve 1970). Here the principle is based on the difference in rotational diffusion rates between the free analogue-analyte and the receptor bound analogue-analyte. When the analogue-analyte is bound to the large molecular receptor, its rotation rate is slowed so that the depolarization of emitted light is reduced. Thus, an increase in the amount of polarized fluorescence is directly related to amount of analogue bound. In the immunoassay kits based on this principle low molecular weight analogues can be used because conservation of reactants is not an issue. For biosensor applications, the analogue would have to be large enough to be retained within the dialysis tube and thus a molecular weight on the order of several thousand is required. With larger analogue-analytes the sensitivity of the method will be lessened because the difference in rotational diffusion rates between the free and bound analogue will be reduced.

Normal optical fibres scramble polarized light, but recent developments in the use of graded index glass allow retention of polarization for short lengths of fibres. Configurations similar to that shown in Fig. 32.7 could be used with the fluorescence depolarization approach.

Turbidimetric methods
Another method for estimating the extent of reaction between macromolecular analogue-analytes and receptors is by measuring changes in the intensity of back scattered light in sensors in the form shown in Fig. 32.7. For polymers with diameters on the order of tens of angstroms, the intensity of back scattered light is proportional to the square of molecular weight. If, for example in a glucose sensor, dextran with a size equal to Con A (molecular-weight about 60 000) is chosen as the competing analyte, then the intensity of scattered light from the complex dextran-Con A will be about four times that of either component alone. Thus there will be a decrease in scattered light as reaction 32.3 proceeds in the left direction as glucose enters the sensor chamber.

32.4 Approximate models for response characteristics

Assuming that the reactions involved are at equilibrium, the mathematical representation of response characteristics for biosensors based on reversible binding can be obtained fairly directly for simple univalent binding systems. The practical attainment of chemical equilibrium should be considered in the light of the kinetics of other processes that are involved in the sensor response. For example, in most biosensors a membrane will be interposed between the chemical constituents and the sample fluid. Then the rate of analyte diffusion through the membrane(s) will be an important factor in the overall sensor response. For example, the time constant for diffusion of glucose through a hollow dialysis fibre with a 30 micron wall thickness is about five minutes (Schultz *et al.* 1982). The time constant for glucose binding to Con A is on the order of milliseconds, and thus the reaction is always at equilibrium with respect to the diffusion dynamics. On the other hand, the kinetics of some antibody-antigen interactions is fairly slow. For example, Kranz *et al.* (1982) report on antifluorescyl monoclonal antibodies with dissociation half-lifes from 10^{-2} to 10^3 seconds. For antibodies it generally appears that the higher the affinity constant the lower the dissociation rate, in some cases as long as hours. Obviously, in the latter situation an equilibrium assumption will not be valid.

32.4.1 Direct method
The chemistry of simple binding can be represented as

$$A \quad + \quad R \quad \rightleftharpoons \quad A:R \qquad\qquad (32.7)$$
$$\text{analyte} \quad \text{receptor} \quad\quad\quad \text{bound analyte}$$

$$[R]_t = [R] + [A:R] \tag{32.8}$$
$$K_a = [A:R]/[A][R] \tag{32.9}$$
$$[R]/[R]_t = 1/[1 + ([A]K_a)] \tag{32.10}$$

where $[R]$ is concentration of free receptor, $[R]_t$ is total receptor concentration and K_a is equilibrium binding constant between analyte and receptor.

Thus if the receptor (R), normally fluoresces but is quenched when A is bound, then $[R]/[R]_t$ is the residual fluorescence as a function of the concentration of A. As with systems that obey Langmuir isotherms, the response is one half maximum when $[A]$ is numerically equal to K_a^{-1}. Note that the sensitivity of this type of system is independent of receptor concentration, and if the detection system were able to measure R over the range $0.1 < [R]/[R]_t < 0.9$, this corresponds to an analyte range of $(1/9)/K_a < [A] < 9/K_a$.

32.4.2 Indirect methods

As shown in Fig. 32.5 for our glucose sensor, the calibration curves for sensors based on equilibrium binding are generally hyperbolic in nature.

For practical reasons, i.e. attempting to obtain the maximum performance from the sensor, it is desirable to have the background output as close to zero as possible and about 50 to 80% maximal response at the operational expected concentration of the analyte for a given application. The selection criteria for receptor and analogue-analyte as related to binding constants, and concentration effects can be estimated from a simplified mathematical analysis of the system.

$$\begin{array}{ccc} \text{A} & + & \text{R} \rightleftharpoons \text{A:R} \\ \text{analyte} & & \text{receptor} \quad \text{bound analyte} \end{array} \tag{32.11}$$

$$\begin{array}{ccc} \text{A*} & + & \text{R} \rightleftharpoons \text{A*:R} \\ \text{analogue-analyte} & \text{receptor} & \text{bound analogue-analyte} \end{array} \tag{32.12}$$

If it is assumed that the binding reactions are unimolecular (more complex behaviour will be discussed later), then assuming chemical equilibrium between all of the constituents, the following algebraic equations will pertain:

$$K_a = [A:R]/[A][R] \tag{32.13}$$
$$K_a^* = [A^*:R]/[A^*][R] \tag{32.14}$$

where $[A]$, etc., are the concentration of the various species.

Because of the construction of the sensor, the total amount of receptor and analogue ligand are conserved over time and thus the following material balance equations can be written.

$$[R]_t = [R] + [A:R] + [A^*:R] \tag{32.15}$$
$$[A^*]_t = [A^*] + [A^*:R] \tag{32.16}$$

where $[R]_t$ and $[A^*]_t$ are the total (or initial) concentrations of these two species within the sensor chamber.

These four equations can be solved for the ratio of unbound to total detector ligand concentration:

$$\left(\frac{[A^*]}{[A^*]_t}\right)^2 + \frac{[A^*]}{[A^*]_t}\left[\left(\frac{[R]_t}{[A^*]_t} - 1\right) + \left(\frac{K_a[A] + 1}{[A^*]_t K_a^*}\right)\right] - \left(\frac{K_a[A] + 1}{[A^*] K_a^*}\right) = 0. \tag{32.17}$$

The normalized response is given as $[A^*]/[A^*]_t$; this ratio, between 0 and 1, of the free analogue-analyte to the total analogue-analyte concentration represents the range of output of the sensor. The sensitivity of the sensor will depend somewhat on the amount of analogue-analyte used in preparing the sensor $[A^*]_t$. From practical considerations minimum concentration of the analogue ligand that can be used in the sensor depends on the capability of the optical system for measuring low levels of fluorescence and the presence of other possible interfering substances, e.g. bilirubin in blood.

From eqn 32.17 it can be seen that the normalized response is a function of two groups of parameters $[R]_t/[A^*]_t$ and $(K_a[A] + 1)/([A^*]_t K_a^*)$. The latter group contains the independent variable of interest, $[A]$ the concentration of

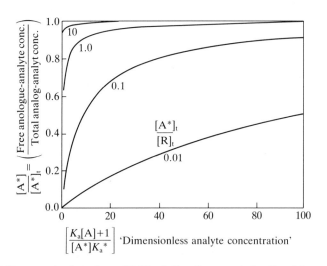

Fig. 32.8 Parametric plot of eqn 32.17 relating the expected ratio of free analogue-analyte to total analogue-analyte in the detection chamber as a function of the dimensionless group $[K_a[A] + 1]/[A^*]K_a^*]$ which is directly related to the free analyte concentration. Parametric curves of $[A^*]_t/[R]_t$ give the effect of relative levels of analogue-analyte concentration within the detector chamber.

analyte. Thus a dimensionless plot of $[A^*]/[A^*]_t$ *vs.* $(K_a[A] + 1)/([A^*]_t K_a^*)$ provides a complete characterization of the system as shown in Fig. 32.8.

From this figure it is clear that at low values of $[R]_t/[A^*]_t$, the responsiveness of the sensor to changes in analyte concentration will be very slight. Physically this condition represents the situation where the analogue-analyte concentration is so high relative to the amount of available receptor sites that there is a great excess of unbound analogue ligand. Thus the additional release of analogue ligand from receptor sites by analyte does not appreciably affect the free and measurable $[A^*]$. Thus in designing biosensors of this type it is clear that in order to obtain an analyte calibration curve over a range of concentrations of interest a reasonable rule of thumb is to maintain the ratio of $[R]_t/[A^*]_t$ greater than 1.

This same principle can be seen from another point of view. Operationally, it is desirable for the signal to be low at low analyte concentration, and high at the maximum analyte concentration expected for a given application. This behaviour can be met if $[R]_t/[A^*]_t$ is on the order of 10. On the other hand, if $[R]_t/[A^*]_t$ is much larger, (e.g. on the order of 100), some other problems may result, namely that the actual concentration of analogue-analyte may be too low for dependable detection by the optical system.

These considerations can be used to estimate the physical chemical constants required for a given sensor application. First, it is desirable for the output of the sensor to be low when the analyte concentration is zero. Substituting the values $[A] = 0$, $[R]_t/[A^*]_t = 10$, and a minimal sensor response, i.e. $[A^*]/[A^*]_t = 0.1$, we find from eqn 32.17 that the group $[A^*]_t K_a^*$ needs to be on the order of 1.0.

Now in order to obtain a 50% response when the analyte concentration is in mid-range, let $[A^*]/[A^*]_t = 0.5$, and we find that the group $K_a[A']$ should be on the order of 10 (where $[A']$ is the mid-range analyte concentration).

Using the glucose sensor as an example, the range of blood glucose in diabetics is on the order of 1 to 5 mg/ml, thus $[A'] = 5$ mg/ml or 0.025 M. The association binding constant of glucose to Con A (K_a) is about 320 M^{-1}.

The maximum amount of Con-A that we were able to immobilize to the interior surface of the hollow dialysis fibre resulted in an effective concentration of 10^{-5} M. The affinity binding constant between FITC dextran (70 000 MW) and Con-A is about $7.5 \times 10^{+4} M^{-1}$ and the total concentration of FITC dextran was about 1.5×10^{-6} M. The value of the $K_a[A']$ group was about 6 at a glucose value of 2.5 mg/ml, and $[R]_t/[A^*]_t$ was 7. Thus for our particular glucose sensor these dimensionless group are approximately in the range of the criteria given above.

From these considerations a rational approach to designing a biosensor can be outlined for a specific analyte.

1. Estimate the mid-range analyte concentration of interest $[A']$.

2. Select a bioreceptor with a binding constant with a numerical value on the order of $10/[A']$.

3. Estimate the minimum concentration of analogue-analyte ligand that can be detected by the optical system. $[A]_m$ and presume that $[A^*]_t$ will be on the order of $50 [A]_m$.

4. Select, synthesize, or modify competing analogue candidate compounds so that the criteria $K_a^* = 1/[A]_m$ is satisfied.

5. Develop methodologies to load the sensor transducer compartment with the bioreceptor so that the total concentration of sites is on the order of $100[A^*]_t$.

32.4.3 Multivalent binding behaviour

So far in this discussion we have limited the analysis to monovalent interactions between ligands and receptors. Actually, most antibodies are at least divalent (i.e. have two receptor sites) and many are multivalent. Concanavalin A has four receptor sites. Also, haptens (analogue-analytes) usually have multiple active groups. Thus the simple models given above are not exact for these more complex systems, and general mathematical approaches are still being developed (Perelson 1984). However, as a first approximation for estimating biosensor behaviour one can use the above formulations with pseudo-univalent binding constants. For example, as mentioned above the binding constant between glucose and Con A is 320 M^{-1} whereas for FITC-dextran, linear glucose polymer with many pendant glucose units, the effective binding constant with Con A is about 7.5×10^4 M^{-1} or a factor 20 times higher.

32.5 Summary

The capabilities of fibre-optic systems for miniaturizing analytical techniques based on the properties of light provides an enormous resource that can be harnessed for biosensor applications. The fast pace of developments in opto-electronic devices, i.e. solid state lasers, integrated opto-electronic chips, new types of optical fibres, connectors, multiplexers, portends a future where not only the sensor is miniaturized but the measuring equipment as well. In addition, modern developments in molecular biology and protein engineering in particular will make it possible to design bioreceptors with the desired characteristics for specific use in biosensors. These two trends should result in a completely new generation of highly selective, miniature, portable, stable, and inexpensive biosensors that can be used in both biomedical and industrial applications.

Acknowledgement

This work was partially supported by NIH Grant RO1 AM 26858.

References

Andrade, J. D., VanWagenen, R. A., Gregonis, D. E., Newby, K. and Lin, J.-N. (1985). Remote fibre-optic biosensors based on evanescent-excited fluoro-immunnoassay: Concept and Progress. *IEEE Trans. Electron Devices* **ED-32**, 1175-9.

Chabay, I. (1982). Opical waveguides. *Anal. Chem.* **54**, 1071A-80A.

Chaiken, I., Wilchech, M., Paritch, I. (eds.) (1984). *Affinity chromatography and biological recognition*. Academic Press, New York.

Dandlicker, W. and Saussuve, V. A. (1970). Review of fluorescence polarization in immunochemistry. *Immunochem.* **7**, 799-805.

Goldstein, I. J. and Hayes, C. E. (1978). The lectins: carbohydrate-binding proteins of plants and animals. In *Advances in carbohydrate chemistry and biochemistry*. (eds. R. S. Typson and D. Horton). Vol. 35, 127-145.

Kranz, D. M., Herron, J. N. and Voss E. W., Jr. (1982). Mechanisms of ligand binding by monoclonal antifluoresyl antibodies, *J. Biol. Chem.*, **257**, 6987-95.

Kronick, N. M. and Little, W. A. (1975). *J. Immunol. Methods.* **8**, 235-240.

Lacey, E. A. (1982). *Fiber optics*. Prentice Hall, Englewood, NJ, USA.

Landich, R. and Oxender, D. (1982). Periplasmic binding proteins. In *Membranes and Transport*, (ed. Martonosi) Vol. 2, pp. 81-88. Plenum, New York.

Lehninger, A. (1970). *Biochemistry*. Worth, New York.

Leung, C. and Mears, C. (1977). Attachment of fluorescent metal chelated to macromolecules using 'bifunctional' chelating agents. *Biochem. Biophys. Res. Comm.* **75**, 149-55.

Lubbers, D. W. and Opitz, N. (1983). Blood gas analysis with fluorescent dyes as an example of their usefulness as quantitative chemical sensors. In *Proc. intl. mtg. chemical sensors*, Fukuoda, Japan. Elsevier, Amsterdam.

Mansouri, S. (1983). Optical glucose sensor based on affinity binding. Ph.D. Thesis, University of Michigan.

Mansouri, S. and Schultz, J. S. (1984). A miniature optical sensor based on affinity binding. *Bio/technology* **2**, 385-90.

Perelson, A. S. (1984). Some mathematical models of receptor clustering by multivalent ligands. In *Cell surface dynamics: concepts and models* (eds. A. S. Perelson, C. DeLisi, and F. W. Wiegel) pp. 223-276. Marcel Dekker, New York.

Peterson, J. I., Goldstein, S. R., Fitzgerald, R. V. and Ruckold, D. K. (1980). Fiberoptic pH probe for physiological use. *Anal. Chem.* **52**, 864-9.

Peterson, J. I. and Vurek, G. G. (1984). Fiber-optic sensors for biomedical applications. *Science.* **224**, 123-7.

Saari, L. and Seitz, W. R. (1982) pH sensor based on immobilized fluorescein amine. *Anal. Chem.* **54**, 821-3.

Schultz, J. S., Mansouri, S. and Goldstein, I. J. (1982). Affinity sensor: a new technique for developing implantable sensors for glucose and other metabolites. *Diabetes Care.* **5**, 245-53.

Schultz, J. S. and Sims, G. (1979). *Biotech. Bioeng. Symp.* **9**, 65-71.

Seitz, W. R. (1984). Chemical sensors based on fiber optics. *Anal. Chem.* **56**, 16A-34A.

Sirinivasan, K. R., Mansouri, S. and Schultz, J. S. (1986). Coupling of Concanavalin

A to cellulose hollow fibers for use in a glucose affinity sensor. *Biotech. Bioeng.* **28**, In press.

Shaw, E. J., Watson, R. A. A., London, J., Smith, D. S. (1977). Estimation of serum gentamicin by quenching fluoroimmunoassay. *J. Clin. Pathol.* **30**, 562–31.

Smith, D. S., Al-Hakiem, M. and Landon, J. (1981). A review of fluorimmunassay and immunofluorimetric assay. *Anal. Clin. Biochem.* **18**, 253–274.

Soini, E. and Hemmila, I. (1979). Fluorimmunoassay: present status and key problems. *Chin. Chem.* **25**, 353–61.

Soini, E. and Kojola, H. (1983). Time-resolved fluorometer for lanthamide chelates — a new generation of nonisotopic immunoassays. *Clin Chem.* **29**, 65–8.

Ullman, E. F., Schwarzberg, M. and Rubenstein, K. (1976). Fluorescent excitation transfer immunoassay, a general method for determination of antigens. *J. Biol. Chem.* **251**, 4172.

Vureck, G. G. and Bowman, R. L. (1969). Fiber-optic colorimeter for submicroliter samples. *Anal. Biochem.* **29**, 238–47.

33

IRS devices for optical immunoassays

RANALD M. SUTHERLAND and CLAUS DÄHNE

33.1 Introduction

Internal Reflection Spectroscopy (IRS) is an established technique for monitoring reaction systems within the order of a wavelength of light at a continuous surface (Harrick 1967). IRS is based on the optical reflection characteristics between two transparent media of different refractive indices. When a light beam is totally internally reflected within the optically denser medium, an electromagnetic wave-form is generated in the optically rarer medium close to the reflecting surface. This evanescent wave is part of the internally reflected light beam and penetrates a fraction of a light wavelength into the lower refractive index medium. The evanescent wave is the 'sensing' component and can optically interact with compounds close to or at the surface. This optical interaction can be followed as a change in the intensity of light which exits from the optically denser medium. The latter is commonly called the internal reflection element (IRE) and can be designed as a single (Fig. 33.1a) or multiple (Fig. 33.1b) reflection element. Other common terms for multiple reflection elements are light-guide or waveguide. The characteristics of this type of sensor allow the continuous monitoring of reactions at the interface with minimal interference from compounds distant from the wave-guide surface (of the order of a light wavelength).

Previous biological applications of IRS devices are mainly based on the interaction of proteins with or at surfaces, the latter pretreated to make them hydrophobic or hydrophilic. The two optical techniques most frequently used for measuring these interactions are attenuated total reflection (ATR) and total internal reflection fluorescence (TIRF). ATR is defined as 'reflection which occurs when an absorbing coupling mechanism acts in the process of total internal reflection to make the reflectance less than unity' (Harrick 1967). That is, when an optically absorbing film is present on the waveguide interface, light energy absorbed from the evanescent wave can be monitored as an attenuation of the internally reflected light beam. ATR spectroscopy has been extensively applied to monitoring protein interactions at surfaces (Baier and Dutton 1969; Brash and Lyman 1971) in the infra-red (IR) region. Gendreau and co-workers have combined ATR and Fourier-

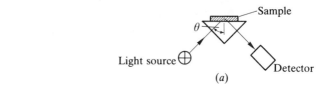

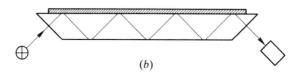

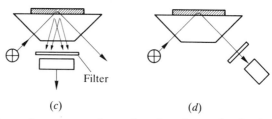

Fig. 33.1 Schematic representations of various internal reflection elements; (a) a single reflection prism; (b) a multiple-internal reflection element; (c) detection of right-angle fluorescence; (d) detection of in-line fluorescence.

transform infra-red spectroscopy to rapidly generate complete spectra of proteins adsorbed to a Germanium waveguide (Gendreau *et al.* 1981, 1982).

TIRF has also been applied to the study of protein interactions at surfaces using a number of fluorescence techniques. It can be considered that TIRF is a form of ATR spectroscopy, as in TIRF the absorption of evanescent photons by surface bound molecules is the first of a two-step process where, in a second step the photons are re-emitted at a longer wavelength as fluorescence. Harrick and Loeb (1973) applied TIRF to monitoring bovine serum albumin (BSA)-dansyl chloride bound to the surface of a quartz wave-guide, using TIRF. Watkins and Robertson (1977) measured fluoresceine (FITC)-bovine-γ-globulin binding to the surface of silicon rubber, and Lok *et al.* (1983*a*, *b*) presented data on the binding of FITC-BSA also to silicon rubber. Van Wagenen *et al.* (1980, 1982) used the intrinsic fluorescence of protein tryptophan residues to analyse BSA bound to a quartz waveguide.

Two other techniques have been applied to TIRF measurement. Burghardt and Axelrod (1981) used photobleaching recovery to study tetramethyl-rhodamine-BSA adsorbed to a quartz slide, and Thompson *et al.* (1981) developed a fluorescence correlation spectroscopic method to measure the interaction of rhodamine-labelled IgG and rhodamine-labelled insulin with a BSA-coated quartz slide.

The potential advantages of using IRS devices for immunoassay lie mainly in the ability to monitor surface reactions with high sensitivity. Conventionally (e.g. Kirkham and Hunter 1971), immunoassays are a multi-step procedure involving several incubations and penultimately the separation of antibody-bound materials from non-bound components prior to measurement of the specific binding signal. This separation step is a major source of assay imprecision, is tedious, and is technically demanding. There has been considerable research into producing non-separation (i.e. homogeneous) immunoassays (e.g. fluorescence polarization (Dandliker *et al.* 1980), laser nephelometry (Deaton *et al.* 1976), homogeneous enzyme immunoassays (EMIT, Syva Corporation) all of which have been applied in a routine clinical laboratory environment. However, there is still the requirement for a generally applicable method both for research and for routine immunoassays. IRS devices seem to offer an alternative approach as a novel form of homogeneous immunoassay with the advantage of being able to use a number of different optical detection techniques.

The key characteristic in the context of immunoassay is the ability to monitor surface reactions without major interferences from the bulk of solution. The concept lies in fixing one of the immunological binding pair to the surface of the waveguide, and monitoring its reaction with the complementary antigen (or antibody) without the need to carry out a formal separation step. This is because an '*in situ*' separation occurs at the waveguide surface within the optically sensitive region of the evanescent wave thus precluding the physical separation of antibody-bound from 'free' molecules.

The following paragraphs describe the optical theory behind some of the techniques used for measuring surface reactions with an evanescent wave, the important factors of optical system design with respect to commonly used IREs, a review of available literature on IRS devices for immunoassay, and finally some comments on what the future may hold.

33.2 Theoretical aspects

33.2.1 Principles of internal reflection spectroscopy

When a light beam irradiates the interface between two transparent media (Fig. 33.2), striking from the medium of higher refractive index ($n_1 > n_2$), total internal reflection occurs (Harrick 1967) when the angle of reflection θ is larger than the critical angle θ_c:

$$\theta_c = \sin^{-1}(n_2/n_1). \tag{33.1}$$

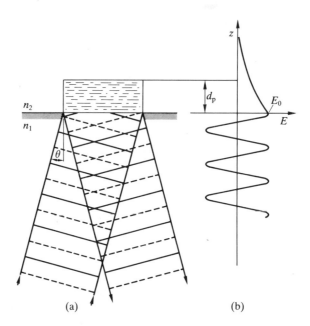

Fig. 33.2 Generation of the evanescent wave at an interface between two optical media; (a) where $n_1 > n_2$ and $\theta > \theta_c$, θ_c is the critical angle at which refraction occurs; the evanescent wave is generated at the reflecting surface. (b) Same as (a), but representing the electric field amplitude E, on both sides of the reflecting surface (Z = distance into the rarer medium, d_p = the characteristic penetration depth of the evanescent wave).

In this case the evanescent wave penetrates a distance (d_p), of the order of a fraction of a wavelength, beyond the reflecting surface into the rarer medium (n_2). According to Maxwell's equations, a standing sinusoidal wave, perpendicular to the reflecting surface, is established in the denser medium (Fig. 33.1b). Although there is no net flow of energy into a non-absorbing, rarer medium, there is an evanescent field in that medium. Because of continuity conditions of the field vectors the electric field amplitude (E) is largest at the surface interface (E_0) and decays exponentially with distance (Z) from the surface:

$$E = E_0 \cdot \exp(-Z/d_p). \tag{33.2}$$

The depth of penetration (d_p), defined as the distance required for the electric field amplitude to fall to $\exp(-1)$ of its value at the surface, is given by

$$d_p = \frac{\lambda/n_1}{2\Pi\{\sin^2\theta - (n_2/n_1)^2\}^{1/2}}. \tag{33.3}$$

This quantity d_p decreases with increasing θ and increases with closer index matching (i.e. as $n_2/n_1 \rightarrow 1$). Also, because d_p is proportional to wavelength, it is greater at longer wavelengths.

Thus, by an appropriate choice of the refractive index n_1 of the IRE, of the incident angle, and of the wavelength, one can select a d_p to promote optical interaction mainly with compounds close to or affixed at the interface and minimally with bulk solution.

As an example, if the waveguide is made of quartz ($n_1 = 1.46$), and the rarer medium is an aqueous sample ($n_2 = 1.34$), θ_c is $66°$ (eqn 33.1). If θ is selected as $70°$, λ as 500 nm, the resultant d_p is approximately 270 nm into the solution (see eqn 33.3). The estimated size of an IgG molecule (i.e. an antibody) is approximately 10 nm by 6 nm (Amzel and Poljak 1979). Thus a 'sandwich-type' immunological complex at the surface, consisting of three layers of IgG may have an average diameter of around 25 nm. At 25 nm the field strength is still 91% of E_0 (see eqn 33.2). However at double or treble this distance, the field strength falls off to 83% and 76% respectively, due to the exponential decay characteristics.

The depth of penetration is one of four factors which determine the attenuation caused by absorbing films in internal reflection. The other factors are, the polarization dependent electric field intensity at the reflecting interface, the sampling area which increases with increasing θ, and matching of the refractive index of the denser medium to that of the rarer medium which in turn controls the strength of the optical coupling. The appropriate quantity which takes account of all these factors in the effective thickness, d_e. It represents the actual thickness of film that would be required to obtain the same absorption in a transmission experiment.

In order to enhance sensitivity, multiple reflection elements are often used. The number of reflections (N) is a function of the length (L), thickness (T) of the waveguide and angle of incidence (θ).

$$N = L/T . \cot\theta \qquad (33.4)$$

The longer and thinner the waveguide, the larger is N and the more frequently the evanescent wave interacts with the surface layer of antibody–antigen complexes. If for one reflection the reflectivity (R) is

$$R = 1 - \alpha . d_e \qquad (33.5)$$

where α is the absorption coefficient and d_e is the effective thickness of a weakly absorbing layer, after N reflections the reflection loss is

$$R^N = 1 - N . \alpha . d_e \qquad (33.6)$$

i.e. it is increased by a factor of N.

The evanescent wave can be used to monitor surface reactions by a number of optical techniques. Emphasis will be placed on two major forms of optical detection. Firstly, systems which are based on the optical absorbance or fluorescence characteristics of the compound to be measured, i.e. ATR and TIRF. Secondly, systems based on the change in the thickness/refractive index of the immunological film will be discussed. The latter includes surface plasmon resonance (SPR).

33.2.2 *Attenuated total reflection (ATR) and total internal reflection fluorescence (TIRF)*

When an absorbing material is placed in contact with the reflecting surface of an IRE, the resultant internally reflected light beam is said to be attenuated (Harrick 1967). In the case of ATR techniques, what is measured is the attenuated intensity as a function of incident wavelength. In TIRF, fluorescent materials are used, and thus the absorbed energy is partly re-emitted as fluorescent light which is in turn detected.

To collect the fluorescence at a waveguide/liquid interface different signal collection techniques can be employed. Fluorescence emitted at an interface can be detected either conventionally where the detector is placed at right angles to the interface (Fig. 33.1c) or in-line with the primary light beam (Fig. 33.1d). Considering the very small solid angle of emission in in-line detection compared with the emission angle of right-angle geometry detection, the former would not seem to be very efficient. However, there is an enhancement effect, and theory predicts that for a fused silica waveguide with water as the n_2 medium, the in-line fluorescence intensity can be 50 times higher than the fluorescence emitted at right-angles to the waveguide. This effect, that fluorescence is tunnelled back into the waveguide is verified both theoretically and experimentally (e.g. Lee *et al.* 1979; Carniglia *et al.* 1972).

The following is a verbal explanation: in a first step, an incident plane wave generates an evanescent wave which excites molecules near the surface with a local distribution proportional to the evanescent electric field intensity (see eqn 33.2). After a characteristic excited-state lifetime, these molecules emit fluorescent radiation with a local distribution in the vicinity of the surface very similar to the exciting intensity distribution described by eqn 33.2, i.e. that of an evanescent wave, but at the fluorescent wavelength. The question of what happens to the fluorescent evanescent wave can be answered by applying the principle of optical reciprocity, which states that this light is coupled back into the waveguide as a plane wave in the same way as the primary process when a plane wave generates an evanescent wave. Theory shows that the fluorescent intensity emission peaks at the critical angle of total internal reflection so that it can be internally reflected. To increase sensitivity, the IRE can be structured to collect fluorescent light from several reflections and guide it to the detector.

This is especially advantageous when an optical fibre is used as an IRE, as fluorescent light emitted at right-angles from an elongated fibre cannot be easily collected onto a detector. In-line detection also avoids measurement of fluorescence through the bulk of the sample solution surrounding the fibre, which otherwise can give significant interference, depending on the fluorescent dye used (Soini and Hemmilä 1979).

33.2.3 Surface plasmon resonance (SPR)

Surface plasmon resonance (also called Surface Plasmon Oscillation) is a well-established concept that has been studied both theoretically and experimentally for a number of years. Detailed reviews of Surface plasmon oscillations are given by Raether (1977, 1980). However, it is a new technique in the field of chemical and biological measurement.

Surface plasmons exist in the boundary of a solid (metal or semiconductor) whose electrons behave like those of a quasi-free electron gas. The plasmons represent the quanta of the oscillations of surface charges, which are produced by exterior electrical fields in the boundary. These charge oscillations are coupled with high frequency electromagnetic fields extending into space. Surface plasmons can be excited by electron beams or by light. Two types of surface plasmons can be distinguished: radiative and non-radiative. For sensing applications, non-radiative plasmons excited by light are of most interest. This plasmon is characterized by an exponential decrease of the electric field with distance from the boundary. Non-radiative surface plasmons are not produced by 'direct' illumination (i.e. using light reflected at a metal surface) as the momentum of the incoming photons is too small. The method mainly applied for sensing applications is the excitation of plasmons by evanescent waves. The optical configuration is the ATR, or prism arrangement called the Kretschmann configuration (Kretschmann and Raether 1968). Figure 33.3 illustrates the system, and the resemblance with the basic ATR approach can be seen (e.g. Fig. 33.1a) as an IRE in the form of a glass prism with refractive index n_1 is irradiated with light incident at the prism base at an angle θ. The probed region below the prism base has a refrac-

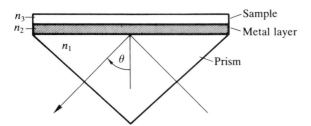

Fig. 33.3 Attenuated total reflection method of exciting non-radiative plasmons using the Kretschmann arrangement (Kretschmann and Raether 1968). θ is the incident angle of the light n_1, n_2, and n_3 are the refractive indices of the glass prism, metal layer, and sample, respectively.

tive index n_3 where $n_1 > n_3$. The characteristic of SPR is the metal layer between the prism and sample. When the incident field is p-polarized and the angle of incidence θ is such that the photon momentum along the surface matches that of the plasmon, light can couple to the electron plasma in the metal. This is the surface plasmon resonance. It can be seen in the intensity of the totally-reflected light as a sharp drop in transmission as a function of the angle of incidence. The depth and width of this resonance minimum is determined by the characteristic absorption and the thickness of the metal film. For a given metal a thickness can be selected to give a reflected intensity of effectively zero (e.g. *ca.* 60 nm for silver). Variation of the wavelength of the incident light can displace the position and width of the minimum.

Figure 33.4 illustrates the spatial distribution of the energy density, $|H|^2$, for three different angles of incidence and a 60 nm layer of silver as the metal; $\theta_0 = 50°$, this is outside the resonance and the field energy decays exponentially inside the plasma; $\theta_0 = 45.4°$, this is near the resonance and the field energy drops at first before reaching a higher value at the boundary; $\theta_0 = 45.2°$, this is at resonance and the field energy is maximum at the boundary. In this case, the energy density is about eighty times higher as compared to the value without resonance. That is, there is an evanescent

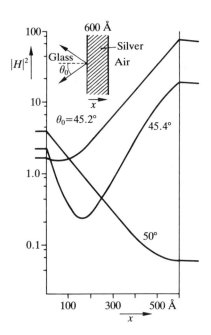

Fig. 33.4 The calculated electromagnetic density $|H(x)|^2$ in a 600-Å silver film (left medium: glass, right medium: air) with the angle of incidence as the parameter ($\lambda = 6000$ Å). (After Raether 1980, with permission).

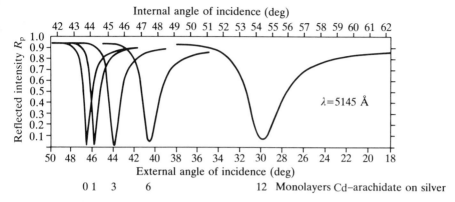

Fig. 33.5 Attenuated total reflectivity curves for silver films covered with different numbers of Cd-arachidate monolayers, as indicated ($\lambda = 5145$ Å) (after Pockrand *et al.* 1977, with permission).

wave outside the metal (in air in Fig. 33.4) which has the same penetration depth but is amplified eighty-fold when compared to ATR without a metal film. This is one reason for the high sensitivity of SPR. The other is that the angular position of the resonance minimum is very sensitive to variations in refractive index of the medium just outside the metal film, e.g. changing from air ($n = 1.0$) to water ($n = 1.33$) results in shifting the resonance angle from 43° to 68°, using a silver film and a HeNe light source (Liedberg *et al.* 1983). Since the electric field probes the medium only a few hundred nm from the metal surface, the resonance is very sensitive to thin films at that surface. This is the effect used for sensing applications.

As an example, Fig. 33.5 shows the dependence of the resonance minimum on the number of Cd-arachidate monolayers each 26.8 Å thick. It can be seen that the resonance position shifts to greater angles and its width increases with increasing numbers of layers. In terms of sensitivity, if the optical system can resolve better than 0.05°, coatings of a few angstroms thick can be measured.

33.2.4 Ellipsometry

Ellipsometry is probably one of the most commonly used techniques for measuring thin films deposited on a solid substrate. For detailed explanations of the theory, instrumentation, and applications, the reader is referred to the many review articles available (e.g., Poste and Moss 1972; Rothen 1974; Muller 1976; Azzam and Bashara 1977; Hauge 1980). Ellipsometry is mentioned in this chapter as it is one of the most sensitive techniques for measurement of thin films. Although it is based on external, not internal, reflection techniques, Carter *et al.* (1982) have suggested that ellipsometric measurements of thin biological films can be carried out using either single- or multiple-internal reflection waveguide systems. Published information on combining ellipsometry with IRS devices is very limited. It is not clear how useful this technique is, and it will not be discussed in any detail.

33.3 Practical considerations in choosing and using IREs

33.3.1 IRE

The key element to an IRS system is the IRE. The geometry of the IRE is a function of both the nature of the sample (in this instance usually a small quantity of liquid) and the IRS technique employed. It is not intended to review each of these techniques with reference to the detailed optical require- ments and the reader is referred to the references in each of the preceding sections for such detail. However it is useful to pick out some of the important factors required to generate an evanescent wave at a liquid/wave- guide interface.

A large variety of IREs have been developed (Harrick 1967), the simplest of which is the single reflection prism (Fig. 33.1a). The prism is generally used at a fixed angle (θ) and liquids can be held at the reflecting surface using a flow cell arrangement (Van Wagenen *et al.* 1982). The single reflection prism is generally not sufficiently sensitive to allow the absorption measure- ments of immunoassays. However, fluorescence emission spectra can be obtained in right-angle geometry (Fig. 33.1c) (e.g. Van Wagenen *et al.* 1982). To obtain the high sensitivity required for ATR immunoassay, multiple internal reflection elements (e.g. plates, Fig. 33.1b) must be employed as increasing the number of reflections, N, enhances the contrast of a measured spectrum (see eqn 33.6). N is increased by making the plate longer and/or thinner (see eqn 33.4). Because of practical considerations both the length (L) and the thickness (T) are limited. For example, with fast reactions the plate has to be sufficiently long to maximize sensitivity, but short enough to avoid filling delays. Also as T decreases, the aperture is reduced limiting the usable light power. When T is so small that light focused on the entrance aperture fills it completely, there may be problems designing a flow cell as gaskets may contact the light-guiding area. In this case the gasket is a poten- tial source of light loss through absorption, refraction and scattering. Also the gasket may 'creep' during the test protocol. The design shown (Fig. 33.6) avoids contact of light with the gasket as light is introduced via a quartz prism which directs light away from the gasket. Variable-angle prisms were used to allow changing the angle of incidence (θ) and thus control the depth of pene- tration (see eqn 33.3) such that the spectral contrast can be optimized. In this case θ is varied by the linear movement or rotation of a mirror (Fig. 33.6).

A very promising multiple-reflection IRE is the optical fibre. Here light is

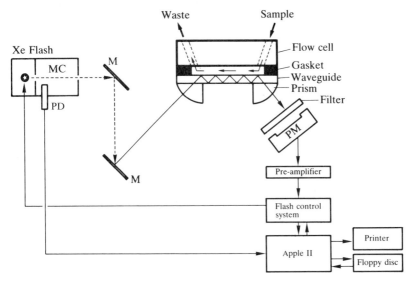

Fig. 33.6 Diagram of instrumental layout used for measuring immunoassays with a multiple-internal reflection plate. PM, photomultiplier tube; PD, photodiode; MC, monochromator; M, mirrors.

also introduced at angles exceeding θ_c and propagates down the fibre by total internal reflection. Optical fibres manufactured for communication purposes are available with high optical quality. Fibres have been employed as IREs because of their small diameter and (potentially) unlimited length so that the effective number of reflections can be very large. To allow the fibre surface to interact with the sample, the protective coating and cladding have to be removed from communication fibres. This is relatively easy for plastic clad silica fibres (available core diameters from 0.2 to 1.5 mm, e.g. Fibre Optique Industries, Pithiviers, France). Figure 33.7 shows a diagram of a fibre optic assembly (0.6 mm diameter fibre core). Within a cylindrical flow cell, the straight fibre is exposed to the sample solution along an active length of 64 mm. The fibre ends are held in metal fittings and polished. The lenses define the angular aperture of around 70°.

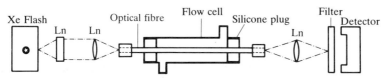

Fig. 33.7 Diagram of fibre optic assembly with flow cell and light coupling optics. Ln are lenses.

Other types of fibres, e.g. quartz long distance communications fibres (core diameters 5–50 μm), are difficult to handle because of their small size. Similarly, because of the complicated optical paths and mode conversion effects introduced by bends in longer optical fibres, calculations of angles of incidence and hence effective thickness cannot easily be made. There are no data available using such fibres for immunoassay.

33.3.2 SPR

The experimental components used for SPR are similar to those of an ATR system (*c.f.* Fig. 33.3 and Fig. 33.1a). The IREs are prisms coated on the sensor side with a thin film of metal (e.g. Au, Ag, Al, or Cu).

Several methods are used for detecting the plasmon resonance. The most common is measuring the attenuated reflection as a function of incident angle at a fixed wavelength, or as a function of wavelength for a fixed incident angle. Using the former approach angular shifts of the order of 0.0005° have been measured (Eagen and Weber 1979). By choosing an angle of incidence half-way down the reflectance minimum and measuring the intensity of reflected light at that constant angle, changes in the refractive index of the order of 0.00001 were detected (Liedberg *et al.* 1983). Another method measures the scattered light coupled out by the surface roughness of the film as a function of incident angle at a fixed wavelength. This geometry is similar to that of TIRF with right-angle detection see Fig. 33.1d).

33.3.3 Material requirements

When choosing an optical material for IREs consideration is given to optical characteristics (refractive index, wavelength transmission limits, surface quality), mechanical characteristics (hardness, brittleness), and chemical characteristics (inertness, adsorption efficiency of proteins, availability of chemical groups for covalent protein attachment).

The optical and mechanical aspects are discussed in detail by Harrick (1967) who gives refractive indices and transmission limits for a number of materials for the visible, UV, IR, and far IR regions. Opposing surfaces must be flat and parallel, and the surface quality must be sufficiently high to minimize light losses due to scattering. Hardness and brittleness are also important to reduce physical handling problems both in producing an IRE and particularly in preparation of the surface.

The material most often used for IREs is quartz due to its well-characterized optical qualities and chemical properties. The transmission range of quartz is from 0.3 to 2.3 μm allowing measurements to be carried out in the UV visible and near-IR. Also its hardness makes it a relatively simple material to handle. Quartz IREs are readily available as microscope slides and as the core material of plastic clad silica fibres.

33.3.4 Antibody immobilization

The immobilization of one of the immunological binding pair to the IRE surface is a key factor in the successful development of an IRS device for immunoassay. Not only does the immobilization procedure have to meet requirements of reproducibility, high protein uptake, retained immunological activity, and stability, but also the procedure should not cause chemical or physical changes to the surface which cause undesirable optical effects (e.g. light scattering). Since most references apply to quartz or glass, this discussion will be limited to these materials. Also the following paragraphs will deal with protein immobilization only. Many non-protein antigens may be immobilized to IRE surfaces but the individual chemistries are not generally applicable and will not be discussed here. However, one approach is to coat the IRE with a protein (e.g. bovine serum albumin) and then couple with non-protein antigen to this material (Kronick and Little 1975).

The two most commonly used techniques for protein immobilization to silica surfaces are physical adsorption and covalent coupling. There is a considerable quantity of information available on this subject (e.g. see reviews: Weetall, 1972, 1974, 1975; Jakoby and Wilchek 1974; Mosbach 1976) and the reader is referred to these reviews for detailed procedures as the following discussion will be limited to general principles.

Physical adsorption of proteins to silica surfaces is probably the result of weak-force interactions such as charge–charge (e.g. ionic, salt-bridge) or hydrogen-bonding (Messing 1976). However, protein-glass bonds formed during adsorption are so tight that strong acids or alkalis are required to recover the proteins. Physical adsorption as a method of preparing antibody-coated IREs, is attractive as proteins can be rapidly adsorbed onto glass surfaces in a single-step procedure. Also adsorption does not change the optical characteristics. A typical approach would be to first wash the surface clean using one or a combination of strong acids, detergents, organic solvents, and physical means such as heating to high temperatures or ion bombardment (Burghardt and Axelrod 1981; Thompson 1982). A hydrophobic surface can then be generated (e.g. by washing the IRE in dichloromethyl silane, (Elwing and Stenberg 1981)) which encourages protein adsorption. The IRE is then dipped into the appropriate protein solution for several hours, washed to remove unbound materials, incubated with a non-specific protein solution to block unfilled binding sites, washed again and stored dry at 4°C until required.

Adsorption of proteins to surfaces is a complex and generally poorly understood reaction (Lundström 1983). As such, the reproducible preparation of antibody-coated waveguides is based on an empirical 'trial and error' approach. Also with such a technique it is difficult to predict the configuration of proteins on the surface and the effects of the surface adsorption event on availability of antibody-binding sites. Covalent linkage is a more attractive approach as it potentially allows control of the immobilization reaction and a certain degree of predictability.

Most work of the covalent attachment of proteins to silica has been carried out with controlled pore glass particles as the solid-phase (for a review see Lynn 1975). The most often used and probably the simplest technique is reaction with silane coupling agents. These agents are monomeric silanes which have organo-functional groups at one end and groups which will react with the inorganic surface at the other end. A typical agent is γ-aminopropyltriethoxy silane (APTS) which can be used in a three-step procedure to attach proteins to silica. In an aqueous acid environment, the ester groups on the ATPS hydrolyse to form hydroxyls which can then condense with surface silanol groups to give a silica surface with pendant amino groups (eqn 33.7).

$$\text{Silica} - \text{SiOH} + C_2H_5\text{-OSi}(OC_2H_5)_2(CH_2)_3 \rightarrow$$
$$\text{Silica} - \text{SiOSi}(OC_2H_5)_2(CH_2)_3 - NH_2 \tag{33.7}$$

In a second step, the amino groups are used to prepare an active aldehyde intermediate by reaction with glutaraldehyde at neutral pH (eqn 33.8):

$$\text{Silica} - NH_2 + OCH(CH_2)_2CHO \rightarrow \text{Silica} - N = CH(CH_2)_2CHO \tag{33.8}$$

The final step is to react the aldehyde group with a primary amine on the protein to form an imine coupling (eqn 33.9):

$$\text{Silica} - CHO + NH_2\text{-Antibody} \rightarrow \text{Silica} - CH = N\text{-Antibody} \tag{33.9}$$

This approach has been applied to antibody immobilization to planar quartz and optical fibre IREs (Sutherland *et al.* 1984). However, there are a number of potential pitfalls with this chemistry as the optimum concentration of active aldehyde groups on the surface falls within a narrow useful range. A minimum number of these groups is required for a stable antibody preparation and too many groups can result in multiple site attachment of the antibody to the surface resulting in decreased immunological activity. Also, the silane layer thickness is a function of many factors including pH, temperature, time of reaction, surface area, silane concentration and the reaction solvent (Schroder *et al.* 1967). Thus for reproducibility each of these factors has to be considered when optimizing the coupling conditions.

Alternative covalent systems have been used with reflectance devices (Nilsson and Mosbach 1981). Here silicon wafers are alkylated, hydroxyl groups formed on the alkylated surface and then activated with tresyl chloride. The tresylate groups can then react with amino groups on the protein. This technique was applied to the attachment of concanaualin A to silicon surfaces which were subsequently reacted with *S. aureus* cells and the reaction monitored by ellipsometry (Mandenius *et al.* 1984).

33.4 Application of IRS devices to immunoassay: review

33.4.1 ATR

ATR has been applied to monitoring immunoassays in the IR, visible, and ultra-violet (UV) regions of the spectrum. The basic principles are those given in the above theoretical section, where sequestration of antigen (or antibody) at a waveguide/liquid interface is measured as an attenuation of the internally reflected light beam. This attenuation is wavelength specific for an absorption maximum characteristic of one of the immunological binding pair.

In the IR region, Ockman (1978) has applied ATR to monitoring the reaction between various sera albumin and their respective antisera, at a germanium/liquid interface. The waveguide surface was initially immersed in the antigen solution and the transmission spectra obtained of the absorbed protein layer. Following reaction with dilute antiserum solution, bound antibody was identified as a decrease in transmission in the Amide 1 region (1650 cm^{-1}). The change in optical density was 0.032 units for specific binding (antibody-antigen reaction) while only 0.007 units for non-specific binding (in the absence of antigen).

This end-point approach, though successful, does not make full use of the potential of IRS methods which should allow continuous monitoring of the immunological reaction as it occurs. Such continuous analyses have been carried out in both the visible and UV regions.

As a model system, the reaction between haemoglobin and rabbit anti-haemoglobin antisera has been monitored by ATR techniques (Sutherland, R. M., Kulhanek, E., and Dähne, C., unpublished observations). In this case, rabbit antibodies were covalently immobilized to the surface of a quartz microscope slide, then reacted with different concentrations of haemoglobin. By monitoring the attenuation of the reflected light at 410 nm (absorption maximum of haemoglobin) a three-phase response curve was obtained (Fig. 33.8). Initially a base-line was established in the presence of a physiological buffer system containing sheep serum (to minimize non-specific binding of haemoglobin to the surface). On introduction of the antigen solution there was an immediate fall in transmission due to light absorption by haemoglobin molecules diffusing within the penetration depth of the evanescent wave. This was followed by a rapid attenuation in transmission as the haemoglobin molecules were bound close to the surface by antibodies. Finally as the antibody-binding sites became saturated the rate of change in transmission became smaller. Also shown are the results of repeating the experiment with BSA replacing the antibody of the surface. The difference between the two curves represents specific binding of haemoglobin at the surface.

Similar results were found in the UV region, where specific antibody-

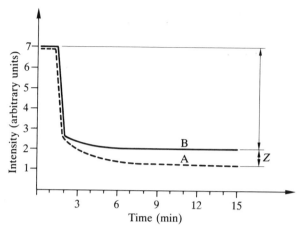

Fig. 33.8 Injection of a 10 mg/ml solution of haemoglobin into the flow cell illustrated in Fig. 33.6, with (A) rabbit anti-haemoglobin (code No. A118, Dako Immunoglobulins, Copenhagen, Denmark) attached to the surface of the multiple-internal reflection element by a covalent bond (aminopropyltriethoxy silane; see text for details) and (B) bovine serum albumin similarly immobilized to a second IRE. The reaction was monitored by the attenuation of the internally-reflected light beam at 410 nm. The difference between the two curves (Z) is taken to represent specific binding (Sutherland, R. M., Kulhanek E. and Dähne, C.; unpublished observations).

binding of the chemotherapeutic agent methotrexate, at a quartz/liquid interface was monitored by the attenuation in transmission at 310 nm (Sutherland *et al.* 1984*a*). Plots of the absolute change in transmission, or rate of change in transmission, gave a dose-response curve with an estimated limit of detection of 0.3 μmol/l for methotrexate.

33.4.2 TIRF

The original work using TIRF to measure immunological reactions was carried out by Kronick and Little (1973, 1975, 1976). Haptens such as phenylarsonic acid or morphine were immobilized to the surface of a quartz microscope slide via a hapten-albumin conjugate. FITC-labelled antibody which bound to the immobilized hapten could be detected by exciting fluorescence at the surface using the evanescent wave. On addition of free hapten to the bulk of solution the binding rate of the FITC-antibody to the surface was reduced in a concentration-dependent fashion. Monitoring the fluorescence at right-angles (see Fig. 33.1c), a minimum detection limit of 0.2 μmol/l of morphine could be measured.

Thompson (1982) used a similar approach combined with fluorescence correlation spectroscopy. Here, dinitrophenol was immobilized to a quartz slide via adsorbed albumin. Both monovalent and bivalent rhodamine-labelled antibodies were reacted with the surface-bound hapten. One of the main findings associated with these experiments was the large proportion of non-specifically bound antibody (up to 60% of the signal). One conclusion by Thompson was that the high level of non-specific binding prevented continuous measurement of the kinetics of binding.

Sutherland *et al.* (1984*b*) used the reaction between human IgG and two antisera to investigate some of the critical factors which might overcome the non-specific binding in a TIRF system, with FITC as the label. Preliminary experiments demonstrated that inclusion of an excess (200-fold relative to the antibody) of an appropriate non-immune animal serum into the buffer, reduced non-specific binding of the FITC-labelled protein to acceptable levels. The non-immune serum probably competed for and saturated, non-specific binding sites on the waveguide surface and similarly competitively inhibited non-specific interactions between the fluorescently-labelled proteins and immobilized antibody.

With assay buffers containing the animal serum, experiments were carried out to partially optimize a two-site immunofluorometric assay for IgG. A sheep anti-IgG was covalently immobilized to the waveguide surface and reacted with standard solutions of human IgG. Following rinsing with buffer to remove unbound materials, the reaction between immunologically immobilized IgG and a second (FITC-labelled) rabbit antibody was monitored by measuring the right-angle fluorescence. The signal generated using this approach is illustrated (Fig. 33.9), with an explanation of the various signal components. The detection limit of this system was approximately 5 μg/ml of IgG.

All these TIRF systems are based on right-angle detection of the fluorescent signal. It is also possible to use in-line detection (Fig. 33.1d). Sutherland *et al.* (Sutherland *et al.*, 1984*a*; Dähne *et al.* 1984) have used both quartz microscope slides and quartz optical fibres to monitor the two-site immunofluoremetric assay for IgG, with signal detection in the in-line mode. After a ten minute incubation with the FITC-antibody, these authors achieved a detection limit of 3.0 and 1.5 μg/ml of IgG, for the slide and fibre waveguides respectively.

33.4.3 SPR

Nylander *et al.* (1982) first suggested using SPR as a technique to monitor immunological reactions and measured changes as small as 30 Å in the thickness of an immunological layer. In later work, using the reaction between human IgG and anti-IgG as a model, the antigen was absorbed to the silvered surface of a prism to give a layer of protein up to 50 Å thick (Liedberg 1983). Various concentrations of anti-IgG were individually incubated with the absorbed protein and the shift in resonance angle monitored at a fixed angle

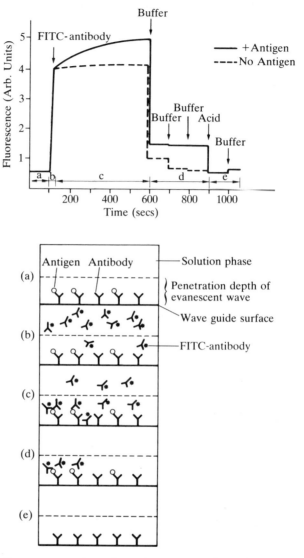

Fig. 33.9 Binding curves and a schematic representation of a two-site immuno-fluoremetric assay monitored by TIRF. Here the IRE surface is coated with antibody raised against Human IgG. Following reaction of the coated waveguide with a standard IgG solution (10 μg/ml) a second FITC-labelled anti-IgG is allowed to react with the immobilized antigen and the reaction monitored by measuring fluorescence either at right-angles (Sutherland *et al.* 1984*b*) or with an in-line geometry (Sutherland *et al.*, 1984*a*). (a) The prepared IRE; (b) Signal generated by unbound FITC-anti-IgG within the d_p of the evanescent wave; (c) Binding curves of FITC-anti-IgG in the

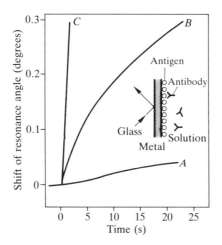

Fig. 33.10 Shift in resonance angle versus time for three different anti-IgG concentrations; A, B and C for 2, 20 and 200 μg/ml of IgG respectively. The shift is measured as an increase of the reflected light intensity. The insert illustrates the antibody binding event. (After Liedberg *et al.* 1983, with permission).

of incident light (Fig. 33.10). Using this approach the SPR system could differentiate between 0.2 and 2 μg/ml of antibody after 25 s.

Flanagan and Pantell (1984) carried out similar experiments using human serum albumin as the antigen. The initial layer of antigen was 60 Å thick. This increased to 200 Å following reaction with the antibody, corresponding to up to 4 layers of IgG. The authors suggested that there was a proportion of non-specifically adsorbed antibodies in this second layer, although cooperativity between antibodies may also be a factor.

33.5 Discussion

The potential for IRS devices in immunoassay is based on the ability to monitor surface reactions without major interferences from the bulk of solution components. The above examples demonstrate the basic feasibility of this concept. However considerable effort will have to be expended before these systems achieve their potential in both research and commercial environments. Two factors are essential to the successful application of IRS devices for immunoassays. Firstly, antibodies as reagents allow the specific measurement of a compound (or family of compounds) from complex

---

presence (solid line) and absence (dotted line) of antigen; (d) Washing away unbound materials leaving the specific (solid line) and non-specifically (dotted line) bound signals; (e) Disrupting the immunologically bound materials with dilute acid.

mixtures such as found in clinical samples (e.g. serum, plasma, or whole blood). Considerable research has been carried out to adopt procedures in conventional immunoassays, which do not compromise this specificity. However, with IRS devices some new (and old) problems may occur. Each of the three systems, ATR, TIRF, and SPR, will be sensitive to non-specific optical and/or physical interactions at the interface. Both the ATR and TIRF techniques will be sensitive to substances which will optically interfere within the penetration depth of the evanescent wave (e.g. substances which absorb at the same wavelength, or quench fluorescence). All three systems, but probably SPR in particular will be sensitive to physical non-specific binding events at the interface. As SPR is essentially a measure of an effective layer thickness and refractive index, non-specific changes in either of these parameters may be difficult to differentiate from specific binding events.

A second factor is that conventional immunoassays involving a separation step (i.e. they are heterogeneous), are *sensitive* systems which can detect compounds down to femtomolar levels using radioactive labels. As yet the ATR, TIRF, and SPR available data show detection limits of approximately 1 μmol/l, 10 nmol/l, and <5 nmol/l. For assay systems approaching the sensitivity of conventional heterogeneous assays significant progress will have to be made.

One key element in enhancing sensitivity is the use of multiple internal reflections, as yet applied to ATR and TIRF systems. Using thinner and/or longer waveguides is rewarded by an increase in sensitivity factorially related to the number of reflections (see eqn 33.6). In this context, optical fibres seem to offer considerable advantages, as they can be manufactured very thin and, with appropriate optics, effectively all of the external surface is used as the sensor. One design for a disposable optical fibre diagnostic is available (Fig. 33.11). There may be, however, a considerable challenge in manufacturing such a device.

If adequate sensitivity can be achieved with reasonable assay times (minutes, not hours) IRS devices such as optical fibres may find application *in vivo* as well as *in vitro*. Optical fibres have already enjoyed success in the fields of surgery, optical investigative procedures (e.g: endoscopy), and *in vivo* analyses (e.g. blood pressure, blood oxygenation, pH). This is due to their small size and physical flexibility as well as light guiding properties. Used as *in vivo* IRS devices for immunoassay other characteristics may be equally important, such as being chemically inert, the possibility of construction from biocompatible materials and fabrication costs may be sufficiently low to warrant a disposable system. Two major problems will have to be addressed however. Firstly how to sterilize such a disposable without destroying the antibodies. Secondly how to use the device to continuously monitor. The latter problem is due to the affinity constant of the antibody which makes binding effectively irreversible, and thus the sensor may not

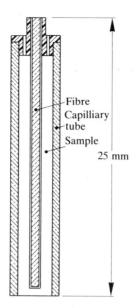

Fibre
Capilliary
tube
Sample

25 mm

Fig. 33.11 A disposable fibre optic IRE for TIRF immunoassays. The fibre is held within a capillary tube which allows easy sampling (the sample is introduced into the cuvatte by capillary action) and the capillary tube accurately defines the sample volume. (After Hirschfeld 1984, with permission).

respond rapidly to changes (reductions) in antigen concentration.

One of the aims for an IRS device applied to optical immunoassays must be to supply easier test systems useful in clinical diagnostics. Due to the lack of a separation step such assay systems could be operated in a relatively non-skilled environment. To achieve this potential requires not only suitable IRE development but also design of a simple photometric system in which to carry out measurements. As yet such a system is not readily available.

In conclusion, IRS devices for immunoassays have great potential for both research and commercial applications as they offer a relatively flexible and simple alternative to the conventional immunoassay. As such, appropriate development could result in these devices entering the *in vitro* and even *in vivo* diagnostics market place.

Acknowledgements

We wish to acknowledge the technical assistance of Mr. A. Bregnard in the development of the fibre optic system, Mr. A. Ringrose for his considerable efforts in designing the planar waveguide system used in our laboratories, and also to Ms. E. Kulhanek for her work on the haemoglobin system reported above. We also acknowledge the help of the secretarial staff of the Battelle Institute for their typing of this manuscript under a tight schedule and especially Ms. J. Boëque for proof-reading the manuscript. Some of the above work was financially supported by Prutec Ltd.

References

Amzel, L. M. and Poljak, R. J. (1979). Three-dimensional structure of immuno-globulins. *Ann. Rev. Biochem.* **48**, 961–98.

Azzam, R. M. A. and Bashara, N. M. (1977). *Ellipsometry and polarized light*. North Holland Publishing Co., Amsterdam.

Baier, R. E. and Dutton, R. C. (1969). Initial events in interaction of blood with a foreign surface. *J. Biomed. Mater. Res.* **3**, 191–206.

Brash, J. L. and Lyman, D. J. (1971). Adsorption of proteins and lipids to non-biological surfaces. In *The chemistry of biosurfaces* (ed. M. L. Hair). pp. 177–232. Marcel Dekker Inc., New York.

Burghardt, T. P. and Axelrod, D. (1981). Total internal reflection/fluorescence photobleaching recovery study of serum albumin adsorption dynamics. *Biophys. J.* **33**, 455–68.

Carniglia, C. K., Mandel, L. and Drexhage, H. (1972). Absorption and emission of evanescent photons. *J. Opt. Soc. Amer.* **62**, 479–86.

Carter, T., Dähne, C. and Place, J. F. (1982). European Patent Application EP 81-801255.0.

Dähne, C., Sutherland, R. M., Place, J. F. and Ringrose, A. R. (1984). Detection of antibody-antigen reactions at a glass-liquid interface: a novel fibre-optic sensor concept. In *OFS '84*, Proceedings of the second international conference on optical fibre sensors (eds. R. T. Kersten and R. Kist) pp. 75–9. VDE-Verlag, Berlin.

Dandliker, W. B., Hsu, M.-L. and Vanderlaan, W. P. (1980). Fluorescence polarization immuno/receptor assays. In *Immunoassays, clinical laboratory techniques for the 1980's* (eds. R. M. Nakamura, W. R. Dito, and E. S. Tucker) pp. 65–88. Alan R. Liss Inc., New York.

Deaton, C. D., Maxwell, K. W., Smith, R. S. and Creveling, R. L. (1976). The use of laser nephelometry in the measurement of serum proteins. *Clin. Chem.* **22**, 1465–70.

Eagen, C. F. and Weber, W. H. (1979). Modulated surface-plasmon resonance for adsorption studies. *Phys. Rev.* **19**, 5068–82.

Elwing, H. and Stenberg, M. (1981). Biospecific bimolecular binding reactions — a new ellipsometric method for their detection, quantitation and characterization. *J. Immunol. Methods.* **44**, 343–9.

Flanagan, M. T. and Pantell, R. M. (1984). Surface plasmon resonance and immunosensors. *Electr. Lett.* **20**, 968–70.

Gendreau, R. M., Winters, S., Leininger, R. I., Fink, D., Hassler, C. R. and Jakobsen, R. J. (1981). Fourier-transform infrared spectroscopy of protein adsorption from whole blood: *Ex-vivo* dog studies. *App. Spectr.* **35**, 355–7.

—— Leininger, R. I., Winters, S. and Jacobsen, R. J. (1982). Fourier-transform infrared spectroscopy for protein-surface studies. In *Biomaterials: Interfacial phenomena and applications* (eds. S. L. Cooper and N. A. Peppas). *Adv. Chem. Ser.* **199**, 371-95.

Harrick, N. J. (1967). *Internal reflection spectroscopy.* Interscience, New York.

—— and Loeb, G. I. (1973). Multiple internal reflection spectrometry. *Anal. Chem.* **45**, 687-91.

Hauge, P. S. (1980). Recent developments in instrumentation in ellipsometry. *Surf. Sci.* **96**, 108-40.

Hirschfeld, T. E. (1984). US Pat. 4,447,546.

Jakoby, W. B. and Wilchek, M. (eds.) (1974). Affinity techniques. *Methods in enzymology.* Vol. 34, Academic Press, New York.

Kirkham, K. E. and Hunter, W. M. (1971). *Radioimmunoassay methods.* Churchill-Livingstone, Edinburgh.

Kretschmann, E. and Raether, H. (1968). Radiative decay of non-radiative surface plasmons excited by light. *Naturforschung* **123**, 2135-6.

Kronick, M. N. and Little, W. A. (1973). A new fluorescent immunoassay. *Bull. Amer. Phys. Soc.* **18**, 782.

Kronick, M. N. and Little, W. A. (1975). A new immunoassay based on fluorescence excitation by internal reflection spectroscopy. *J. Immunol. Methods.* **8**, 235-42.

—— (1976). US Pat. No. 3,939,350.

Lee, E. H., Benner, R. E., Fenn, J. B. and Chang, R. K. (1979). Angular distribution of fluorescence from liquids and monodispersed spheres by evanescent wave excitation. *App. Opt.* **18**, 862-70.

Liedberg, B., Nylander, C. and Lundström, I. (1983). Surface plasmon resonance for gas detection and biosensing. *Sens. Act.* **4**, 299-304.

Lok, B. K., Cheng, Y.-L. and Robertson, C. R. (1983*a*). Protein adsorption on cross-linked polydimethylsiloxane using total reflection fluorescence. *J. Coll. Interf. Sci.* **91**, 104-116.

—— (1983*b*). Total internal reflection fluorescence: A technique for examining interaction of macromolecules with solid surfaces. *Ibid.* 87-103.

Lundström, I. (1983). Surface physics and biological phenomena. *Phys. Scrip.* **T4**, 5-13.

Lynn, M. (1975). Inorganic support intermediates: covalent coupling of enzymes on inorganic supports. In *Immobilized enzyme, antigens, antibodies and peptides* (ed. H. H. Weetall) pp. 1-48. Marcel Dekker Inc., New York.

Mandenius, C. F., Welin, S., Danielsson, B., Lundström, I. and Mosbach, K. (1984). The interaction of proteins and cells with affinity ligands covalently coupled to silicon surfaces as monitored by ellipsometry. *Anal. Biochem.* **137**, 106-14.

Messing, R. A. (1976). Adsorption and inorganic bridge formation. In *Immobilized enzymes* (ed. Mosbach, K.). *Methods in enzymology.* Vol. 64, pp. 148-169. Academic Press, New York.

Mosbach, K. (ed.) (1976). *Immobilized enzymes. Methods in enzymology.* Vol. 64. Academic Press, New York.

Muller, R. H. (1976). Present state of automatic ellipsometers. *Surf. Sci.* **56**, 19-36.

Nilsson, K. and Mosbach, K. (1981). Immobilization of enzymes and affinity ligands to various hydroxyl group carrying supports using highly reactive sulfonyl chlorides. *Biochem. Biophys. Res. Comm.* **102**, 449-57.

Nylander, C., Liedberg, B. and Lund, T. (1982). Gas detection by means of surface plasmon resonance. *Sens. Actuators* **3**, 79–88.

Ockman, N. (1978). The antibody–antigen interaction at an aqueous-solid interface: a study by means of polarized infrared ATR spectroscopy. *Biopolymers* **17**, 1273–84.

Pockrand, I., Swalen, J. D., Gordon, I. and Philpott, M. R. (1977). Surface plasmon spectroscopy of organic monolayer assemblies. *Surf. Sci.* **74**, 237–44.

Poste, G. and Moss, C. (1972). Antigen-antibody reactions in thin films. In *The study of surface reactions in biological systems by ellipsometry.* (eds. G. Poste and C. Moss). pp. 206–231. Pergamon Press, New York.

Raether, H. (1977). Surface plasmon oscillations and their applications. In *Physics of thin films, advances in research and development* (eds. G. Haas and M. H. Francombe) Vol. 9, pp. 145–261. Academic Press, New York.

Raether, H. (1980). Excitation of plasmons and interband transitions by electrons. *Springer, tracts in modern physics.* Vol. 88. Springer–Verlag, Berlin, FRG.

Rothen, A. (1974). Ellipsometric studies of thin films. In *Progress in surface and membrane science* (eds. J. F. Danielli and M. D. Rosenberg), pp. 81–118. Academic Press, New York.

Schroder, M. E., Lerner, I. and D'Oria, F. J. (1967). Radioisotope study of coupling agents in reinforced plastics. *Med. Plast.* **45**, 195–7.

Soini, E. and Hemmilä, I. (1979). Fluoroimmunoassay: Present status and key problems. *Clin. Chem.* **25**, 353–61.

Sutherland, R. M., Dähne, C., Place, J. F. and Ringrose, A. R. (1984*a*). Optical detectin of antibody-antigen reactions at a glass liquid interface. *Clin. Chem.* **30**, 1533–8.

—— (1984*b*). Immunoassays at a quartz-liquid interface: theory, instrumentation and preliminary application to the fluorescent immunoassay of human immuno-globulin G. *J. Immun. Methods.* **74**, 253–65.

Thompson, N. L. (1982). Ph.D. Thesis. University of Michigan.

—— Burghardt, T. P. and Axelrod, D. (1981). Measuring surface dynamics of biomolecules by total internal reflection fluorescence with photobleaching recovery and correlation spectroscopy. *Biophys. J.* **33**, 435–54.

Van Wagenen, R. A., Rockhold, S. and Andrade, J. D. (1982). Probing protein adsorption: total internal reflection intrinsic fluorescence. In *Biomaterials. Interfacial phenomena and applications* (eds. S. L. Cooper and N. A. Peppas). Adv. Chem. Ser. Vol. 199, pp. 351–370.

—— Zdasiuk, B. J. and Andrade, J. D. (1980). Total internal reflection fluorescence studies of albumin adsorption onto quartz. *Org. Coat. Plast. Chem.* **42**, 749–53.

Watkins, R. W. and Robertson, C. R. (1977). A total internal reflection technique for the examination of protein adsorption. *J. Biomed. Mater. Res.* **11**, 915–38.

Weetall, H. H. (1972). *Insolubilized antigens and antibodies. The chemistry of biosurfaces* (ed. M. L. Hair) Vol. 2, pp. 597–631. Marcel Decker, New York.

—— (1974). Preparation, characterization and application of enzymes immobilized on inorganic supports. *Adv. Exp. Med. Biol.* **42**, 191–2.

—— (ed.) (1975). *Immobilized enzymes, antigens, antibodies and peptides: Preparation and characterization.* Marcel Decker, New York.

34

Laser light scattering and related techniques

*ROBERT J. G. CARR, ROBERT G. W. BROWN, JOHN
G. RARITY, and DAVID J. CLARKE*

34.1 Introduction

Optical techniques have long been central to the analysis of biological systems and have been utilized in a wide variety of forms. In recent years however the development of new and improved optical measuring mechanisms has been stimulated by the advent of the laser. The laser celebrated the 25th anniversary of its invention last year (1985). Since its appearance it has contributed to some of the most significant advances in measurement science, not only in the research laboratory environment but increasingly in the industrial world as well.

The laser is a light source having unique properties. It is an emitter of collimated monochromatic light that can range from X-ray to microwave (Maser) through the ultra-violet, visible, and infra-red regions of the electromagnetic spectrum. The light output can be continuous or pulsed, with pulse lengths as short as a few femto-seconds (approx. 1×10^{-15} seconds) and output powers ranging from microwatts to megawatts and more. Laser light can be highly polarized (electric field oscillation in one direction only) and is usually coherent both temporally and spatially (with field phase relationships being maintained along the beam and across it). There exists an extensive introductory literature describing the wide range of lasers that exist, their properties, and their uses (e.g. Brown 1980; Forsyth and Wilson 1980; Butler 1980; O'Shea *et al.* 1979).

Laser light is very different from that produced by conventional white light sources. Its properties can be individually exploited to great effect in laser based optical measuring systems.

Concomitant with the development of the laser has been the development of optical fibre technology (Cherin 1983), the major thrust being provided by the rapid expansion of the optically-based data communications systems industry. It is the combination of laser and fibre optic technologies that promises the development of a new generation of optical sensors that will enable the application of many of the existing optical techniques to situations previously considered inaccessible or inappropriate to optically based analysis or monitoring.

Optical fibre sensors can be broadly classified into two categories: intrinsic and extrinsic sensors (Culshaw 1983). Intrinsic sensors, in which propagation time (or group or phase velocity), intensity, or polarization state of the light propagating down a fibre may be modulated by an external force acting on the fibre, have been developed for a wide range of physical variables, for example, electrical, magnetic, and acoustic fields; angular and linear displacement; velocity and acceleration; temperature, pressure, stress, and strain; and radiation dosage (Dakin 1983; Moore and Ramer 1983; Giallorenzi *et al.* 1982; Brenci *et al.* 1983). Extrinsic sensors merely use the fibre as a means of transporting light to and from an analyte- or measurand-sensitive element or volume that is responsible for modifying one or more properties of the light used (such as intensity, state of polarization, or wavelength).

Fibre sensors have been demonstrated for the measurement of an increasing number of analytes in biological systems *in vitro* (Milanovich *et al.* 1984) and *in vivo* (Vurek 1984) by modification of the fibre cladding or tip (endface) with analyte sensitive reagents or biological molecules. The advantages afforded by such remote optical fibre sensors, for example, miniaturization, electromagnetic immunity, ruggedness, physical flexibility, and ease of manipulation, longevity, and the ability to be multiplexed, have ensured a great deal of interest in their development (Cramp and Ried, 1982*a,b*; Carter *et al.* 1982). Thus, a wide variety of optical techniques lend themselves to fibre optic technology including the monitoring of light scattered by particles.

Light scattering has long been a method of deriving information as to the size, shape, and composition of particles but new more powerful techniques of analysis by laser light scattering have been developed in recent years that are likely to find application in fibre optic sensors. This chapter will discuss how laser light can be scattered by particles (macromolecules to micro-organisms and above in size) and used to study particle size, shape, velocity, and other potentially useful parameters for the biotechnologist and further how these techniques may be configured into biosensors.

34.2 Theory and principles of light scattering

A laser beam possesses a number of properties that can be very stable with time and easily and specifically modified by interactions with many types of materials, the modification to be later analysed with high precision. Some of these properties were mentioned in the introduction; intensity, mono-chromaticity phase, polarization, etc. The specific advantages afforded by the laser concern its ability to yield these parameters to often better than 1% accuracy and yet non-intrusively (i.e. without perturbation or contamination).

The scattering of light by small particles has been the subject of intensive study for over 100 years and is well reviewed and documented (e.g. van de Hulst 1957; Kerker 1969; Huglin 1972; Degiorgio 1983; Ford 1985). For bio-sensing we are primarily concerned with three types of light scattered by particles in particular size ranges and all of which are interrelated: 1) Rayleigh scattering, 2) Rayleigh–Gans–Debye scattering, and 3) Mie scattering.

34.2.1 Rayleigh scattering

Consider a particle of dielectric (non-absorbing) material illuminated by collimated plane polarized light of wavelength much greater than its largest dimension.

The incident field induces a fluctuating dipole moment, and the particle acts as a point source radiating equally in all directions perpendicular to the dipole axis. The intensity (I) scattered by the particle in this plane is inversely proportional to the fourth power of the wavelength (λ) and directly proportional to the square of the particle volume (V):

$$I \propto \frac{V^2}{\lambda^4} \, .$$

In the plane parallel with the induced dipole (thus parallel to the incident field polarization) the scattered intensity falls to zero at 90 degrees (longitudinal waves are not supported in electromagnetic radiation). The scattering polar diagram is shown schematically in Fig. 34.1a.

34.2.2 Rayleigh–Gans–Debye (RGD) scattering

For particles of dimension comparable with the wavelength of incident light and refractive index close ($\Delta n \leqslant 0.05$) to its surrounding medium, i.e. a weak scatterer, the polar diagram shows less light is scattered back towards the original laser beam (Fig. 34.1b). The forward lobe can be crudely explained by saying that in all but the forward direction destructive interference occurs between light scattered from different points within the particle. Thus

$$I \propto \frac{V^2}{\lambda^4} \cdot P(K)$$

where $P(K)$ contains the interference effects caused by the particle dimension approaching that of the incident wavelength, and the angular dependence arises through the scattering vector modulus

$$|K| = \frac{4\pi n_1}{\lambda} \sin \frac{\theta}{2}$$

where n_1 is the refractive index of the medium surrounding the particle, λ is the wavelength of the incident beam, and θ is the angle of measurement

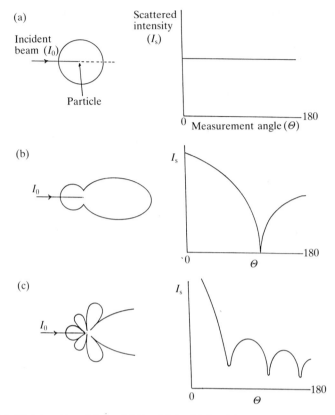

Fig. 34.1 Light scattered from (a) Rayleigh, (b) Reyleigh–Gans–Debye, and (c) Mie scattering particles. For each type of scatterer the light scattered (I_s) in the plane perpendicular to the plane of polarization of the incident beam (I_0) is shown both graphically (intensity as a function of measuring angle, θ) and as a polar scattering diagram (representing the change in scattering intensity over $\pm 180°$ circle for a symmetrical particle).

relative to the beam direction. At certain values of θ, no light is scattered, thus forming a pattern of scattering lobes surrounding the particle. Many biological macromolecules and micro-organisms are RGD scatterers, close to forward scattering angles (Koch 1968).

34.2.3 Mie scattering

For particles of dimension $\geqslant 1$ wavelength and of arbitrary refractive index the Mie theory of light scattering is required. Again forward scattering predominates (Fig. 34.1c) with several lobes appearing in the polar diagram. The minima are more numerous but less pronounced than in the RGD approximation due to phase differences in the distribution of the light energy around the particles surface.

The Mie formula for scattering intensity involves a series summation of complex functions thus its evaluation is computationally expensive. However, there exist two simpler analytic approximations that are often applicable. The Fraunhofer approximation (Swithenbank *et al.* 1977) assumes opaque particles of size larger than the wavelength of light giving rise to the familiar Airy pattern. The anomalous diffraction (van de Hulst 1957) approximation assumes similar size but particle refractive index close to that of the medium.

34.3 Light scattering techniques

There are a large number of techniques that utilize light scattering as a sensing or analysis method. Such methods may be conveniently divided into two areas: (1) static light scattering in which the magnitude of scattering is observed directly and (2) dynamic light scattering in which one observes the timescale of intensity fluctuations (which is not dependent on the absolute or relative magnitudes of intensity).

34.3.1 Static light scattering techniques

Static light scattering techniques include those long familiar to biochemistry, microbiology, and other biological disciplines. Thus turbidimetry, nephelometry, and angular or differential light scattering, etc. are well characterized and common methods for the routine analysis of biological samples and need not be discussed in any detail here. Whilst there remain many aspects of light scattering that are poorly defined, e.g. the problem of arbitrary shape (Drain *et al.* 1982; Williams 1984; Walters 1980), in general, light scattering has proved an important means of particle sizing (Barth and Sun 1985; Barth, 1984) and characterization.

Latimer (1982) has comprehensively reviewed the theoretical and practical aspects of light scattering by cells and subcellular particles and Koch (1968) and Koch and Ehrenfeld (1968) have similarly discussed extensively light scattering by bacteria and bacteria-like particles. Light scattering principles are widely employed, for instance in the assessment of nuclear and cellular morphology using forward and perpendicular scatter in a flow cytometry system (Benson *et al.* 1984), in the characterization of epidermal cells using goniometric techniques (Bruls and van der Luen 1984) and laser light is used in the monitoring or erythrocyte deformation (Plasek and Marik 1982). Lasers have also been used in the rapid screening of urine for the presence of bacteriuria in a nephelometer configuration (Bayardelle and Richet 1984).

Multi- and low-angle laser scattering techniques may be used in the study of particles as small as lysozyme (Jones and Midgley 1984) or can be used as the basis of a technique for the characterization of microbial populations, i.e. angular or differential light scattering (Wyatt 1975*a*,*b*). More recent techniques, such as circular intensity differential scattering (CIDS; Salzman and Gregg, 1984) have evolved from established light scattering techniques, in this case circular dichroism (e.g. Kreuger 1984), and are under commercial development (Mesa Diagnostics Inc., San Diego) for application in the area of clinical microbiology. Related to the above are the electric dichroism and electric birefringence techniques (Oakley *et al.* 1982) used to study samples orientated in electric field. Such techniques have been widely employed in the study of DNA by, for instance, Yamaoka and his co-workers (Yamaoka and Yueda 1982; Charney and Yamaoka 1982; Yamaoka and Matsuda 1980, 1981).

Lasers are also used in Raman and Brillouin scattering (Yariv 1975). Brillouin scattering arises from the interaction of monochromatic (laser) light with thermally driven acoustic fluctuations within the substance being studied. Brillouin scattering and its use in the analysis of biological systems has been discussed by Randall and Vaughan (1979). Raman scattering arises from the interaction of coherent laser incident light with the substance and results in frequency shifted scattered light containing information about the molecular vibrational properties of the sample. Raman spectroscopy has been used in the *in vitro* study of many biological molecules (Theophanides 1979; Prescott *et al.* 1984) and, more recently, of intact cells (Jeannesson *et al.* 1983).

A further technique that has been employed primarily in the size analysis of inorganic and mineral (e.g. fuel sprays, exhaust gas) particles of size greater than 1 μm is diffraction light scattering usually assuming the Fraunhofer approximation. Its potential as a technique of use to the biotechnologist makes it worthy of further discussion. In diffraction light scattering it is usual to direct an expanded parallel beam of continuous laser light through an ensemble of static or moving macromolecules or particles and analyse the spatial distribution of diffracted optical energy by means of detecting the back focal plane intensity distribution (or Airy pattern) of a lens symmetrically centred in the laser beam and focussed at infinity (Fig. 34.2). For a monodisperse sample the particle radius (a) is

$$a = \frac{0.61\,\lambda f}{r}$$

where λ is the wavelength of the incident beam, f is the focal length of the (Fourier) lens, and r is the radius of the first zero intensity ring in the diffracted intensity distribution. For polydisperse samples, the particle size distribution is calculated through a Bessel function transformation. Particle sizes from approx 1 μm to 1 mm can be measured, particularly at high concentration, using this technique (Bertero and Pike 1983; Swithen-

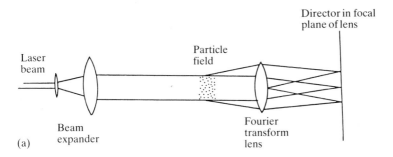

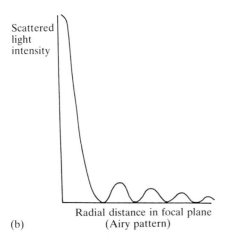

Fig. 34.2 Fraunhofer diffraction.
(a) The optical arrangement for the measurement of Fraunhofer diffraction.
(b) The intensity distribution (Airy pattern) of scattered light. The diameter of the diffraction patterns is inversely proportional to the diameter of the particles and the pattern obtained is independent of the position of the particle and therefore measurements can be made with particles moving at any speed.

bank *et al.* 1981; Nakadate and Saito 1983; Bayvel and Jones 1981; Bayvel *et al.* 1982).

34.3.2 Dynamic light scattering techniques

The above text briefly describes a few examples of the various analytical methods based on static light scattering from macromolecules and particles. When, however, an ensemble or particles are suspended in a medium they will move under Brownian motion and the various elemental scatterings from each particle will, at some distance from the scatterers, add to some resultant intensity and phase. As the particles move randomly under Brownian motion, so the observed intensity at a distance fluctuates with time; the time-scale of the intensity fluctuations carries information about the particles' size and size distribution. This is the basis of dynamic light scattering or intensity fluctuation spectroscopy (also known as quasi-elastic light scattering spectro-scopy or QELS). Examination of the timescales of intensity fluctuations is performed by electronic signal processors to yield particle size distribution, etc. When the processor is a photon-correlator, as is nowadays usual, then the technique is referred to as photon-correlation spectroscopy or PCS.

There is a second branch of dynamic light scattering which may be useful as a sensor technique, for example, in the measurement of fluid flow inventory. In this variation, known as laser Doppler velocimetry (LDV), one or more laser beams probe the liquid containing the macromolecular or particulate suspension. The geometry of the laser beams and the light detection systems depend on the nature of the sample to be analysed and is discussed later. The timescales of intensity fluctuations from translating particles measures their velocity.

These new and powerful techniques, PCS and LDV, are potentially of great value to the study of biological macromolecules and particles. Although comparatively recent in their development and unfamiliar to most biotechnologists, there exist several commercially produced instruments that are beginning to be used in the biological sciences.

34.3.2.1 Photon correlation spectroscopy   PCS is now a well developed and widely used research technique in which (Fig. 34.3) light from a con-tinuous, visible laser beam is directed through an ensemble of macromole-cules or particles in suspension and moving under Brownian motion. Some of the laser light is scattered by the particles and this scattered light is collected by a lens and detected by a photo-detector which generates an electrical signal proportional to the light intensity detected. The light intensity fluctuates on a timescale related to the time taken for a particle to diffuse a distance

---

Fig. 34.3 Photon correlation spectroscopy.
(a) Diagram showing the component parts of a PCS system.
(b) Graphical representation of the fluctuation in light intensity at the detector which contains information about the diffusion rates of the scattering particles.
(c) The fluctuating intensity is converted into a train of standardized photoelectron pulses in the photon counting detector. Peaks in intensity are thus observed as 'bunching' in the pulse train.
(d) The signal arising from the above is fed into a digital correlator and used to generate a correlation function. The diagram shows a normalized correlation function from which the background has been removed. See text for details.

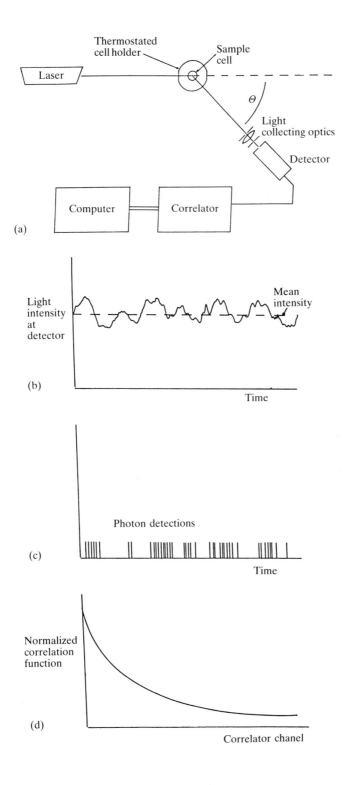

(a)

Laser

Thermostated cell holder

Sample cell

Θ

Light collecting optics

Detector

Computer

Correlator

(b)

Light intensity at detector

Mean intensity

Time

(c)

Photon detections

Time

(d)

Normalized correlation function

Correlator chanel

comparable with the light wavelength which in turn is related to the particle's hydrodynamic radius.

The electrical output signal of the photo-detector is analysed in a hard-wired digital signal processor known as a photon correlator. The correlator computes averages of the signal compared (multiplied) with itself at different delay times, i.e. the autocorrelation function of the signal. The autocorrelation function formed is characteristically an exponentiality decaying function of delay time. The decay time is related to the size of the macromolecules or particles that scattered the light. By examining in detail the multi-exponentiality of the decaying function, a particle size distribution, etc. can be constructed.

Mathematically we can briefly describe the above process in the following manner. For Brownian diffusing spherical macromolecules of identical size the electric field correlation function of the scattered light is

$$g^{(1)}(\tau) = e^{(-D_t K^2 \tau)} e^{(i\omega_0 \tau)}$$

where D_t is the translational diffusion coefficient of the macromolecules, τ is the delayed time, K is the modulus of the scattering vector, related to the angle of observation, and ω_0 is the angular frequency of the incident light. When large numbers of scatterers are illuminated, then the measured intensity auto-correlation function can be shown to be

$$g^{(2)}(\tau) = 1 + B\,|g^{(1)}(\tau)|^2 = 1 + B\,e^{(-2D_t K^2 \tau)}$$

which is an exponentially decaying function. But D_t is related to the particles size by the Stokes–Einstein equation

$$D_t = \frac{k\,T}{6\pi\eta\,R_h}$$

where k is Boltzmann's constant, T is temperature, η is viscosity, and R_h is the hydrodynamic radius of the macromolecules. Thus R_h can be estimated from the autocorrelation function.

Of course, most particulate systems are polydisperse and thus $|g^{(1)}(\tau)|$ is the sum of many differing exponential decays. Formally $|g^{(1)}(\tau)|$ is given by

$$|g^{(1)}(\tau)| = \int_0^\infty G(\Gamma)\, e^{-\Gamma\tau}.d\Gamma$$

where the linewidth $\Gamma = D_t K^2$ and $G(\Gamma)$ is the intensity weighted linewidth distribution. An estimate of $G(\Gamma)$ and hence the radius distribution can be obtained using Laplace inversion techniques (Bertero *et al.* 1985). Further details of this and the rigorous details behind the simple statements above can be found in Cummins and Pike (1974, 1977), Earnshaw and Steer (1983), Schulz–DuBois (1983), Dahneke (1983), Chen *et al.* (1982), Pusey and

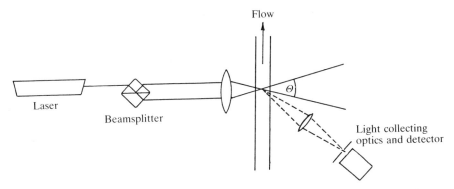

Fig. 34.4 Laser Doppler velocimeter. Schematic representation of a laser Doppler velocimeter (incoherent detection arrangement). See text for details.

Vaughan (1975), and Pecora (1985).

Typically PCS operates successfully with between 10^4 and 10^{10} particles/ml with particle sizes between a few nanometers and a few microns.

34.3.2.2 Laser Doppler velocimetry Laser velocimetry is a non-instrusive means of acquiring velocity information through analysis of light intensity fluctuations caused by the motion of macromolecules or particles through one or more laser beams. Velocities ranging from μm/min to km/sec may be studied with the same instrumentation. A schematic diagram of a typical experimental arrangement is shown in Fig. 34.4. Continuous, plane polarized monochromatic laser light of typically a few mW power is usually divided into two equally intense beams that are focussed and made to intersect in the fluid flow at a position where the velocity is varying. Small particles embedded in the flow traversing the laser beam intersection region (or measuring volume) scatter laser light from each laser beam with a slightly different Doppler frequency due to their motion relative to the different laser beam directions. Some of the scattered laser light is collected by a lens placed at some convenient position and the light 'beats' at a photodetector. The electrical signal from the photodetector contains frequency information linearly related to the difference in the Doppler frequencies created from each laser beam and thus to the particles velocities. In the event of strong light signals, analogue signal processing such as frequency analysis may be employed to yield an estimate of the velocities of the particles; much weaker optical signals are processed by a photon-correlator as in PCS, to obtain the velocity statistics. With the optical geometry described the flow velocity component measured is that one perpendicular to the bisector of the angle between the propagating laser beams and lying in the plane that the laser beams define. It may be shown that for statistically independent orthogonal velocity fluctuations the form of the intensity auto-correlation function is

$$g^{(2)}(\tau) = \int_0^\infty P(u) \exp\left(\frac{-u^2\tau^2}{r^2}\right)\left[1 + \frac{m^2}{2}\cos\left(\frac{2\pi u\,\tau}{s}\right)\right] du$$

where $g^{(2)}(\tau)$ is as above, r is the laser beam radius, m is a measure of the signal contrast, u is the velocity component measured, $P(u)$ its probability distribution, and $s(=\lambda/2\sin(\theta/2))$ is the fringe spacing. The correlogram takes the form of an exponentially decaying cosine oscillation, and when $u^2\tau^2 \ll r^2$:

$$g^{(2)}(\tau) = 1 + \frac{m^2}{2} \times \int_0^\infty P(u)\cos\left(\frac{2\pi u\tau}{s}\right) du.$$

$P(u)$ and the velocity statistics may be recovered through a Fourier-cosine transformation (Cummins and Pike 1977; Schulz–DuBois 1983).

34.4 Applications of dynamic light scattering techniques in biology

Although dynamic light scattering techniques have yet to become widespread in research· into the structure and behaviour of biological systems, a significant amount of work has been carried out that demonstrates their potential usefulness in a wide range of applications. Reviews of the impact and use of light scattering and dynamic light scattering techniques in the biological sciences have been written by Cummins (1973, 1983) and Burchard and Cowie (1972). Bloomfield (1985) has discussed more recent studies in this area. Steer (1983b) has discussed aspects of biological samples that must be considered in light scattering studies. Sample preparation (Tabor 1972) and the effect of choice of solvent and other factors such as temperature and pressure have been discussed (Huglin 1972) as have fundamental aspects of light scattering by biological polyelectrolyte macromolecules (Eisenberg 1973; Nagasawa and Takahashi 1972) and their study by QELS (Giordano and Micali 1983).

Light scattering from polymers is the subject of a comprehensive text (Huglin 1972) within which a variety of aspects pertinent to biological samples have been considered. The use of Raman and Brillouin scattering in the study of bulk polymers and solutions of polymers as well as amorphous polymers and polymer gels has been discussed by Vaughan (1982) and Patterson (1985).

The study, by light scattering techniques, of polymerization, association, and aggregation of molecules and macromolecules has been concisely reviewed by Elias (1972). Similarly, interparticle interactions and their effect on particle size determination by QELS has been discussed using micelles and charged proteins as examples (Nicoli and Dorshow 1983; Mazer 1985). Interestingly, in the analysis of the immunoassay reaction by dynamic light scattering methods PCS has been shown to offer a 100-fold increase in sensitivity compared to conventional assays (1000-fold when in the inhibition mode). It compares in sensitivity with radioimmunoassay but uses no radiochemicals and can be performed rapidly with no prior separation of bound and unbound antigen yet work with sample volumes as low as 1 μl (Cohen and Benedek 1975; von Schulthess *et al.* 1976*a*,*b*). Rate nephelometry, using laser light has been employed in the measurement of the immunoprecipitin reaction (Sittampalam and Wilson 1984*a*) and light scattering techniques in general for the immunoassay of specific proteins has been reviewed by Price *et al.* (1983). Other optical immunoassay techniques have been developed that employ light reflected at an angle close to the pseudo-Brewster angle off an antibody coated silicon surface (Arwin and Lundstrom 1985).

The study of gels and gel formation has been carried out using dynamic light scattering methods (Vaughan 1982; Tanaka, 1985). Sellen (1983) studied the diffusion of macromolecules within gels, in particular the movement of dextran fractions within calcium alginate and agarose gels. DNA has been studied using dynamic light scattering techniques (Cummins and Pike 1974; Dahneke 1983; Earnshaw and Steer 1983). The changes in comformation of superhelical DNA following binding of intercalating agents was studied by Newman (1984). 'Splitting' of the diffusion coefficient of dinucleosomal-sized DNA (average 375 base pairs) following lowering of ionic strength has been demonstrated using QELS implying that the simple relating of hydrodynamic radius to particle size may lead to erronous conclusions regarding the conformation of the molecule (Schmitz and Lu 1984). Folding-unfolding transitions of ribonuclease A over a range of temperatures has been studied with dynamic light scattering (Wang *et al.* 1980) indicating that the technique should prove valuable in protein denaturation and DNA melting studies. The ability of PCS and other light scattering techniques to give data as to the size and shape of particles has been shown to be of value in the determination of tertiary structure and behaviour of macromolecules of biological importance for instance, gramicidin (De La Torre *et al.* 1984) and bovine factor VIII (Gabriel *et al.* 1984).

The animal protein collagen has been studied by the use of PCS (Hwang and Cummins 1982) employing a new approach to simultaneously determine both the length of the molecule and the viscosity of the solution. Proteoglycan aggregates were studied using both static and dynamic light scattering (Shogren *et al.* 1983) and data obtained of the size of the molecule was shown to be in good agreement with that obtained by electron microscopy, indicating that the aggregates visualized by electron microscopy were also present in solution.

Studies on micelle structure and interaction are well suited to dynamic light scattering techniques (Corti *et al.* 1983; Hirsch *et al.* 1984; Mazer 1985) and in particular casein micelles have been investigated (Griffin and Anderson 1983; Holt 1983). Vesicles have been studied using similar techniques (Steer 1983*a*; Yu 1983).

The ease with which it is possible to obtain a regular and monodisperse sample of the tobacco mosaic virus (TMV) has meant that it has become, like the polystyrene spheres, a model object for dynamic light scattering studies. More realistically, polydisperse solutions of TMV virus were characterized by PCS (Wiltzius 1982), the technique demonstrating its ability to resolve a number of different sized particles simultaneously. A number of other virus particle suspensions have been characterized (Pusey *et al.* 1974; Camerini–Otero *et al.* 1974).

Typing of blood cells has been attempted (Arefyev *et al.* 1978) using the immunoprecipitation technique and was found to be an improvement on the methods employed routinely in forensic science. The chemotactic response of *Escherichia coli* cells has been followed using PCS and other light scattering methods (Wang and Chen 1983). Similarly the phototactic response of unicellular motile algae was analysed by PCS (Ascoli and Frediani 1983). The motility of another type of cell, spermatozoa, has also received considerable attention, concise reviews of which may be found in Volochine (1983) and Earnshaw (1983).

The motility of cells and micro-organisms in general and its study by dynamic light scattering techniques has been reviewed in detail by Boon (1983) and its biochemical significance discussed by Klein (1984). Carlson (1983) and Carlson and Fraser (1973) have shown PCS to be a powerful technique in the understanding of cellular movement of a very specific kind, muscle contraction.

The transient electrical birefringence of rodlike molecules when combined with QELS studies has been used to determine the length and diameter of such particles. Flexible molecules can be characterized in terms of their persistence length from deviations from rodlike behaviour (Eden and Elias 1983; Elias and Eden 1981).

Using these methods the electric polarizability and behaviour of DNA fragments and the filamentous virus Pf3 were studied. Jennings (1972) has reviewed electric field light scattering and, more recently, Ware (1983) has discussed in some detail the application of LDV in electrophoretic light scattering and its use in studies on living cells, vesicles, and counterion condensation onto DNA. Automated instruments combining LDV and electrophoretic systems are now available and have been used to study, with high precision and rapidity (1–3 min), the electrophoretic mobility of leucocytes and lymphocytes from several types of leukemia (Steiner *et al.* 1985) and similarly, the electrophoretic mobility of erythrocytes (Spendley *et al.* 1982).

34.5 The future

The development of increasingly sophisticated and sensitive instrumentation in conjunction with advances in the understanding of the theoretical complexities underlying many light scattering techniques have resulted in a large variety of instruments being made available to the researcher in the biological sciences. Whilst the routine analysis and study of more complex biological parameters would benefit from advances in instrument and component design and performance in general it is the very complexity and variability of biological systems that commonly results in poor reproducibility or ambiguous data. These problems are common to all of the light scattering and other light interaction techniques discussed above, and highlight the problem of attaining specificity from optical measurements of biological processes.

Methods of achieving specificity include the use of labels, either chemical (e.g. fluorescent) or biochemical (e.g. polystyrene spheres attached to monoclonal material), and the use of combinations of the various sensing techniques. One such multi-parameter light scattering technique, a derivative of CIDS currently under development, (Salzmann and Gregg 1984) would appear to be a promising technique for differentiating between different species and types of microbial cell. As the technique is dependent on the analysis of the total cell genome it may prove problematical to ensure reproducibility of data from a given cell type in the face of the significant effects that variations in the cell growth medium and conditions and time of sampling can have on the conformation and composition of nuclear material. In addition, it remains to be seen whether the presence of cell wall and virus coat material which represent significant refractive index boundaries will obscure the genetic material within the cell.

When changes in the scattered light are used as a means of monitoring the formation of aggregates, e.g. the nephelometric or PCS determination of the immunoprecipitin reaction, the presence of significant amounts of scattering background material as is found in serum samples can seriously reduce the sensitivity of the techniques. Sensitivity can be enhanced by the attachment to the reactants of optical markers such as polystyrene spheres of relatively large size (100 nm) that scatter more than the macromolecules of interest or the background (Price *et al.* 1983). However, in monoepitopic antibody–antigen reactions only lower order aggregates are formed, thus with high background, more specific labelling (e.g. fluorescence) is required.

Light scattering techniques may find future areas of new application in such industrial activities as fermentation process monitoring, immunoassays (as discussed earlier), down-stream processing and other areas where monitoring of small particles is required.

The techniques outlined above, have, in the most part, evolved from early, crude optical instruments and theories into the powerful analytical tools that exist today in the research laboratory. However, even these modern systems are restricted in their application to certain situations due to the bulky and inflexible nature of their component parts (e.g. lenses, mirrors, apertures, etc.). Most of the techniques suffer from a number of disadvantages of which the most obvious include high cost, large size, the requirement for frequent and careful calibration (except PCS), a high level of operator expertise and more often than not, a considerable amount of sample preparation and manipulation. Samples are usually analysed, with varying degrees of rapidity, one at a time and often only after some isolation or separation stage. Furthermore, it is usual for the sample in question to have to be taken from the site of interest to the created instrument.

Optical fibres offer a revolutionary alternative to existing optical designs. It may prove possible to adapt a large number of the above techniques to configuration possessing several major additional advantages. Modern fibre optics are capable of maintaining a particular polarization state or phase (a prerequisite for many optical analytical mechanisms), allow remote (many kilometers distant) points of analysis or measurement and are of increasingly low cost. Their small diameter enable very small sample volumes to be addressed (down to 1 μl) with a consequent saving in possibly expensive reagents. This small size makes possible *in situ* or *in vivo* measurements previously considered inaccessible and their inherent inertness and ruggedness makes optical fibres suitable for hostile environments.

The capacity for a large number of optical fibres to be addressed very rapidly by a single source and detector by means of optical multiplexers should reduce significantly the 'cost per channel' of a multi-analyser instrument. The simultaneous revolution in microelectronics and the advent of smaller, faster, and more powerful electronic 'chips', particularly through uncommitted array and VSLI technologies, will accelerate the development of true biosensor devices capable of employing the most sophisticated of current optical techniques.

One can therefore conceive of analysis equipment being centrally positioned within a laboratory or, more importantly, an industrial environment and coupled to perhaps hundreds of light scattering, parameter gathering sensors remotely positioned. Examples of such a labour un-intensive philosophy are starting to emerge, e.g. 1 km distance remote laser Raman, to and from a measuring point, via multimode fibres and using material embedded into porous glass welded to the far (measurement) end of the fibre (Hirschfield 1984).

Already PCS and LDV have been successfully demonstrated in millimeter dimension packages via optical fibres and we confidently expect demonstration of other light scattering techniques via fibres also.

References

Arefyev, I. M., Barsegyanz, L. O., Eskov, A. P. and Alekseyeva, V. I. (1978). Species diagnosis of blood by light beating spectroscopy. *Sudebno-Meditsinskaya Ekspertiza Moskva* **21(1)**, 26–7.

Arwin, H. and Lundstrom, I. (1985). A reflectance method for quantification of immunological reactions on surfaces. *Anal. Biochem.* **145**, 106–12.

Ascoli, C. and Frediani, C. (1983). The application of laser light scattering to the study of photo-responses of unicellular motile algae. In *The application of laser light scattering to the study of biological motion* (eds. J. C. Earnshaw and M. W. Steer) NATO Advances Science Institute Series, Vol. 59, pp. 669–679. Plenum Press, New York.

Barth, H. G. (1984). *Modern methods of particle size analysis*. Wiley, New York.

—— and Sun, S.-T. (1985). Particle size analysis. *Anal. Chem.* **57**, 151R–175R.

Bayardelle, P. and Richet, H. (1984). Rapid screening for bacteriuria with a laser nephelometer. *Can. J. Microbiol.* **30**, 927–9.

Bayvel, L. P. and Jones, A. R. (1981). *Electromagnetic Scattering and its Application*, Applied Science Publishers, Englewood, N.J.

—— Eisenklam, P. and Jones, A. R. (1982). A light scattering instrument for measuring drop sizes in the range of 0.1 to 1000 μm. *Proc. 2nd. Int. Conf. on Liquid Atomization and Spray Systems (ICLASS)*, June 1982, Wisconsin. pp. 329–34.

Benson, M. C., McDougal, D. C. and Coffey, D. S. (1984). The application of perpendicular and forward light scattering to assess nuclear and cellular morphology. *Cytometry*, **5**, 515–22.

Bertero, M. and Pike, E. R. (1983). Particle size distributions from Fraunhofer diffraction. I. An analytical eigenfunction approach. *Optica Acta* **30(8)**, 1043–9.

—— Brianzi, P., Pike, E. R., DeVilliers, G., Lan, K. H. and Ostrowsky, N. (1985). Light scattering polydispersity analysis of molecular diffusion by Laplace transform inversion of weighted spaces. *J. Chem. Phys.* **15**, 1551–6.

Bloomfield, V. A. (1985). Biological applications. In *Dynamic light scattering* (ed. R. Percora), pp. 363–416. Plenum Press, New York.

Boon, J. P. (1983). Motility of living cells and micro-organisms. In *The application of laser light scattering to the Study of Biological Motion* (eds. J. C. Earnshaw and M. W. Steer) NATO Advanced Science Institute Series, Vo. 59, pp. 561–606. Plenum Press, New York.

Brenci, M., Falciai, R. and Scheggi, A. M. (1983). Multimode optical fibre sensors. *Alta Frequenza*, **52(3)**, 206–8.

Brown, D. C. (1980). Solid state lasers. In *Applied optics and optical engineering*. Vol. VI, Chapter 1. Academic Press, New York.

Bruls, W. A. G. and van der Luen, J. C. (1984). Forward scatter properties of human epidermal layers. *Photochem. and Photobiol.* **40(2)**, 231–42.

Burchard, W. and Cowie, J. M. G. (1972). Selected topics in biopolymeric systems. In

Light scattering from polymer solutions, (ed. M. B. Huglin) pp. 725–787. Academic Press, New York.

Butler, J. F. (1980). Semiconductor diode lasers. In *Applied optics and optical engineering* Vol. VI, Chapter 3, pp. 53–88. Academic Press, New York.

Camerini-Otero, R. D., Pusey, P. N., Koppel, D. E., Schaefer, D. W. and Franklin, R. M. (1974). Intensity fluctuation spectroscopy of laser light scattered by solutions of spherical viruses: R17, $Q\beta$, BSV, PM2 and T7. I. Diffusion coefficients, molecular weights, solvation and particle dimensions. *Biochemistry* 13(5), 960–72.

Carlson, F. D. (1983). The application of quasi-electric light scattering to the study of muscular contraction. In *The application of laser light scattering to the study of biological motion* (eds. J. C. Earnshaw and M. W. Steer) NATO Advanced Science Institute Series, Vol. 59, pp. 405–58. Plenum Press, New York.

—— and Fraser, A. (1973). Intensity fluctuation autocorrelation studies of the dynamics of muscle contraction. In *Photon correlation and light beating spectroscopy* (eds. H. Z. Cummins and E. R. Pike) NATO Advanced Study Institute Series B: Physics, Vol. 3, pp. 519–38. Plenum Press, New York.

Carter, T., Dahne, C. and Place, J. F. (1982). Method for the determination of species in solution with an optical waveguide, Eur. Pat. Appl. No. 0-075-353.

Charney, E. and Yamaoka, K. (1982). Electric dichroism of deoxyribonucleic acid in aqueous solutions: electric field dependence, *Biochemistry* 21, 834–42.

Chen, S-H., Chu, B. and Nossal, R. (eds.) (1981). *Scattering techniques applied to supramolecular and non-equilibrium systems*. Plenum Press, New York.

Cherin, A. H. (1983). *An introduction to optical fibres*, McGraw-Hill, New York.

Cohen, R. J. and Benedek, G. B. (1975). Immunoassay by light scattering spectroscopy. *Immunochemistry* 12, 349–51.

Corti, M., Minero, C. and Degiorgio, V. (1983). Light scattering from micellar solutions — proposal for a light scattering standard. In *The application of laser light scattering to the study of biological motion* (eds. J. C. Earnshaw and M. W. Steer) NATO Advanced Science Institute Series, Vol. 59, pp. 333–46. Plenum Press, New York.

Cramp, J. H. W. and Ried, R. F. (1982a). Sensitive optical fibre, Eur. Pat. Appl. No. 0-062-443.

—— (1982b). Optical Fibre Sensor, Eur. Pat. Appl. No. 0-061-884.

Culshaw, B. (1983). Optical systems and sensors for measurement and control. *J. Phys. E: Sci. Instrum.* 16, 978–86.

Cummins, H. Z. (1973). Application of light beating spectroscopy to biology. In *Photon correlation and light beating spectroscopy* (eds. H. Z. Cummins and E. R. Pike) NATO Advanced Study Institute Series B: Physics, Vol. 3, pp. 285–330. Plenum Press, New York.

—— (1983). Analysis of diffusion of biological molecules by quasi-elastic light scattering. In *The application of laser light scattering to the study of biological motion* (eds. J. C. Earnshaw and M. W. Steer) NATO Advanced Science Institute Series, Vol. 59, pp. 171–208. Plenum Press, New York.

—— and Pike, E. R. (eds.) (1974). *Photon correlation and light beating spectroscopy*. NATO Advanced Study Institute Series B: Physics, Vol. 3, Plenum Press, New York.

—— (eds.) (1977). *Photon correlation spectroscopy and velocimetry*. Plenum Press, New York.

Dahneke, B. E. (1983). *Measurement of suspended particles by quasi-elastic light scattering*. John–Wiley, New York.

Dakin, J. P. (1983). Optical fibre sensors — principles and applications. *Fibre Optic '83, SPIE* **374**, 172–82.

Degiorgio, V. (1983). Physical principles of light scattering. In *The application of laser light scattering to the study of biological motion* (eds. J. C. Earnshaw and M. W. Steer). NATO Advanced Science Institutes Series, Vol. 59, Plenum Press, New York.

De La Torre, G., Martinez, M. C. L. and Tirado, M. M. (1984). Dimensions of short, rodlike macromolecules from translational and rotational diffusion coefficients. Study of the gramicidin dimer. *Biopolymers* **23**, 611–15.

Drain, L. E., Smith, N. and Dalzell, W. (1982). Aspects of light scattering by spherical particles. *Proc. Max. Born Conf., SPIE* **369**, 610–15.

Earnshaw, J. C. (1983). Laser doppler velocimetry in a biological context. In *The application of laser light scattering to the study of biological motion* (eds. J. C. Earnshaw and M. W. Steer) NATO Advanced Science Institute Series, Vol. 59, pp. 123–142. Plenum Press, New York.

—— and Steer, M. W. (eds.) (1983). *The application of laser light scattering to the study of biological motion*. NATO Advanced Science Institutes Series, Series A, Life Sciences, Vol. 59. Plenum Press, New York.

Eden, D. and Elias, J. G. (1983). Transient electrical birefringence of DNA restriction fragments and the filamentous virus Pf3. In *Measurement of suspended particles by quasi-elastic light scattering* (ed. B. E. Dahneke) pp. 401–38. John–Wiley, New York.

Eisenberg, H. (1973). Light scattering intensity studies in multicomponent solutions in biological macromolecules. In *Photon correlation and light beating spectroscopy* (eds. H. Z. Cummins and E. R. Pike) NATO Advanced Study Institute Series B: Physics, Vol. 3, pp. 151–68. Plenum Press, New York.

Elias, H.–G. (1972). The study of association and aggregation via light scattering. In *Light scattering from polymeric solutions* (ed. M. B. Huglin) pp. 397–457. Academic Press, New York.

—— and Eden, D. (1981). Transient electric birefringence study of the persistence length and electric polarizability of restriction fragments of DNA. *Macromolecules* **14**, 410–19.

Ford, N. C. (1985). Light scattering apparatus. In *Dynamic light scattering* (ed. R. Pecora) pp. 7–57. Plenum Press, New York.

Forsyth, J. M. and Wilson, J. (1980). Gas lasers. *Applied optics and optical engineering*, Vol. VI, Chapter 2, pp. 29–52. Academic Press, New York.

Gabriel, D. G., Kirkland, J. A., Cooper, H. A. and Wagner, R. H. (1984). A light scattering study of bovine factor VIII. *Arch. Biochem. Biophys.* **231**(1), 189–92.

Giallorenzi, T. G., Bucaro, J. A., Dandridge, A., Sigel, G. H., Cole, J. H., Rashleigh, S. C. and Priest, R. G. (1982). Optical fibre sensor technology. *IEEE J. of Quantum Elect.* **QE18**(4), 626–65.

Giordano, R. and Micali, N. (1983). Correlation spectroscopy and structural properties of macromolecular solutions. In *The application of laser light scattering*

to the study of biological motion ...Milanovich entries

to the study of biological motion (eds. J. C. Earnshaw and M. W. Steer) NATO Advanced Science Institute Series, Vol. 59, pp. 221–6. Plenum Press, New York.

Griffin, M. C. A. and Anderson, M. (1983). Laser light scattering study of the fractionation of casein micelles in skim milk by controlled pore glass chromatography. In *The application of laser light scattering to the study of biological motion* (eds. J. C. Earnshaw and M. W. Steer) NATO Advanced Science Institute Series, Vol. 59, pp. 347–52. Plenum Press, New York.

Hirsch, E., Candau, S. and Zana, R. (1984). Micellar structure and inter-micellar interactions in solutions in tetradecyltrimethylammonium bromide in the presence of l-pentanol: light scattering and viscosity study. *J. Coll. Interface Sci.* **97(2)**, 318–26.

Hirschfield, T. (1984). Proc. ICO '84, Sapporo, Japan. *Remote analysis by fibre optics.*

Holt, C. (1983). Structural studies on bovine casein micelles by laser light scattering. In *The application of laser light scattering to the study of biological motion* (eds. J. C. Earnshaw and M. W. Steer) NATO Advanced Science Institute Series, Vol. 59, pp. 353–8. Plenum Press, New York.

Huglin, M. B. (ed.) (1972). *Light scattering from polymer solutions.* Academic Press, New York.

Hwang, J. S. and Cummins, H. Z. (1982). Dynamic light scattering studies of collagen. *J. Chem. Phys.* **77(2)**, 616–21.

Jeannesson, P., Manfait, M. and Jardillier, J. (1983). A technique for laser Raman spectroscopy studies of isolated cell populations. *Anal. Biochem.* **129**, 305–9.

Jennings, B. R. (1972). Electric field light scattering. In *Light scattering from polymer solutions* (ed. M. B. Huglin) pp. 527–79. Acad. Press. New York.

Jones, M. N. and Midgley, P. J. W. (1984). Low angle laser light scatter from surfactant solubilised biological macromolecules. Proc. 607th Meeting ('Lasers in Biochemistry') *Biochem. Soc. Trans.* **12**, 625–7.

Kerker, M. (1969). *The scattering of light and other electromagnetic radiation.* Academic Press, New York.

Klein, R. A. (1984). The measurement of motility in micro-organisms and its biochemical significance. Proc. 607th Meeting ('Lasers in Biochemistry') *Biochem. Soc. Trans.* **12**, 627–30.

Koch, A. L. (1968). Theory of the angular dependence of light scattering by bacteria and similar-sized biological objects. *J. Theoretical. Biol.* **18**, 133–56.

—— and Ehrenfeld, E. (1968). The size and shape of bacteria by light scattering measurements. *Biochim. Biophys. Acta* **165**, 262–73.

Korpel, A. (1980). Acousto-optics In *Applied optics and optical engineering* Vol. VI, Chapter 4, pp. 89–109. Academic Press, New York.

Kreuger, R. (1984). The effect of low ionic strength on the circular dichroic spectrum of chromatin and nucleosomal subunits. *Arch. Biochem. Biophys.* **231(1)**, 183–8.

Latimer, P. (1982). Light scattering and absorption as methods of studying cell population parameters. *Ann. Rev. Biophys. Bioeng.* **11**, 129–50.

Mazer, N. A. (1985). Laser light scattering in micellar systems. In *Dynamic light scattering* (ed. R. Pecora) pp. 305–46. Plenum Press, New York.

Milanovich, F. P., Hirschfeld, T. B. and Wang, F. T. (1984). Clinical measurements using fibre optics and optrodes. In *Novel optical fibre techniques for medical applications. SPIE*, Vol. **494**, pp. 18–24.

Moore, E. L. and Ramer, O. G. (eds.) (1983). *Fiber optic and laser sensors.* Proceedings of SPIE, Vol. 412, April 5–7, 1983, Arlington, Virginia, USA.

Nagasawa, M. and Takahashi, A. (1972). Light scattering from polyelectrolyte solutions. In *Light scattering from polymer solutions* (ed. M. B. Huglin) pp. 672–723. Academic Press, New York.

Nakadate, S. and Saito, H. (1983). Particle size distribution measurement using a Hankel transform of a Fraunhofer diffraction spectrum. *Optics Letts.* **8(11)**, 578–80.

Newman, J. (1984). Dynamic light scattering as a probe of superhelical DNA-inter-calating agent interaction. *Biopolymers* **23**, 1113–19.

Nicoli, D. F. and Dorshow, R. B. (1983). Effects of interparticle interactions on particle size determinations by QELS. In *Measurement of suspended particles by quasi-elastic light scattering* (ed. B. E. Dahneke) pp. 501–28. John–Wiley, New York.

Oakley, D. M., Jennings, B. R., Wateman, D. R. and Fairey, R. C. (1982). An electro-optic birefringence fine-particle sizer. *J. Phys. E.* **15**, 1077–82.

O'Shea, D. C., Callen, W. R. and Rhodes, W. T. (1979). *Introduction to Lasers and their applications.* Addison–Wesley Mass, USA.

Patterson, G. D. (1985). Dynamic light scattering in bulk polymers. In *Dynamic light scattering* (ed. R. Percora) pp. 245–76. Plenum Press, New York.

Pecora, R. (ed.) (1985). *Dynamic light scattering; applications of photon correlation spectroscopy.* Plenum Press, New York.

Plasek, J. and Marik, T. (1982). Determination of undeformable erythrocytes in blood samples using laser light scattering. *Appl. Opt.* **21(23)**, 4335–8.

Prescott, B., Steinmetz, W. and Thomas, G. J. (1984). Characterization of DNA structure by laser Raman spectroscopy. *Biopolymers* **23**, 235–56.

Price, C. P., Spencer, K. and Whicher, J. (1983). Light scattering immunoassay of specific proteins: a review. *Ann. Clin. Biochem.* **20**, 1–14.

Pusey, P. N. (1984). Detection of small polydispersities by photon correlation spectroscopy. *J. Chem. Phys.* **80(8)**, 3513–20.

—— and Vaughan, J. M. (1975). Light scattering and intensity fluctuation spectro-scopy. In *Dielectric and related molecular processes*, Vol. 2, Chapter 2, 48–105. Chem. Soc. Specialist Periodical Report.

—— Koppel, D. E., Schaefer, D. W., Camerini-Otero, R. D. and Koenig, S. H. (1974). Intensity fluctuation spectroscopy of laser light scattered by solutions of spherical viruses: R17, Qβ, BSV, PM2 and T7. I. Light scattering technique. *Biochemistry* **13(5)**, 952–60.

Randall, J. J. and Vaughan, J. M. (1979). Brillouin scattering in systems of biological importance. *Phil. Trans. R. Soc. Lond.* **A293**, 341.

Salzman, G. C. and Gregg, T. G. (1984). Current and experimental methods of rapid microbial identification. *Biotechnology* March, 243–8.

Schulz–DuBois, E. O. (ed.) (1983). *Photon correlation techniques in fluid mechanics*, Springer Verlag, Berlin.

Schmitz, K. S. and Lu, M. (1984). Quasielastic light-scattering studies on dinucleo-somal-sized DNA: ionic-strength dependence. *Biopolymers* **23**, 797–808.

Sellen, D. B. (1983). The diffusion of compact macromolecules through biological gels. In *The application of laser light scattering to the study of biological motion* (eds J. C. Earnshaw and M. W. Steer) NATO Advanced Science Institute Series, Vol. 59, pp. 209-220. Plenum Press, New York.

Shogren, R. L., Blackwell, J., Jamieson, A. M., Carrino, D. A., Pechak, D. and Caplan, A. I. (1983). Light scattering studies of chick limb bud proteoglycan aggregate. *J. Biol. Chem.* **258(24)**, 14741-4.

Sittampalam, G. and Wilson, G. S. (1984*a*). Experimental observations of transient light scattering formed during immunoprecipitin reactions. *Anal. Chem.* **56**, 2170-5.

—— (1984*b*). Theory of light scattering measurements as applied to immunoprecipitin reactions. *Anal. Chem.* **56**, 2176-80.

Spendley, D. G., Jones, D. P., Smith, A. T., Lloyd, D. S. and Cooke, E. D. (1982). Inexpensive laser Doppler instrument for cell electrophoresis. Proc Max Born Conf., SPIE Vol. 369, 174-177.

Steer, M. W. (1983*a*). Vesicles, In *The application of laser light scattering to the study of biological motion* (eds. J. C. Earnshaw and M. W. Steer) NATO Advanced Science Institute Series, Vol. 59, pp. 359-66. Plenum Press, New York.

—— (1983*b*). Applications of laser light scattering to biological systems. In *The application of laser light scattering to the study of biological motion* (eds. J. C. Earnshaw and M. W. Steer) NATO Advanced Science Institute Series, Vol. 59, pp. 43-52. Plenum Press, New York.

Steiner, R., Ottmann, O., Kaufmann, R., Light, P. A. and Hoffmann, W. (1985). Cell electrophoresis: automatic measurements by light scattering with Lazypher. *Electrophoresis* **6**, 82-9.

Swithenbank, J., Beer, J. M., Taylor, D. S., Abbot, D. and McCreath, G. C. (1977). A laser diagnostic technique for the measurement of droplet and particle size distribution. *Prog. Astronautics and Aeronautics* **53**, 421-47.

Tabor, B. E. (1972). Preparation and clarification of solutions. In *Light scattering from polymer solutions* (ed. M. B. Huglin) pp. 1-25. Academic Press, New York.

Tanaka, T. (1985). Light scattering from polymer gels. In *Dynamic light scattering* (ed. R. Pecora) pp. 347-62. Plenum Press, New York.

Theophanides, T. (1979). *Infrared Raman spectroscopy of biological molecules.* NATO Advanced Study Institute Series. D. Reidel, Dordecht, Holland.

van de Hulst, H. C. (1957). *Light scattering by small particles.* Wiley, New York. (Also 1981, Dover Books.)

Vaughan, J. M. (1982). Quasi-elastic light scattering from polymer solutions. In *Static and dynamic properties of the polymeric solid state* (eds. R. A. Pethrick and R. W. Richards) pp. 305-347. D. Reidel, Dordecht, Holland.

Volochine, B. (1983). Light scattering studies of biological populations. In *The application of laser light scattering to the study of biological motion* (eds. J. C. Earnshaw and M. W. Steer) NATO Advanced Science Institute Series, Vol. 59, pp. 635-656. Plenum Press, New York.

von Schulthess, G. K., Cohen, R. J. and Benedek, G. B. (1976*a*). Laser light scattering spectroscopic immunoassay in the agglutination-inhibition mode for human chorionic gonadotropin (hCG) and human luteinizing hormone (hLH), *Immunochemistry* **13**, 963-66.

—— Sakato, N. and Bendek, G. B. (1976*b*). Laser light scattering spectroscopic immunoassay for mouse IgA. *Immunochemistry* **13**, 955-62.

Vurek, G. G. (1984). *In vivo* chemical sensors. In *Novel optical fibre techniques for medical applications*. SPIE, Vol. 494, pp. 2–6.

Walters, P. T. (1980). Practical applications of inverting spectral turbidity data to provide aerosol size distributions. *Appl. Opt.* **19(14)**, 2353–65.

Wang, C.-C., Holland Cook, K. and Pecora, R. (1980). Dynamic light scattering studies of ribonuclease. *Biophysical Chem.* **11**, 439–42.

Wang, P. C. and Chen, S. H. (1983). Chemotaxis and band formation of *Escherichia coli* studied by light scattering. In *The application of laser light scattering to the study of biological motion* (eds. J. C. Earnshaw and M. W. Steer) NATO Advanced Science Institute Series, Vol. 59, pp. 607–28. Plenum Press, New York.

Ware, B. R. (1983). Electrophoretic light scattering: modern methods and recent applications to biological membranes and polyelectrolytes. In *The application of laser light scattering to the study of biological motion* (eds. J. C. Earnshaw and M. W. Steer) NATO Advanced Science Institute Series, Vol. 59, pp. 89–122. Plenum Press, New York.

Wiliams, D. J. (1984). Organic polymeric and non-polymeric materials with large optical nonlinearities. *Angew. Chem. Int. Ed. Engl.* **23**, 690–703.

Wiltzius, P. (1982). Light scattering study on polydisperse TMV solutions. *Appl. Opt.* **21(11)**, 2022–6.

Wyatt, P. J. (1975a). Differential light scattering techniques for microbiology. In *Methods in microbiology*. (ed. J. R. Norris) Vol. 7A, Chapter 6, pp. 183–263. Academic Press, New York.

—— (1975b). *Atlas of the light scattering characteristics of microparticles*. Science Spectrum Inc., Santa Barbara, Calif., USA.

Yamaoka, K. and Matsuda, K. (1980). Electric dipole moments of DNA in aqueous solutions as studied by the reversing-pulse electric birefringence. *Macromolecules* **13**, 1558–60.

—— (1981). Electric dichroism study of a sonicated DNA and its complex with an acridine dye in aqueous solutions: Field-strength dependence and linear dichroic spectra. *Macromolecules* **14**, 595–601.

—— and Yueda, K. (1982). Reversing-pulse electric birefringence study of helical poly(β-l-glutamic acid) in *N,N*-dimethylformamide with emphasis on a new data analysis for the polydisperse system. *J. Phys. Chem.* **86**, 406–13.

Yariv, A. (1975). *Quantum electronics*. Wiley, New York.

Yu, H. (1983). Structure and dynamics of disc membrane vesicles. In *The application of laser light scattering to the study of biological motion* (eds. J. C. Earnshaw and M. W. Steer) NATO Advanced Science Institute Series, Vol. 59, pp. 367–382. Plenum Press, New York.

Applications of microprocessors

35

The use of microprocessors for the evaluation of the analytical performance of enzyme-based sensors

DANIEL R. THÉVENOT, THIERRY TALLAGRAND, and ROBERT STERNBERG

35.1 Introduction

Biosensors such as enzyme electrodes, using enzymatic membranes and electrochemical detectors, usually present a great specificity for a given metabolite such as sugar or amino acid (Thévenot *et al.* 1978, 1979; Sternberg *et al.* 1980). The operating properties and the analytical characteristics of these biosensors are dependent upon a large number of physical, chemical and enzymatic parameters (Sternberg 1983*a*) which are often difficult to discriminate. Programmable calculators and microcomputers have been used by several research groups for instrument development (Skogberg *et al.* 1979; Jaenchen *et al.* 1982; Kernevez *et al.* 1983; Wieck *et al.* 1984). Numerous Japanese patents on enzyme-based sensors refer to automation involving microcomputers or microprocessors (Kawana *et al.* 1979; Kyoto Daiichi Kagaku K. K. 1982; Tsuji *et al.* 1983; Mitsubishi Rayon Co. 1983). These instruments may alternatively be of great help in a more direct association with enzyme electrodes:

firstly, for the study and optimisation of their analytical properties, especially their precision, repeatability, and extention of measurable concentration domain (De Laforcade, 1980),

secondly, for the direct or indirect determination of some parameters which play an important role in the sensor response (Thévenot 1982; Dubois 1984).

This chapter presents attempts to use programmable calculators and microcomputers to evaluate the analytical performances of amperometric glucose electrodes (Tallagrand *et al.* 1983).

35.2 Material and methods

35.2.1 Enzyme electrodes

All the enzyme electrodes used in this study consisted of glucose oxidase

(GOD) membranes maintained in close contact with a platinum disk. Enzymatic membranes were either prepared by acyl-azyde activation of reconstituted collagen films (Thévenot *et al.* 1979) or by entrapment of enzyme in cellulose acetate films (Sternberg *et al.* 1983*b*). The latter membrane was fabricated manually, in steps, from a solution consisting of 5% cellulose diacetate, 91.5% acetone, 1% polyvinylpyrrolidone, 2.5% water, and an enzyme solution of 5 mg glucose oxidase (EC 1.1.3.4 Boeringer grade II) in 3 ml of acetate buffer; 3 ml of cellulose acetate solution and 0.2 ml of enzyme solution were mixed for 5 min, then spread on a glass plate with the aid of a 5, 15, or 30 micron speader to produce a thin film. After drying for 2–5 min, the membrane was rinsed with distilled water and then stored in acetate buffer, pH 5.6.

Electrochemical measurements were made using a Solea PRGDEL potentiostat and current amplifier connected to a strip chart recorder. When a differential set up was used i.e. when both an enzymatic and a non-enzymatic sensor were placed in contact with stirred or flowing samples, both working electrodes were connected to a Solea DELTAPOL differential current amplifier, linked to the potentiostat. This set up (Thévenot *et al.* 1979) permitted the measurement of the difference between the current corresponding to the enzymatic reaction (I_1) and of the background current (I_2) i.e. calculation of $I_1 - k.I_2$ with k ranging between 0.5 and 2. When the first and second derivative of current outputs were needed, an analogic derivative amplifier (Solea Derivol) and 1 second time base (Solea GCMR) were used.

Electrodes housings were either modified gas electrodes dipped into a thermostated stirred solution (Thévenot *et al.* 1979) or modified electrochemical cells for HPLC (Solea Tacussel type DEL-1). The latter consisted of two blocks of polyethylene separated by a Teflon spacer. One block contained the entry and exit holes for liquid, the other accommodated two platinum electrodes (working and auxiliary) and a reference electrode (Ag/AgCl, sat. KCl). The Teflon spacer was hollowed out in the middle in order to permit circulation of liquid and to define the volume of the reaction chamber (0.02 ml). A cellulose acetate membrane containing enzyme was placed in the cell between the sensing electrodes and the Teflon spacer. Solution was circulated to the cell using a Gilson Minipuls II peristaltic pump at a flow rate ranging between 0.1 and 2 ml/min.

35.2.2 Programmable table calculator for an enzyme electrode

In order to evaluate the linearity and repeatability of glucose sensors, we added to the previous equipment a Hewlett Packard 97 S programmable table calculator (De Laforcade 1980). Its binary coded decimal input and four outputs were interfaced to the potentiostat and to an electric buret through a Solea Ionomate 80 digital Millivoltmeter (range ± 2000 mV,

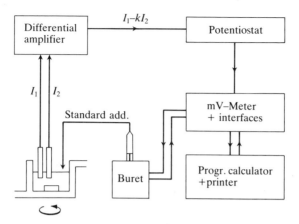

Fig. 35.1 Block diagram of electrodes and electronics using a programmable calculator for an automated enzyme-based electrode, (from Thévenot *et al.* 1982).

precision 0.1 mV) (Fig. 35.1). We have developed a program that perform two main functions:

a) determination of steady-state response by detecting stable output currents before and after sample addition into the reaction vessel where electrodes are dipped in and print-out of steady-state current
b) control of glucose standard additions by the electronic buret (Solea EBX with Solea EBX–INT interface) and statistical analysis of responses to several equal additions (1 to 50) with print-out of each response as well as mean, standard deviation and coefficient of variation.

For determination of unknown glucose concentrations, this program has been modified, replacing the second step by the automatic calibration of the glucose sensor with two successive standard glucose additions and calculation of glucose level, in unknown samples, using the response to the second glucose standard. In order to check for interferences, a post-calibration procedure has been developed: after several sample additions, another glucose standard is added into the vessel and the steady-state response variation is printed.

35.2.3 Microcomputer for an enzyme electrode

The above mentioned calculator does not allow storage of more than 26 variables and thus does not permit storage of the entire response curves, therefore an alternative set up was developed using an Apple II 64 K microcomputer (Fig. 35.2). The data acquisition interface connected to the potentiostat consisted of a 12 bit, 16 channel, 4 range A.D.C. (GD 16V 12B 4G) and a programmable offset 8 bit D.A.C. (GD Offset Prog). Data

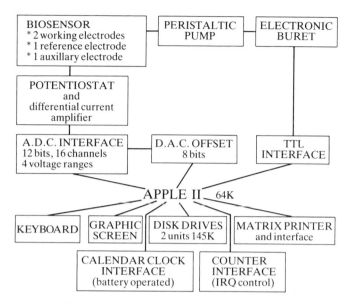

Fig. 35.2 Block diagram of electrodes and electronics using a microcomputer for an automated enzyme-based electrode.

acquisition was controlled by IRQ interrups generated by a programmable timer module (CCS 7440A). A battery operated real-time calendar clock interface (Mountain Hardware Apple Clock) allowed identification of experiments by exact start time. The electronic buret Solea EBX was interfaced to the microcomputer by a 8 TTL input and 8 relay card (MID CR8C).

35.2.4 Electrode responses

When a glucose-containing sample is added to a solution of 0.2 M acetate buffer, 0.1 M KCl (pH 5.7) into which both electrodes are dipped or circulating through modified HPLC electrode, several different current *vs.* time curves may be recorded:

a) I_2 is the output current of the non-enzymatic, compensating electrode E_2. I_2 is the background response and is usually very low except if the sample contains electrochemical reducing species (ascorbate, urate, sulphites etc.) and if the GOD membrane presents no permselectivity (reconstituted collagen films).

b) $(I_1 - k.I_2)$ where k is close to 1, and corresponds to the detection of enzymatically generated hydrogen peroxide; it reaches a steady-state value after 2–3 min (0.3–0.5 mm thick collagen films) or 0.5–3 min (0.005–0.025 mm thick cellulose acetate films); this is the steady-state response of the sensor.

c) $d(I_1 - k.I_2)/dt$ is maximum after 20–50 s (collagen) or 10–60 s (cellulose acetate); the height of the peak is the dynamic response of the sensor. Thus 3 different current *vs.* time curves are available and usually recorded on a 3-channel Linear 395 recorder. When non-enzyme compensating electrode E_2 is absent, only I_1 and dI_1/dt signals are recorded. The calculator or microcomputer are linked to either $I_1 - k.I_2$ or to I_1 and I_2 current outputs.

35.2.5 Analytical evaluation of sensors

Methods of analytical evaluation of glucose electrodes are different for dipped-in and flow-through sensors.

In the first case, glucose oxidase and compensating electrodes are dipped in a 20 ml thermostated stirred buffer solution or incorporated into the wall of a special 1–5 ml thermostated vessel capable of supporting horizontal glass rods. All assays are performed by small volume additions of samples or standard glucose solutions into the vessel. Prior to the experiment buffer solutions are saturated with air at the given experimental temperature, i.e. 30 or 37°C. Background current is measured in buffer solution after 0.5–2 h polarization of the platinum working electrodes. Calibration, linearity, and repeatability assays are performed simultaneously by 10 to 50 additions of equal amounts of glucose standard into the reaction vessel. These additions are usually made by electronic buret when stable output current is detected by the calculator, i.e. when previous response to glucose addition has reached a steady state. Responses are calculated either by comparing steady-state current to background current I_{bg} prior to any glucose addition or by subtracting the steady-state current corresponding to previous addition: thus either $I - I_{bg}$ *vs.* C or delta I/delta C *vs.* C curves are plotted (C is the total glucose concentration in reaction vessel).

When the flow-through cell is used, either buffer solution or glucose containing buffer solution is pumped through the sensor. In both cases these solutions are carefully thermostated and saturated with air at the experimental temperature (37°C) prior to experiment. Calibration, linearity, and repeatability assays are performed, as mentioned above, by recirculating the output solution into the storage vessel.

35.3 Automation of glucose enzyme electrodes using programmable calculator

Determination of analytical patterns of enzyme in standard solutions is usually performed by accurate tests of electronic equipment alone as well as careful study of the whole instrument, including biosensor, electronic equipment, and recording or display devices. Although the potentiostat, the differential curent amplifier, and the derivating current amplifier used in this

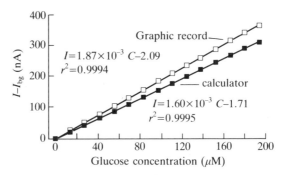

Fig. 35.3 Calibration curves of steady-state responses to 15 additions of a glucose standard: comparison of responses determined on chart recorder and with a programmable calculator. GOD collagen membrane, $30.0 \pm 0.1°C$, 50 μl additions of 5.55 mM glucose into 20 ml of acetate buffer (from De Laforcade 1980).

study gives good accuracy, linearity, repeatability, and very low drift, the 3-channel recorder offers poor reproducibility yielding a coefficient of variation (CV) of 1.73% for 50 successive measurements on a dummy cell (De Laforcade 1980). On the contrary the programmable calculator, connected to the output signals by a BCD interface and a mV-meter presents a much better repeatability (CV = 0.64% for 50 assays). Thus, it seems important to use both the calculator and the graphic recorder during repeatability assays of the whole instrument.

In order to simultaneously determine the background current I_{bg} and the calibration curve of the instrument, successive additions of glucose standard may be made and the steady-state current measured before all additions and after each addition. These steady-state currents are either directly measured on recorded response curve or determined using the calculator when signal drift is lower than a threshold value (usually 0.2 nA/min). Besides this steady-state current determination, the calculator is also able to perform two other functions: it controls additions of glucose standards, by electronic buret into the vessel where sensor is dipped, and it calculates and prints mean values and coefficients of variation for several equal additions of standard. Thus the whole experiment may be performed without interruption in a very accurate and reproducible way (Fig. 35.1).

Printouts and graphics curve responses may be plotted as calibration curves, i.e. as $I - I_{bg}$ vs. C. Fig. 35.3 presents typical results obtained with 15 successive 50 μl additions of 5.55 mM glucose standard into 20 ml acetate buffer. Linear regression of these plots gives following equations:

for steady-state graphic responses:

$$I(A) = 1.87 \times 10^{-3} C - 2.09 \text{ with } r^2 = 0.99945,$$

for steady-state printed responses:

$$I(A) = 1.60 \times 10^{-3} C - 1.71 \text{ with } r^2 = 0.99949,$$

glucose concentration C being expressed in mole/l in reaction vessel. As such plots do not allow an accurate determination of linearity, we prefer to plot the increase of steady-state current *vs.* the increase of glucose concentration in the vessel, i.e. delta I *vs.* delta C. In all experiments such plots give a better linearity or repeatability if they are measured using the calculator: coefficients of variation equal, for example, 6.5 and 8.0% for 15 successive steady-state calculator and graphic responses, respectively. It appears on almost all such assays that response to the first glucose addition is significantly smaller than to the following ones: indeed, when unknown glucose solutions are determined by addition of samples into the same buffer, we prefer to use the response to the second glucose standard as the reference for calculation of the calibration curve equation. When the derivative current amplifier is used, it is also possible to measure the maximum of the first derivative dI/dt. This dynamic response is proportional to the glucose concentration increase and usually presents a better reproductibility than the graphic steady-state response (CV = 5.7% for 15 assays).

The use of this automated glucose electrode enables rapid characterization of sensors prepared with various enzymatic membranes electrode housings and reaction vessels, avoiding time-consuming production and interpretation of graphs. For example, it appears that better stirring of buffer solution gives better reproductibility of steady-state responses (Fig. 35.4): an increase of the 1 cm stirring bar rotation rate from 320 to 530 rpm slightly decreases the steady-state calibration curve slope from 1.7 to 1.6 mA/M and significantly decreases the steady-state coefficient of variation from 9.4 to 2.0% (n = 8). Thus a better definition of hydrodynamic conditions in the enzymatic membrane vicinity is necessary: a flow-through cell derived from an electro-chemical detector for HPLC has been tested. An alternative to such hydro-dynamic cell is a rotating membrane electrode in which diffusion layer thickness may be defined with great accuracy: such a set-up is especially suitable for permeability and diffusion coefficients determination of the enzymatic membrane (Dubois 1984).

Since the noise level increases with total concentration and current levels, the absolute precision on delta I/delta C is better for the first standard additions than for the following ones: for example CV = 2.0% for the first eight glucose standard additions, whether CV = 10.9% for the following seven standard additions (Fig. 35.4 bottom, steady-state response on calculator). Thus, when the enzyme-based sensor is used in a stirred reaction vessel where both standard and samples are added, one should change the buffer solution and rinse the sensor often enough to keep the precision at a suitable level.

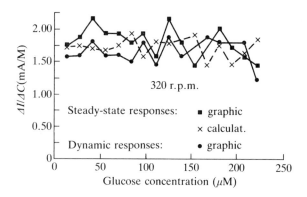

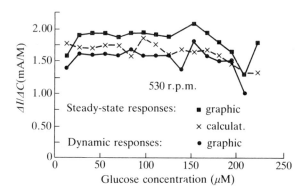

Fig. 35.4 Comparison of the reproducibility of response to 16 additions of glucose under different stirring conditions: (top) 320 and (bottom) 530 rpm of a 1 cm stirring bar in 20 ml buffer solution. (+) Graphic and (●) calculator steady-state, and (×) dynamic responses; same conditions as Fig. 35.3.

Such a set-up is able to evaluate analytical performances of steady state responses, but it is unable to characterize transient responses and to store a whole response curve for a more detailed study. Thus we developed a more powerful device which uses a microcomputer for data storage and treatment.

35.4 Microcomputer for automation of glucose enzyme electrodes

35.4.1 Development of an automated device for enzyme electrode evaluation

The use of personal microcomputers enables much wider possibilities for data storage and versatility than any table calculator. The previously described calculator and mV-meter interface can be replaced by a commercially available 12 bit A.D.C. interface connected to a stable 8 bit D.A.C. used as programmable offset for increasing precision of analogue to digital conversion (Fig. 35.2). Whereas in the previous set-up the acquisition rate was fixed to the maximum possible value at *ca.* 0.5 Hz, this device allows a much more accurate and versatile control of acquisition rate: this is achieved with IRQ interrupts generated by a time counter card containing three 16 bit chained counters. The buret is controlled by a TTL input, relay output card and may add given amounts of glucose standard to the reaction vessel.

Software has been developed for this application using two input channels respectively connected to the enzymatic E_1 and compensating E_2 electrodes. As shown in Fig. 35.5, this software is organized around a branching 'menu' and contains several programs linked together by a parameter file. Depending upon the speed necessary for each of these programs, either 6502 machine or compiled basic language is used. For example, the installation procedure during which all experimental parameters such as (a) identification numbers, (b) potential range (± 20, ± 100, ± 500, or ± 2500 mV), (c) signal units (nA or mA), (d) actual ranges (ex: 200 nA for 5000 mV), (e) acquisition frequency, and (f) number of data (lower than 2000) is stored in a random access file during a conversational compiled basic program.

The actual experimental program consists of several linked compiled basic programs during which:

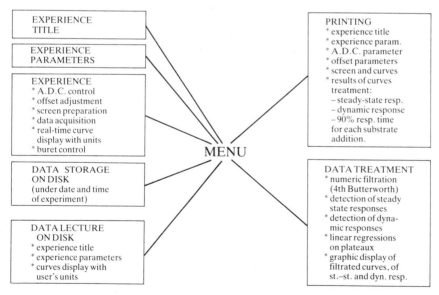

Fig. 35.5 Block diagram of software developed for the automated enzyme-based electrodes using an Apple II + microcomputer.

a) the A.D.C. card is tested for zero drift,
b) the offsets for both channels are optimized for decreasing background signals prior to the experiment,
c) the high resolution screen is prepared and axes are graduated in user defined units,
d) the actual starting date and time is measured and stored on the parameter file,
e) the time counters are initiated for IRQ interrups at the controlled frequency,
f) and the acquisition procedure is started under a manually operated switch.

Then several machine language programs

a) control data acquisition on both channels,
b) store numerical values as most significant and less significant bytes,
c) and display points corresponding to both channels on the high resolution screen.

Such a procedure of acquisition and real-time curve display is not limited by execution time of these programs but by response times of A.D.C. and D.A.C. With these commercially available devices a period of 30 ms is necessary when potential ranges and offset values are different for each channel. If the system is used with a single channel, the acquisition frequency reaches 2.5 kHz; it may ultimately reach 15 kHz when curve display on the screen is performed at the end of the experiment. Finally, addition of given volumes of standard at a given periodicity may be achieved using a machine language program which controls the step motor of the buret and counts delivered volume as TTL signals.

Results may be stored on the user's disk as parameter and data files named under starting date and time. Alternatively, a previous experiment may be completely recalled by reading corresponding experimental parameters and data files and by displaying curves on the high-resolution screen in the user's unit.

In order to keep track of each experiment all parameters including A.D.C. zeros and offset values, actual screen displays, and untreated or treated curves and results of data treatment may be hard-copied on a dot-matrix printer (Fig. 35.6 top).

The last component of this automated device is a data treatment unit which is a set of linked compiled basic programs. These programs, placed on the second side of the program disk, perform several treatments on previously stored data:

a) a 4th order Butterworth numeric filter attenuates the signal at a frequency larger than a threshold value, chosen by user,

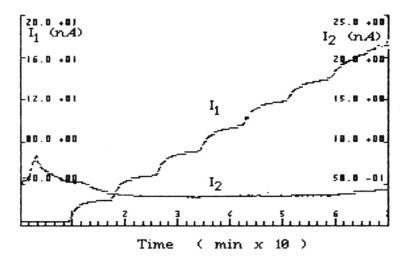

Time (min x 10)

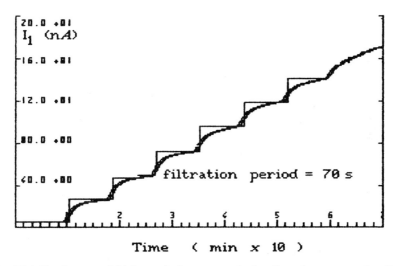

Time (min x 10)

Fig. 35.6 Hard copy of high resolution screen during linearity assays of a flow-through glucose electrode at high concentration: (top) experimental and (bottom) treated response curves to seven increases of glucose concentration by 5 mM steps. GOD cellulose acetate membrane, $37.0 \pm 0.1°C$, seven 30 μl additions of 0.50 M glucose into 3 ml of acetate buffer placed in a closed loop (additions every 500 s).

b) steady-state signals are detected on filtered data when their slopes are smaller than a user chosen value, the equations of these almost horizontal parts of curves are calculated by linear regression and the corresponding steady-state response, i.e. delta I are determined,

c) when the first derivative of the filtered data reaches a maximum, the corresponding dynamic responses $(dI/dT)_{max}$ are determined,

d) all these operations are controlled by the user, since filtrated curves, plateaux and inflexion points are displayed on screen (Fig. 35.6 bottom).

Simultaneously a file is created with all steady-state and dynamic responses, in users units, and all dynamic and steady-state response times: the user may either validate these data and store them on the corresponding parameter file, or discriminate undesirable values, or even resume the whole treatment procedure.

Finally, software has been created for reading all parameters and data on previously mentioned files and for storing both channels and time coordinates, in user's units, under the data-interchange format (D.I.F.) used by most commercial software such as worksheets: thus any systematic calculation may be performed on either all data or on a selection of them made by experimenter.

35.4.2 Use of the automated device for glucose electrode evaluation

This set-up and software allows large number of repetitive experiments designed for comparison of various GOD membranes and glucose sensors to be performed. Figure 35.6 presents typical results of repeatability and linearity assays at high glucose concentration using a cellulose acetate enzyme membrane placed in a flow-through cell: seven increases of glucose concentration by 5 mM steps give steady-state responses (upper curve); the value of these responses may be determined using the data treatment programs (lower curve) as ranging between 21.9 and 23.7 nA using a filtration period of 70 s; corresponding dynamic response range between 21.7 and 24.4 nA/s demonstrating a good linearity of this glucose sensor response up to 30 mM glucose.

During similar evaluation of glucose sensors we have tested their response to an artificial glucose concentration *vs.* time profile. Figure 35.7 presents such a profile (upper curve) for simulated intravenous glucose tolerance tests (IVGTT) of various kinetic patterns. It appears that such a device responds to increasing and decreasing glucose level but that its steady-state response time may be somewhat too large for such an application.

Such membranes are suitable for some *in vivo* glucose determination, as tested on an external blood shunt of conscious rats (Thévenot *et al.* 1985) but present relatively low response values (1 to 10 μA $\times$ M^{-1} $\times$ mm^{-2}) and sometimes excessive response values (0.4 to 3 min). Further experiments are

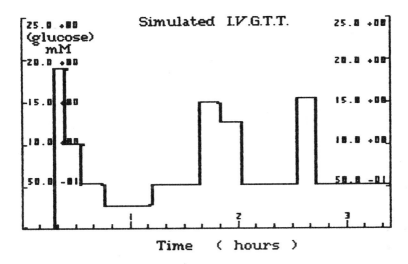

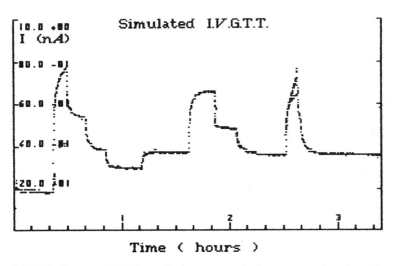

Fig. 35.7 Hard copy of high resolution screen during assays of a flow-through electrode to simulated intravenous glucose tolerance tests: (top) variations of glucose level simulating IVGTT under different physiological conditions and (bottom) response of the glucose electrode to this concentration profile. GOD cellulose acetate membrane, $37.0 \pm 0.1°C$, 0.2 to 19 mM glucose concentration profiles performed by addition of either glucose standard or buffer in acetate buffer placed in a closed loop.

in progress to prepare glucose sensors with similar linearity for highly concentrations of glucose but with larger response amplitudes and shorter response times.

35.5 Conclusions

Good characterization of any sensor and especially biosensors such as enzyme-based electrodes implies a large number of linear and repeatable assays, and the treatment of corresponding steady-state or dynamic responses. As a matter of fact, several thousands of such glucose assays have been performed using the same reconstituted collagen membrane for periods of up to four successive months of operation at 30°C and storage at room temperature (Thévenot *et al.* 1982). Such numerous assays would not have been possible without using automation of both the addition of 10 to 50 glucose standards in the reaction vessel and the detection of steady-state responses and their statistical treatment. This chapter presents two different set-ups for such automation: on the one hand, a simple programmable calculator carries out all these operations with a precision often better than a manual experiment, using a chart recorder; on the other hand, it may be of considerable interest to store the whole response curve and to analyse carefully its shape: such a situation is encountered when the substrate follows the non step-like increase of concentration common in industrial or clinical processes. This second set-up, which exploits microcomputers and commercially available interface cards, enables both acquisition and real-time display on a high resolution screen, and various types of data treatments. It is currently used in our laboratory for comparing the principal analytical parameters of various enzyme membranes and reaction vessels, and also for recording and treatment of *in vivo* assays of flow-through glucose sensors under different physiological conditions of conscious animals (Thévenot *et al.* 1985).

Acknowledgements

The support of the Caisse Nationale de l'Assurance Maladie des Travailleurs salariés (France) Grant CNAMTS-INSERM 85.3.54.8.E, of National Institute of Health (US) Grant AM30718, and of Association des Jeunes Diabétiques (Paris, France) is grateful acknowledged.

References

Dubois, C. (1984). Electrochemical characterization of membranes used in enzyme electrodes. Research report, Université Paris–Val de Marne, 42 pp.
De Laforcade, V. (1980). Study of a table set-up for glucose determination with an enzyme-based electrode. Research report, Université Paris–Val de Marne, 106 pp.
Jaenchen, M., Scheller, F., Pfeiffer, D., Pittelkow, R., Wiegand, P. and Nentwig, J. (1982). GKM 01: a new measuring instrument for glucose using enzyme electrodes. *Z. Med. Laboratoriumsdiagn.* **23(1)**, 39–42.

Kawana, S., Nihira, K., Miyashiro, H. and Takada, Y. (1980). Analyzer using immobilized enzymes. Jpn. Kokai Tokyo Koho JP 55/10523 (80/10523), 25 Jan 1980, 3 p. Appl. or Pr. 78/83098, 10 Jul 1978.

Kernevez, J. P., Konate, L. and Romette, J. L. (1983). Determination of substrate concentrations by a computerised enzyme electrode. *Biotechnology and Bioengineering* **25**, 845–55.

Kyoto Daiichi Kagaku, K. K. (1982). Apparatus for automatic and continuous analysis of blood. Patent Belg. BE 892964 A1, 16 g 1982, 50 p. Appl. 2079, 26 Apr 1982; JP Appl. 81/63160, 24 Apr 1981; JP Appl. 81/150924, 9 Oct 1981.

Mitsubishi Rayon Co. Ltd. (1983). Automatic electrode apparatus for determination of biological components. Jpn. Kokai Tokyo Koho JP 58/135950 A2 (83/135950), 12 g 1983, 4 p., Appl. 82/18477, 8 Feb 1982.

Skogberg, D., Richardson, T. and Blasczyk, T. (1979). Automatic sampling and monitoring of potentiometric electrodes: steady-state response by first and second derivative techniques. *Analytical Chemistry* **51**(12), 2054–7.

Sternberg, R., Apoteker, A. and Thévenot, D. R. (1980). Trace glucose electrode for clinical, food and environmental determinations. In *Analytical chemistry symposia Series* Vol. 2 (ed. W. F. Smith) pp. 461–473. Elsevier, Amsterdam.

—— Tallagrand, T. and Thévenot, D. R. (1983a). Experimental and theoretical studies of enzymatic membranes used in enzyme electrodes. Communication to the Electroanalysis International Symposium, Cardiff (Great Britain) abstract no. 82.

—— Tallagrand, T. and Thévenot, D. R. (1983b). Enzymatic membranes used in enzyme-based electrodes. Communication to 1st National colloquium of the French Bioelectrochemistry Group, Port–Leucate (France) abstract n. 24, pp. 93–96.

Tallagrand, T., Grunberg, M. and Thévenot, D. R. (1983). Microcomputers for specific electrodes using immobilised enzyme. Communication to 1st National Colloquium of the French Bioelectrochemistry Group, Port Leucate (France) abstract no. 25, pp. 97–101.

Thévenot, D. R. (1982). Use of electrochemical methods in the characterization of enzymatic membranes. Communication to the 33rd congress of the International Society of Electrochemistry, Lyon (France), abstract p. 784.

—— Sternberg, R. and Coulet, P. (1982). A glucose electrode using high-stability glucose-oxidase collagen membranes. *Diabetes Care* **3**, 203–6.

—— Coulet, P. R., Sternberg, R. and Gautheron, D. C. (1978). A highly sensitive glucose electrode using glucose oxidase collagen film. *Bioelectrochemistry and Bioenergetics* **5**, 548–53.

—— Sternberg, R., Coulet, P. R., Laurent, J. and Gautheron, D. C. (1979). Enzyme collagen membrane for electrochemical determination of glucose. *Analytical Chemistry* **51**, 96–100.

—— Tallagrand, T., Velho, G. and Reach, G. (1985). Enzyme electrodes for use *in vivo*. 30th I.U.P.A.C. Meeting, Manchester, UK.

Tsuji, N., Nakamura, K., Endoh, K., Hamada, T. and Ishida, K. (1983). Blood sugar analyzing apparatus. US Patent 4407959 A, 4 Oct 1983, 11 p. Appl. 313666, 21 Oct 1981; JP Appl. 80/150756, 29 Oct 1980; JP Appl., 80/172665, 9 Dec 1980; JP Appl. 80/172666, 9 Dec 1980.

Wieck, H. J., Heider, G. H. and Yacynych, A. M. (1984). Simple approach to microcomputer-controlled electrochemistry. *Anal. Chim. Acta* **166**, 315–19.

Commercialization and future prospects

36

Biosensors in medicine: the clinician's requirements

P. D. HOME and K. G. M. M. ALBERTI

While the practice of modern medicine still depends heavily on the traditional skills of the doctor in observation, taking a clinical history, and examining the patient, the advent of effective therapy this century has been matched by a rapid growth in techniques of making objective determinations of measures of illness (pathology) and their response to treatment. Chemical and biochemical measurement in medicine has evolved into a specialty of its own ('chemical pathology', more lately 'clinical biochemistry'), generally as an offshoot of the more traditional laboratory based pathology disciplines, tissue pathology and microbiology. This laboratory bias has led increasingly towards the use of more sophisticated and automated analytical devices, particularly under the pressure of increased clinical demand. The necessary batch processing makes the laboratory less able to respond flexibly to urgent demands, and removes local services at small hospitals in favour of a major installation in population centres.

A number of trends in medicine are seeking to reverse these pressures (Marks and Alberti 1985). It has always been the case that seriously ill patients, in intensive care units, could show rapid swings in biochemical variables, and that recognition and appropriate action were equally urgent. A rapid increase in open heart surgery and renal transplantation in particular has meant that many more people are requiring intensive life support for short periods. Furthermore it is now possible to offer more successful treatment in cases of natural catastrophe, when associated with acute renal or hepatic failure or acute severe heart failure, for example. The need for a quick answer to the request for a particular biochemical measurement has often been met by the establishment of small ward-based laboratories, often at first using traditional analytical techniques, but later by the development of dedicated single specimen devices capable of giving rapid results. Measurement of blood gases, potassium, and glucose are familiar examples.

A second major pressure to move away from the 'routine laboratory' comes from the increasing pace and pressures of modern medicine, coupled to some extent to economic considerations. Both on the wards and in their offices clinicians find it increasingly less satisfactory to analyse a problem, implement investigations, and then have to arrange to reassess the problem at some later timepoint in the light of the results of those investigations. Patients, too, are not unnaturally keen to have their problems sorted out as rapidly as possible. The drive here, then, is to have the ability to perform some types of investigation in the doctor's office, hospital out-patient clinic, or on the ward. Examples are given below. In some cases instant investigation can be important even in the home, blood glucose in some diabetic states being the obvious example.

A further major pressure has come from the availability of reagent strips based on glucose oxidase for the determination of capillary blood glucose. Because subcutaneous insulin therapy in diabetes is a very erratic and unsatisfactory tool, knowledge of blood glucose levels both at home and on the ward is very helpful to both the patient and clinician. Capillary blood is easily collected from a finger-prick, and a widescale and reasonably successful implementation of blood glucose monitoring by this method (Tattersall 1979) has both opened clinicians' eyes to the possibilities of 'instant' biochemical determinations, and led to demands for even more convenient, robust, and operator proof blood glucose systems.

The erratic nature of the response to subcutaneous insulin therapy has also led to the drive to produce devices capable of physiologically appropriate intravenous insulin delivery. Because the amount of insulin required varies considerably with meals, exercise, stress, injury, and infection, and even the time of day, some kind of device which monitored blood glucose continuously, and whose output was used to control an insulin pump, has attracted considerable attention and speculation. Somewhat inevitably it has been the glamour of this 'artificial pancreas' (Fogt *et al.* 1978) which has proved a magnet for those interested in the application of biosensors to medicine, rather than the more mundane measurement only devices.

This chapter will attempt to identify some of the areas where clinicians have a requirement that might be fulfilled by the use of a biosensor, and will then consider what is required in putting such a device to practical use in medicine.

36.1 Openings for biosensors in medicine

36.1.1 The intensive care unit

It is fairly easy to understand that the availability of continuous monitoring, or high frequency continual monitoring, in the intensive care unit can be a great aid to patient care. This is already achieved for many physical measurements (heart rate, blood pressure, temperature) and to some extent for a limited range of biochemical measurements (oxygen, pH, glucose). It is also possible to define the range of biochemical parameters that would be useful in such circumstances (Table 36.1), but it is less easy to predict how these

Table 36.1 Biochemical measurements which would be useful when monitored continuously (or at high frequency) in the intensive care unit

In blood
  Oxygen, carbon dioxide, pH
  Lactate
  (Amino acids, ketone bodies)

In blood or subcutaneous tissue
  Glucose
  Sodium, potassium
  Calcium
  Creatinine, urea

In urine
  Sodium, potassium
  Creatinine, urea

systems would be put into operation. The problem is not just one of clinical requirements, for the nature and ease of use of such devices will also determine their practical applicability. At present, even in units with access to blood glucose controlled insulin infusion systems (artificial pancreas, Biostator), in practice blood glucose is often determined with a bedside reagent strip meter and the insulin infusion pump adjusted from experience or using written algorithms.

Blood gas (oxygen, carbon dioxide, pH) and electrolyte (sodium, potassium) estimation will presumably continue to be by chemical sensors, but it is instructive to consider how different will be the clinical use of the information derived from these measurements. Blood oxygen tensions and saturation in the ill patient are largely determined by the condition of the lungs and circulation, and are not easily correctable by changing the inspired oxygen concentration or rate of administration. Furthermore rapid changes in oxygen tension can occur. The demand is therefore for true continuous monitoring, but with the response loop closed by the human brain. Electrolytes and water balance are much more directly affected by input and output however. In the situation where blood concentrations, urine concentrations, and fluid output can be measured it is relatively easy to conceive of an automatic 'fluid balance centre', controlling input in closed loop fashion, though here the lessons of the Biostator must be learnt. Note that in most circumstances hourly estimations would suffice, provided an option was retained for emergency overide.

The requirements for blood glucose estimation are similar to the pattern for electrolytes. Thus a bedside device, operated manually by application of blood samples at 15 minute to 4 hour intervals, is the major advance from relying on laboratory measured samples. Reagent strip meters meet this market already to some extent, but their response time is inconveniently long (2 min) and careful operator training is required. Continuous monitoring would be a worthwhile advance not only in diabetic patients on the unit, but also in those receiving high doses of inotropic agents (which can be diabetogenic) for cardiac support, and those receiving high osmolarity glucose solutions for intravenous nutrition. While it is desirable to move to blood glucose controlled insulin infusion in such circumstances, in practice the patients are additionally receiving glucose solutions, both to 'buffer' diabetic control and to provide free water. It may therefore be that when sophisticated blood glucose control systems are available for use in intensive care units, it will be in conjunction with fluid balance centres.

The role of the monitoring of other aspects of intermediary metabolites in the critically ill patient has yet to be explored, and indeed such research awaits the advent of biosensors for the continuous monitoring of blood lactate, alanine, and ketone bodies (Noy and Alberti 1981*a*, *b*). In these circumstances it is at present difficult to predict how the information might be used clinically, except in lactic acidosis, and at first it may merely allow the physician to monitor metabolic status more closely.

Intensive care units would also find instant and repeated measurements of renal function (creatinine, urea) extremely useful.

36.1.2 Casualty/emergency rooms and general wards

In the circumstance of seeing an acutely ill patient in whom the diagnosis is uncertain the clinician's primary need is for instant results to biochemical tests to complement the clinical history and examination, both of which already provide answers on which an immediate assessment can based. Whether the results are required for diagnostic purposes or as a guide to therapy is immaterial, except insofar as the latter are more likely to be repeated at intervals of hours.

The list of tests which account for 95% of such urgent investigations is not large, and they are listed (Table 36.2) irrespective of whether biosensors, physico-chemical sensors, reagent strip meters or standard biochemical techniques are likely to form the basis of usable devices. Glucose and amylase would probably be in greatest demand in medical and surgical emergencies, followed sadly by estimations of paracetamol and salicylate levels in blood. Creatine kinase is an enzyme used to confirm the diagnosis of coronary thrombosis. The overall level of demand for electrolytes and creatinine (or urea) would be high, particularly when wards are included, but generally the urgency and importance of these requests will not be of such high priority. It will again be noted that there will be a requirement for urine based, as well as blood based, estimation of electrolytes and creatinine.

While the commonest need for emergency drug investigations is for para-

Table 36.2   Biochemical tests for which instant results would be invaluable in emergency situations

Amylase
Glucose
Paracetamol
Salicylate
Creatine kinase
Aspartate aminotransferase
Ammonia
Sodium
Potassium
Calcium
Creatinine or urea
Oxygen, pH, carbon dioxide

cetamol and salicylate, emergency admissions for overdosage of other drugs is also common. Estimation of drug levels is performed not just to confirm the diagnosis, but also so that specific measures may be taken to counteract the deleterious effects of the drug (paracetamol) or to enhance its elimination (salicylate). Unfortunately neither of these is possible for most pharmacological agents, and treatment is therefore supportive (e.g. artificial ventilation) without the need for identification of specific drugs. Though exceptions do exist (phenobarbitone), and in other cases prognostic information can be helpful (paraquat), the local rate of poisoning with any individual agent will always be low.

If antigen–antibody interactions can be successfully harnessed into biosensors then detection of hepatitis B antigen or HTLV-III (AIDS) virus antigen in blood samples would be much in demand for protection of laboratory personnel. Similarly drugs can be detected by antibody interactions, and the heart drug digoxin is an obvious candidate where fast answers are often required.

36.1.3 Physician's consulting rooms

Again the need here is for instant information to aid diagnosis. The convenience of office based measurements will vary from country to country, for unlike the UK many consulting rooms are not hospital based. Occasionally diagnostic tests are urgent even in the physician's office, and glucose, amylase, and creatine kinase would be most useful. Glucose is already widely measured in routine practice (reagent strips with or without meters), in diabetic clinics, as a diagnostic measure, and in the management of the ill diabetic patient. Blood cholesterol and triglycerides are likely to be more in demand as the results of the lipid intervention studies (Lipid Research Clinics

Program 1984) become more widely appreciated, both for selective screening and to save the extra patient visits presently necessary to have a current result available at the time of consultation. Creatinine and potassium would also be useful investigations to have 'on tap' at the clinic.

The viral antigen and drug tests mentioned above would also be useful in this situation. Another example from current use is the measurement of anti-convulsant levels in neurology.

36.1.4 Diabetes and the patient

The attention of sensor engineers has focused upon diabetes for a number of reasons. Diabetes can be regarded as a disease of relative or absolute deficiency of the messenger/effector (hormone) insulin, a protein produced by one of the ultimate natural biosensors, the B cell of the Islets of Langerhans in the pancreas (Malaisse *et al.* 1979). Insulin has a very short half life in blood (4 to 5 min) and hence its concentration, a major determinant of its action, depends on its rate of secretion. The B cells are sensitive to a wide range of substances, as befits the many biochemical actions of insulin, the most important of these being blood glucose. The blood glucose concentration in blood is normally tightly regulated by this means (between 3.5 and 5.5 mmol/l), but in diabetes insulin deficiency results in high blood glucose levels with consequent short term ill health and long term tissue damage.

The obvious treatment is to give insulin, and indeed before insulin became available patients usually died after a few months. Without the continuous monitoring of glucose (and other substances) it is not possible to give insulin in a normal physiological fashion however, and so diabetic patients still have periods of high blood glucose levels, and, through excessive and inappropriate insulin administration low blood glucose levels.

Improvements in control of diabetes, and the life style of the diabetic patient, came with the introduction of the glucose oxidase based reagent strips (Tattersall 1979), at first read by rather clumsy meters, which are however now much refined. A further major advance was the visually read strip (by colour matching), effectively freeing the patient from needing to carry or buy a meter. To compete with visually read reagent strips direct reading biosensors (working on a drop of blood) will need to be competitive on cost (say UK£0.25 per test), and use very light, portable, and reliable hardware. In its basic form the latter should retail at no more than UK£70, but it is increasingly likely that such devices will form the basis of more sophisticated recording devices, which will be able to advise on insulin dosage.

Patients will however continue to suffer from hypoglycaemic reactions due to low blood glucose concentrations on occasion, for reasons as diverse as exercise or alcohol consumption. Considerable effort has gone into attempting to build 'hypoglycaemia detectors' (Levandowsky *et al.* 1983), but to date these have depended on changes in skin conductivity (due to perspiration).

These changes are however very non-specific, and after a few false alarms the patient (or his parents) abandons its use. An evident way around this is to sense actual blood glucose levels, or a related measurement such as subcutaneous blood glucose concentration. This use of needle type indwelling glucose sensors is likely to precede their use in controlling insulin delivery pumps, for much troublesome hypoglycaemia is at night and the sensor need

Table 36.3 Potential uses of biosensors in diabetes

Type of device	Circumstance of use	Place of use
Glucose sensors		
Spot blood glucose sensor	Routine measurement	At home (by patient)
		Diabetic clinics
		Consulting rooms
		Medical/surgical wards
	Emergency measurement	As for routine measurement
		Casualty/emergency rooms
Needle sensors	Hypoglycaemia alarms	Overnight at home
(subcutaneous)	Blood glucose profiles	Outpatient monitoring
		Conventional insulin delivery
	Continuous monitoring	Hybrid feedback insulin delivery
Intravenous sensors	Continuous monitoring	Automatic insulin delivery
Ketone body sensors		
Spot blood ketone sensor	Diagnosis of keto-acidosis	Casualty/emergency rooms
		Diabetes wards/units
Skin, breath sensors	Guard against keto-acidosis	Home or hospital
Subcutaneous sensors	Adjunct to insulin infusion systems	Outpatient use
Combined glucose/ ketone sensor	Continuous monitoring	Automatic insulin delivery
Lactate sensor		
Intravenous sensor	Critically ill patients	Intensive care unit
Combined glucose/ lactate sensor	Continuous monitoring	Automatic insulin delivery
Amino acid sensor		
Combined glucose/ amino acid sensor	Continuous monitoring	Automatic insulin delivery

only be worn for the period spent asleep. Aside from reassuring the patient at home, a few overnight profiles of blood glucose concentration would greatly help in adjusting insulin regimens.

The technical prerequisites for the use of sensors in medicine are discussed in some detail below. Evidently however the signal from a rapidly responding blood glucose sensor could be used to control an insulin delivery pump, given reliability, selectivity, and absence of signal drift. Combined with the necessarily sophisticated implantable insulin infusion pumps (which should be tested in patients in 1986), an effective replacement for the B cell could be made available. Subcutaneous sensors (Schichiri *et al.* 1982) offer obvious advantages in terms of access, but the signal at mealtimes is delayed compared to changes in blood glucose concentrations, a problem that may be difficult to resolve as physiological insulin concentrations rise very quickly after meals (Ahmed *et al.* 1976). Furthermore in order to control an implanted pump the signal will have to be transmitted back across the skin to any implantable pump. Early subcutaneous sensors are therefore likely to be used with conventional subcutaneous insulin administration by injection or infusion pump, with the human brain intervening to interpret the data, probably with the aid of dosage computers (Schiffrin *et al.* 1985).

It would be useful to measure other substrates in the diabetic patient (Table 36.3). With more physiological day to day insulin delivery the risks of acute deterioration of diabetes due to other illness (e.g. infection) appear to be increased, and a device warning of high blood ketone body levels (e.g. 3-hydroxybutyrate) would be welcome. Again skin or subcutaneous sensors (or acetone breath detectors) might be more feasible. Aside from the intensive care unit rapid rises in blood lactate concentrations may, in the absence of exercise, indicate an over-rapid increase in the glucose turnover rate, suggesting overinsulinization. Incorporating a lactate sensor into the glucose sensor controlling insulin delivery might be the first step to approaching the complexity of the natural B cell response, with amino acids being the next candidates.

36.2 The application of biosensors in medicine

The application of technology to medicine imposes special demands which inevitably vary with the proximity of any device to human tissues, and the importance of its output, whether information or action, to vital functions. In many situations detection and measurement devices, although capable of warning of abnormalities, only result in modifications to treatment through human intervention, so that for example, an abnormal cardiac rhythm does not result in the patient receiving direct current cardioversion (DC shocks) without medical intervention. In more sophisticated applications this link may be missing and impossible to restore, the most familiar example being cardiac pacemakers, whose output can be life saving but also fatal.

These differences result in very different requirements in terms of reliability, accuracy, precision, bioavailability, patient acceptability, and patient interfacing. From the engineering point of view an external measurement device subjected to routine quality control monitoring may be constructed to little better than ordinary consumer standards, while life dependent devices used continuously at home will need to meet military/aerospace specifications.

36.2.1 Accuracy/precision/sensitivity

It is readily apparent that any measurement device must give a result that approximates to the real value (accuracy), and must do this with sufficient reproducibility (precision) for individual readings to be dependable. Accuracy will not generally be a problem with devices calibrated against known reference methods, except insofar as calibration drift occurs. Clinical medicine is surprisingly undemanding on precision when compared to mechanical or chemical engineering, with doctors generally unresponsive to differences of $\pm 10\%$ in making spot decisions, though for serial measurements this kind of difference may be of value in detecting trends due to treatment. In some circumstances (measurement of serum uric acid, or high levels of blood amylase or paracetamol for example) even less precision is necessary.

There is a need however to be careful in interpreting clinical requirements in terms of current medical practice. Many patients currently read their blood glucose monitoring strips to $\pm 30\%$ (being the steps on the colour chart), and present the data to their physicians, who find the results a satisfactory basis on which to adjust insulin dosage. Such imprecision would not however be acceptable if each individual measurement were used for adjustment of insulin dosage in an attempt to maintain constant physiological blood glucose concentrations, as might be the case if subcutaneous insulin delivery was therapeutically more effective. It can be anticipated that when more sophisticated use is made of blood glucose data (in computations of dose, absorption of food and insulin sensitivity, or for feedback control of intravenous insulin delivery) then much better precision will be required.

It is important to recognize that the effective range of a measurement device for use in clinical medicine will generally relate to the patho-physiological range for that parameter and not the physiological range. Blood glucose is normally maintained between 3.5 and 5.5 mmol/l, as discussed above, but it is important to be able to distinguish 1.0 mmol/l from 2.0 mmol/l, and to know that a recorded change from 50 to 40 mmol/l is real. The hormone TSH is important in monitoring low levels of thyroid gland activity (it rises under these circumstances), and endocrinologists have long used an assay that is incapable of distinguishing concentrations below the upper limit of the physiological range. The sensitivity of a device has therefore to be tailored to its role in medicine.

The availability of more portable, precise, and reliable measurement devices will inevitably be a further stimulus to the demands of the medical research establishment. Those involved in the development of biosensors will be approached for devices of high accuracy and precision for use in clinical and fundamental physiological research.

36.2.2 Response time

A blood sample sent to the routine hospital laboratory for analysis will generally produce a result anywhere between 30 minutes and several days later. During this time the clinician will proceed with therapy on the basis of clinical judgement. Paradoxically where bedside monitoring is undertaken the response time of the device becomes more important as there will usually be the intention of making an instant decision. As discussed above this is where biosensors should have an early impact on modern clinical management. While waiting for a result from a sensor type device staff will not have time to complete another activity, so in general response times of over 120 seconds are unsatisfactory. This should include any calibration or preparative procedures. A suitable aim would be 30 seconds, and it is very important that no opportunity should be given of making a reading before the intended interval has elapsed.

36.2.3 Calibration

It is at present difficult to conceive of biosensors that will maintain their accuracy with repetitive or continuous usage over a period of time. The problem will not occur of course with single use devices. Furthermore while physical devices such as reflectance meters can be calibrated using prepared dry strips or filters, biosensors may need calibration with fluid incorporating the substance to be measured. Such fluids may themselves need to incorporate fixed concentrations of interfering substances where necessary. Unless response times are very fast it would be unsatisfactory to perform calibration at each usage, but it is highly desirable that devices are pre-programmed to demand recalibration after a fixed number of tests and at fixed time intervals. External calibration against a laboratory based machine is inpracticable for routine purposes, and should be reserved for quality control schemes organized by clinical and laboratory personnel.

In vivo monitoring presents further problems, and drifts in accuracy will often be the limit to the useful lifetime of a sensor. In general any intravenous or subcutaneous needle should have a minimum expected lifetime of 24 hours before replacement is contemplated (and transcutaneous wires and cannulae generally must be changed after a maximum of 3 days). Within the hospital external calibration against a blood sample would usually be the method of choice, though care would be necessary where blood concentrations were to be related to tissue concentrations in ill patients. Equally, looking to the future, there is no good reason why external calibration from a capillary blood sample should not be used to reset an indwelling implanted sensor, probably through a dedicated external unit, but again this could not be done more than once every 24 hours by the patient at home.

36.2.4 Interfering substances

The problem of non-specificity of biosensors in relation to measurements in biological fluids is well recognized. It is important for bioengineers to realise that the range of interfering concentrations of any substance present in blood is not its physiological range. The very ill patient may have very abnormal blood levels of glucose, oxygen, organic acids, urate, etc., and it is in just such patients that *in vivo* monitoring may at first be contemplated. Furthermore multiple drug therapy is almost the rule in medicine, and these compounds and their metabolites are another potential source of interference.

36.2.5 What sample

Clinicians will use for measurement any fluid sample that they can obtain — urine, cerebro-spinal fluid, saliva, sweat, effusions, and exudates — but most commonly blood. Blood is often the fluid most easily obtained, especially in an emergency, and is also highly representative of chemical disturbances in the body. Unfortunately blood poses two special problems. Firstly a variable proportion of it is compartmentalized into erythrocytes, themselves around 30% protein as haemoglobin, and whose internal composition is distinct to plasma. Secondly blood contains a series of agents purposefully designed by evolution to react with surfaces. Though centrifugation may be used to separate erythrocytes from plasma, it does take time and equipment, and can be difficult with smaller samples. Furthermore mechanical breakage of vessels can present a real health hazard through the formation of aerosols of plasma.

Sensors therefore need to be incorporated into systems which accept blood, and which estimate concentrations within the plasma compartment for these substances which do not equilibrate rapidly across the erythrocyte membrane.

36.2.6 Safety and reliability

It might seem logical to say that a device could be used in medicine if its chances of saving life were higher than its risks to life. This simple idea is unacceptable in practice, even if the risks were quantifiable, which is generally not the case. Furthermore many treatments in medicine are aimed at relieving morbidity (suffering) rather than reducing mortality, and setting risks to health (and life) against such treatments or means to treatment is fraught with philosophical and social difficulties. In general then the benefits from any new treatment or device have to far outweigh potential problems before being medically acceptable.

36.2.6.1 False results   Malfunction of any sensor causing a false result and a subsequently inappropriate automatic or informed response to it must remain of major concern. Examples of a dangerous response might include an *in vivo* blood glucose monitoring device, controlling an insulin infusion system, generating a falsely high signal. Even a home blood glucose meter, making the same error, could result in a patient taking dangerous action to correct the perceived abnormality. Equally failure to detect a real abnormality could resist in clinicians not taking appropriate measures in potentially fatal circumtances. High ketone body levels in the blood (diabetic ketoacidosis) or paracetamol poisoning might be pertinent examples.

Sophisticated *in vivo* monitoring devices can be provided with circuits to monitor electronic malfunction, though there can be no guard against an incorrect sensor signal, unless duplication of sensors is used. Within certain limits devices can be programmed to monitor the rate of change of measured parameters and alert users when the result changes outside present limits, but this is heavily dependent on the error developing more quickly than changes might be expected to occur as a result of the disease. Thus the design of all parts of sensor devices needs continuing attention to reliability, and the use of the highest practicable engineering standards.

Bedside and patient-operated devices present a more difficult judgement, partly because to be useful they must be offerred at a sensible retail price. Part of the answer here lies in the hands of the doctors themselves, so that users are educated not to react to a single result that could cause a dangerous change in treatment without thought and perhaps cross-checks.

36.2.6.2 Toxicity   It is self evident that *in vivo* monitoring devices must be made of materials that are non-toxic, and considerable commercial expertise is available for structural materials (metals and plastics) used in heart valves, pacemaker wires, and bone and vessel prostheses. Attention must also be paid to novel organic substances, including enzymes, that might leach from sensors or otherwise be picked up by the body's scavenger cells (macro-phages). The anticipated problem would be activation of the immune system and production of antibodies, with the potential of organ damage through immune complex disease or amyloidosis. These risks are remote however, given the likely load of toxic or antigenic materials to the body, and the containment of most of them behind diffusion barriers.

36.2.6.3 Mechanical dangers   Every breach of the skin is a destruction of anatomical integrity, and every advance deeper into the body carries with it further risks of disturbing vital functions. Sensors placed in the subcutaneous tissue, and associated with a transcutaneous wire, provide a entry portal for infection. They must therefore be sterile and need changing every 1 to 3 days. The risk is higher for devices placed within the circulation (the infection is more serious), while the procedural risks of placing such devices in deep veins means that regular changing is not practicable outside the intensive care unit or operating theatre. Such devices should therefore be totally implantable and have a long life (over two years). Furthermore the risks of thrombosis are not fully understood, and it appears from experience with pacemaker wires that anything lying up against the vessel wall may be incorporated within it. This might obviate sensor function!

The other risk from intravascular devices is that of mechanical disintegration resulting from long term placement in fluid at 37°C in an environment that never stops moving. It is for all these reasons that sensors intended for permanent intravascular placement in man will have to be proved over some years in dogs or pigs, and will only then be in a position for approval by the regulatory authorities.

References

Ahmed, M., Gannon, M. C. and Nuttall, F. Q. (1976). Postprandial plasma glucose, insulin, glucagon and triglyceride responses to a standard diet in normal subjects. *Diabetologia* **12**, 61–7.

Fogt, E. J., Dodd, L. M., Jenning, E. M. and Clemens, A. H. (1978). Development and evaluation of a glucose analyser for a glucose-controlled insulin infusion system (Biostator). *Clin. Chem.* **24**, 1366–72.

Levandowski, L. A., White, N. H., Popp, D. and Santiago, J. V. (1983). Teledyne sleep sentry — a possible aid for the detection of symptomatic nocturnal hypoglycaemia in insulin-dependent diabetes. In *Artificial systems for insulin delivery* (eds. P. Brunetti, K. G. M. M. Alberti, K. D. Hepp, A. M. Albisser, and M. Massi-Benedetti) pp. 353–6. Raven Press, New York.

Lipid Research Clinics Program (1984). The lipid research clinics coronary prevention trial results. *J. Am. Med. Assoc.* **251**, 351–64.

Malaisse, W. J., Sener, A., Herchuelz, A. and Hutton, J. C. (1979). Insulin release: the fuel hypothesis. *Metabolism* **28**, 373–86.

Marks, V. and Alberti, K. G. M. M. (eds.) (1985). *Clinical biochemistry nearer the patient.* Churchill Livingstone, Edinburgh.

Noy, G. A. and Alberti, K. G. M. M. (1981a). *In vivo* monitoring of intermediary metabolites. In *Advances in clinical biochemistry* (eds. K. G. M. M. Alberti and C. P. Price) Vol. 2, pp. 229–41. Churchill Livingstone, Edinburgh.

—— (1981b). *In vivo* monitoring of metabolites using enzyme based analytical techniques. In *Applied biochemistry and bioengineering* (eds. L. B. Wingard, Jr., E. Katzin-Katalski, and L. Goldstein) Vol. 3, pp. 233–52. Academic Press, New York.

Schichiri, M., Kawamori, R., Yamasaki, Y., Hakui, N. and Abe, H. (1982). Wearable artificial endocrine pancreas with needle-type glucose sensor. *Lancet* **ii**, 1129–31.

Schiffrin, A., Mihic, M., Leibel, B. S. and Albisser, A. M. (1985). Computer assisted insulin dosage adjustment. *Diabetes Care* **8**, 545–52.

Tattersall, R. B. (1979). Home blood glucose monitoring. *Diabetologia* **16**, 71–4.

37

Exploiting biosensors

JAMES MCCANN

Biosensors have attracted considerable attention in recent years as successors to a wide range of analytical techniques in process control, in the clinical laboratory, in veterinary health care, and in the food industry. Indeed, the potential applications of the technology are so widespread that a short chapter in this book can merely indicate some of the major trends affecting the exploitation of these devices over the new few years. Furthermore, one is faced with the problem of defining exactly what is a biosensor. For example, consider the clinical biochemistry market where analysers have been around for at least ten years. These analysers range from small hand held models, costing a few hundreds of pounds, to vast automated systems costing many thousands. Clearly many of these demand the epithet biosensor, yet they have been rarely discussed as such.

Given the problems of definition, and the wide range of existing products that cleary fall into the category, I have decided to adopt a permissive definition of the word biosensor. Thus I make no apologies for the inclusion of items and technologies which are not normally classified under the title biosensor. Their inclusion is not merely to provide background material, but also to provide precedents for what may or may not happen to some of the new devices that are discussed elsewhere in this book. Moreover, these earlier analytical techniques can provide insight into those forces that can lead to the successful commercialization or demise of a biosensor — 'the invisible hand' of the market place so beloved of by eighteenth century economists.

In order to add structure to a discussion of how and where the biosensors are to be exploited I shall appeal to a conceptual framework well known to the doyens of Madison Avenue — the product life cycle. This concept gained widespread currency during the 1970s as an explanation of how markets behave and the reasons for this behaviour. Its importance arises from the fact that certain types of market behaviour are usually observed at different stages in the product life cycle, irrespective of the product involved. For example, the degree of competition, size of the market, advertising, and distribution methods can all be related to the stage of the product life cycle. For the purposes of this discussion the product in question is a biosensor and we shall examine the following markets for the devices:

1) human health care,
2) veterinary health care,
3) fermentation and process control.

I have selected these three categories because they represent markets at different stages of the product life cycle, and therefore widely different opportunities for biosensors. Taken together, they also represent the major markets. But first, I shall digress for a short introduction to the product life cycle.

37.1 The product life cycle

The product life cycle is usually divided into four separate stages: introduction, growth, maturity, and decline. The introduction phase of the life cycle represents the initial sales following product introduction. As sales increase the market enters a growth phase characterized by increasing sales. When this growth slackens the market reaches a period of decline. Figure 37.1 shows a sketch of a typical product life cycle.

The introduction phase of a product is usually the result of many years of research and development by a single company. In the case of biosensor devices the product development will entail laboratory work, prototype testing, regulatory approval from appropriate bodies, and extensive clinical testing.

Once the product is introduced the company will also have to expend considerable resources in establishing distribution, marketing, and service networks and in educating consumers. The success of a product is crucially dependent upon the effectiveness of this programme. Thus relatively inferior products may enjoy success because of adept marketing and distribution, while better designed products may flounder. An analogy may be drawn here with computers, where IBM have always exploited their superior marketing,

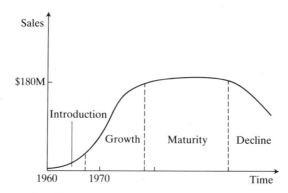

Fig. 37.1 The product life cycle: the market for radioimmunoassays in the USA.

service and distribution to dominate the market, despite inferior product design.

In the case of medical products the introduction phase of a product is usually very long. There are a number of reasons for this including high complexity; the large number of people involved in adopting the new method (doctors, nurses, administrators); the risks associated in moving to a new method as opposed to staying with an established one; the expense involved in purchasing new equipment; and the innate conservatism of some parts of the medical profession. The cost of overcoming these hurdles and obtaining market acceptance for a medical product will be many times greater than the cost of the research and development effort. Thus many small innovative companies, which are adept at product invention and development, will fail to earn a return on their investment because they lack the resources to overcome these problems. During this introductory phase the pioneer company will typically be in a monopoly position, which will be reinforced by patents developed during the research period.

The growth phase is usually characterized by a rapid increase in product sales. However, the increase in sales and high prices usually charged by the monopoly supplier attracts new competition and products. These new products will typically be as close to the existing product in performance as possible, while, at the same time, avoiding patent infringement. In many cases these new competitors will be large health care companies that hope to expand primary demand for the product with their large advertising and marketing budgets, worldwide distribution, and sales forces. These new entrants usually employ large staffs of legal counsel and development teams to circumvent the advantages of the pioneering company. Their focus on development, rather than innovation, means they are unlikely to be as adept at product innovation as the pioneer.

Sales growth during the growth phase will be rapid due to increased consumer acceptance, a history of reliable product use, large marketing and advertising budgets, and widespread product availability. However, as the market reaches saturation, this sales growth will decline and the market will reach a period of maturity.

This stage is characterized by a large number of competitors all selling products using very similar technology, the novelty afforded by patent protection having been eroded by time, cross licensing agreements, and endless efforts at circumvention. Since the consumer is now faced by a plethora of products all performing in roughly the same way there will be intensive price competition, with widespread price cutting. Some competition may leave the market entirely or try to distinguish their product by means of 'product differentiation' — changing some of the product characteristics such that the consumer may be willing to pay a premium for it. As can be imagined, trying to enter a market at this stage is very difficult indeed, unless one has something that is clearly and demonstrably superior. Even then, the consumers may have invested large amounts in existing capital equipment and trained staff, and will thus be unwilling to change.

Eventually the market may begin to decline in real terms due to obsolescence, the introduction of radical new technology, or a substitute product.

Arguably the best example of this type of market behaviour related to biosensors is the market for radioimmunoassays.

This market was pioneered during the early sixties following the discovery that a radioisotope tag could be used to quantitate the reaction of a specific antibody with its specific antigen. At the time of its discovery this method was the only available means of carrying out many standard assays. As a result the market grew rapidly during the 1960s and 1970s with many companies entering the field. Technological improvement, although rapid at first, slowed and most competitors were selling a similar product by the middle of the 1970s. Since most of the products could be read on any available gamma-counter, and most clinical chemistry laboratories had purchased one, switching between various suppliers became endemic. Purchase decisions became dominated by price concerns and the profitability of many of the participants fell correspondingly. The market displayed all the characteristics of maturity.

However, the market has now entered a period of slow decline because new analytical technologies, most notably those using an enzyme or fluorescent molecule to tag the antibody, have been developed. These new methods offer ease of disposal, stability during storage and transport, and lower equipment costs. Nevertheless, the demise of radioimmunoassays will be very slow due to the large amount of capital invested in gamma counters and trained staff. Indeed, radioimmunoassays still account for at least 40% of the U.S. market for immunoassays, despite the advent of enzyme labels almost ten years ago. Table 37.1 lists the estimated market sizes of the various types of immunoassay reagents in the USA during 1984. The largest category was radioimmunoassay with annual sales of up to $250 million. Table 37.2 breaks

Table 37.1   Estimated 1984 immunoassay reagent sales by product category and market share with USA

Category	Market size ($ millions)
Immunology	40
Blood banking	80
Serology (testing)	80
Radioimmunoassays	250
Non-isotopic assays (mostly enzyme linked systems)	160
Total	$610 million

Table 37.2 Estimated US Market shares of the ten largest radioimmuno-assay (RIA) tests in the USA in 1983

RIA test	Approximate market size ($ millions)
Hepatitis	50
T_4	30
Digoxin	20
Human chorionic gonadotropin	20
B_{12}/folate	12
Thyroid stimulating hormone	11
Carcinogenic embryonic antigen	10
Cortisol	8
T_3	7
Ferritin	6
	$174 million

The total market for RIA tests in the USA in 1983 was estimated to be $250 million.

down the radioimmunoassay market still further into the ten largest selling tests.

The second largest category of immunoassay was non-isotopic assay, the majority of which used an enzyme to replace the radioactive label. This segment is the most rapidly growing because it offers the user a combination of ease of use, low equipment cost, simple protocols, and rapid response. Table 37.3 breaks the market for enzyme immunoassays down further and gives details of the six largest selling tests.

Table 37.3 Estimated US market shares of enzyme immunoassays in the USA in 1984

Test	Approximate market size ($ millions)
Theophylline	30
Phenytoin	11
Digoxin	6
Phenobarbital	8
Tobramycin	9
Gentamicin	8
	$72 million

Total US market size in 1983 for enzyme immunoassays in the USA was estimated to be $120 million, divided between approximately forty tests. The market was estimated to be growing at over 10% per annum.

The remainder of the market for immunoassays comprises reagents used for immunology, blood banking and serology. The immunology area comprises reagents for the characterization of immunoproteins. The blood banking segment comprises tests used for the screening of blood prior to transfusion, including blood typing. The serology segment comprises reagents used for the testing of bacterial and viral antigens, and for various metabolic diseases such as lupus and arthritis.

With this brief overview of the way that markets behave and the current US market for immunoassays, we shall now move on to examine the market for biosensors in each of our chosen categories.

37.2 Human health care

The traditional home of analytical chemistry in the health care field has been the centralized clinical laboratory. These laboratories are situated in the larger general hospitals and are charged with the analysis of patient samples from the entire hospital, or even from an entire hospital district. This structure has developed because the complex nature of the tasks to be carried out required the use of a small cadre of highly trained staff in one laboratory. With time, the ever increasing volume of samples led to the application of automated sample handling and dilution equipment. Thus instrument manufacturers have focused on the provision of large clinical chemistry analysers capable of handling hundreds of samples per day. The high cost of these machines has further increased centralization of testing in the clinical laboratory. Indeed, the high cost of the large analysers has become the primary reason why testing is concentrated in one centralized laboratory.

The clinical laboratory market now shows all the characteristics of maturity. In 1971 the market had approximately five competitors, a market for reagents and instruments of approximately £600 million and a growth rate of 15% per annum. By 1983 the market had grown to approximately £1.4 billion, but the number of competitors had grown to 17 and market growth was estimated at between 0 to 4%. Some competitors, such as Eastman Kodak, were actually making substantial losses. Most of the assays on offer use exactly the same technology: typically a UV spectrophometric based assay with complex automatic sample handling techniques. Thus patent protection appears to be unimportant. More importantly, the recent analysers are virtually indistinguishable to the consumer; one just pushes a few buttons and gets a computer printout a few seconds later. The market is therefore becoming very price sensitive as consumers make their purchase decisions on price alone.

The potential for new biosensors in this market is very limited indeed. The existing analysers are rapid, easy to use, and accurate. Competition is well entrenched and is highly regarded by the medical profession. Moreover, even if new biosensor technologies allowed a reduction in the actual cost of reagents and the sensor element; the realizable reduction in the price of the whole machine would be minimal because most of the system cost is embedded in the sample and data handling functions.

The most promising market for new biosensors lies in areas other than the central clinical laboratory. These new markets have developed primarily because of legislative attempts to reduce the overall cost of supplying health care. The forerunner in the field is the USA, which was spending 10% of its gross national product on health care by 1983, twice the current UK level.

During 1984 the USA introduced new methods of reimbursing hospitals so as to give them an incentive to reduce the cost of treating patients. In effect this induced hospitals to reduce the length of patient stay and move therapy to out-patient departments, hospices, and off site delivery sites where the costs of treatment are considerably less. In many cases these changes require the development of new low cost methods for diagnosis, for monitoring of patient condition, and for therapy. In short, these changes demand biosensors that can be employed in low technology environments outside the clinical chemistry laboratory.

The requirements for these devices are very different from the large clinical chemistry analysers. The medical profession will have to buy large numbers of them so that they can be situated in each ward, out patient department, or physician's office. They must therefore be low cost. They will be used in an unsophisticated environment and must therefore be easy to use and require minimal sample pretreatment. At the same time they must retain acceptable accuracy and precision. A comparison of instruments developed to measure blood glucose in the clinical chemistry laboratory and the 'off site' market serves to illustrate these points. Details of the two instruments are given in Table 37.4. On one side there is the Yellow Spring's Instrument, an amperometric system for measuring glucose that relies upon the oxidation of glucose according to:

$$\text{Glucose} + O_2 \xrightarrow{\text{Glucose oxidase}} H_2O_2 + \text{Glucose-lactone}$$

H_2O_2 is then electrochemically reduced at a platinum electrode. The system is

Table 37.4 Clinical chemistry instrument versus off site instrument

	Off site	Clinical chemistry instrument
	Glucometer	Yellow springs instrument
Cost	$150	$6000
Weight	1 kg	30 kg
Sample	50 μl whole blood	20 μl plasma

commonly used in a centralized laboratory to measure emergency glucose samples.

In contrast the Glucometer is a small hand held instrument that uses a small disposable element to quantitate the amount of glucose present, according to:

$$\text{Glucose} + O_2 \xrightarrow{\text{Glucose oxidase}} H_2O_2 + \text{Glucono-lactone}$$

$$H_2O_2 \xrightarrow{\text{Horseradish peroxidase}} H_2O + \text{Oxidized chromogen}$$

The oxidized chromogen then produces a colour change that is used to quantitate the amount of glucose present. Note the difference in cost, weight, and degree of sample pretreatment.

The 'off site' testing market displays all the characteristics of a market in the early growth phase. Sales are smaller than the clinical chemistry market, but are growing rapidly. Patent protection and proprietary technology appear to be important. Indeed, there are many technologies still under development and many specific opportunities for small innovative companies to fill.

37.3 Veterinary health care

Veterinary health care is concerned with the diagnosis, therapy, and treatment of animals used for commercial enterprises and as pets. The whole market is valued in the range of $5–$6 billion per annum in the USA, but this includes antibiotics, vaccines, vitamins, general veterinary services, feed additives such as amino acids, growth stimulants and hormones, and steroids. It is certain that diagnostic tests only comprise a very small proportion of the total — probably in the range $100–$200 million per annum. Thus the existing market is very small in comparison to human health care.

There clearly are a number of possible opportunities for biosensor type products in veterinary health care, particularly for those devices that are robust, easy to use, and amenable to a low technology environment. However many of the potential users are totally unfamiliar with diagnostic testing procedures. Furthermore, the unsanitary conditions of a farm or slaughterhouse compare very unfavourably to those of a domestic household or an out patients department. Thus new devices will have to be particularly user friendly and robust. In addition, the considerable costs associated with consumer education, the establishment of new distribution channels, service and product support, and meeting the regulatory requirements must not be underestimated. The prognosis, therefore, is rather less favourable than some of the opportunities in the human health care sector. Indeed, the prohibitive costs of developing the market argues against commercial enterprises aiming for these applications in isolation. Rather, one will see companies developing products for a human health care applications and then modifying them slightly for a veterinary use. This model of development is already happening. For example the Ames division of Miles Laboratories Inc. of Ekhart, Indiana, now sells some of its human diagnostic tests to the veterinary market.

37.4 Fermentation and process control

Once again the ambit of the fermentation and process control market extends far beyond the space available to the writer. However, it is clear to say that there are a number of potential applications for biosensors in this area. These include the monitoring and control of industrial pollutants such as methane, carbon dioxide, carbon monoxide; the monitoring of microbial contamination in enclosed processes (e.g. heating and ventilation systems, water distribution networks); and the control of standard fermentation processes by monitoring substrate levels, microbial biomass or substrate formation. The biological sensing element of a biosensor may, furthermore, lend a biosensor device particular advantages over competing technologies. For example, enzymes or immunological components offer a unique degree of specificity coupled with an ability to select a target molecule in a highly complex soup of other molecules. Biosensors may also offer a high degree of sensitivity. On the other hand, they are highly sensitive to temperature, pH, and osmotic pressure and deteriorate relatively rapidly with time.

Industrial processes may also have particular characteristics that make them singularly inappropriate for biosensors. For example, many processes require sensors at remote parts of the system where it is difficult to obtain access to replace delicate biological sensor elements at regular intervals. Many food processing applications demand a steam sterilization procedure to prevent microbial contamination. Clearly this is incompatible with a biosensor, unless one has a separate bleed off from the main process to a remote testing site. My own experiences tell me that individuals in the fermentation would be loath to compromise their well established steam sterilization procedures with something as innocuous as a small line leading to a biosensor!

37.5 Conclusions

As you may have gathered the commercial potential of biosensors varies greatly from one application to another. The commercial future prophesized by many can be compromised by a whole range of unforeseen problems including product recalls, entrenched competition, lack of demand, technical difficulties, legislative or patent problems, poor marketing or distribution, and poor product design. The route to successful commercialization of a biosensor will require thorough market analysis, a good understanding of potential benefits, sound financial backing, comprehensive marketing and distribution, and tenacity. Provided that appropriate commercial decisions are made, the potential of these devices is very great indeed. However, the commercialization of biosensors is not a field for one who subscribes to the old Cromwellian dictum of he who goes furthest knows not whither he goes!

Index

tobramycin 741
total assimilable sugars 14
total internal reflection fluorescence
  (TIRF) 656, 660, 666, 670, 671, 672, 674
  TIRF immunoassays 675
toxicity 734
Toxi-guard 591
transaminases 340
transcription 103
transcutaneous glucose monitor 367
transcutaneous oxygen tension 358
transcutaneous partial pressure of oxygen
  ($TcPO_2$) 360
  $TcPO_2$ monitoring 359
transcutaneous PO_2 electrode 359
transducers v, 7, 56
transfer junction 453
transfer of electrons 3
transfer of electrons across cell walls 295
transformation 103
translation 103
transmission 670
transport 55
  mechanism 54, 55
  process 56
Trichosporium cutaneum 25, 28
Trichosporon brassicae 17–19, 28
triglyceride determination 584
triglycerides 325, 586, 727
trinitrobenzene sulphonate 125
trinitrotoluene (TNT) 621
  reductase 621
trypsin 122, 576, 581
tryptophan 148, 642
TSH, *see* thyroid stimulating hormone
TTF, *see* tetrathiafulvalene
tumour antigens 60
tunnelled fluorescence 660
turbidimetric methods 23, 648
turbidimetry 683
turnover number 113
two-phase flows in bioreactors 553
two-site immunofluorometric assay 671, 672
tyramine 125
tyrosinase 52
tyrosine 31, 52, 148, 399
  biosensor 52ff
L-tyrosine 144, 148, 149
tyrosyl tRNA 118

ultrasonic absorption spectroscopy 651
ultra sound fields 563
undiluted whole blood 3, 10
unsaturated region of operation 492
urate 399, 708
urea 30, 31, 34, 37, 47, 50, 135, 141, 143, 144,
  146, 147, 150, 327, 473, 512, 545, 546,
  547, 586, 725, 726, 727
  biosensor 50
  calibration curve 474
  determination 543
  as interference 475
  -sensitive ENFET 472, 510, 512
  sensor 50ff, 471
  in serum 583
urease 3, 30, 50, 66, 89, 143, 144, 146, 147,
  150, 512, 531, 533, 543, 545, 576, 586,
  591
  -containing electrodes 446
  immobilized 472
  probe based in IrMoS capacitor 546
uric acid 255, 331, 586, 731
uric acid analyser 329
uricase 90, 329, 576, 586
  electrodes 330
urinary-tract infections 539
urine 20, 27, 148, 333, 339, 340, 544, 545,
  587, 683, 725
  glucose 86, 149, 317, 329
USA spending on health care 743

vacuum deposition 287
vacuum level 482
valence band 482, 473–7
valine 34, 47
valinomycin 138, 140, 364, 504
vapour deposition 476
variable angle prisms 664
variations of oxygen 401
vector quantity 429
velocity statistics 690
very high/frequency audio signal 418
very high/frequency methodologies 447
venous oxygen saturation 363, 364
veterinary vi
  health care 737, 738, 744ff
Vibrio harveyi 620
viral DNA 82
virus 60, 692
vitamin B_1 28, 295
vitamin C assays 584
vitamin D deficiency 333
volatile dehydrogenase substrates 541
volatile organoleptic compounds 557
voltammetric immunoassay 64
Beta-vulgaris altissima 52

wall jet electrode 167
Warburg impedance 435
waste water 26, 291, 561
waste water treatment 13, 25
waveguide–liquid interface 660, 669